Automatic Control Engineering

McGRAW-HILL SERIES IN MECHANICAL ENGINEERING

KARL H. VESPER, *Stanford University,*
Consulting Editor

Automatic Control Engineering

Francis H. Raven
Professor of Mechanical Engineering
University of Notre Dame

McGraw-Hill Book Company
New York, St. Louis, San Francisco, Toronto,
London, Sydney

Automatic Control Engineering

Library of Congress Catalog Card Number
68-11619

ISBN 07-051227-2

8910 KPKP 7654

Preface

In recent years, automatic control systems have been rapidly advancing in importance in all fields of engineering. The applications of control systems cover a very wide scope, ranging from the design of precision control devices such as delicate instruments used for inertial guidance to the design of massive equipment such as that used for controlling the manufacture of steel or other industrial processes. New applications for automatic controls are continually being discovered.

This text is the outgrowth of the notes developed by the author to teach control engineering at the University of Notre Dame. The author has endeavored to give the principles a thorough presentation and yet make them clear and easy to understand. It is presupposed that the reader has the general maturity and background of a third- or fourth-year engineering student, but no previous training in control engineering.

Although the principles of feedback control systems are presented in a manner which is appropriate to the interests of mechanical engineers, this text has also been successfully used to teach students in other fields of engineering. In addition, the author has taught night courses for practicing engineers. In the light of their enthusiastic comments, it is felt that this book will be of much value to the engineer in industry who did not have the opportunity to take such a course while in college.

The basic principles and fundamental concepts of feedback control systems are presented in the first portion (Chaps. 1 through 10). The next four chapters (11 through 14) provide a general introduction to advanced topics. The last four chapters (15 through 18) correlate basic theory with the more practical aspects involved in the design of control systems. Because the usual pattern encountered is that new engineers are strong in theory but weak in practice, it is felt that this latter portion will help bridge the gap between theory and practice.

In particular, the study of control engineering is begun by showing how typical control systems may be represented by block diagrams. This is accomplished by first demonstrating how to represent each component or part of a system as a simple block diagram. Next, it is explained how

v

these individual diagrams may be connected to form the overall block diagram, just as the actual components are connected to form the complete control system. Because actual control systems frequently contain nonlinear components, considerable emphasis is given to such components. The preceding material is presented in the first three chapters. In the fourth chapter it is shown that much important information concerning the basic or inherent operating characteristics of a system may be obtained from a knowledge of the steady-state behavior.

This introduction to control theory differs from the usual "black-box" approach, in which the block diagram for a system is given outright. The black-box approach permits introducing Laplace transforms and other methods for system analysis at an earlier stage. However, it has been the author's experience that the student is better able to appreciate the value of the more specialized techniques used in system analysis if he is first familiarized with the physical significance of feedback controls, and that he thus arrives at a far deeper understanding.

In Chaps. 5 through 10, the various methods and techniques used for determining the performance of control systems are thoroughly described. In Chap. 5 in particular it is shown how linear differential equations which describe the operation of control systems may be solved algebraically by the use of Laplace transforms. Chapter 6 explains how the roots of the characteristic equation govern the transient response, and in Chap. 7 it is shown how these roots may be ascertained by use of the root-locus method. Application of the analog computer for simulating control systems is presented in Chap. 8. The use of frequency-response techniques for evaluating dynamic performance is explained in Chaps. 9 and 10. Although the first ten chapters in the second edition bear the same titles as the corresponding chapters in the first edition, the chapters have been completely rewritten and expanded to provide a broader and deeper coverage of the material.

Chapters 11 through 14 provide a general introduction to advanced control topics. The purpose of these chapters is to bridge the gap between basic and advanced control topics. One of the most versatile methods for handling nonlinear control systems, the describing function, is presented in Chap. 11. Chapter 12 begins by explaining the phase-plane method, which is a general procedure for investigating second-order nonlinear systems. It is then shown how, with the aid of State-Space concepts, the Liapunov method is in reality but an extension of the phase-plane method to general higher-order nonlinear systems. When digital computers are employed as part of a control system, the resulting system may then be regarded as a sampled-data system as is explained in Chap. 13. The topic of Chap. 14 is statistical methods and adaptive control systems.

More specialized considerations which arise in the design of hydraulic systems, pneumatic systems, and electrical systems, and in inertial navigation are treated in Chaps. 15 through 18.

The author wishes to express his appreciation for the many fine suggestions of teachers who used the first edition. Their suggestions have greatly aided in the preparation of this revised edition. In particular, the author wishes to acknowledge the suggestions of Professor J. C. Chou, University of Hawaii; Professor Lyle G. Clark, University of Texas; Professor E. C. Fitch, Oklahoma State University; Professor J. Miro, Ohio University; Professor K. E. Scott, Worcester Polytechnic Institute; Professor Thomas B. Sheridan, and Professor D. E. Whitney, Massachusetts Institute of Technology. Students have also been very helpful in their comments. Particular recognition is due John G. Allen and R. V. Dave for their valuable assistance in the preparation of this text.

The author wishes to express his gratitude for the continued encouragement of his colleagues at the University of Notre Dame, especially to Dr. Edward W. Jerger, Head of the Department of Mechanical Engineering. Thanks are also due Mrs. Ella Levee, who typed the manuscript.

Renewed appreciation is expressed to all those previously acknowledged in the first edition.

The author's wife, Therese, has faithfully worked with him throughout the development of this text. She has made innumerable suggestions and has been a constant source of encouragement.

Francis H. Raven

To Therese

Contents

1

Introduction to automatic controls

1.1 Historical Development. Early man had to rely upon his own brute strength or that of beasts of burden to supply energy for doing work. By use of simple mechanical devices such as wheels and levers, he accomplished such feats as the building of high pyramids and Roman highways and aqueducts. He first supplemented his energy and that of beasts by utilizing power from natural sources such as the wind for powering sailing vessels and windmills, and waterfalls for turning water wheels. The invention of the steam engine was a milestone in man's progress because it provided him with useful power that he could harness at will. Since then, man has devised many different means for obtaining abundant and convenient sources of energy. Engineering effort is primarily concerned with the practical applications of using power to serve the purposes of man. That is, the engineer designs and develops machines and equipment by which man can utilize power.

Early machines and equipment had controls which were predominantly of a manual nature, and the adjustments had to be reset frequently in order that the desired output or performance could be maintained. The design of newer equipment with greater usefulness and capabilities is bringing about an ever-increasing growth in the development of control equipment. The reason is twofold. First, automatic controls relieve man of many monotonous activities so that he can devote his abilities to other endeavors. Second, modern complex controls can perform functions which are beyond the physical abilities of man to duplicate. For example, an elaborate automatic control system operates the engine of a modern jet airplane with only a minimum amount of the pilot's attention so that he is free to maneuver and fly his airplane.

It is interesting to note that, as the applications and uses for controls have increased, so also have the demands upon the performance of these systems increased. There is no doubt that a major concern of the engineer today, and even more so in the future, is, and will be, the design and development of automatic control systems.

1.2 Feedback Control Systems.   The controlling of temperature is
a typical example of a feedback control system.   The position of the
temperature dial sets the desired temperature (i.e., the reference input).
The actual temperature of the system is the controlled variable (i.e.,
the quantity which is being controlled).   The thermostat, or comparator,
compares the actual temperature with the desired temperature in order
to measure the error.   This error signal is the actuating signal, which
is then sent to the heating units in order to correct the temperature.
For example, if the actual temperature is less than the desired temperature, the actuating signal causes the control elements to supply more
heat.   If there is no error, the control elements do not change the amount
of heat which is being supplied.   When the actual temperature is greater
than the desired value, then the actuating signal calls for a decrease in
the amount of heat.

For a system to be classified as a feedback control system, it is necessary that the controlled variable be fed back and *compared* with the
reference input.   In addition, the resulting error signal must *actuate* the
control elements to change the output so as to minimize the error.   A
feedback control system is also called a closed-loop system.   Any system which incorporates a thermostat to control temperature is a feedback,
or closed-loop, system.   Well-known examples are electric frying pans,
irons, refrigerators, and household furnaces with thermostatic control.

For speed control systems, the device which subtracts the feedback
signal from the reference input (i.e., the comparator) is usually a centrifugal governor.   The governor serves the same purpose that the thermostat does for temperature controls.   That is, the governor compares the
actual speed which is to be controlled with the desired value and measures
the error.   This error signal then actuates the control elements.   The
same basic concepts apply to all types of feedback control systems, whether
the controlled variable be temperature, speed, pressure, flow, position,
force, torque, or any other physical quantity.

In an open-loop system there is no comparison of the controlled variable
with the desired input.   Each setting of the input determines a fixed
operating position for the control elements.   For example, for a given
input temperature setting, the heating units are positioned to supply
heat at a fixed rate.   (Note that there is no comparator, or thermostat,
which measures the error and resets the heating units.)   The disadvantage
of such a system is illustrated by the fact that, for a fixed rate of heat
supplied to a house, the inside temperature varies appreciably with
changes in the outside temperature.   Thus, for a given set input to an
open-loop system, there may be a big variation of the controlled variable
depending on the ambient temperature.

In this example, the ambient temperature is an external disturbance.

By an external disturbance is meant something external to the system which acts to change or disturb the controlled variable. A major advantage of employing feedback control is that, because of the comparator, the actuating signal continually changes so that the controlled variable tends to become equal to the reference input regardless of the external disturbance. Another consideration is that with feedback one can generally use relatively inexpensive components and yet obtain better control than is possible by using very expensive components in an open-loop system. The primary effort of this text will be devoted to feedback control systems.

1.3 System Representation. The mathematical relationships of control systems are usually represented by block diagrams. These diagrams have the advantage of indicating more realistically the actual processes which are taking place, as opposed to a purely abstract mathematical representation. In addition, it is easy to form the overall block diagram for an entire system by merely combining the block diagrams for each component or part of the system.

A comparator subtracts the feedback signal from the reference input r. For the case in which the controlled variable c is fed back directly (i.e., for unity-feedback systems), the signal coming from the comparator is $r - c$, which is equal to the actuating signal e. The mathematical relationship for this operation is

$$e = r - c \tag{1.1}$$

A circle is the symbol which is used to indicate a summing operation, as is illustrated in Fig. 1.1. The arrowheads pointing toward the circle

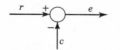

FIG. 1.1. Block diagram of a comparator.

indicate input quantities, while the arrowhead leading away signifies the output. The sign at each input arrowhead indicates whether the quantity is to be added or subtracted.

The relationship between the actuating signal e, which enters the control elements, and the controlled variable c, which is the output of the control, is expressed by the equation

$$c = G(D)e \tag{1.2}$$

where $G(D)$ represents the operation of the control elements. In Chaps. 2 and 3, it is shown how the actual values of $G(D)$ for specific control systems are obtained. The block-diagram representation for the preceding equation is shown in Fig. 1.2. A box is the symbol for multiplication. In this case, the input quantity e is multiplied by the function in

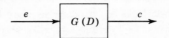

FIG. 1.2. Block diagram of the control elements.

the box $G(D)$ to obtain the output c. With circles indicating summing points and with boxes, or blocks, indicating multiplication, any linear mathematical expression may be represented by block-diagram notation.

The complete block diagram for an elementary unity-feedback control system is obtained by combining Figs. 1.1 and 1.2 to yield Fig. 1.3. This

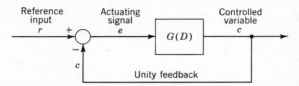

FIG. 1.3. Block diagram of an elementary unity-feedback control system.

diagram shows the controlled variable c being fed back to the summing point, where it is compared with the reference input r. This diagram pictorially shows why a feedback control system is also called a closed-loop system.

When the controlled variable is fed back to the comparator, it is usually necessary to convert the form of the controlled variable to a form that is suitable for the comparator. For example, in a temperature control system the controlled temperature is generally converted to a proportional force or position for use in the comparator. This conversion is accomplished by feedback elements $H(D)$. The block-diagram representation for this more general case of a feedback control system is shown in Fig. 1.4. The signal which is fed back is

$$b = H(D)c \tag{1.3}$$

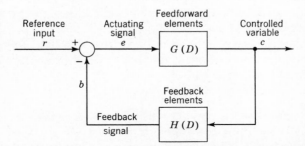

FIG. 1.4. Block diagram of an elementary feedback control system.

The elements represented by $H(D)$ are called the feedback elements because they are located in the feedback portion of the control. The control elements represented by $G(D)$ are the feedforward elements because of their location in the feedforward portion of the loop. The actuating signal e is now $r - b$. This actuating signal e is a measure or indication of the error.

The term "feedback control system" is a general term which applies to any system in which the controlled variable is measured and fed back to be compared with the reference input. The terms "servomechanism" and "regulator" are distinguished as follows: A servomechanism is a particular type of feedback control system in which the controlled variable is a mechanical position (e.g., the angular position of a shaft). A regulator is distinguished as a feedback control system in which the reference input, although adjustable, is held fixed, or constant, for long periods of time (e.g., most temperature controllers).

2

Representation of control components

To investigate the performance of control systems, it is necessary to obtain the mathematical relationship $G(D)$ relating the controlled variable c and the actuating signal e of the feedforward elements. This is accomplished by first obtaining the mathematical representation for each component between the actuating signal and the controlled variable and then expressing each of these equations as a block diagram. The combination of the block diagrams for each component yields the desired representation for $G(D)$. The value of $H(D)$ is obtained by applying the same technique to the components in the feedback portion of the control.

The quantity $G(D)$ could be obtained by writing the mathematical equation describing the operation of each component between e and c and then combining these individual equations algebraically to obtain the overall relationship between e and c. However, for all but the simplest systems, this procedure proves cumbersome because of the interaction between the various components in a typical control system. In addition, the block-diagram method gives one a better understanding of the system because of its visual representation.

The obtaining of block diagrams for typical elements used in control devices is illustrated in this chapter. In the next chapter, it is shown how these individual diagrams are combined to form entire control systems.

2.1 Operational Notation. In writing equations for control systems, it is convenient to use the operational notation

$$D^n = \frac{d^n}{dt^n} \qquad n = 1, 2, 3, \ldots \tag{2.1}$$

The operator D is a symbol which indicates differentiation with respect to time. For example, if x and y are functions of time, then

$$D(x + y) = \frac{d}{dt}(x + y) = \frac{dx}{dt} + \frac{dy}{dt} = Dx + Dy$$

This shows that the operator D obeys the distributive law, that is

$$D(x + y) = Dx + Dy \tag{2.2}$$

It may also be shown that if a and b are constants, then

$$(D + a)(D + b)y = (D + a)\left(\frac{dy}{dt} + by\right)$$

$$= \frac{d}{dt}\left(\frac{dy}{dt} + by\right) + a\left(\frac{dy}{dt} + by\right)$$

$$= \frac{d^2y}{dt^2} + (a + b)\frac{dy}{dt} + aby$$

$$= [D^2 + (a + b)D + ab]y$$

Thus, the commutative law also holds. That is

$$(D + a)(D + b)y = (D + b)(D + a)y \tag{2.3}$$

Consider the differential equation

$$x = \frac{1}{D + a}f(t) \tag{2.4}$$

From calculus it is known that the solution is

$$x = e^{-at}\int f(t)e^{at}\,dt$$

Operating on both sides by $D + a$ shows that

$$(D + a)x = \frac{d}{dt}\left[e^{-at}\int f(t)e^{at}\,dt\right] + ae^{-at}\int f(t)e^{at}\,dt$$

$$= e^{-at}[f(t)e^{at}] - ae^{at}\int f(t)e^{-at}\,dt + ae^{-at}\int f(t)e^{at}\,dt$$

Thus, $$(D + a)x = f(t) \tag{2.5}$$

Equations (2.4) and (2.5) are equivalent forms of the same differential equation. These forms verify the fact that operators may be cross-multiplied. Consider now the differential form

$$y = (D + a)\frac{1}{D + a}f(t) \tag{2.6}$$

With the aid of Eq. (2.4) it follows that

$$y = (D + a)x = (D + a)[e^{-at}\int f(t)e^{at}\,dt]$$
$$= e^{-at}[f(t)e^{at}] - ae^{-at}\int f(t)e^{at}\,dt + ae^{-at}\int f(t)e^{at}\,dt$$

Thus,

$$y = f(t)$$

This shows that the operators in Eq. (2.6) may be canceled. In general, it may be shown that

$$(D + a)^n\frac{1}{(D + a)^m}f(t) = (D + a)^{n-m}f(t) \tag{2.7}$$

where n and m are positive integers.

Interchanging the operators in Eq. (2.6) yields the differential form

$$y = \frac{1}{D + a}(D + a)f(t) \tag{2.8}$$

Cross multiplying yields

$$(D + a)y = (D + a)f(t)$$

This equation is satisfied when $Dy = Df(t)$ and $ay = af(t)$. Because $ay = af(t)$, then $y = f(t)$ when a is not equal to zero. Hence, for $a \neq 0$ the operators in Eq. (2.8) may be canceled. In general, it may be shown that

$$\frac{1}{(D + a)^m}(D + a)^n f(t) = (D + a)^{n-m} f(t) \qquad a \neq 0 \tag{2.9}$$

For the case in which $a = 0$, then Eq. (2.8) becomes

$$y = \frac{1}{D} Df(t) = \frac{1}{D} f'(t) \tag{2.10}$$

Cross-multiplying to obtain $Dy = f'(t)$ and then integrating shows that

$$y = \int f'(t)\, dt = f(t) + C \tag{2.11}$$

where C is the constant of integration. Comparison of Eqs. (2.10) and (2.11) reveals the fact that the reciprocal of the derivative $1/D$ indicates integration. Evaluation of Eq. (2.11) at time $t = t_0$ shows that

$$y(t_0) = f(t_0) + C \qquad \text{or} \qquad C = y(t_0) - f(t_0)$$

Thus, the constant of integration depends on the initial conditions. The substitution of C into Eq. (2.11) gives

$$y = f(t) - f(t_0) + y(t_0) = f(t) \Big|_{t_0}^{t} + y(t_0)$$

The cancellation of operators in Eq. (2.10) gives the erroneous result

$$y(t) = \frac{1}{D} Df(t) = f(t) \qquad \text{invalid result}$$

In general, it may be shown that

$$\frac{1}{D^m} D^n f(t) \neq D^{n-m} f(t) \tag{2.12}$$

The algebraic cancellation of operators in Eq. (2.12) does not regard the constant of integration that arises from the integration indicated by Eq. (2.11). Thus, it is not possible to cancel operators when a derivative is to be integrated unless the constant of integration is zero, as is the case when all initial conditions are zero. Because no initial condition terms arise from the differentiation process, then Eq. (2.7) holds for $a = 0$. That is

$$D^n \frac{1}{D^m} f(t) = D^{n-m} f(t)$$

In summary, the operator D obeys all algebraic laws except for that indicated by Eq. (2.12). This exception seldom occurs in obtaining the equations for engineering systems.

2.2 Mechanical Components. The load-deflection characteristics for a mechanical spring are shown in Fig. 2.1a. The spring force F_s required

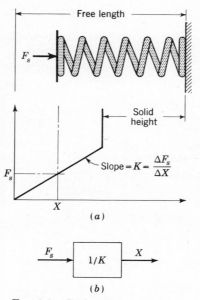

(a)

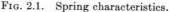

(b)

Fig. 2.1. Spring characteristics.

to compress a spring X in. from its free length is given by the equation

$$F_s = KX \tag{2.13}$$

where K, the spring rate, is a constant which is equal to the slope of the curve of the load F_s versus deflection X. The input to a spring is usually the force F_s, and the output is the deflection X, so that the block-diagram representation for Eq. (2.13) is as shown in Fig. 2.1b.

For a viscous damper as illustrated in Fig. 2.2a, the force F_d required to move one end of the dashpot at a velocity V relative to the other end is equal to the product of the damping coefficient B and the velocity.

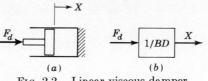

(a)   (b)

Fig. 2.2.   Linear viscous damper.

That is,

$$F_d = BV = B\frac{dX}{dt}$$

The substitution of the operator symbol $D = d/dt$ into the preceding expression yields

$$F_d = B(DX) \tag{2.14}$$

With the force F_d as the input and the displacement X as the output, the block-diagram representation for Eq. (2.14) is shown in Fig. 2.2b.

By Newton's second law of motion, it follows that the summation of the external forces ΣF_e acting on a mass is equal to the product of the mass and acceleration.

$$\sum F_e = MA = M\frac{d^2X}{dt^2} = M(D^2X)$$

The displacement X is given by the equation

$$X = \frac{1}{MD^2}\sum F_e \tag{2.15}$$

This is represented diagrammatically in Fig. 2.3.

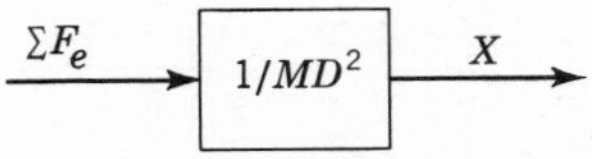

Fig. 2.3.   Acceleration of a mass.

For the mass-spring-damper combination shown in Fig. 2.4a, the spring force and damper force are opposed to, or resist, the motion caused by

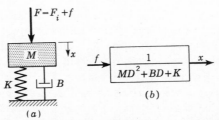

(b)
(a)

Fig. 2.4.   Series mass-spring-damper combination.

the applied load F. The summation of the forces acting on the mass is

$$\Sigma F_e = F + Mg - F_s - F_d = MD^2X$$

or
$$F = (MD^2 + BD + K)X - Mg \tag{2.16}$$

This is the equation for the total forces acting on the system. For control work, it is usually more convenient to make measurements with respect to some reference operating point. A lowercase letter is used to designate the variation or change in displacement x from the reference position X_i so that $x = X - X_i$. The force equation at the reference operating condition is

$$F_i = KX_i - Mg$$

where F_i is the force required to maintain the mass in equilibrium at the reference position X_i. Subtracting the equation for the forces at the reference position from that for the total forces gives the equation of operation for changes about the reference position. That is

$$F - F_i = (MD^2 + BD)X + K(X - X_i)$$

By using lowercase letters to represent changes about the reference position, then the change in force is $f = F - F_i$ and similarly the change in displacement is $x = X - X_i$. Because X_i is a constant, then $DX = D(X_i + x) = Dx$ and $D^2X = D^2x$. As would be expected, velocity and acceleration are independent of the reference position from which displacement is measured. The preceding equation of operation with respect to the reference position may thus be written in the form

$$f = (MD^2 + BD + K)x \tag{2.17}$$

This result could have been obtained directly by summing the change in forces from the reference operating condition. It is to be noted that forces which remain constant, such as the gravitational force, have no change and thus do not appear.

Although x and f are measured from the reference operating point, Eq. (2.17) is a general equation describing the dynamic behavior of the system. It is not necessary that the system be initially at this reference operating point or that the system be initially at rest. As is later explained, it is usually much easier to obtain the equation of operation with respect to some convenient reference point rather than using total values. When total values are desired, it is an easy matter to add the reference value to the variation. The block diagram for Eq. (2.17) is shown in Fig. 2.4b.

Rotational Mechanical Components. A torsional spring is characterized by the equation

$$T_s = K_s\theta \tag{2.18}$$

where T_s = torque tending to twist spring
K_s = torsional spring rate
θ = angular displacement of spring

A well-known example of a torsional spring is a shaft as shown in Fig. 2.5. The right end of the shaft is displaced an angle θ with respect to

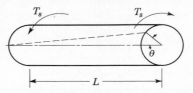

FIG. 2.5.   Shaft acting as a torsional spring.

the left end because of the twisting torque T_s.   For a straight shaft, the torsional spring rate is

$$K_s = \frac{\pi d^4 G}{32L}$$

where G = modulus of elasticity in shear
d = diameter of shaft
L = length of shaft

The torque T_d required to overcome viscous friction of a rotating member is

$$T_d = B_\nu \omega = B_\nu \frac{d\theta}{dt} = B_\nu D\theta \tag{2.19}$$

where B_ν = coefficient of viscous friction
ω = angular velocity

A disk rotating in a viscous medium and supported by a shaft is shown in Fig. 2.6a.   The applied torque tending to rotate the disk is T.   The

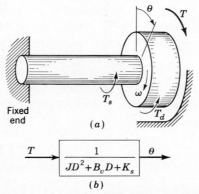

FIG. 2.6.   Torsional inertia-spring-damper combination.

shaft torque and viscous friction oppose the motion so that

$$\Sigma T_e = T - T_s - T_d = J\alpha = JD^2\theta \tag{2.20}$$

where ΣT_e is the summation of external torques acting on the disk. The substitution of T_s from Eq. (2.18) and T_d from Eq. (2.19) into Eq. (2.20) yields

$$T = (JD^2 + B_\nu D + K_s)\theta \tag{2.21}$$

The block-diagram representation for this system is shown in Fig. 2.6b.

2.3 Electrical Components. The resistor, inductor, and capacitor are the three basic components of electrical circuits. The equation for the voltage drop E_R across a resistor is

$$E_R = RI \tag{2.22}$$

where R is the resistance in ohms and I is the current flowing through the resistor in amperes.

For an inductor, the voltage drop E_L is given by the equation

$$E_L = L \frac{dI}{dt} = LDI \tag{2.23}$$

where L is the inductance in henrys.

Similarly, the voltage drop E_C across a capacitor is

$$E_C = \frac{1}{CD} I \tag{2.24}$$

where C is the capacitance in farads.

The diagrammatic representations of Eqs. (2.22) to (2.24) are shown in Fig. 2.7.

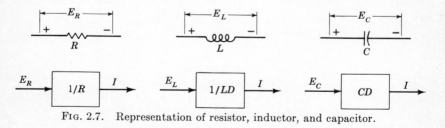

Fig. 2.7. Representation of resistor, inductor, and capacitor.

For the series RLC circuit shown in Fig. 2.8a, the total voltage drop E is the sum of the voltage drop across the inductor E_L, plus that across the resistor E_R and that across the capacitor E_C.

$$E = E_L + E_R + E_C = \left(LD + R + \frac{1}{CD}\right)I \tag{2.25}$$

The charge Q is the time integral of the current, that is, $Q = (1/D)I$. By noting that $LDI = LD^2(I/D) = LD^2Q$, $RI = RD(I/D) = RDQ$, $1/C(I/D) = (1/C)Q$, Eq. (2.25) becomes

$$E = \left(LD^2 + RD + \frac{1}{C}\right)Q \qquad (2.26)$$

The overall block-diagram representation for this RLC circuit is shown in Fig. 2.8b.

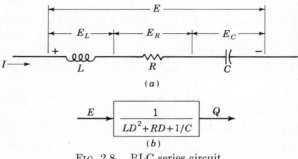

$$(a)$$

$$(b)$$

FIG. 2.8.   RLC series circuit.

2.4 Series and Parallel Laws.   Elements are usually connected in either a series or a parallel arrangement.   Much simplification in arriving at the equation for such systems is afforded by the use of the laws for series and the laws for parallel combinations.

Series Electrical Circuits.   A general series circuit is shown in Fig. 2.9a. In a series circuit, *the total voltage drop E is the sum of the individual voltage*

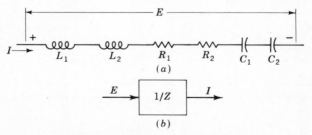

$$(a)$$

$$(b)$$

FIG. 2.9.   General series circuit.

drops across each element and *the same current I flows through each element.* The equation for the summation of the voltage drops is

$$E = \left(L_1 D + L_2 D + R_1 + R_2 + \frac{1}{C_1 D} + \frac{1}{C_2 D}\right)I = ZI \qquad (2.27)$$

The equivalent impedance Z for elements in series is

$$Z = L_1D + L_2D + R_1 + R_2 + \frac{1}{C_1D} + \frac{1}{C_2D} \qquad (2.28)$$

The block-diagram representation is shown in Fig. 2.9b.

Parallel Electrical Circuits. A general combination of electrical elements in parallel is shown in Fig. 2.10a. The distinguishing features of a

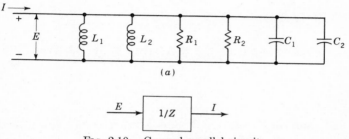

(a)

$$\xrightarrow{E} \boxed{1/Z} \xrightarrow{I}$$

FIG. 2.10. General parallel circuit.

parallel arrangement are that *the voltage drop E across each element is the same,* and *the total current I flowing into the system is the sum of the currents flowing through each element.* Thus

$$I = \frac{E}{L_1D} + \frac{E}{L_2D} + \frac{E}{R_1} + \frac{E}{R_2} + \frac{E}{1/C_1D} + \frac{E}{1/C_2D} \qquad (2.29)$$

or $\quad E = \dfrac{1}{1/L_1D + 1/L_2D + 1/R_1 + 1/R_2 + C_1D + C_2D} I = ZI$

The equivalent impedance Z for elements in parallel is

$$Z = \frac{1}{1/L_1D + 1/L_2D + 1/R_1 + 1/R_2 + C_1D + C_2D} \qquad (2.30)$$

The block diagram representation is shown in Fig. 2.10b.

ILLUSTRATIVE EXAMPLE 1. For the circuit shown in Fig. 2.11, let it be desired to determine the equation relating the output voltage E_2 to the input voltage E_1.

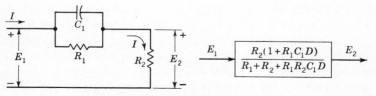

FIG. 2.11. Electrical circuit.

SOLUTION.   The parallel combination of R_1 and C_1 is in series with R_2, so that the total impedance Z is

$$Z = Z_1 + R_2 = \frac{1}{1/R_1 + C_1 D} + R_2 = \frac{R_1}{1 + R_1 C_1 D} + R_2 \quad (2.31)$$

The voltage E_1 is given by the equation

$$E_1 = ZI = \frac{R_1 + R_2 + R_1 R_2 C_1 D}{1 + R_1 C_1 D} I \quad (2.32)$$

and similarly E_2 is

$$E_2 = R_2 I \quad (2.33)$$

The substitution of I from Eq. (2.32) into Eq. (2.33) yields the desired answer

$$E_2 = \frac{R_2(1 + R_1 C_1 D)}{R_1 + R_2 + R_1 R_2 C_1 D} E_1 \quad (2.34)$$

Series Mechanical Elements.   A series arrangement of linear mechanical elements is shown in Fig. 2.12a.   In general, it is better to use the

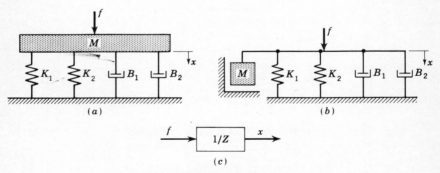

FIG. 2.12.   Mechanical elements in series.

equivalent "grounded-chair" representation for a mass, as shown in Fig. 2.12b, rather than the more common representation of Fig. 2.12a.   The fact that the mass is in series with the other elements is more readily seen from Fig. 2.12b than from Fig. 2.12a.   In determining inertia force, the acceleration of a mass is always taken with respect to ground.   Thus, providing the grounded chair to indicate motion relative to ground is a more justifiable representation than Fig. 2.12a, which shows better the actual physical arrangement of the elements in the system.   For series mechanical elements, *the force f is equal to the summation of the forces acting on each individual component,* and *each element undergoes the same displacement.* Thus

$$f = (K_1 + K_2 + B_1D + B_2D + MD^2)x = Zx \qquad (2.35)$$

where x and f are measured from a convenient reference operating point. The equivalent impedance for mechanical elements in series is

$$Z = K_1 + K_2 + B_1D + B_2D + MD^2 \qquad (2.36)$$

The block diagram representation for this system is shown in Fig. 2.12c.

Parallel Mechanical Elements. A parallel combination of mechanical elements is shown in Fig. 2.13a. For parallel elements, *the same force f is*

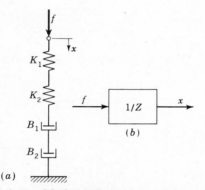

FIG. 2.13. Mechanical elements in parallel.

transmitted through each element. In addition, *the total deflection x is seen to be the sum of the individual deflections of each element.* Thus

$$x = \frac{f}{K_1} + \frac{f}{K_2} + \frac{f}{B_1D} + \frac{f}{B_2D} \qquad (2.37)$$

or

$$f = \frac{1}{1/K_1 + 1/K_2 + 1/B_1D + 1/B_2D} x = Zx$$

The equivalent impedance for mechanical elements in parallel is

$$Z = \frac{1}{1/K_1 + 1/K_2 + 1/B_1D + 1/B_2D} \qquad (2.38)$$

The block-diagram representation is shown in Fig. 2.13b.

A necessary condition for parallel elements is that the same force be transmitted through each element. Springs and dampers satisfy this condition because the force is the same on both sides. However, this is not the case for a mass such as that shown in Fig. 2.14a because the difference in forces acting on both sides of a mass is utilized in acceleration. Thus, a mass located between other elements cannot be in parallel with

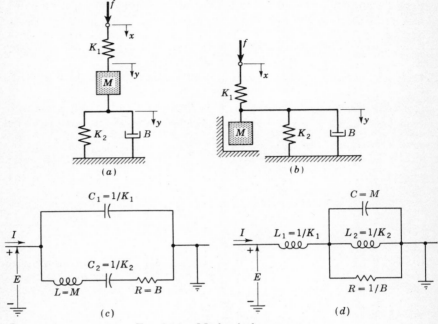

FIG. 2.14.   Mechanical system.

them.   A mass can be in parallel only if it is the last element, as shown in Fig. 2.15.   For this system, the displacement x is

$$x = (x - y) + (y - z) + z = \left(\frac{1}{K} + \frac{1}{BD} + \frac{1}{MD^2}\right)f \qquad (2.39)$$

Parallel and series laws for rotational mechanical components may also be developed by extending the preceding techniques.[1,2]

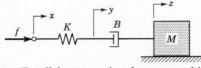

FIG. 2.15.   Parallel mass-spring-damper combination.

[1] H. F. Olson, "Dynamical Analogies," 2d ed., D. Van Nostrand Company, Inc., Princeton, N.J., 1958.
[2] R. L. Sutherland, "Engineering Systems Analysis," Addison-Wesley Publishing Company, Reading, Mass., 1958.

ILLUSTRATIVE EXAMPLE 2. For the mass-spring-damper combination shown in Fig. 2.14a, determine the equation relating f and x, the equation relating f and y, and the equation relating x and y.

SOLUTION. The first step is to draw the equivalent grounded-chair system, in which the motion of the mass with respect to ground is clearly indicated as shown in Fig. 2.14b. The spring K_1 is in parallel with the series combination of M, K_2, and B. Thus

$$f = Zx = \frac{1}{1/K_1 + 1/Z_2} x = \frac{K_1 Z_2}{K_1 + Z_2} x \qquad (2.40)$$

or

$$\frac{f}{Z_2} = \frac{f}{MD^2 + BD + K_2} = \frac{K_1 x}{MD^2 + BD + K_1 + K_2} \qquad (2.41)$$

where $\qquad Z_2 = MD^2 + BD + K_2$

The force f is transmitted through the spring K_1 and acts upon the series combination of M, K_2, and B. Thus, the equation of motion for this part of the system which relates f and y is

$$\frac{f}{MD^2 + BD + K_2} = y \qquad (2.42)$$

Equating (2.41) and (2.42) yields the desired relationship between x and y. That is,

$$y = \frac{K_1}{MD^2 + BD + K_1 + K_2} x \qquad (2.43)$$

Grounded-chair Representation. The general procedure for constructing the grounded-chair representation is as follows:

1. Draw coordinates such that the coordinate at which the force acts is at the top and ground is at the bottom.
2. Insert each element in its correct orientation with respect to these coordinates.

For the system shown in Fig. 2.16a, the coordinates are x, y, and ground. Step 1 is carried out by drawing the coordinates as shown in Fig. 2.16b. To do step 2 we must note that for the spring K_1 and mass M_1 the coordinates are x and ground, for the spring K and damper B the coordinates are x and y, and finally for the mass M_2 and spring K_2 the coordinates are y and ground. Inserting these elements between the proper coordinates as shown in Fig. 2.16c completes the grounded-chair representation. The series and parallel combinations are now recognized directly from this grounded-chair representation. The equation for the

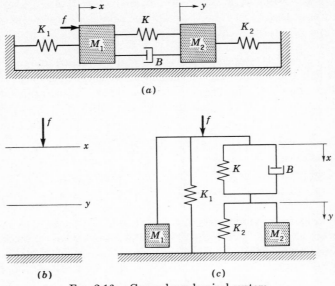

FIG. 2.16.   General mechanical system.

force f is

$$f = \left[M_1 D^2 + K_1 + \frac{1}{1/(K + BD) + 1/(K_2 + M_2 D^2)} \right] x$$

Degrees of Freedom.   By degrees of freedom is meant the number of coordinates required to specify the position of all the elements in a mechanical system.   Thus, the system shown in Fig. 2.14b has two degrees of freedom, while that shown in Fig. 2.15 has three degrees of freedom.

Rather than using the series and parallel laws, an alternate method of determining the equation of operation of mechanical systems is to write the force balance at each coordinate.   For example, the force equation at the x coordinate of Fig. 2.14b is

$$K_1(x - y) = f \tag{2.44}$$

The compression of the spring K_1 is $x - y$, and as x increases, so does the spring force, but as y increases, the spring force decreases.   The force balance at the y coordinate is

$$K_1(x - y) = (K_2 + BD + MD^2)y \tag{2.45}$$

The two preceding force equations may be written in the form

$$\begin{aligned} K_1 x & & -K_1 y = f \\ K_1 x & - (K_1 + K_2 + BD + MD^2)y = 0 \end{aligned} \tag{2.46}$$

These two equations may be solved simultaneously to yield any of the desired relationships between x, y, and f. For example, solving for y gives

$$y = \frac{\begin{vmatrix} K_1 & f \\ K_1 & 0 \end{vmatrix}}{\begin{vmatrix} K_1 & -K_1 \\ K_1 & -(K_1 + K_2 + BD + MD^2) \end{vmatrix}}$$

$$= \frac{K_1 f}{K_1[(K_1 + K_2 + BD + MD^2) - K_1]} = \frac{f}{K_2 + BD + MD^2} \quad (2.47)$$

Suppose that it is desired to consider y positive for upward motion rather than for downward motion. (Downward motion is shown in Fig. 2.14b.) This reversal would change the sign of each y term in Eqs. (2.44) and (2.45), which would change the sign of y in the resultant expression given by Eq. (2.47). In effect, reversing the positive sense of a coordinate merely changes its sign.

In applying the series or parallel laws to mechanical elements, care must be exercised to take the positive sense of motion of each coordinate (this is indicated by the arrow at each coordinate) in the same direction as that of the applied force. It is a simple matter to later change the positive sense of a coordinate by merely changing the sign of the corresponding term in the derived equation.

2.5 Analogies. The equation of operation for the series mechanical system of Fig. 2.4a is given by Eq. (2.17), and the equation for the series electrical circuit of Fig. 2.8a is given by Eq. (2.26). Comparison of corresponding terms in Eqs. (2.17) and (2.26) shows that the differential equation of operation for each system has the same form. The terms which occupy corresponding positions are called analogous quantities. This particular analog is referred to as the direct analog. The analogous quantities for a direct analog are shown in Table 2.1.

TABLE 2.1. ANALOGOUS QUANTITIES IN A DIRECT (FORCE-VOLTAGE) ANALOG

Translational mechanical system	Force	Mass	Viscous damping coefficient	Spring constant	Displacement	Velocity
	f	M	B	K	x	$\dot{x} = Dx$
Electrical system	Volt-age	In-duct-ance	Resistance	Reciprocal of capacitance	Charge	Current
	E	L	R	$\dfrac{1}{C}$	Q	$I = DQ$

The total force acting on a group of mechanical elements in series is equal to the sum of the forces exerted on each element. Similarly, the total voltage drop across a group of electrical elements in series is equal to the sum of the voltage drops across each element. Thus, in constructing a direct analog, series mechanical elements are replaced by analogous series electrical elements.

For parallel mechanical elements, the force acting on each element is the same, and for parallel electrical elements the voltage drop across each element is the same. Thus, in a direct analog, parallel mechanical elements should be replaced by equivalent electrical elements in parallel. A direct analog is also called a force-voltage analog in that force and voltage are analogous quantities.

The other type of analog is the inverse analog. To construct an inverse analog, it should first be noted that the *total current* flowing through a group of electrical elements in parallel is the *sum* of the currents in each element. This is analogous to the fact that the *total force* acting on a group of mechanical elements in series is the *sum* of the forces acting on each element. Thus, to construct an inverse analog, series mechanical elements must be replaced by parallel electrical elements. Similarly, in an inverse analog, it may be shown that parallel mechanical elements should be replaced by series electrical elements. Thus, the arrangement of series and parallel elements is inverted in constructing an inverse analog (i.e., series elements are replaced by parallel elements and vice versa). An inverse analog is also called a force-current analog in that force and current are analogous quantities.

Analogous quantities for an inverse analog may be determined by comparing the equation of operation for the parallel mechanical system of Fig. 2.15 with that for the series electrical system of Fig. 2.8a. The equation of operation for the parallel mechanical system of Fig. 2.15 is given by Eq. (2.39). Multiplication of both sides of Eq. (2.39) by D gives

$$\dot{x} = \left(\frac{D}{K} + \frac{1}{B} + \frac{1}{MD} \right) f \qquad (2.48)$$

The operation of the series electrical circuit of Fig. 2.8a is described by Eq. (2.25), which has the same form as Eq. (2.48). Comparison of corresponding terms in Eqs. (2.25) and (2.48) yields the analogous quantities for an inverse analog that are shown in Table 2.2.

ILLUSTRATIVE EXAMPLE. Let it be desired to determine the electrical analog for the mechanical system of Fig. 2.14b by using (1) the direct analog, (2) the inverse analog.

SOLUTION. (1) The direct analog for the mechanical system of Fig. 2.14b is shown in Fig. 2.14c. Note that the capacitor C_1 is in parallel with the

TABLE 2.2. ANALOGOUS QUANTITIES IN AN INVERSE (FORCE-CURRENT) ANALOG

Translational mechanical system	Force	Velocity	Spring constant	Damping coefficient	Mass
	f	x	K	B	M
Electrical system	Current	Voltage	Reciprocal of inductance	Reciprocal of resistance	Capacitance
	I	E	$\dfrac{1}{L}$	$\dfrac{1}{R}$	C

series combination of L, C_2, and R, just as the spring K_1 of Fig. 2.14b is in parallel with the series combination of M, K_2, and B. The equation of operation for the electrical circuit of Fig. 2.14c is

$$E = ZI = \frac{1}{\dfrac{1}{1/C_1D} + \dfrac{1}{LD + R + 1/C_2D}}\, I$$

or $$E = \frac{C_2(LD^2 + R\,D + 1/C_2)}{C_1C_2[LD^2 + RD + (1/C_1 + 1/C_2)]}\frac{I}{D}$$

or $$\frac{E}{LD^2 + RD + 1/C_2} = \frac{1/C_1}{LD^2 + RD + (1/C_1 + 1/C_2)}\,Q \qquad (2.41a)$$

Comparison of corresponding terms in Eqs. (2.41) and (2.41a) verifies the analogous quantities given in Table 2.1.

(2) The resulting inverse analog for Fig. 2.14b is shown in Fig. 2.14d. In Fig. 2.14d, it is to be noted that the inductor L_1 is in series with the parallel combination of C, L_2, and R, whereas in Fig. 2.14b the spring K_1 is in parallel with the series combination of M, K_2, and B. The equation of operation for the electrical circuit of Fig. 2.14d is

$$E = ZI = \left(L_1D + \frac{1}{CD + 1/R + 1/L_2D}\right)I$$

or $$I = \frac{RL_2[CD^2 + (1/R)D + 1/L_2]}{RL_1L_2[CD^2 + (1/R)D + (1/L_1 + 1/L_2)]}\frac{E}{D}$$

or $$\frac{I}{CD^2 + (1/R)D + 1/L_2} = \frac{1/L_1}{CD^2 + (1/R)D + (1/L_1 + 1/L_2)}\frac{E}{D}$$

$$(2.41b)$$

Comparison of corresponding terms in Eqs. (2.41) and (2.41b) verifies the analogous quantities given in Table 2.2. In the inverse analogy, velocity is analogous to voltage, and thus displacement is analogous to the integral of voltage.

Comparison of corresponding terms in Eqs. (2.17) and (2.21) shows that a direct (torque-force) analog may be developed in which series translational mechanical elements are replaced by series rotational elements. Similarly, parallel translational elements should be replaced by parallel rotational elements.

2.6 Scale Factors. Because of the convenience of working with electrical equipment, ordinarily an electrical analog is constructed for some other system. Scale factors ensure that the values of the voltages and currents in the electrical analog will be reasonable. For example, in a direct analog, analogous quantities are force-voltage and velocity-current, hence

$$f = k_E E \qquad (2.49)$$

$$\frac{dx}{dt} = k_I I \qquad (2.50)$$

Thus, if the maximum value of f is 1,000 lb and the maximum desired voltage is 100 volts, then

$$k_E = \frac{f}{E} = 10 \text{ lb/volt}$$

In this case, one volt corresponds to 10 lb of force.

To determine the other analogous relationships, first write the force equations for a mass, a damper, and a spring. That is,

$$f = M \frac{d}{dt}\left(\frac{dx}{dt}\right) \qquad (2.51)$$

$$f = B \frac{dx}{dt} \qquad (2.52)$$

$$f = Kx \qquad \text{or} \qquad \frac{df}{dt} = K \frac{dx}{dt} \qquad (2.53)$$

The voltage equations for an inductor, resistor, and capacitor are

$$E = L \frac{d}{dt} I$$

$$E = RI$$

$$\frac{dE}{dt} = \frac{1}{C} I$$

The preceding expressions may be written in the form

$$k_E E = \frac{k_E}{k_I} L \frac{d}{dt} k_I I \qquad (2.54)$$

$$k_E E = \frac{k_E}{k_I} R k_I I \qquad (2.55)$$

$$\frac{d}{dt} k_E E = \frac{k_E}{k_I} \frac{1}{C} k_I I \qquad (2.56)$$

By comparison of Eqs. (2.51) and (2.54), it follows that to have $f = k_E E$ and $dx/dt = k_I I$, then $M = (k_E/k_I)L$ or

$$L = kM \tag{2.57}$$

where $k = k_I/k_E$.

Comparison of Eqs. (2.52) and (2.55) shows that

$$R = kB \tag{2.58}$$

Comparison of Eqs. (2.53) and (2.56) yields

$$C = \frac{1}{kK} \tag{2.59}$$

For the case in which $k = 1$, the preceding analogous relationships are the same as those given in Table 2.1.

Time Scale. For systems which are extremely fast acting, it may be desired to slow down the solution on the electric analog. Similarly, for extremely slow systems it may be desired to speed up the solution. By letting t represent actual time for a phenomenon to occur in the actual system and τ represent the time for the corresponding phenomenon to take place in the analog, then

$$\tau = at \tag{2.60}$$

where t = actual time of phenomenon
τ = time in analog

If a phenomenon takes 1 sec to complete in actual time t and if $a = 10$, then $\tau = at = 10$ or the solution has been slowed down on the analog by a factor of 10. Hence, for $a > 1$ the solution is slowed down and for $a < 1$ the solution is sped up.

When a time scale change is effected, events in the electric analog occur in analog time τ; hence, writing Eqs. (2.54), (2.55), and (2.56) in terms of τ gives

$$k_E E = \frac{L}{k}\frac{d}{d\tau}k_I I$$

$$k_E E = \frac{R}{k}k_I I$$

$$\frac{d}{d\tau}k_E E = \frac{1}{kC}k_I I$$

Differentiation of Eq. (2.60) shows that $d\tau/dt = a$, hence

$$\frac{dI}{d\tau} = \frac{dt}{d\tau}\frac{dI}{dt} = \frac{1}{a}\frac{dI}{dt} \qquad \text{and} \qquad \frac{dE}{d\tau} = \frac{1}{a}\frac{dE}{dt}$$

Expressing the equations for the electrical elements in terms of time t gives

$$k_E E = \frac{L}{ka} \frac{d}{dt} k_I I \tag{2.61}$$

$$k_E E = \frac{R}{k} k_I I \tag{2.62}$$

$$\frac{d}{dt} k_E E = \frac{a}{kC} k_I I \tag{2.63}$$

By comparison of Eqs. (2.51) and (2.61), it follows that to have $f = k_E E$ and $dx/dt = k_I I$, then $M = L/ka$ or

$$L = akM \tag{2.64}$$

Comparison of Eqs. (2.52) and (2.62) shows that

$$R = kB \tag{2.65}$$

Comparison of Eqs. (2.53) and (2.63) shows that

$$C = \frac{a}{k} \frac{1}{K} \tag{2.66}$$

For the case in which $a = 1$ and $k = 1$ the preceding results are identical to those given in Table 2.1.

The corresponding relationships for an inverse analog are developed in a similar manner. In this analog, force and current are analogous quantities as are voltage and velocity; hence, the desired scale factors are

$$f = k_I I \tag{2.67}$$

$$\frac{dx}{dt} = k_E E \tag{2.68}$$

Replacing k by k_I/k_E in Eqs. (2.61), (2.62), and (2.63) shows that all of the scale factors cancel out. Hence, these equations are merely modified forms of the basic relationships for an inductor, resistor, and capacitor respectively. Solving Eqs. (2.61), (2.62), and (2.63) for $k_I I$ gives

$$\frac{d}{dt} k_I I = \frac{ka}{L} k_E E \tag{2.69}$$

$$k_I I = \frac{k}{R} k_E E \tag{2.70}$$

$$k_I I = \frac{kC}{a} \frac{d}{dt} k_E E \tag{2.71}$$

Comparison of Eqs. (2.53) and (2.69) reveals that to have $f = k_I I$ and $dx/dt = k_E E$, then $K = ka/L$ or

$$L = ak \frac{1}{K} \tag{2.72}$$

Similarly comparing Eq. (2.52) with (2.70) and comparing Eq. (2.51) with (2.71), shows that

$$R = k\frac{1}{B} \tag{2.73}$$

$$C = \frac{a}{k}M \tag{2.74}$$

For the case in which $a = 1$ and $k = 1$, these relationships become identical to those given in Table 2.2.

2.7 Thermal Systems. For small temperature differences, the rate of heat transferred into a body is proportional to the temperature difference across the body.

$$Q = hA(T_1 - T) = \frac{T_1 - T}{R_T} \tag{2.75}$$

where Q = rate of heat flow
h = coefficient of heat transfer of the surface of the body
A = surface area
T = the temperature of the body
T_1 = temperature of the surrounding medium

and the symbol $R_T = 1/hA$ means equivalent thermal resistance and will soon be shown to be analogous to the electrical resistance R.

The rate of change of temperature of the body dT/dt is related to the rate of heat transfer into the body by the expression

$$Q = Mc\frac{dT}{dt} = C_T DT \tag{2.76}$$

where c = average specific heat of the body
M = mass
$C_T = Mc$ is the equivalent thermal capacitance

The equation for a resistor and a capacitor may be written in the form

$$I = \frac{1}{R}E \tag{2.77}$$

and
$$I = CDE \tag{2.78}$$

Comparison of Eq. (2.77) with Eq. (2.75) and of Eq. (2.78) with Eq. (2.76) shows the following quantities to be analogous.

$$\begin{matrix} T \sim E & Q \sim I \\ R_T \sim R & C_T \sim C \end{matrix} \tag{2.79}$$

This is the direct, or temperature-voltage, analog.

In Fig. 2.17*a* is shown an insulated container. The liquid is stirred so that the temperature T of the liquid is constant throughout. The equation for the heat transfer into the liquid is given by Eq. (2.75). Because

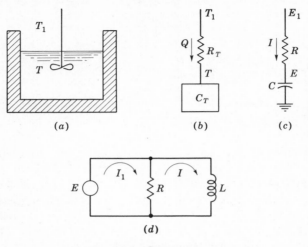

(a) (b) (c)

(d)

FIG. 2.17. Thermal system.

this equation has the same form as the resistor equation, it is represented as a thermal resistor R_T in the equivalent thermal circuit of Fig. 2.17*b*. Similarly, the equation for the heat stored in the liquid is given by Eq. (2.76). Because this equation has the same form as the capacitor equation, it is represented as a thermal reservoir in Fig. 2.17*b*. The equation of operation for this thermal circuit is

$$Q = \frac{T_1 - T}{R_T} = C_T D T$$

Solving for T gives

$$T = \frac{T_1}{1 + (R_T C_T)D} \tag{2.80}$$

The electrical circuit which is the direct analog of the thermal circuit is shown in Fig. 2.17*c*. The equation of operation for the electrical circuit is

$$I = \frac{E_1 - E}{R} = C D E$$

Solving for E gives

$$E = \frac{E_1}{1 + (RC)D} \tag{2.81}$$

In the direct analog, series thermal elements are replaced by analogous electrical elements in series. Similarly, parallel thermal elements are replaced by analogous electrical elements in parallel. For thermal systems, there are only two elements.

The inverse, or temperature-current, analog is developed by first writing the equation for a resistor and inductor in the form

$$E = RI \tag{2.82}$$
$$E = LDI \tag{2.83}$$

Comparison with Eqs. (2.75) and (2.76) reveals the following analogous relationships:

$$T \sim I \qquad Q \sim E$$
$$R_T \sim \frac{1}{R} \qquad C_T \sim L \tag{2.84}$$

The inverse analog of Fig. 2.17*b* is constructed by replacing the thermal resistor R_T and thermal capacitor C_T which are in series by an electrical resistor R and inductor L as shown in Fig. 2.17*d*. Because the thermal elements R_T and C_T have the same rate of heat flow Q then each electrical element R and C must have the same voltage E. The temperature of the thermal reservoir is T and thus the inductor current is I. Similarly, the temperature difference across the thermal resistor is $T_1 - T$, and the electrical resistor current is $I_1 - I$. The equation of operation for the inverse analog, Fig. 2.17*d*, is

$$E = R(I_1 - I) = LDI$$

Solving for I gives

$$I = \frac{I_1}{1 + (L/R)D} \tag{2.85}$$

For any circuit, there are but two possible analogs: the inverse analog in which the series-parallel arrangement is inverted, and the direct analog in which the series-parallel arrangement is retained.

2.8 Fluid Systems. In working with fluid systems, it is necessary to distinguish if the fluid is incompressible or compressible. For incompressible fluids, it suffices to work with volume rate of flow. For compressible fluids, it is necessary to work with the mass rate of flow.

Incompressible Fluids. When the pressure difference across a flow restriction is small, the volume rate of flow Q is proportional to the pressure drop $P_1 - P$ across the restriction.

$$Q = \frac{P_1 - P}{R_F} \tag{2.86}$$

where R_F is the equivalent fluid resistance.

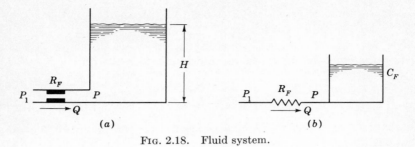

FIG. 2.18.   Fluid system.

The rate of flow into a tank, such as that shown in Fig. 2.18a, is equal to the cross sectional area A of the tank times the rate of change of height.

Thus
$$Q = ADH = \frac{A}{\rho} DP = C_F DP \qquad (2.87)$$

where $P = \rho H$ in which ρ is the density of the fluid
H = the head
$C_F = A/\rho$ = equivalent fluid capacitance

The equation of operation for the fluid system of Fig. 2.18a is

$$Q = \frac{P_1 - P}{R_F} = C_F DP$$

Solving for P gives

$$P = \frac{P_1}{1 + (R_F C_F)D} \qquad (2.88)$$

Replacing P by ρH yields the equation for the head H. In Fig. 2.18b is shown the fluid circuit representation for this system.

Comparison of Eqs. (2.86) and (2.87) with Eqs. (2.77) and (2.78) shows the following quantities to be analogous.

$$\begin{array}{cc} P \sim E & Q \sim I \\ R_F \sim R & C_F \sim C \end{array} \qquad (2.89)$$

These are analogous quantities for the direct, or pressure-voltage, analog. The electrical circuit which is the direct analog for the fluid system of Fig. 2.18b is the same as shown in Fig. 2.17c.

Comparison of Eqs. (2.86) and (2.87) with Eqs. (2.82) and (2.83) yields the analogous relationships for the inverse, or pressure-current, analog. Thus,

$$\begin{array}{cc} P \sim I & Q \sim E \\ R_F \sim \dfrac{1}{R} & C_F \sim L \end{array} \qquad (2.90)$$

The inverse analog for the fluid system of Fig. 2.18b is the same as that shown in Fig. 2.17d.

Compressible Fluids. For small pressure differences, the mass rate of flow M through a restriction is proportional to the pressure difference $P_1 - P$.

$$M = \frac{P_1 - P}{R_F} \tag{2.91}$$

where R_F is the equivalent fluid resistance. In Fig. 2.19a is shown a tank of constant volume V. The equation of state for the fluid in the

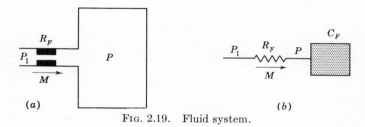

(a)

(b)

FIG. 2.19. Fluid system.

tank is

$$PV = WRT$$

The flow into such a tank is usually isothermal. Thus, differentiation of both sides of the equation of state with respect to time and solving for $M = dW/dt$ gives

$$M = \frac{dW}{dt} = \frac{V}{RT} \frac{d}{dt} P = \frac{V}{RT} DP = C_F DP \tag{2.92}$$

where $C_F = V/RT$ is equivalent fluid capacitance. In Fig. 2.19b is shown the fluid circuit representation for this system. The equation of operation is

$$P = \frac{P_1}{1 + (R_F C_F)D} \tag{2.93}$$

The analogous relationships for the direct, or pressure-voltage, analog are the same as those given by Eq. (2.89) except that Q is replaced by M. The electric circuit which is the direct analog is the same as Fig. 2.17c.

Similarly, the analogous relationships for the inverse, or pressure-current, analog are the same as those given by Eq. (2.90) with Q replaced by M, and the electric circuit which is the inverse analog is the same as Fig. 2.17d.

A major use of analogs is that often it is easier to study experimentally one type of system rather than another. For example, it may be easier to change a resistor rather than a coefficient of viscous friction. Whenever possible, it is best to work with the system directly rather than to consider the operation of an analogous system. This eliminates the

chance of error in construction of the analogy. Also, when carried far
enough analogies usually break down because things which are physically possible for one component may be impossible for the analogous
component.

2.9 Comparators and Integrators.   When the reference input and the
feedback signal are each represented by the angular position of a shaft,
then a differential gear train may be used to measure the difference.   A

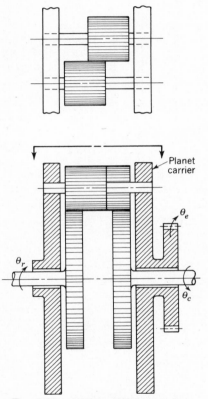

FIG. 2.20.   Differential gear train.

schematic representation of such a gear train is shown in Fig. 2.20.
The equation of operation is

$$\theta_e = \frac{\theta_r - \theta_c}{2} \tag{2.94}$$

where θ_e is the angular position of the planet carrier or cage which is a
measure of the error, the shaft position θ_r is the reference input, and θ_c is

the feedback angular position. Such a device might be used as the comparator of a system used for the remote control of the angular position θ_c of a large mass such as a radar tracking antenna. The use of two differentials, one for azimuth and one for elevation, is required for orientation of an object in space.

For a typical control system, the planet carrier is connected to a power-amplifying device such that when θ_e is positive a torque is transmitted to increase θ_c and when θ_e is negative a torque is applied to decrease θ_c. When θ_e is zero, then the value of θ_c remains constant. For this case, it is seen from Eq. (2.94) that $\theta_c = \theta_r$.

To understand the operation of this device better, suppose initially that $\theta_e = 0$ and also $\theta_c = \theta_r = 0$. If the reference input position is instantaneously increased by 10°, then from Eq. (2.94) it follows that θ_e changes by 5°. This in turn causes a torque to be transmitted to increase θ_c. As θ_c increases, the planet carrier gradually returns to its initial position. Thus, when $\theta_c = \theta_r = 10°$, then θ_e is again zero.

For subtracting linear motions, one could use a rack and pinion to convert the linear motions to rotations and then use a differential gear train. However, the device shown in Fig. 2.21 subtracts linear motions

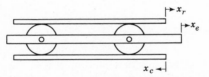

Fig. 2.21. Translational differential mechanism.

directly. With the position of the lower rack x_c held fixed, then it is seen that the motion x_e is one-half the motion of the upper rack x_r. Similarly, with the upper rack held fixed, the motion x_e is one-half that of x_c. However, it should be noticed that x_e decreases as x_c increases. Because it makes no difference whether the movements of x_r and x_c occur at different times or simultaneously, the total movement of x_e is that due to a change in x_r plus that due to a change in x_c. Thus the equation for this mechanism is

$$x_e = \frac{x_r - x_c}{2} \tag{2.95}$$

It should be noted that changing the positive sense of motion for x_c in Fig. 2.21 changes the sign in front of x_c in Eq. (2.95) so that a summing device results.

Integrating Devices. In control systems, the error signal coming from the comparator is often fed into an integrating device. The reason for this is that because of friction, backlash, etc., the system might not detect a very small error, but the integral of a small error continually increases with time so that the system eventually detects it.

A device for integrating mechanically is shown in Fig. 2.22. This is called a ball-and-disk type of integrator. A differential rotation $d\theta$ of

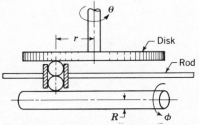

FIG. 2.22.   Ball-and-disk integrator.

the input position θ produces a linear motion $r\, d\theta$ which is transmitted through the two balls to the output shaft of radius R and angular position ϕ. The term r is the distance from the centerline of the input shaft to the balls. The reason for the two balls is to ensure that pure rolling exists between the elements even when the position r is being varied. There could not be pure rolling if there were only one ball. The differential equation of operation for this device is

$$R\, d\phi = r\, d\theta \qquad (2.96)$$

Because this is a continuously acting device, it sums up or integrates all incremental motions. Thus, integration of the preceding expression gives

$$\phi = \frac{1}{R} \int r\, d\theta \qquad (2.97)$$

The value of r is varied in proportion to the function that is to be integrated. The application of this device to integrate an error signal is demonstrated as follows: Let the distance r be varied in proportion to the error signal ($r = C_1 e$), and let the input shaft be driven at a constant angular velocity $\omega = d\theta/dt$ or $d\theta = \omega\, dt$, so that Eq. (2.97) becomes

$$\phi = \frac{1}{R} \int C_1 e\omega\, dt = \frac{C_1\omega}{R} \int e\, dt \qquad (2.98)$$

Thus the position ϕ of the output shaft is seen to be proportional to the time integral of the error. A more thorough treatment of computing mechanisms may be obtained by referring to other publications.[1-3]

A hydraulic valve-and-piston combination which in effect integrates hydraulically is shown in Fig. 2.23a. The position of the valve is

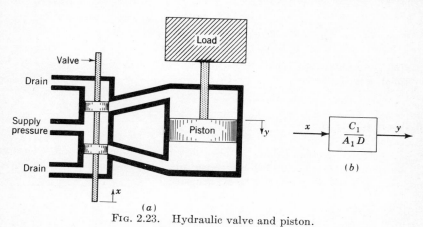

(a)

(b)

FIG. 2.23. Hydraulic valve and piston.

designated by x, and the position of the large piston which moves the load is y. This type of valve is called a balanced valve because the pressure forces acting on it are all balanced so that it requires little force to change its position. When the valve is moved upward, the supply pressure admits oil to the upper side of the piston and the fluid in the lower side of the piston is returned to the drain, where it is recirculated in the system through the pump. For the reverse process, the valve is moved downward so that the supply pressure is connected to the bottom side of the big piston. The upper side of this piston is connected to the upper drain to permit return flow to the pump.

For a constant pressure drop across the valve, the rate of flow to the piston is proportional to the area uncovered by the valve, which is seen to be proportional to the position x. Thus

$$q = C_1 x \qquad (2.99)$$

where q is the rate of flow through the valve into the piston chamber. This rate of flow q into the piston chamber is equal to the rate of change in volume of the chamber, which is equal to the piston velocity Dy times

[1] W. W. Soroka, "Analog Methods in Computation and Simulation," McGraw-Hill Book Company, New York, 1954.
[2] G. W. Michalec, Survey and Evaluation: Analog Computing Mechanisms, *Machine Design*, **31**: (6), 157–179 (Mar. 19, 1959).
[3] H. H. Mabie and F. W. Ocvirk, "Mechanisms and Dynamics of Machinery," 2d ed., pp. 196–225, John Wiley & Sons, Inc., New York, 1963.

the area A_1 of the piston.

$$q = A_1 Dy \tag{2.100}$$

Equating the preceding expressions for q and solving for y gives

$$y = \frac{C_1}{A_1 D} x \tag{2.101}$$

The block-diagram representation for this hydraulic integrator is shown in Fig. 2.23b.

Problems

2.1 For each case given below, perform the indicated operation and determine the constants of integration. For $f(t)$ use the function $f(t) = t^2$. The initial conditions are specified to the right of each case.

(a) $x(t) = \dfrac{1}{D} Df(t)$ $x(0) = 7$

(b) $x(t) = \dfrac{1}{D} D^2f(t)$ $x(0) = 7$

(c) $x(t) = \dfrac{1}{D^2} Df(t)$ $x(0) = 7$

                                    $x'(0) = 4$

(d) $x(t) = \dfrac{1}{D^2} D^2f(t)$ $x(0) = 7$

                                    $x'(0) = 4$

2.2 For each of the mechanical systems shown in Fig. P2.2,

    (a) Determine the equation which relates f and x.

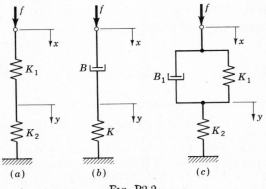

FIG. P2.2

(*b*) Determine the equation which relates *f* and *y*.

(*c*) Determine the equation which relates *x* and *y*.

2.3 For each of the mechanical systems shown in Fig. P2.3, construct the equivalent grounded-chair representation and

(*a*) Determine the equation which relates *f* and *x*.

(*b*) Determine the equation which relates *f* and *y*.

(*c*) Determine the equation which relates *x* and *y*.

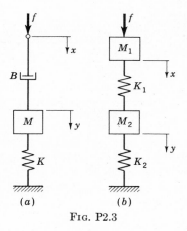

(*a*)   (*b*)

Fig. P2.3

2.4 For the electrical networks shown in Fig. P2.4*a* and *b*,

(*a*) Determine the equation which relates E_1 and I.

(*b*) Determine the equation which relates E_1 and E_2.

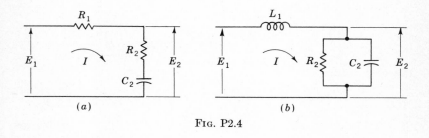

(*a*)   (*b*)

Fig. P2.4

2.5 A schematic diagram of an accelerometer for measuring the linear acceleration d^2x/dt^2 is shown in Fig. P2.5. Determine the operational form for the differential equation which relates *y* (the change in the position of the mass relative to the frame) to the acceleration D^2x of the frame.

Fig. P2.5

2.6 Determine the equation for the torsional spring rate of the stepped shaft shown in Fig. P2.6. Are the individual spring rates for the left and right portion of the stepped shaft added by the parallel or by the series law?

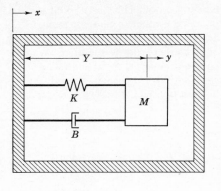

Fig. P2.6

2.7 (*a*) The torque T which is applied to the shaft shown in Fig. P2.7*a* is transmitted directly to the load, which consists of inertia $JD^2\phi$, viscous friction $B_vD\phi$, and external load torque T_L. Determine the equation relating T and the position ϕ of the load.

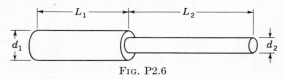

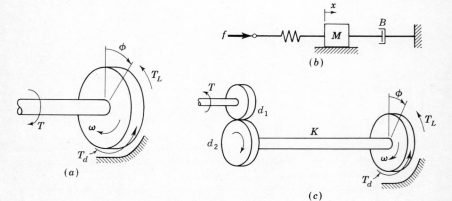

Fig. P2.7

(b) Figure P2.7b shows the direct (force-torque) analog for the system of Fig. P2.7a. Compare the equation relating f and x of this analog with that obtained for T and ϕ in part a.

(c) In Fig. P2.7c the two shafts are connected by gears of diameter d_1 and d_2, respectively. Determine the equation relating T and the position ϕ of the load. (Neglect inertia of the gears.)

2.8 (a) In Fig. P2.8a is shown the stable element of a stable platform for an inertial-guidance system. This stable element consists primarily of two disks which are connected by a flexible post. The torque transmitted through the post is $K_s(\phi_2 - \phi_1)$, where ϕ_1 and ϕ_2 designate the angular positions of the upper and lower disks, respectively. Write the expression for the summation of torques acting on each disk, and then eliminate the parameter ϕ_2 in order to determine the operational form of the differential equation relating the motor torque T and the position ϕ_1. Assume that the viscous damping in the bearing which supports the post is negligibly small.

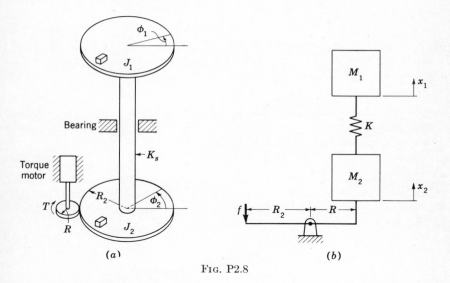

(a)   (b)

Fig. P2.8

(b) In Fig. P2.8b is shown the direct (force-torque) analog for the rotational system shown in Fig. P2.8a. For the mechanical system shown in Fig. P2.8b, determine the equation relating f and x_1. Compare this with the equation relating T and ϕ_1 that was obtained in part a.

(c) Same as Prob. 2.8a except that the torque motor is connected to the upper table rather than the lower table. Determine the equation relating T and ϕ_1.

2.9 For the lever shown in Fig. P2.9a and b, the variation in the applied force is f, and the variation in spring position is x. (The horizontal line represents the reference position of the lever.) For each system,

(a) Determine the equation relating f and x.

(b) Determine the relationship between t and ϕ (where $t = fL_f$ is the variation in applied torque).

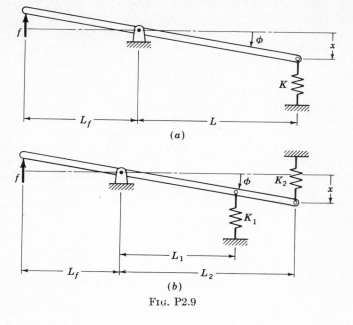

FIG. P2.9

2.10 The lever system shown in Fig. P2.10 is drawn in its reference position. The variation in spring position is designated by x. The variation in applied force is designated by f. (f and x are zero at the reference position.)

   (a) Determine the equation relating f and x;

   (b) determine the relationship between t and ϕ;

where $t = fL_f$ and $x = L\phi$.

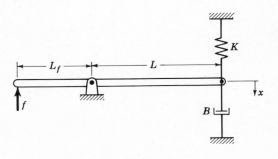

FIG. P2.10

2.11 For the lever system shown in Fig. P2.11,

   (a) Determine the equation relating f and x;

   (b) determine the relationship between t and ϕ;

where $t = fL_f$ and $x = L\phi$.

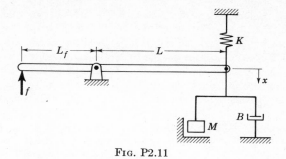

FIG. P2.11

2.12 Two mechanical vibration absorbers are shown in Fig. P2.12. Construct the grounded-chair representation and determine the equation relating f and x for each case.

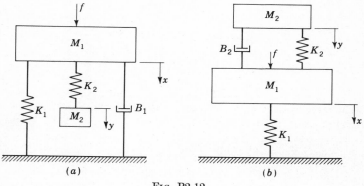

FIG. P2.12

2.13 For each of the mechanical systems shown in Fig. P2.13, construct the grounded chair representation and determine the equation relating f and x.

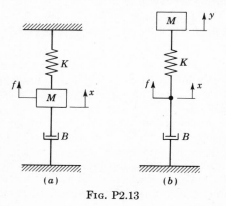

FIG. P2.13

2.14 For the mechanical system shown in Fig. P2.2c, construct the electrical circuit which is the

(a) Direct analog. Determine the equation relating E and I of this electrical system and compare this equation with that relating f and x of Fig. P2.2c.

(b) Inverse analog. Determine the equation relating E and I of this electrical system, and compare this equation with that relating x and f of Fig. P2.2c.

2.15 For the electrical system shown in Fig. P2.4b, construct the mechanical circuit which is the

(a) Direct analog. Determine the equation relating f and x of this mechanical system, and compare this equation with that relating E_1 and I of Fig. P2.4b.

(b) Inverse analog. Determine the equation relating x and f of this mechanical system, and compare this equation with that relating E_1 and I of Fig. P2.4b.

2.16 For the mechanical system shown in Fig. P2.16,

(a) Determine the differential equation relating f and x.

(b) Construct the direct (force-voltage) analog.

(c) Construct the inverse (force-current) analog.

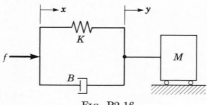

FIG. P2.16

2.17 The parameters for a mechanical system are $M = 10$ lb$_f$/(in.)(sec^2), $B = 5{,}000$ lb$_f$/(in.)(sec), and $K = 2{,}500$ lb$_f$/in. It is estimated that $f_{max} = 500$ lb$_f$ and $\dot{x}_{max} = 5$ in./sec. Determine what size resistor, inductor, and capacitor to use in the direct analog such that $E_{max} = 100$ volts and $I_{max} = 10$ amps.

After the analog has been made, it is found that $E_{max} = 50$ volts and $I_{max} = 4$ amps. What were the actual values of f_{max} and $\dot{x}_{max}$?

What size resistor, inductor, and capacitor should be used to speed up the solution of this problem by a factor of 10?

2.18 Same as Prob. 2.17, except for an inverse rather than direct analog.

2.19 The differential equation for a series RLC circuit is

$$E = \left(LD + R + \frac{1}{CD}\right) I$$

(a) Construct the mechanical circuit which is the direct (force-voltage) analog for the series RLC circuit. Determine the equation for the force f as a function of velocity $\dot{x}$. (Label mass M_a, spring K_a, and damper B_a.)

(b) Construct the mechanical circuit which is the inverse analog for the series RLC circuit. Determine the equation for velocity $\dot{x}$ as a function of force f. (Label mass as M_b, spring K_b, and damper B_b.)

(c) Compare the results of parts (a) and (b) above, and then suggest analogous quantities in constructing the dual of a mechanical circuit. (Duals are two different mechanical circuits whose differential equations have the same form.)

2.20 For the manometer shown in Fig. P2.20 determine the equation of motion relating the pressure P at the open end to the position x. The length of the measuring column is L, the cross-sectional area is A, and the density is ρ.

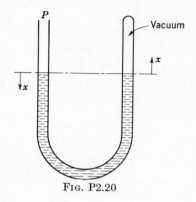

P

Vacuum

x

x

FIG. P2.20

2.21 For the thermometer shown in Fig. P2.21, the temperature of the sur-rounding medium is T_1, the temperature of the glass enclosure is T_2, and the temperature of the fluid in the thermometer is T. The rate of heat flow from the surrounding medium to the glass is $Q_1 = (T_1 - T_2)/R_{T_1}$. The rate of heat flow from the glass to the fluid is $Q_2 = (T_2 - T)/R_{T_2}$.

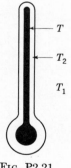

T

T_2

T_1

FIG. P2.21

The rate of temperature change of the glass is $DT_2 = (Q_1 - Q_2)/C_{T_1}$, and the rate of change of temperature of the fluid is $DT = Q_2/C_{T_2}$.

Construct the thermal circuit representation for this system and then deter-mine the equation for the temperature T of the fluid as a function of the surround-ing temperature T_1.

2.22 In Fig. P2.22 is shown an oven which is supplied with heat from an electric source. The rate of heat supplied is proportional to the voltage, $Q_s =$

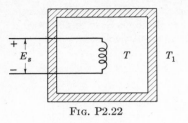

FIG. P2.22

KE_s.   The rate at which heat is lost through the walls is $Q = (T - T_1)/R_T$. The rate of change of temperature of the oven is

$$DT = \frac{Q_s - Q}{C_T}$$

Construct the thermal circuit representation for this system and then determine the equation for the temperature T of the oven as a function of the applied voltage E_s and the surrounding temperature T_1.

2.23   In Fig. P2.23 is shown a fluid system of two tanks in series.   Construct the fluid circuit representation for this system.   Determine the equation for the head H as a function of the inlet pressure P_1 (P_2 should not appear in this equation).

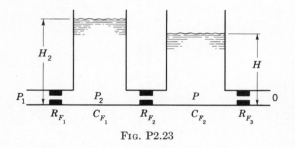

FIG. P2.23

2.24   Same as Prob. 2.23 except for the system shown in Fig. P2.24.

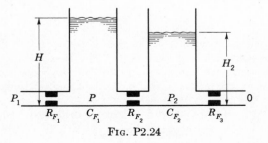

FIG. P2.24

2.25 In Fig. P2.25 is shown a tank in which flow is supplied at a rate Q_s. Construct the fluid circuit representation for this system. Determine the equation for the head H as a function of P_1 and Q_s.

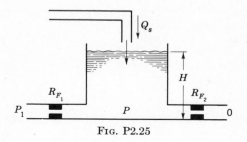

FIG. P2.25

2.26 In Fig. P2.26 is shown a tank with two inlets. Determine the equation for the pressure P as a function of P_1 and P_2.

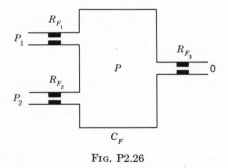

FIG. P2.26

2.27 In Fig. P2.27 are shown two tanks in series. Determine the equation for the pressure P as a function of the inlet pressure P_1 (P_2 should not appear in the equation).

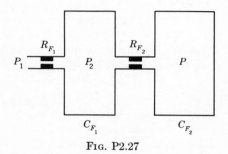

FIG. P2.27

3

Representation of control systems

In this chapter it is shown how to obtain the overall block-diagram representation for some typical control systems. In brief, the method employed is to obtain the block diagram for each component or process and then "hook up," or connect, the corresponding inputs and outputs for each diagram to obtain the one overall representation for the system. The techniques which are presented in later chapters for determining the operating characteristics of control systems are based on a knowledge of the overall block-diagram representation for the system.

3.1 Linearization of Nonlinear Functions. The most powerful methods of system analysis have been developed for linear control systems. For a linear control system all of the relationships between the variables are linear differential equations, usually with constant coefficients. The reason that differential equations rather than algebraic equations are obtained is that in feedback control systems the variables are functions of time. For example, in controlling temperature, the actuating signal causes a change in heat flow, but time is required for this added heat to bring the temperature to its desired value. In speed control systems, the actuating signal causes a change in power of the prime mover, but time is required for the engine to accelerate or decelerate to its desired speed. Similarly, in pressure control systems, it takes time to bring the pressure in a chamber to some desired value.

Actual control systems usually contain some nonlinear elements. Such elements would in turn yield nonlinear differential equations for the system. In the following it is shown how the equations for nonlinear elements may be linearized. Thus, the resulting differential equation of operation for the system becomes linear.

In Fig. 3.1a is shown a mechanical linkage which is used for obtaining the square of a number. The point B is the center of the right-angle linkage ($\alpha + \beta = 90°$) and is constrained to move in the vertical track. One leg of this right-angle linkage passes through the slider, which pivots at point A. The other leg of the linkage must always pass through the

46

slider at point C, which in turn is constrained to move in the horizontal track. Because of the geometry of this device, triangles BOC and AOB will always be similar. Therefore

$$\frac{Y}{X} = \frac{X}{K}$$

or

$$Y = \frac{X^2}{K} \tag{3.1}$$

where K is a constant.

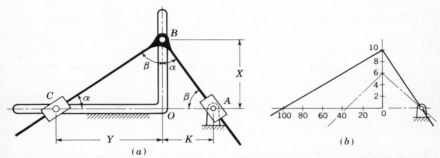

FIG. 3.1. (a) Mechanical squaring device; (b) skeletal representation of squaring device.

Considering X as the input quantity, the position of point C and thus Y, the output, will vary as the square of X. If the operation were reversed so that Y were the input and X the output, this mechanism would be a square-root device in which $X = \sqrt{KY}$. Depending on which scale is used for the input, this device may be used for obtaining squares or square roots, as is illustrated by the skeletal diagram of Fig. 3.1b. The scale of this diagram is for the case in which $K = 1$.

For an equation to be linear, each variable term $X_1, X_2, X_3, \ldots, X_n$ in the equation for Y must be of the first power, and the contribution of each term must be added independently as in the general linear equation

$$Y = C_1 X_1 + C_2 X_2 + C_3 X_3 + \cdots + C_n X_n \tag{3.2}$$

A plot of the nonlinear relationship given by Eq. (3.1) is shown in Fig. 3.2. It is to be noticed that, in the vicinity of the point of interest (X_i, Y_i), the nonlinear function $Y = X^2/K$ is closely approximated by the tangent to the function. For example, consider a new operating point (X, Y) on the curve of the nonlinear function. The abscissa X is seen to be displaced a distance x from X_i. This abscissa X intersects the nonlinear function a vertical distance $y + \epsilon$ from Y_i, and it intersects the tangent a distance y from Y_i. The equation for Y is

$$Y = Y_i + y + \epsilon \approx Y_i + y \tag{3.3}$$

Lowercase letters indicate the variation of the capital-letter parameters from the point of interest or the reference point. From the geome-

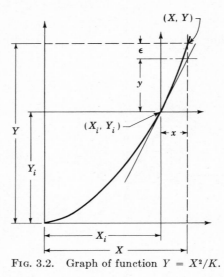

Fig. 3.2.   Graph of function $Y = X^2/K$.

try of Fig. 3.2, it is seen that the slope of the tangent line is

$$\frac{y}{x} = \frac{dY}{dX}\bigg|_i = \text{slope at point } (X_i, Y_i)$$

The symbol $\bigg|_i$ means that the derivative is to be evaluated at the reference condition. Thus

$$y = \frac{dY}{dX}\bigg|_i x = \frac{d}{dX}\left(\frac{X^2}{K}\right)\bigg|_i x = \frac{2X_i}{K} x \tag{3.4}$$

Substitution of y from Eq. (3.4) into Eq. (3.3) yields the following linear approximation for Y:

$$Y \approx Y_i + \frac{2X_i}{K} x \tag{3.5}$$

ILLUSTRATIVE EXAMPLE 1.   Effect a linear approximation for the equation $Y = X^2$ for values of X in the neighborhood of 10, and find the error when using this approximation for $X = 11$. The reference values are $X_i = 10$ and $Y_i = X_i^2 = 100$. Substitution of $x = X - X_i = 1$ and

$K = 1$ into Eq. (3.5) gives

$$Y \approx 100 + \frac{2(10)(1)}{1} = 120$$

The exact value is $Y = X^2 = 121$; thus the error is 1 part in 121, less than 1 percent.

A more general procedure for obtaining a linear approximation is to use the expression derived in calculus[1,2] for approximating the incremental variation ΔY for a function $Y = F(X_1, X_2, \ldots, X_n)$ of n independent variables. That is,

$$\Delta Y = \frac{\partial Y}{\partial X_1}\Big|_i \Delta X_1 + \frac{\partial Y}{\partial X_2}\Big|_i \Delta X_2 + \cdots + \frac{\partial Y}{\partial X_n}\Big|_i \Delta X_n \qquad (3.6)$$

By using the lowercase letters to represent variations from the reference condition, it follows that

$$
\begin{aligned}
Y - Y_i &= \Delta Y = y \\
X_1 - X_{1_i} &= \Delta X_1 = x_1 \\
X_2 - X_{2_i} &= \Delta X_2 = x_2 \\
X_n - X_{ni} &= \Delta X_n = x_n
\end{aligned}
\qquad (3.7)
$$

Thus, the general expression for obtaining a linear approximation for a nonlinear function is

$$y = C_1 x_1 + C_2 x_2 + \cdots + C_n x_n \qquad (3.8)$$

where
$$C_1 = \frac{\partial Y}{\partial X_1}\Big|_i \qquad C_2 = \frac{\partial Y}{\partial X_2}\Big|_i \qquad \text{etc.}$$

Evaluation of these partial derivatives at the reference condition yields constants.

The application of the general expression Eq. (3.8) to the nonlinear equation $Y = (1/K)X^2$ is effected as follows: The independent variable is X, which corresponds to X_1 in the general equation. Thus

$$C_1 = \frac{\partial Y}{\partial X}\Big|_i = \frac{\partial}{\partial X}\left(\frac{X^2}{K}\right)\Big|_i = \frac{2X}{K}\Big|_i = \frac{2X_i}{K}$$

From Eq. (3.8)

$$y = C_1 x = \frac{2X_i}{K} x$$

The total value of Y is

$$Y \approx Y_i + y = Y_i + \frac{2X_i}{K} x \qquad (3.9)$$

[1] Louis A. Pipes, "Applied Mathematics for Engineers and Physicists," 2d ed., McGraw-Hill Book Company, New York, 1958.

[2] I. S. Sokolnikoff and E. S. Sokolnikoff, "Higher Mathematics for Engineers and Physicists," 2d ed., McGraw-Hill Book Company, New York, 1941.

This is the result obtained by the preceding geometric interpretation and given by Eq. (3.5).

The need for linearizing nonlinear relationships is frequently encountered in control engineering. For example, most mechanical speed control systems incorporate a flyball governor for sensing the speed error. This is a centrifugal device, so that a force is obtained which is proportional to the square of the speed. In the design of hydraulic equipment in which the working medium is an incompressible fluid, one encounters the nonlinear equations which govern such fluid flow. Similarly, the working medium for pneumatic equipment is air, whose flow is described by nonlinear relationships.

ILLUSTRATIVE EXAMPLE 2. Effect the linear approximation for P in the equation of state $PV = WRT$. The reference conditions are $P_i = 100$ lb$_f$/ft^2, $V_i = 100$ ft^3, $W_i = 10/53.3$ lb$_m$, and $T_i = 1{,}000°$R. Determine the percent error in using this approximation for P when $V = 110$ ft^3, $T = 1{,}200°$R, and W remains the same. The constant R is 53.3 ft-lb$_f$/lb$_m$/°R.

SOLUTION. From the equation of state and the fact that W remains constant, it is seen that P is a function of the independent variables T and V, or $P = F(T,V)$. Application of Eq. (3.8) to obtain the variation p of the pressure from its reference value yields

$$p = \frac{\partial P}{\partial T}\Big|_i t + \frac{\partial P}{\partial V}\Big|_i v \tag{3.10}$$

The partial derivatives are evaluated from the equation of state as follows:

$$\frac{\partial P}{\partial T}\Big|_i = \frac{\partial}{\partial T}\left(\frac{WRT}{V}\right)\Big|_i = \frac{WR}{V}\Big|_i = \frac{(10)(53.3)}{(53.3)(100)} = 0.10$$

$$\frac{\partial P}{\partial V}\Big|_i = \frac{\partial}{\partial V}\left(\frac{WRT}{V}\right)\Big|_i = \frac{-WRT}{V^2}\Big|_i = -1.0$$

The linearized approximation for P is

$$P \approx P_i + p = P_i + 0.1t - v \tag{3.11}$$

From the given information, it follows that

$$v = V - V_i = 110 - 100 = 10$$
$$t = T - T_i = 200$$

Thus $\qquad P \approx 100 + (0.1)(200) - (10) = 110$ lb$_f$/ft^2

The exact value of P is

$$P = \frac{WRT}{V} = \frac{(10)(53.3)(1{,}200)}{(53.3)(110)} = 109.1$$

Therefore, the percent error is

$$\frac{(109.1 - 110)100}{109.1} = 0.82\%$$

ILLUSTRATIVE EXAMPLE 3. The equation for the flow of an incompressible fluid through a restriction is

$$Q = C_c A \sqrt{\frac{2g}{\rho} (P_1 - P_2)} \tag{3.12}$$

where Q = rate of flow, in.^{3}/sec
$\quad C_c$ = coefficient of discharge (dimensionless)
$P_1 - P_2$ = pressure drop across restriction, psi
$\quad \rho$ = density of fluid, lb$_m$/in.^{3}

Determine the linear approximation for the variation q.

SOLUTION. Because Q is a function of the area A and pressure drop $P_1 - P_2$, then

$$Q = F[A,(P_1 - P_2)]$$

The variation q is

$$q = \frac{\partial Q}{\partial A}\bigg|_i a + \frac{\partial Q}{\partial (P_1 - P_2)}\bigg|_i (p_1 - p_2)$$

The partial derivatives are

$$\frac{\partial Q}{\partial A}\bigg|_i = C_c \sqrt{\frac{2g}{\rho} (P_1 - P_2)}\bigg|_i = \frac{Q}{A}\bigg|_i$$

and

$$\frac{\partial Q}{\partial (P_1 - P_2)}\bigg|_i = \frac{C_c A}{2} \sqrt{\frac{2g}{\rho}} \frac{1}{P_1 - P_2}\bigg|_i = \frac{1}{2} \frac{Q}{P_1 - P_2}\bigg|_i$$

Thus

$$q = Q_i \left[\frac{a}{A_i} + \frac{1}{2} \frac{p_1 - p_2}{(P_1 - P_2)_i} \right] \tag{3.13}$$

ILLUSTRATIVE EXAMPLE 4. For sonic flow of air through a restriction, the mass rate of flow is

$$M = \frac{0.528}{\sqrt{T}} AP \tag{3.14}$$

where T = the inlet temperature, °R
$\quad A$ = area of restriction, in.^{2}
$\quad P$ = inlet pressure, psi

Determine the linearized approximation for the variation m when the inlet temperature T is constant.

SOLUTION.   Because the temperature is constant, the mass rate of flow is a function of A and P.   Thus

$$m = \frac{\partial M}{\partial A}\Big|_i a + \frac{\partial M}{\partial P}\Big|_i p$$

The partial derivatives are

$$\frac{\partial M}{\partial A}\Big|_i = \frac{0.528}{\sqrt{T}} P\Big|_i = \frac{M}{A}\Big|_i$$

and

$$\frac{\partial M}{\partial P}\Big|_i = \frac{0.528}{\sqrt{T}} A\Big|_i = \frac{M}{P}\Big|_i$$

Thus, $$m = M_i \left(\frac{a}{A_i} + \frac{p}{P_i}\right) \qquad (3.15)$$

ILLUSTRATIVE EXAMPLE 5.   For subsonic flow of air through a restriction, the mass rate of flow is

$$M = \frac{1.05}{\sqrt{T}} A \sqrt{(P_1 - P_2)P_2} \qquad (3.16)$$

where T = inlet temperature, °R
     A = area of restriction, in.²
     P_1 = inlet pressure, psi
     P_2 = outlet pressure, psi

Determine the linearized approximation for the variation m when the inlet temperature is constant.

SOLUTION.   The mass rate of flow is a function of A, $P_1 - P_2$, and P_2. Thus

$$m = \frac{\partial M}{\partial A}\Big|_i a + \frac{\partial M}{\partial(P_1 - P_2)}\Big|_i (p_1 - p_2) + \frac{\partial M}{\partial P_2}\Big|_i p_2$$

Evaluating the partial derivatives yields

$$m = \left[\frac{a}{A_i} + \frac{p_1 - p_2}{2(P_1 - P_2)_i} + \frac{p_2}{(2P_2)_i}\right] M_i \qquad (3.17)$$

The same result is obtained if P_1 and P_2 are regarded as the variables rather than $P_1 - P_2$ and P_2.

Geometric Interpretation of Error Introduced by a Linear Approximation. From the linear approximation for the area of a rectangle, it is possible to represent geometrically the error which is introduced.   In Fig. 3.3 is shown a rectangle in which the reference length is L_i and the width W_i. The area of a rectangle is a function of the length L and width W, so that

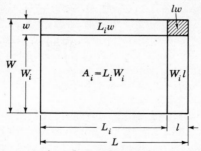

FIG. 3.3. Geometric representation of error incurred from the linear approximation for a rectangle.

the variation in the area from its reference size is obtained as follows:

$$A = F(L,W)$$

$$a = \frac{\partial A}{\partial L}\bigg|_i l + \frac{\partial A}{\partial W}\bigg|_i w$$

The preceding partial derivatives are evaluated from the equation $A = LW$,

$$\frac{\partial A}{\partial L}\bigg|_i = W_i \qquad \text{and} \qquad \frac{\partial A}{\partial W}\bigg|_i = L_i$$

Thus the linearized expression for the area A is

$$A \approx A_i + a = A_i + W_i l + L_i w \tag{3.18}$$

Each term in the preceding expression is represented by an area in Fig. 3.3. The difference between this approximation and the actual area LW is the small shaded portion lw.

ILLUSTRATIVE EXAMPLE 6. Determine the linearized representation for Eq. (2.16), that is

$$F = (MD^2 + BD + K)X - Mg$$

SOLUTION. Because F is a function of X, it follows that

$$f = \frac{\partial F}{\partial X}\bigg|_i x$$

The operator D is not a function of X. Thus, the operator is regarded as a constant in evaluating the preceding partial derivative. That is

$$\frac{\partial F}{\partial X}\bigg|_i = MD^2 + BD + K$$

The resulting linearized equation is

$$f = (MD^2 + BD + K)x$$

This verifies the linearized form given by Eq. (2.17). As illustrated by this example, for equations which are already linear the substitution of lowercase letters for the capital-letter variable terms and dropping out the constant terms (for example, $-Mg$) yields directly the linear equation of operation about the reference point. Constant terms drop out because the partial derivative of a constant is zero.

3.2 Linearization of Operating Curves. In the preceding section, it was shown how equations which are nonlinear could be linearized. However, for many components encountered in control systems, the operating characteristics are given in the form of general operating curves rather than equations. For example, Fig. 3.4 shows a typical family of operat-

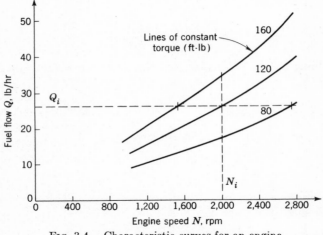

Fig. 3.4. Characteristic curves for an engine.

ing curves for an engine. Usually such curves are determined experimentally, and it would be quite tedious and difficult to express these curves as equations. The linearized equation for the operation of the engine about some reference operating point is obtained as follows: From Fig. 3.4, it is seen that the speed N is a function of the rate of fuel flow Q and the engine torque T, thus

$$N = F(Q,T)$$

Linearization gives

$$n = \frac{\partial N}{\partial Q}\Big|_i q + \frac{\partial N}{\partial T}\Big|_i t$$

The term $\partial N/\partial Q\big|_i$ is the change in speed per change in fuel flow with all other parameters held constant (in this case with T constant). This partial derivative is equal to the reciprocal of the slope of the line of constant torque evaluated at the reference point. That is,

$$\frac{\partial N}{\partial Q}\bigg|_i = \frac{2{,}400 - 1{,}600}{32 - 20} = 66.7$$

The partial derivative $\partial N/\partial T\big|_i$ is the change in speed per change in torque with Q held constant. This is evaluated from a horizontal interpolation of the characteristic operating curves as follows:

$$\frac{\partial N}{\partial T}\bigg|_i = \frac{2{,}730 - 1{,}530}{80 - 160} = -15$$

The minus sign indicates that for a constant Q the speed decreases as the torque increases. Thus, for operation in the vicinity of the point $N_i = 2{,}000$, $Q_i = 26$, and $T_i = 120$, the linearized approximation for N is

$$N \approx N_i + n = N_i + 66.7q - 15t \qquad (3.19)$$

The main difference in working with characteristic operating curves for a component rather than equations is that the partial derivatives are evaluated from a physical interpretation of the curves rather than mathematically from the equation.

3.3 Hydraulic Servomotor. A hydraulic servomotor is shown in Fig. 3.5. A linkage called a *walking beam* connects the input position x, the valve position e, and the piston position y. The center line of the lever when the servomotor is in its reference position is indicated in Fig. 3.5. The

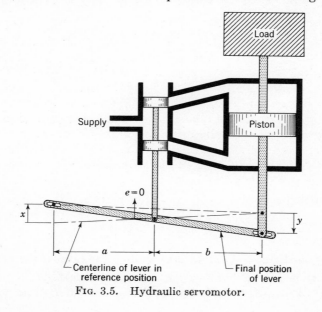

Fig. 3.5. Hydraulic servomotor.

variations in x, e, and y from their reference positions are also indicated. When e is zero, the valve is "line on line" and no flow can go to or from the big piston.

The operation of this servomotor may be visualized as follows: When the input x is changed from the reference position, the walking beam first pivots about the connection at y because the large forces acting on the piston hold it in place temporarily.   This position of the walking beam is shown by the dashed line in Fig. 3.5.   Because of the corresponding movement of e, the valve now admits fluid to the big piston to move it in the direction which makes e zero.   The final position of the walking beam, in which e is again zero and the piston has moved a distance y, is indicated in Fig. 3.5.   For steady-state operation ($e = 0$), the relationship between the input x and the output y is

$$\frac{y}{b} = \frac{x}{a} \qquad \text{or} \qquad y = \frac{b}{a} x$$

The overall block diagram which describes the dynamic as well as the steady-state operation of this servomotor is obtained as follows: In Fig. 3.6a is shown the walking-beam linkage.   For small variations about the

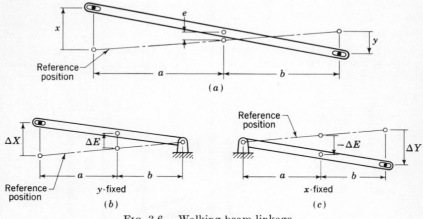

Fig. 3.6.   Walking-beam linkage.

reference position

$$e = \frac{\partial E}{\partial X}\bigg|_i x + \frac{\partial E}{\partial Y}\bigg|_i y \qquad (3.20)$$

The value of $\partial E/\partial X \big|_i$ is obtained by finding the ratio of the change in E for a change in X with all other parameters held constant at the reference condition.   Figure 3.6b illustrates the linkage with Y fixed in the reference position.   From similar triangles,

$$\frac{\partial E}{\partial X}\bigg|_i = \lim_{\substack{\Delta E \to 0 \\ \Delta X \to 0}} \frac{\Delta E}{\Delta X} = \frac{b}{a+b}$$

Similarly, from Fig. 3.6c in which X is fixed in the reference position,

$$\frac{\partial E}{\partial Y}\bigg|_i = \lim_{\substack{\Delta E \to 0 \\ \Delta Y \to 0}} \frac{\Delta E}{\Delta Y} = \frac{-a}{a+b}$$

The minus sign arises because e decreases as y increases.   The substitution of the preceding results into Eq. (3.20) yields the following expression for the walking-beam linkage.

$$e = \frac{b}{a+b}\, x - \frac{a}{a+b}\, y \qquad (3.21)$$

This equation shows that the walking-beam linkage is actually a comparator or summing point.   The preceding result could have been obtained directly by a closer examination of Fig. 3.6a.   It is apparent that the motion of e is the sum of the contribution due to changing x with y fixed, that is, $[b/(a + b)]x$, and that due to changing y with x fixed, that is, $[-a/(a + b)]y$.

For the case in which $a = b$

$$e = \frac{x - y}{2} \qquad (3.22)$$

The block-diagram representation for Eq. (3.22) is shown in Fig. 3.7a.

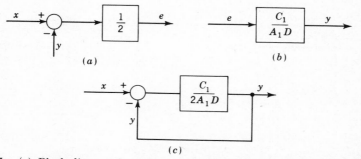

(a)

(b)

(c)

FIG. 3.7.   (a) Block diagram for walking-beam linkage; (b) block diagram for valve and piston; (c) block diagram for servomotor.

The equation for the valve-and-piston combination is given by Eq. (2.101), in which x is replaced by e.   Thus

$$y = \frac{C_1}{A_1 D}\, e \qquad (3.23)$$

The block-diagram representation for the preceding expression is shown in Fig. 3.7b.   Combining Fig. 3.7a and b yields the overall block diagram for the servomotor as shown in Fig. 3.7c.

The overall relationship between the input x and the output y is obtained as follows from the block diagram of Fig. 3.7c:

$$(x - y) \frac{C_1}{2A_1D} = y$$

or

$$\left(1 + \frac{2A_1}{C_1} D\right) y = x$$

Thus

$$(1 + \tau D)y = x \qquad (3.24)$$

where

$$\tau = \frac{2A_1}{C_1}$$

Equation (3.24) is the differential equation relating x and y.   For steady-state operation, both x and y are constant.   The quantity $Dy = dy/dt$ is zero when y is constant, and thus for steady-state operation Eq. (3.24) becomes

$$y = x$$

To determine the transient response of y for a given change in x, it is necessary to solve Eq. (3.24), which is a first-order linear differential equation with constant coefficients.   If, at some arbitrary time $t = 0$, the input x changes instantaneously from its reference position in which $x = 0$ to a new or final position at which $x = x_f$, then a step change, as is illustrated graphically in Fig. 3.8a, has occurred.

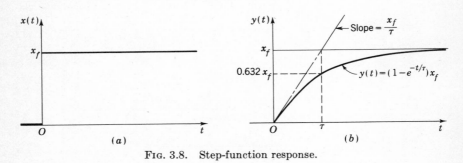

FIG. 3.8.   Step-function response.

The solution of the differential equation given by Eq. (3.24) is

$$y(t) = (1 - e^{-t/\tau})x_f \qquad (3.25)$$

A graph of the response $y(t)$ is shown in Fig. 3.8b.   A characteristic feature of such an exponential response curve is that, when $t = \tau$, then $y(t)$ has undergone 63.2 percent of its total change.   This is proved by letting $t = \tau$ in Eq. (3.25); thus

$$y(\tau) = (1 - e^{-1})x_f = (1 - 0.368)x_f = 0.632x_f \qquad (3.26)$$

Another unique feature of such an exponential response is that the tangent to the curve at $t = 0$ intersects the final value at time $t = \tau$. This is proved as follows:

$$\left.\frac{dy}{dt}\right|_{t=0} = \frac{1}{\tau}\, e^{-t/\tau}x_f \Big|_{t=0} = \frac{x_f}{\tau} \qquad (3.27)$$

Thus, as shown in Fig. 3.8b, the slope of the tangent line is such that it intersects the final value $y(t)_f = x_f$ at $t = \tau$. The term τ is called the time constant and is a measure of the speed of response. When τ is small, the system approaches its new operating condition very fast, and when τ is large, more time is required for the change to occur.

3.4 Temperature Control System. In Fig. 3.9 is shown a system for controlling the output temperature T_o of a chamber, such as an industrial

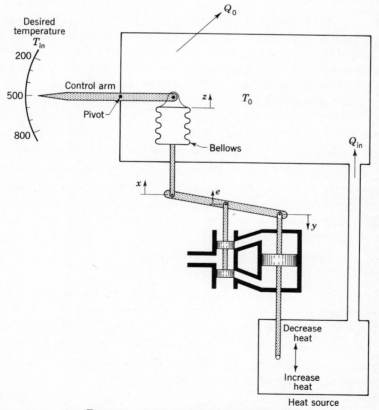

Fig. 3.9. Temperature control system.

oven, a heat-treating furnace, etc. The desired temperature T_{in} is indicated by the pointer on the control arm, which pivots about its center. The other end of the control arm determines the position of the top of the temperature-sensitive bellows. When the pointer is moved to a higher temperature setting, the control arm raises the input position x of the linkage through the liquid-filled bellows. The bellows acts as a rigid connecting link in transmitting this motion because its length is fixed by the temperature of its liquid. This then raises the valve, which admits fluid to the top of the piston to move the piston extension, which actuates the heat source to increase the heat supply.

For the case in which the control arm is set for a desired temperature T_{in}, if the oven temperature T_o decreases, the bellows contracts. (The bellows is filled with a liquid which expands as T_o increases and contracts as T_o decreases.) Thus, as T_o decreases, so does the length of the bellows, which in turn increases x. As just described, when x increases, the piston moves in such a direction as to increase the heat Q_{in} to the oven. This in turn tends to bring the oven temperature T_o back to the desired value.

The overall block-diagram representation of this system for operation in the neighborhood of any reference temperature T_i is obtained by working from the input to the output as follows: The variation z of the position of the top of the bellows from its reference position (i.e., the position when $T_{in} = T_i$) is a function only of the desired temperature T_{in}. That is, $Z = F(T_{in})$, and thus

$$z = \frac{\partial Z}{\partial T_{in}}\bigg|_i t_{in} = C_2 t_{in} \tag{3.28}$$

where $t_{in} = T_{in} - T_i$ is the variation in the desired temperature and $C_2 = \partial Z / \partial T_{in}\big|_i$ is the change in position Z of the top of the bellows per change in T_{in}. Thus, C_2 is equal to the slope of the curve of position Z versus T_{in} evaluated at the reference temperature.

The length L of the temperature-sensitive bellows is a function of the oven temperature T_o, or $L = F(T_o)$. Thus

$$l = \frac{\partial L}{\partial T_o}\bigg|_i t_o = C_3 t_o \tag{3.29}$$

where $l = L - L_i$ is the change in the length of the bellows (L_i is the length of the bellows at the reference temperature), $t_o = T_o - T_i$ is the variation in the oven temperature (note that $T_o|_i = T_{in}|_i = T_i$), and $C_3 = \partial L / \partial T_o\big|_i$ is the change in the length of the bellows per change in temperature of the oven. This is the slope of the curve of L versus T_o evaluated at the reference temperature.

From the geometry of Fig. 3.9, it follows that the change in length l of the temperature-sensitive bellows is equal to the change in the position z

of the top of the bellows minus the change in the position x of the bottom. Thus, $l = z - x$, whence

$$x = z - l \tag{3.30}$$

The block-diagram representation for Eqs. (3.28) to (3.30) is shown in Fig. 3.10. It should be noted from Fig. 3.10 that this is, in effect, the comparator for this temperature controller.

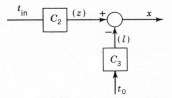

Fig. 3.10. Block diagram for comparator.

The block diagram for the walking-beam, valve-and-piston combination is the same as that shown in Fig. 3.7c.

The rate of heat flow Q_{in} into the oven is a function of the position of the piston Y [that is, $Q_{in} = F(Y)$]; thus

$$q_{in} = \frac{\partial Q_{in}}{\partial Y}\bigg|_i y = C_4 y \tag{3.31}$$

where $C_4 = \partial Q_{in}/\partial Y\big|_i$ is the change in heat supplied per unit change in piston position at the reference condition. It is necessary to obtain experimentally the curve of Q_{in} versus position Y in order to evaluate C_4. The net rate of heat flow into the oven is $q_{in} - q_o$. The total heat accumulated is the time integral $\int(q_{in} - q_o)\,dt$, which is equal to the product $C_5 W t_o$; that is,

$$\int (q_{in} - q_o)\,dt = \frac{q_{in} - q_o}{D} = C_5 W t_o \tag{3.32}$$

where C_5 is the average specific heat of the substance in the oven, W is the total weight, and $t_o = T_o - T_i$ is the corresponding temperature change.

The rate of heat loss Q_o is a function of the temperature difference $T_o - T_a$,

$$Q_o = F(T_o - T_a) \tag{3.33}$$

where T_a is the ambient temperature. Linearization gives

$$q_o = \frac{\partial Q_o}{\partial(T_o - T_a)}\bigg|_i (t_o - t_a) = C_6(t_o - t_a) \tag{3.34}$$

where $\qquad C_6 = \dfrac{\partial Q_o}{\partial(T_o - T_a)}\bigg|_i$

For a given oven, it is possible to plot a curve of Q_o versus $T_o - T_a$. The constant C_6 is the slope of this curve at the given reference point. Eliminating q_o between Eqs. (3.32) and (3.34) gives

$$\frac{q_{in} - C_6(t_o - t_a)}{D} = C_5 W t_o$$

or

$$\frac{q_{in} - C_6 t_o + C_6 t_a}{C_5 W D} = t_o \qquad (3.35)$$

The block-diagram representation for Eqs. (3.31) and (3.35) is shown in Fig. 3.11. Combining the block diagrams of Figs. 3.7c, 3.10, and 3.11 yields the completed overall block diagram shown in Fig. 3.12.

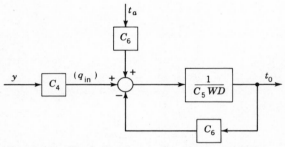

Fig. 3.11. Block diagram for heat source and oven.

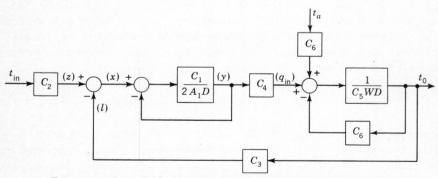

Fig. 3.12. Overall block diagram for temperature control system.

Usually, systems such as this temperature controller are subjected to an external disturbance. By an external disturbance is meant something which acts independently and usually undesirably to affect the operation of the system. In this case, the external disturbance is the ambient temperature t_a. An extraneous or external disturbance may be regarded as an unwanted input to the system which tends to affect the value of the controlled variable.

In determining the dynamic behavior of a system, one is interested in the variation of the system parameters from some reference condition. This is the type of information which is obtainable from the block-diagram representation shown in Fig. 3.12.   If absolute values are desired, it is an easy matter to convert from t_{in} to T_{in} or from t_o to T_o by merely adding the reference value.

In summary, the comparator for this temperature control is the temperature-sensitive bellows assembly.   The desired input is the position z of the top of the bellows, and the variation of the length of the bellows is a measure of the output temperature.   The error $x = z - l$ determines the input position of the walking-beam linkage.   The servomotor serves as an amplifier which produces large hydraulic forces for moving the piston position y to actuate the heat supply.   Thus, the major elements in a feedback control system consist of a comparator and a power amplifier which actuates the system to be controlled.

3.5 Block-diagram Algebra.   It is often desirable to rearrange the form of a block diagram.   In Fig. 3.13 are shown a number of rearrangements which are commonly employed.   It is to be noticed that in all cases the rearrangement does not affect the overall relationship between the input elements (i.e., elements with arrowheads pointing into the diagram) and the output elements (i.e., elements with arrowheads pointing away from the diagram).   There are many possible rearrangements for systems.   However, it is usually desirable to make the ultimate form of the block diagram the same as that shown in Fig. 3.14.   The reason for this is that the methods to be presented later for evaluating the performance of systems are based on systems which are represented in this general form.

By the application of the technique shown in Fig. 3.13*f* to Fig. 3.12 the following results for $G_1(D)$ and $G_2(D)$:

$$G_1(D) = \frac{C_1/2A_1D}{1 + C_1/2A_1D} C_4 = \frac{C_4}{1 + 2A_1D/C_1} = \frac{C_4}{1 + \tau_1 D} \tag{3.36}$$

$$G_2(D) = \frac{1/C_5WD}{1 + C_6/C_5WD} = \frac{1/C_6}{1 + C_5WD/C_6} = \frac{1/C_6}{1 + \tau_2 D} \tag{3.37}$$

where $\qquad \tau_1 = \dfrac{2A_1}{C_1} \qquad$ and $\qquad \tau_2 = \dfrac{C_5W}{C_6}$

The resulting block diagram is shown in Fig. 3.15.   In effect, block-diagram algebra was used to eliminate the minor feedback loops.   A minor feedback loop is an internal feedback loop which takes place within the main loop.

The operational form of the differential equation relating the output t_o

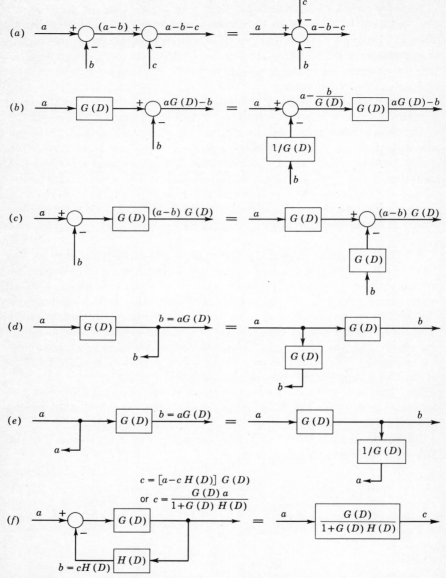

Fig. 3.13. Equivalent block diagrams. (a) Combining interconnected summing points; (b) moving a summing point behind an element; (c) moving a summing point ahead of an element; (d) moving a take-off point behind an element; (e) moving a take-off point ahead of an element; (f) eliminating a minor feedback loop.

of this temperature controller to the input t_{in} and the external disturbance t_a is obtained from Fig. 3.15 as follows: Start with the reference input $C_2 t_{in}$, subtract the feedback signal $C_3 t_o$, and then continue to write the mathematical operations indicated by the feedforward portion of the loop

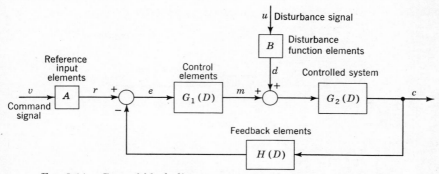

FIG. 3.14. General block-diagram representation for a control system.

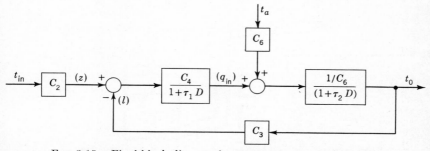

FIG. 3.15. Final block diagram for temperature control system.

until the output t_o is obtained. That is,

$$\left\{\left[(C_2 t_{in} - C_3 t_o)\frac{C_4}{1+\tau_1 D}\right] + C_6 t_a\right\}\frac{1}{C_6(1+\tau_2 D)} = t_o$$

Solving for t_o yields

$$\frac{C_2 C_4 t_{in} - C_3 C_4 t_o + C_6(1 + \tau_1 D)t_a}{C_6(1 + \tau_1 D)(1 + \tau_2 D)} = t_o$$

or

$$t_o = \frac{C_2 C_4 t_{in} + C_6(1 + \tau_1 D)t_a}{C_6(1 + \tau_1 D)(1 + \tau_2 D) + C_3 C_4} \tag{3.38}$$

Equation (3.38) is the operational representation of a linear differential equation with constant coefficients. In Chap. 5, it is shown how linear differential equations with constant coefficients may be solved by use of Laplace transformations.

3.6 Speed Control System. Figure 3.16 shows a typical speed control system for gas turbines, steam turbines, or diesel engines. The position of the throttle lever sets the desired speed of the engine. The speed control is drawn in some reference operating position so that the values of all the lower-case parameters are zero. The positive direction of motion of these parameters is indicated by the arrowhead on each.

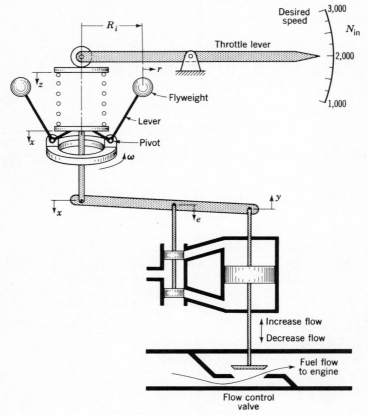

FIG. 3.16. Speed control system.

The center of gravity of the flyweights is at a distance $R = R_i + r$ from the center of rotation. The flyweights are geared directly to the output shaft, so that the speed ω of the flyweights is proportional to the output speed. A lever which is pivoted as indicated in Fig. 3.16 transmits the centrifugal force from the flyweights to the bottom of the lower spring seat. The pivot and lever rotate with the flyweights as a unit. If the speed of the engine should drop below its reference value, then the centrifugal force of the flyweights decreases, thus decreasing the force exerted on the bottom of the spring. This causes x to move downward, which in turn moves e downward. Fluid then flows to the bottom of the big piston to increase y and thus open wider the flow control valve. By supplying more fuel, the speed of the engine will increase until equilibrium is again reached. For steam turbines, the flow control valve controls the flow of steam rather than fuel as is the case with gas turbines and diesels.

Suppose that the throttle lever is moved to a higher speed setting, which in turn causes z to move downward. This in turn causes x to move downward. As just discussed, moving x downward opens the fuel flow valve, which increases the speed.

The overall block-diagram representation for this system is obtained as follows: The position of the top of the spring is a function of the desired speed only. Thus, the variation of the top of the spring z from its reference position is

$$z = C_2 n_{\text{in}} \tag{3.39}$$

where $n_{\text{in}} = N_{\text{in}} - N_i$ is the change in desired speed and $C_2 = \partial Z / \partial N_{\text{in}} \big|_i$ is the slope of the curve of Z versus N_{in} evaluated at the reference point.

The centrifugal force F_c acting on the flyweights is

$$F_c = 2MR\omega^2$$

where M = mass of each of the two flyweights
$\quad R$ = distance from center of rotation to center of gravity of each flyweight
$\quad \omega$ = angular velocity of flyweights

Usually, a governor is geared directly to the output shaft such that ω is equal to the gear ratio times the output speed; i.e.,

$$\omega = C_g \frac{2\pi}{60} N_o$$

where C_g is the gear ratio and the constant $2\pi/60$ converts the output speed N_o from rpm to radians per second. Substitution of this value for ω into the preceding expression for F_c gives

$$F_c = 2 \left(\frac{2\pi C_g}{60} \right)^2 MRN_o{}^2 = C_f MRN_o{}^2 \tag{3.40}$$

where $C_f = 2(2\pi C_g/60)^2$ is a force-conversion constant.

Effects due to inertia, friction, backlash, etc., are generally classified as secondary effects and do not have a marked influence upon the basic operation of a system. In the initial design phases, the designer is chiefly interested in evaluating the primary factors which affect system performance, and thus he disregards secondary effects, as is illustrated in this analysis.

In Fig. 3.17 is shown an enlarged view of the flyweight lever. The distance from the pivot to the center of gravity of the flyweight is b, and

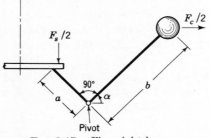

FIG. 3.17.   Flyweight lever.

the distance from the pivot to the spring seat is a.   The angle of inclination of link b is designated as α.   Taking moments about the pivot gives

$$\frac{F_c}{2} b \sin \alpha = \frac{F_s}{2} a \sin \alpha$$

or

$$F_s = \frac{b}{a} F_c = C_r F_c$$

where $C_r = b/a$ is a lever-ratio constant.   Because of the large centrifugal force developed by a flyweight, gravitational effects are negligible. Substitution of F_c from Eq. (3.40) into the preceding expression gives

$$F_s = C_f C_r M R N_o^2 \tag{3.41}$$

The two independent variables in Eq. (3.41) are R and N_o, so that linearization gives

$$f_s = C_3 r + C_4 n_o \tag{3.42}$$

where

$$C_3 = \frac{\partial F_s}{\partial R}\Big|_i = C_f C_r M N_i^2$$

$$C_4 = \frac{\partial F_s}{\partial N_o}\Big|_i = 2 C_f C_r M R_i N_i$$

Note that

$$N_o\Big|_i = N_\text{in}\Big|_i = N_i$$

The compression of the spring from its reference length is $z - x$.   Thus, the variation in force exerted by the spring is

$$f_s = K_s(z - x) \tag{3.43}$$

where K_s is the spring constant. Setting Eqs. (3.42) and (3.43) equal,

$$K_s(z - x) = C_3 r + C_4 n_o$$

The geometry of Fig. 3.16 shows that the motions of r and x are related by a lever so that $r = -C_r x$. The reason for the minus sign is that, as r increases, x decreases. Eliminating r from the preceding equation yields

$$K_s z - K_s x = -C_r C_3 x + C_4 n_0$$

or
$$x = \frac{K_s z - C_4 n_0}{K_s - C_r C_3} \qquad (3.44)$$

The block-diagram representation for Eqs. (3.39) and (3.44) is given in Fig. 3.18, which is the comparator for the speed control system.

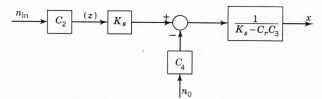

Fig. 3.18. Block diagram for comparator.

The operation of the servomotor was discussed in Sec. 3.3, and the block diagram was given in Fig. 3.7c.

The flow through the flow control valve is a function of the position Y [that is, $Q = F(Y)$]. Linearization gives

$$q = \frac{\partial Q}{\partial Y}\bigg|_i y = C_5 y \qquad (3.45)$$

where C_5 is the slope of the curve of Q versus Y evaluated at the reference condition.

In general, the operating speed N_o of an engine is a function of the fuel flow Q supplied to the engine and the torque T exerted on the engine as it rotates. Thus

$$N_o = F(Q,T)$$

The linearized form of this expression is

$$n_o = \frac{\partial N_o}{\partial Q}\bigg|_i q + \frac{\partial N_o}{\partial T}\bigg|_i t = C_6 q - C_7 t \qquad (3.46)$$

where $C_6 = \partial N_o/\partial Q\big|_i$ is the change in speed per change in fuel and $C_7 = -\partial N_o/\partial T\big|_i$ is the change in speed per change in torque. For a constant flow Q, the speed decreases as the torque on the engine is increased, so that $\partial N_o/\partial T\big|_i$ is a negative number.   However, the minus sign is seen to make C_7 a positive number.   For convenience in using block diagrams, it is desirable that all constants are positive numbers. The values of the preceding partial derivatives are obtained from the curve of the operating characteristics for the particular engine under consideration.   The variation in the torque t is

$$t = (T_L - T_{L_i}) + J\alpha = t_L + \frac{2\pi}{60} JDn_o \qquad (3.47)$$

The variation t of the torque exerted on the engine is composed of the change in torque t_L due to a change in load plus the inertia torque $(2\pi/60)JDn_o$ required to accelerate or decelerate the engine.   (The inertia of a large engine is obviously a prime consideration.)

Substitution of Eq. (3.47) into Eq. (3.46) yields

$$n_o = C_6q - C_7t_L - C_7\frac{2\pi}{60}JDn_o$$

or
$$n_o = \frac{C_6q - C_7t_L}{1 + C_7\dfrac{2\pi}{60}JD} = \frac{C_6q - C_7t_L}{1 + \tau_2 D} = \frac{C_6}{1 + \tau_2 D}(q - C_8t_L) \qquad (3.48)$$

where $\tau_2 = C_7\dfrac{2\pi}{60}J$ and $C_8 = \dfrac{C_7}{C_6} = \dfrac{-\partial N_o/\partial T\big|_i}{\partial N_o/\partial Q\big|_i} = \dfrac{\partial Q}{\partial T}\big|_i$

For an implicit function, the product of the partial derivatives is $(-1)^n$ where n is the total number of variables in the implicit expression.   By writing $N_o = F(Q,T)$ in the implicit form $G(Q,T,N_o) = 0$, then the value of n is seen to be 3.   Thus, the product of the partial derivatives is

$$\frac{\partial Q}{\partial T}\frac{\partial T}{\partial N_o}\frac{\partial N_o}{\partial Q} = (-1)^3 = -1 \qquad \text{or} \qquad \frac{-\partial N_o/\partial T}{\partial N_o/\partial Q} = \frac{\partial Q}{\partial T}$$

The block-diagram representation for Eqs. (3.45) and (3.48) is shown in Fig. 3.19.

The overall block-diagram representation for this speed control system

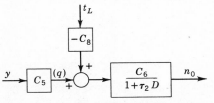

Fig. 3.19.   Block diagram for engine.

is obtained by combining Figs. 3.18, 3.7c, and 3.19, as is shown in Fig. 3.20, in which $\tau_1 = 2A_1/C_1$.

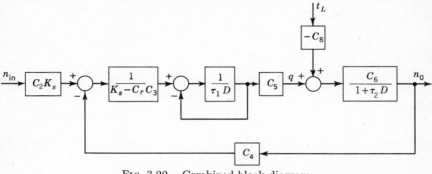

FIG. 3.20. Combined block diagram.

By letting $K_1 = C_5/(K_s - C_rC_3)$ and eliminating the minor feedback loop, then Fig. 3.20 may be represented as shown in Fig. 3.21. The

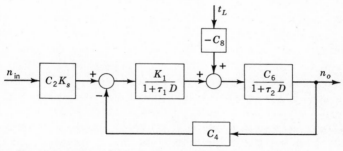

FIG. 3.21. Overall block diagram for speed control system.

operational form of the differential equation relating the output n_o to the input n_{in} and external disturbance t_L for the speed control system represented by the block diagram of Fig. 3.21 is obtained as follows: Subtract the feedback signal C_4n_o from the reference input $C_2K_sn_{in}$, and perform the mathematical operations indicated by the feedforward portion of the block diagram until the output n_o is obtained. That is,

$$\left\{\left[(C_2K_sn_{in} - C_4n_o)\frac{K_1}{1 + \tau_1D}\right] - C_8t_L\right\}\frac{C_6}{1 + \tau_2D} = n_o \quad (3.49)$$

Solving for n_o yields

$$[(1 + \tau_1D)(1 + \tau_2D) + C_4C_6K_1]n_o = C_2C_6K_1K_sn_{in} - C_6C_8(1 + \tau_1D)t_L$$

or
$$n_o = \frac{C_2 C_6 K_1 K_s n_{in} - C_6 C_8 (1 + \tau_1 D) t_L}{(1 + \tau_1 D)(1 + \tau_2 D) + C_4 C_6 K_1} \tag{3.50}$$

In Fig. 3.14 is shown the block diagram representation for a typical feedback control system. The overall equation of operation is

$$\{[r(t) - H_1(D)c(t)]G_1(D) + d(t)\}G_2(D) = c(t)$$

Solving for the output $c(t)$ gives

$$c(t) = \frac{G_1(D)G_2(D)r(t) + G_2(D)\, d(t)}{1 + G_1(D)G_2(D)H(D)} \tag{3.51}$$

The operators $G_1(D)$, $G_2(D)$, and $H(D)$ may be written in the form

$$G_1(D) = \frac{N_{G_1}}{D_{G_1}} \qquad G_2(D) = \frac{N_{G_2}}{D_{G_2}} \qquad H(D) = \frac{N_H}{D_H} \tag{3.52}$$

where N_{G_1} is the numerator of G_1 and D_{G_1} is the denominator of G_1, etc. Substitution of $G_1(D)$, $G_2(D)$, and $H(D)$ from Eq. (3.52) into Eq. (3.51) yields the general form

$$c(t) = \frac{N_{G_1} N_{G_2} D_H r(t) + N_{G_2} D_H D_{G_1}\, d(t)}{N_{G_1} N_{G_2} N_H + D_{G_1} D_{G_2} D_H} \tag{3.53}$$

It is to be noted that the coefficient for $r(t)$ is the product of the numerator terms $N_{G_1} N_{G_2}$ from $r(t)$ to the output and the denominator term D_H from the output back to $r(t)$. Similarly, the coefficient for $d(t)$ is the product of the numerator term N_{G_2} from $d(t)$ to the output and the denominator terms $D_H D_{G_1}$ from the output back to $d(t)$. The denominator for Eq. (3.53) is seen to be the product of all the numerator terms in the loop $(N_{G_1} N_{G_2} N_H)$ plus the product of all the denominator terms $(D_{G_1} D_{G_2} D_H)$. The form given by Eq. (3.53) saves considerable time and effort in obtaining the differential equation of operation for a control system. For example, from Fig. 3.21, it is to be noted that $N_{G_1} = K_1$, $N_{G_2} = C_6$, $N_H = C_4$, $D_{G_1} = (1 + \tau_1 D)$, $D_{G_2} = (1 + \tau_2 D)$, $D_H = 1$, $r(t) = C_2 K_s n_{in}$, $d(t) = -C_8 t_L$, and $c(t) = n_o$. Substitution of these values into Eq. (3.53) yields directly Eq. (3.50).

3.7 Generalized Feedback Control System. A general representation for a feedback control system is shown in Fig. 3.22. It is to be noticed that the command signal, or desired input, does not usually go directly to the comparator but must be converted to a suitable input for this device. Similarly, the controlled variable, or output, in the general case must also be changed by the feedback elements $H(D)$ before it can be measured by the comparator. The actuating signal e is amplified by the control elements $G_1(D)$ before entering the system $G_2(D)$ being controlled. An external disturbance, as shown in Fig. 3.22, is a disturbance which acts independently to affect the operation of the system. Although in Fig. 3.22 the external disturbance is shown entering the system between the control elements and the controlled system, in general, the external disturbance may enter the system at any point.

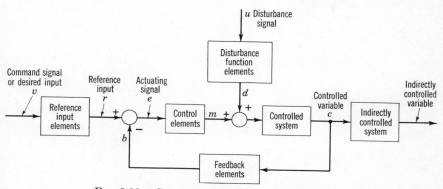

FIG. 3.22. Generalized feedback control system.

It is also to be noticed from this generalized representation of a control system that the controlled variable is not necessarily the quantity which it is desired to control. For example, a household thermostat controls the temperature of the air around the thermostat, and depending upon the circulation of air in the house, the temperature of other areas may vary considerably. In addition, the idealized purpose of this control is to maintain the comfort of the persons of the household, which depends upon humidity, their clothing, their amount of physical activity, etc. Thus, it is apparent that the controlled variable is not necessarily the ultimate quantity which it is desired to control.

3.8 Motion of an Orbiting Satellite. The law of universal gravitation states that the force of attraction between two bodies varies directly as the product of their masses M_1 and M_2, and inversely as the square of the distance R between them, that is

$$F \propto \frac{M_1 M_2}{R^2}$$

or

$$F = G\frac{M_1 M_2}{R^2} \tag{3.54}$$

where G is the universal gravitational constant.

On the surface of the earth the force of attraction of a body of mass M is

$$F = G\frac{M_e}{R_e{}^2}M = gM$$

where M_e = mass of the earth

R_e = radius of the earth

$g = G\dfrac{M_e}{R_e{}^2} = 32.2$ ft/sec^2 = gravitational constant on the surface

of the earth.

The force of attraction at a distance R from the center of the earth is

$$F = G\frac{M_e}{R^2}M = G\frac{M_e}{R_e{}^2}\left(\frac{R_e}{R}\right)^2 M = g\left(\frac{R_e}{R}\right)^2 M = \frac{\mu}{R^2}$$

where $\mu = gR_e{}^2 M$.

In Fig. 3.23 is shown a satellite which is at a distance R from the center of the earth. The coordinate system is called an inertial system

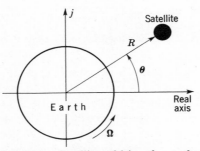

Fig. 3.23. Satellite orbiting the earth.

because it is fixed in space (e.g., to a system of stars). Thus, the angular velocity Ω of the earth relative to this fixed inertial system is one revolution per day. The motion of the satellite relative to the earth depends on Ω. A major advantage of using the inertial coordinate system is that the motion of the satellite relative to the inertial coordinate system is independent of Ω. To obtain the equation of motion of the satellite, it is necessary to obtain the acceleration relative to the fixed coordinate system. The position of the satellite is designated by the vector $Re^{j\theta}$.

A major advantage of employing the exponential form $e^{j\theta}$ is the ease with which it may be differentiated to obtain the velocity and then acceleration. The meaning of the term $e^{j\theta}$ may be ascertained from Euler's equations.

$$\begin{aligned} e^{j\theta} &= \cos\theta + j\sin\theta \\ e^{-j\theta} &= \cos\theta - j\sin\theta \end{aligned} \qquad (3.55)$$

The validity of Euler's equations is proved by expanding $e^{j\theta}$, $\sin\theta$, and cos θ by use of Maclaurin's series. Thus,

$$e^{j\theta} = 1 + j\theta + \frac{(j\theta)^2}{2!} + \frac{(j\theta)^3}{3!} + \frac{(j\theta)^4}{4!} + \frac{(j\theta)^5}{5!} + \cdots$$

$$= \left(1 - \frac{\theta^2}{2!} + \frac{\theta^4}{4!} - \cdots\right) + j\left(\theta - \frac{\theta^3}{3!} + \frac{\theta^5}{5!} - \cdots\right)$$

$$\cos \theta = 1 - \frac{\theta^2}{2!} + \frac{\theta^4}{4!} - \cdots$$

$$\sin \theta = \theta - \frac{\theta^3}{3!} + \frac{\theta^5}{5!} - \cdots$$

The results of Eq. (3.55) follow directly from the preceding expansions.

Because the vector $e^{j\theta}$ is the vector sum of $\cos \theta + j \sin \theta$, the magnitude of $e^{j\theta}$ is always $\cos^2 \theta + \sin^2 \theta = 1$. The physical significance of the unit vector $e^{j\theta}$ is shown in Fig. 3.24. Here it is to be noticed that $e^{j\theta}$ is a unit

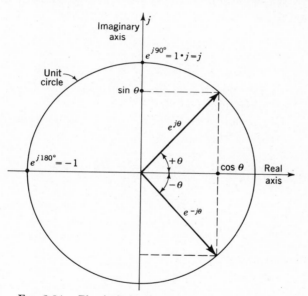

FIG. 3.24. Physical significance of unit vector, $e^{j\theta}$.

vector which is rotated counterclockwise an angle θ from the real axis. For θ equal to 90°, it is seen from the unit circle that $e^{j90°} = j$. Squaring the preceding unit vector yields $j^2 = e^{j90°}e^{j90°} = e^{j180°}$. From the unit circle, this vector is seen to be equal to -1. Thus, $j^2 = -1$, and $j = \sqrt{-1}$.

Differentiation of the position $Re^{j\theta}$ yields for the velocity V of the satellite

$$V = \dot{R}e^{j\theta} + j\dot{\theta}Re^{j\theta} = \dot{R}e^{j\theta} + R\dot{\theta}e^{j(\theta+90°)}$$

Because $e^{j(\theta+90°)}$ is a unit vector rotated 90° from $e^{j\theta}$, then $\dot{R}$ is seen to be the magnitude of the component of velocity along the radius vector $e^{j\theta}$ and $R\dot{\theta}$ is the magnitude of the component along the tangent vector $e^{j(\theta+90°)}$. The acceleration A of the satellite is now obtained by differentiation of the velocity. Thus

$$A = (\ddot{R} - R\dot{\theta}^2)e^{j\theta} + (2\dot{R}\dot{\theta} + R\ddot{\theta})e^{j(\theta+90°)}$$

The first term on the right-hand side is the normal component of acceleration and the second term is the tangential component. That is

$$A_n = \ddot{R} - R\dot{\theta}^2$$
$$A_t = 2\dot{R}\dot{\theta} + R\ddot{\theta}$$

Summing forces in the normal and tangential directions gives $MA_n = F_n$ and $MA_t = F_t$. The only external force acting on the satellite is the gravitational force $-\mu/R^2$ which acts radially inward. Thus,

$$M(\ddot{R} - R\dot{\theta}^2) = -\frac{\mu}{R^2} \tag{3.56}$$

$$M(2\dot{R}\dot{\theta} + R\ddot{\theta}) = 0 \tag{3.57}$$

These two equations which describe the motion of the satellite are seen to be nonlinear differential equations.

It is interesting to derive these equations of motion by use of Lagrange's equations. The Lagrange equations for this system are

$$\frac{d}{dt}\frac{\partial T}{\partial \dot{R}} + \frac{\partial T}{\partial R} = F_R$$

$$\frac{d}{dt}\frac{\partial T}{\partial \dot{\theta}} + \frac{\partial T}{\partial \theta} = F_\theta \tag{3.58}$$

where t = time
T = kinetic energy
$F_R = -\mu/R^2$ = force in the radial direction
$F_\theta = 0$ = force in the tangential direction

The kinetic energy with respect to the fixed coordinate system is

$$T = \tfrac{1}{2}M(\dot{R}^2 + R^2\dot{\theta}^2) \tag{3.59}$$

Substituting T and F_R into the first Lagrange equation and then performing the indicated mathematical operations yields the first equation of motion, Eq. (3.56). Similarly, the second Lagrange equation yields the second equation of motion, Eq. (3.57).

A very valuable result is obtained by writing Eq. (3.57) in the form

$$M(2\dot{R}\dot{\theta} + R\ddot{\theta}) = \frac{M}{R}\frac{d}{dt}R^2\dot{\theta} = 0$$

In order that $(d/dt)R^2\dot\theta = 0$, it is necessary that $R^2\dot\theta = $ constant. In Fig. 3.25 is shown a typical orbital path. The area of the segment (ΔA

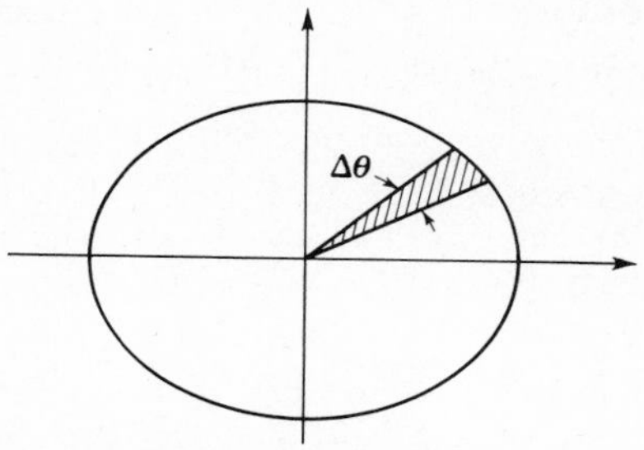

Fig. 3.25. Typical orbital path.

shown shaded) enclosed by the satellite per increment of time Δt is

$$\Delta A = \tfrac{1}{2}R(R\,\Delta\theta)$$

Hence

$$\frac{dA}{dt} = \lim_{\Delta t\to0}\frac{\Delta A}{\Delta t} = \lim_{\Delta t\to0}\frac{1}{2}R^2\frac{\Delta\theta}{\Delta t} = \frac{1}{2}R^2\dot\theta = \text{constant}$$

Because dA/dt is constant, the satellite moves such that the radius vector sweeps out equal areas in equal increments of time. This is referred to as Kepler's second law of planetary motion. Kepler's first law states that planets travel in elliptical paths.

Circular Orbit. When the orbital path is circular, then $R = R_i$ is a constant and $\dot R = \ddot R = 0$. When $R = R_i$ is a constant, then Eq. (3.56) shows that $\dot\theta = \dot\theta_i$ is also constant. That is

$$\dot\theta_i{}^2 = \frac{\mu}{MR_i{}^3} = \frac{32.2}{R_i}\left(\frac{R_e}{R_i}\right)^2$$

The velocity V_i is

$$V_i = R_i\dot\theta_i = \sqrt{32.2R_i}\,\frac{R_e}{R_i}$$

The radius of the earth is about 4,000 miles, hence the velocity of a satellite 100 miles above the earth would be

$$V_i = (32.2)(4,100)(5,280)\,\frac{4,000}{4,100}\,\frac{3,600}{5,280} \approx 17,500 \text{ mph}$$

The term 3,600/5,280 converts the answer from feet per second to miles per hour.

Almost Circular Orbit. Linearization of Eqs. (3.56) and (3.57) yields the equations of motion for an almost circular path. A derivative is linearized just as any other variable. For example, linearization of the term $M\ddot{R}$ in Eq. (3.56) gives

$$\frac{\partial}{\partial \ddot{R}} (M\ddot{R}) \Big|_i \ddot{r} = M \frac{\partial \ddot{R}}{\partial \ddot{R}} \Big|_i \ddot{r} = M\ddot{r}$$

Thus, proceeding to linearize each term in Eq. (3.56) gives

$$M(\ddot{r} - \dot{\theta}_i^2 r - 2R_i \dot{\theta}_i \Delta\dot{\theta}) = \frac{2\mu r}{R_i^3}$$

or

$$\left[MD^2 - \left(M\dot{\theta}_i^2 + \frac{2\mu}{R_i^3} \right) \right] r - 2MR_i \dot{\theta}_i \Delta\dot{\theta} = 0$$

where r is the variation in R from the reference value ($R = R_i + r$) and $\Delta\theta$ is the change in θ from the reference value ($\theta = \theta_i + \Delta\theta$). Evaluating Eq. (3.56) at the reference condition for which $\theta = \theta_i$ and $\ddot{R}_i = 0$ shows that

$$MR_i \dot{\theta}_i^2 = \frac{\mu}{R_i^2} \qquad \text{or} \qquad \frac{\mu}{R_i^3} = M\dot{\theta}_i^2$$

Substituting this result into the preceding equation gives

$$(D^2 - 3\dot{\theta}_i^2)r - 2R_i \dot{\theta}_i \Delta\dot{\theta} = 0 \tag{3.60}$$

Similarly, linearization of Eq. (3.57) gives

$$M(2\dot{\theta}_i \dot{r} + 2\dot{R}_i \Delta\dot{\theta} + \ddot{\theta}_i r + R_i \Delta\ddot{\theta}) = 0$$

Because $\dot{R}_i = 0$ and $\ddot{\theta}_i = 0$, the preceding linearized equation reduces to

$$2\dot{\theta}_i \dot{r} + R_i \Delta\ddot{\theta} = 0$$

or

$$2\dot{\theta}_i Dr + R_i D \Delta\dot{\theta} = 0 \tag{3.61}$$

It is to be noted that the operator D cannot be canceled from this last equation.

Equations (3.60) and (3.61) are the linearized approximations for Eqs. (3.56) and (3.57). These linear equations are much easier to analyze. For example, eliminating $\Delta\theta$ between Eqs. (3.60) and (3.61) yields the following differential equation in $\dot{r}$.

$$(D^2 + \dot{\theta}_i^2)\dot{r} = 0 \tag{3.62}$$

Similarly, eliminating r between Eqs. (3.60) and (3.61) yields the following differential equation in $\Delta\ddot{\theta}$:

$$\frac{R_i}{2\dot{\theta}_i} (D^2 + \dot{\theta}_i^2) \Delta\ddot{\theta} = 0 \tag{3.63}$$

For a given set of initial conditions each of the preceding equations may be solved for $\dot{r}$ and $\Delta\ddot{\theta}$. Integration then yields r and $\Delta\theta$.

Equations (3.60) and (3.61) may also be represented by the block diagram shown in Fig. 3.26. As is indicated by the block diagram, there

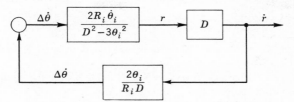

FIG. 3.26. Block diagram for orbiting satellite.

is no input to this system. The motion is determined entirely by the initial conditions (that is, the manner in which the satellite enters the orbit).

As is shown in Chap. 5, it is a relatively easy matter to solve the differential equation (3.62). For example, for $r(0) = \ddot{r}(0) = 0$ and $\dot{r}(0) = 1$ the solution is

$$\dot{r} = \cos \dot{\theta}_i t$$

Integration gives

$$r = \frac{1}{\dot{\theta}_i} \sin \dot{\theta}_i t$$

The resulting orbit is shown dotted in Fig. 3.27.

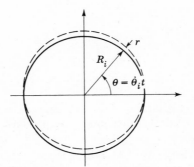

FIG. 3.27. Orbital path for $r(0) = \ddot{r}(0) = 0$ and $\dot{r}(0) = 1$.

Problems

3.1 Linearize each of the following equations:

(a) $Y = \sin KX$
(b) $Y = \tan KX$
(c) $Y = e^{KX}$

What is the resulting linearized expression in each case when $X_i = 0$? When $X_i = 1$?

3.2   Linearize each of the following equations:

(a) $Z = 0.1X^2 + \dfrac{100}{Y}$ (b) $Z = X(2Y + 5)$

If $Y_i = 10$ and $X_i = 20$, what percent error results in each of the above cases when $y = +1$ and $x = -2$?

3.3   The volume V of a sphere is $V = \frac{4}{3}\pi R^3$. Determine the equation for the linear approximation to V. If $R_i = 10$ in., what percent error results by using this approximation for V when $R = 11$? What is the percent error for $R = 9$?

3.4   The equation for the volume of a cylinder is $V = \pi R^2 H$, where R is the radius of the base and H is the altitude. Determine the equation for the variation v in the volume due to a variation r in the radius and a variation h in the altitude.

3.5   The equation for the area of a triangle may be written in the form

$$A = \tfrac{1}{2}XY \sin \theta$$

where X and Y are the lengths of two adjacent sides and θ is the included angle. Designate variations as a, x, y, and $\Delta\theta$, and then determine the linear approximation for the area for the case in which $X_i = 20$, $Y_i = 10$, and $\theta_i = 30°$.

3.6   The period of oscillation of a simple pendulum is

$$T = 2\pi \sqrt{\frac{L}{g}}$$

for $L_i = 100$ in. and $g = 32.2$ ft/sec². Determine the change in the period due to

(a) An increase in L of 1 in.
(b) A decrease in g of 0.1 ft/sec².

3.7   Linearize the following equation,

$$V = \frac{D}{T}$$

where V is velocity, D is distance, and T is time.

(a) Determine the linear approximation for V when $V_i = 60$ mph., $D_i = 1$ mile, and $T_i = 60$ sec.

(b) With the speedometer indicating 60 mph., it is observed that 62 sec are required to travel between successive mile indicator markers on the thruway. Approximately what is the velocity of the vehicle?

3.8   To linearize $V = D/T$ of Prob. 3.7 by the perturbation method, replace V by $V_i + v$, D by $D_i + d$, and T by $T_i + t$. Neglect higher-order variations (differential quantities) and then subtract off the reference condition $V_i T_i = D_i$. Thus, verify the linearized form obtained in Prob. 3.7.

3.9   (a) To linearize Eq. (3.56) by the perturbation method, replace R by $R_i + r$ and θ by $\theta_i + \Delta\theta$. Neglect higher order differential quantities, and then subtract off Eq. (3.56) evaluated at the reference condition. Thus, verify that Eq. (3.60) is the linearized form of Eq. (3.56).

(*b*) Use the perturbation method described in part (*a*) to verify that Eq. (3.61) is the linearized form of Eq. (3.57).

3.10 Typical operating curves for a dc motor are shown in Fig. P3.10. These are curves of torque T versus operating speed N for constant values of voltage E

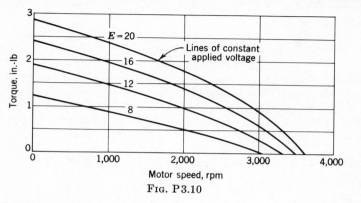

FIG. P3.10

applied to the motor. These curves are a plot of the function $N = F(T,E)$. Effect a linear approximation for N. Evaluate the partial derivatives in this approximation when T_i is 1 in.-lb and E_i is 16 volts.

3.11 In Fig. P3.11 is shown a tank which is used as a mixer. Pure water flows in at a constant rate Q_w. A salt solution at a concentration C_s flows in at a

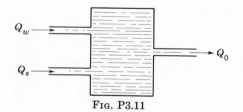

FIG. P3.11

constant rate Q_s. The mixed solution of concentration C_o leaves at the rate Q_o. Because the volume V of fluid in the tank is kept constant, the outflow Q_o is equal to $Q_w + Q_s$. The rate of accumulation of salt in the tank is $Q_sC_s - Q_oC_o = VDC_o$. The salt concentration C_s is controlled by a valve (not shown) such that $C_s = K\theta$.

Determine the differential equation relating the concentration C_o of the tank to the valve position θ in terms of the parameters Q_s, Q_w, and V.

3.12 The linearized equation of operation about a typical operating point for a hydraulic amplifier used in a machine tool is

$$f = 2 \times 10^6 e - 5 \times 10^3 \dot{y}$$

where $\dot{y} = Dy = $ velocity of the power piston
$\quad f = $ change in force acting on the piston
$\quad e = $ position of the valve which controls the piston

The load is that due to the tool reactive force f_L and inertia force MD^2y; hence

$$f = f_L + MD^2y$$

The reference position x and controlled position y are connected by a walking-beam linkage such that

$$e = \frac{x - y}{2}$$

Obtain the overall block-diagram representation for this system in which x is the reference input, y the controlled variable, and f_L the external disturbance.
3.13 A torque-amplifying device is shown in Fig. P3.13. Power for amplification is supplied by a motor which rotates drums I and II at a constant speed.

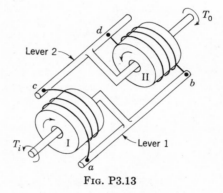

FIG. P3.13

The direction of rotation of each drum is as indicated. The torque balance for lever 1 is

$$T_i = R(F_b - F_a)$$

where F_a = tension in the band at a
F_b = tension at b
R = radius of the drum

(Note that the lever goes through the center of the drum without touching it.) The torque balance for lever 2 is $T_o = R(F_d - F_c)$. For the band on drum I, $F_c = e^{\mu\alpha}F_a$, and for drum II, $F_d = e^{\mu\alpha}F_b$ where μ is the coefficient of friction between the steel band and drum, and α is the angle of wrap in radians. Determine the expression for the torque amplification T_o/T_i.
3.14 In Fig. P3.14 is shown a hydraulic servomotor which is similar to the power-amplifying device used in power steering units. A movement in the x direction of the valve is seen to open passage 1 to the supply pressure, which in turn causes the big piston to move to the right. Because the sleeve is directly connected to this piston, the sleeve also moves to the right to close off flow from the valve. Determine the block diagram relating the input position x to the output y. Identify the time constant.

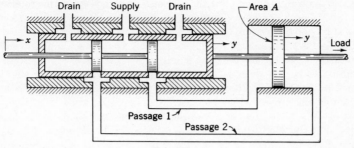

FIG. P3.14

3.15 In Fig. P3.15 is shown a modification of the hydraulic power amplifier discussed in Prob. 3.14. Determine the block-diagram representation for this

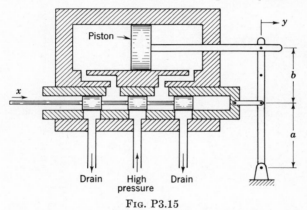

FIG. P3.15

device in which x is the input and y the output. Note that the position of the sleeve is $[a/(a + b)]y$.

3.16 For the hydraulic amplifier shown in Fig. P3.16, determine the block

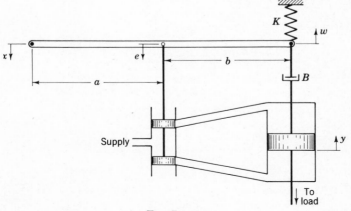

FIG. P3.16

diagram for the walking-beam linkage and also the block diagrams relating e to y and y to w. Combine these diagrams to determine the overall block-diagram representation for the system.

3.17 In Fig. P3.17 is shown a tension-regulating apparatus such as is used in the paper industry. To ensure uniform winding, it is necessary to maintain a constant tension F_c as the sheet is being wound on the wind-up roll. To increase the tension in the paper, the tension control lever is raised. This raises the torque control arm of the motor, which increases the torque T_m applied by the motor to the windup roll. The change in torque provided by the motor is $t_m = K_m e/(1 + \tau p)$. For the wind-up roll, it follows that $F_c = T_m/R$, where R is the radius of the wheel. Determine the overall block diagram relating a variation f_r of the reference or desired tension to a variation of the controlled tension f_c.

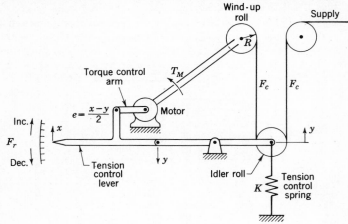

Fᴵɢ. P3.17

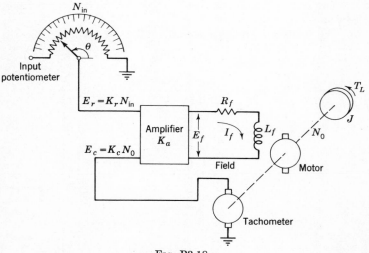

Fᴵɢ. P3.18

3.18 In Fig. P3.18 is shown an electrical speed control system. The input potentiometer provides a reference input voltage E_r proportional to the desired speed N_{in}, that is $E_r = K_r N_{in}$. A voltage signal E_c which is proportional to the controlled output speed N_o is provided by the tachometer ($E_c = K_c N_o$). The error $E_r - E_c$ is amplified by an electronic amplifier whose output is $E_f = K_a(E_r - E_c)$. The voltage E_f is applied to the field of a field-controlled dc motor. The torque exerted on the shaft by the motor (air-gap torque) is proportional to the field current, that is, $T = KI_f$. Determine the overall block diagram for this speed control system for the case in which the load torque consists of an inertia $JD^2\theta = JD(2\pi/60)N_o$ and an external torque T_L.

3.19 In Fig. P3.19 is shown a liquid-level controller. To raise the level of the fluid, the control lever is moved up (i.e., position z is raised). This raises the valve position $e = (z - h_o)/2$, which increases y, thereby admitting more flow Q_{in}. The flow Q_{in} is a function of the flow valve opening Y and the supply pressure P_s. The change in volume of liquid in the tank is the time integral $(q_{in} - q_o)/D$, which is equal to the cross-section area of the tank A_T times the change in level h_o. The flow out Q_o is seen to depend upon the pressure head H_o. Determine the overall block diagram for this controller.

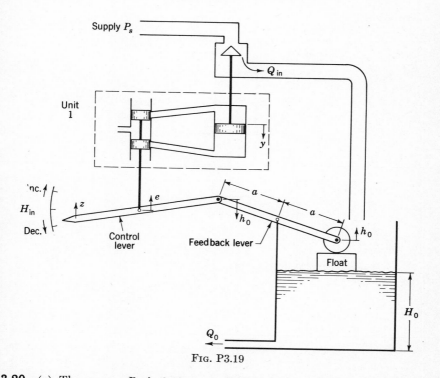

FIG. P3.19

3.20 (a) The same as Prob. 3.19 except that positions e and y are connected by a link to convert the hydraulic integrator to the hydraulic servomotor shown in Fig. P3.20a. That is, unit 2 in Fig. P3.20a is substituted for unit 1 in Fig. P3.19.

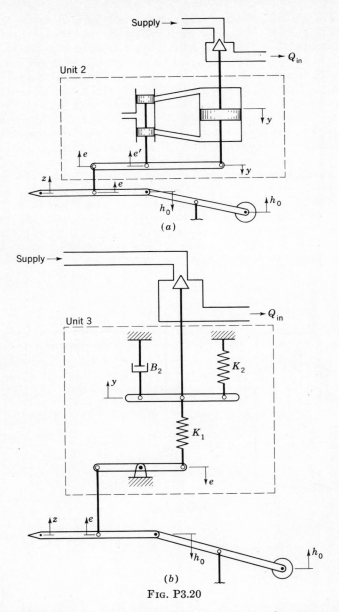

Fig. P3.20

(b) The same as Prob. 3.19 except that positions e and y are connected by unit 3 as shown in Fig. P3.20b. This is in effect replacing the hydraulic integrator by a spring-damper combination.

3.21 A system for controlling flow is shown in Fig. P3.21. Increasing the desired flow setting increases the compression on spring K_1, which causes x and

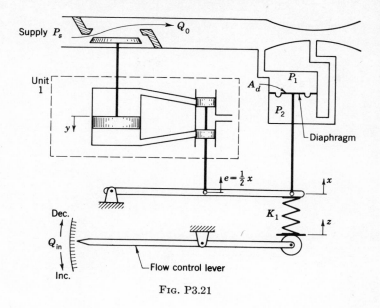

FIG. P3.21

position e of the balanced valve to move up. This in turn causes the flow valve to move down, which increases the flow. The amount of flow out is measured by a venturi-type flowmeter so that the pressure drop $P_1 - P_2$ is a function of Q_o. The diaphragm prevents leakage from the high pressure P_1 to the low pressure P_2, but it permits motion, just as a piston would. The effective area of the diaphragm is A_d. The flow Q_o is seen to be a function of the flow-valve opening Y and the supply pressure P_s. Determine the overall block-diagram representation for this system.

3.22 (a) Same as Prob. 3.21 except that e actuates the valve through unit 2, shown in Fig. P3.20a, rather than unit 1, shown in Fig. P3.21.

(b) Same as Prob. 3.21 except that e actuates the valve through unit 3, shown in Fig. P3.20b, rather than unit 1, shown in Fig. P3.21.

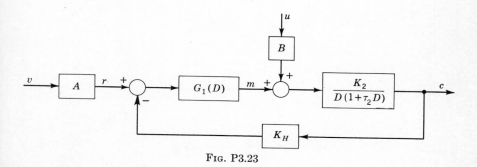

FIG. P3.23

3.23 For the control system shown in Fig. P3.23, determine the differential equation of operation for each of the following cases:

(a) $G_1(D) = \dfrac{K_1}{1 + \tau_1 D}$

(b) $G_1(D) = \dfrac{K_1}{D(1 + \tau_1 D)}$

(c) $G_1(D) = \dfrac{K_1}{D} + \dfrac{K_1}{1 + \tau_1 D}$

4

Steady-state operation

By steady-state operation is meant the equilibrium state attained such that there is no change with respect to time of any of the system variables. The system remains at this equilibrium state of operation until it is excited by a change in the desired input or in the external disturbance. A transient condition is said to exist as long as any of the variables of the system is changing with time. In this chapter, it is shown that considerable information about the basic character of a system may be obtained from an analysis of its steady-state operation.

4.1 Steady-state Analysis. The differential equation relating the output n_o to the input n_{in} and external disturbance t_L for the speed control system represented by the block diagram of Fig. 3.21 is given by Eq. (3.50). For steady-state operation, n_o, n_{in}, and t_L will have constant values, and therefore terms resulting from powers of D operating on these constant quantities will be zero. That is, $Dn_o\big|_{ss} = d(n_o)/dt\big|_{ss} = 0$, etc. Thus, the equation describing the steady-state operation of this speed control system is

$$n_o = \frac{C_2 C_6 K_1 K_s n_{in} - C_6 C_8 t_L}{1 + C_4 C_6 K_1} \tag{4.1}$$

It should be noticed that Eq. (4.1) could also have been obtained by letting $D = 0$ in the overall block diagram of Fig. 3.21. Doing this yields the block diagram for steady-state operation shown in Fig. 4.1a.

In general, the block diagram describing the steady-state operation of a system may be represented as illustrated by Fig. 4.1b, in which

$$K_{G_1} = [G_1(D)]_{D=0} \qquad K_{G_2} = [G_2(D)]_{D=0} \qquad K_H = [H(D)]_{D=0} \tag{4.2}$$

From Fig. 4.1b, the equation for steady-state operation is found to be

$$[(Av - K_H c)K_{G_1} + Bu]K_{G_2} = c$$

or

$$c = \frac{A K_{G_1} K_{G_2}}{1 + K_{G_1} K_{G_2} K_H} v + \frac{B K_{G_2}}{1 + K_{G_1} K_{G_2} K_H} u \tag{4.3}$$

89

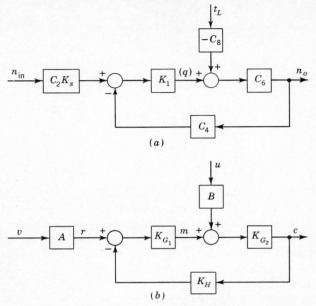

FIG. 4.1.   Block diagram for steady-state operation.

Corresponding quantities for the speed control system are $c = n_o$, $v = n_{in}$, $u = t_L$, $A = C_2 K_s$, $B = -C_8$, $K_{G_1} = K_1$, $K_{G_2} = C_6$, and $K_H = C_4$. Substitution of these results into Eq. (4.3) verifies Eq. (4.1).

The constant A which appears in Eq. (4.3) is, in effect, the scale factor for the input dial.   To have the coefficient of the v term equal to unity, A must be selected such that

$$\frac{A K_{G_1} K_{G_2}}{1 + K_{G_1} K_{G_2} K_H} = 1$$

or
$$A = \frac{1 + K_{G_1} K_{G_2} K_H}{K_{G_1} K_{G_2}} = \frac{1}{K_{G_1} K_{G_2}} + K_H \qquad (4.4)$$

When A is chosen in accordance with Eq. (4.4), the coefficient of the v term is unity and thus Eq. (4.3) becomes

$$c = v + \frac{B K_{G_2}}{1 + K_{G_1} K_{G_2} K_H} u = v + \frac{B}{1/K_{G_2} + K_{G_1} K_H} u \qquad (4.5)$$

To have the controlled variable c equal to the command signal v (that is, $c = v$), it is necessary that the coefficient of the u term be zero.   This coefficient is zero if either K_{G_1} or K_H is infinite.   However, from Eq. (4.4), it follows that an infinite value of K_H would necessitate A being infinite, which is physically impossible.   Thus, only K_{G_1} can be made infinite. This is accomplished by having *an integrator in the control elements* to yield a $1/D$ term which gives the effect of an infinite constant during steady-state operation.   This type of system is called an integral control system.

Satisfactory performance may often be achieved by making the coefficient of the u term sufficiently small so that variations in the external disturbance cause only slight errors.   Control systems for which the coefficient of the u is finite are called proportional control systems. The next two sections treat proportional and integral control systems, respectively.

4.2 Proportional Control Systems.   The speed control system shown in Fig. 3.21 is a proportional control system.   Substitution of the corresponding values for this speed control system into Eq. (4.4) gives

$$A = C_2 K_s = \frac{1}{C_6 K_1} + C_4$$

or

$$C_2 = \frac{1}{K_s}\left(\frac{1}{C_6 K_1} + C_4\right) \tag{4.6}$$

The term $C_2 = \left.\partial Z/\partial N_{\text{in}}\right|_i$ is the scale factor for the speed-setting dial.

Because some of the terms in Eq. (4.6) are partial derivatives evaluated at the reference operating condition, the value of the scale factor C_2 is seen to vary for different reference points.   This would result in a nonlinear scale for the input speed dial.   The use of a nonlinear scale may be avoided by having the input speed-setting position a cam, which in turn sets the desired input position of the top of the spring, as is shown in Fig. 4.2.   It is a relatively easy matter then to set up the speed control

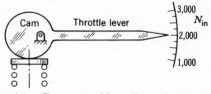

Fig. 4.2.   Cam to avoid nonlinear input scale.

system so that Eq. (4.6) is satisfied for any reference condition.   When this is so, Eq. (4.1) becomes

$$n_o = n_{\text{in}} - \frac{C_6 C_8}{1 + C_4 C_6 K_1} t_L \tag{4.7}$$

Equation (4.7) is the typical form of the steady-state relationship which exists between the input, output, and external disturbance for a proportional control system.   When the load torque T_L is not equal to the reference value T_{L_i} (that is, $t_L \neq 0$), then n_o is not equal to n_{in}.   For example, suppose that this is the speed control system for the gas turbine of a jet airplane and that T_{L_i} is the torque required for the airplane in level flight. When the airplane is inclined to gain altitude, a greater load torque T_L is required than that for level flight (that is, $t_L > 0$). Thus, the output speed is slightly less than the desired value for this flight condition.

The physical reason for this can be seen by looking at the schematic diagram Fig. 3.16 for the speed control system whose block diagram is shown in Fig. 3.21.

For level flight, the system is set up so that $N_o = N_{in}$. When the airplane is gaining altitude, the load torque is increased. This increased torque results in a decreased speed, which in turn causes a lower position for x. Because of the lower position for x, there is a greater flow of fuel. To have the airplane continue to gain altitude, more flow is required than for level flight. To maintain this increased flow, the engine speed must be slightly less than for level flight.

Another method of understanding the operation of a proportional control system is obtained by considering individually the steady-state operating characteristics of the system to be controlled and those of the control elements. For an airplane in level flight, it is possible to plot a curve of fuel flow Q required to maintain various speeds N_o, as shown in Fig. 4.3a by the curve $T_L = T_2$. The curves for different load torques

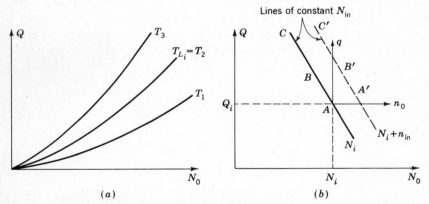

FIG. 4.3. (a) Steady-state engine characteristics; (b) steady-state controller characteristics.

are also shown in Fig. 4.3a. The curve for T_3 would correspond to operation of the airplane at a certain angle of inclination. Similarly, the curve T_1 would correspond to the airplane losing altitude at a certain angle of declination. Thus, Fig. 4.3a represents the operating characteristics of the system to be controlled.

To determine the operating line ABC for the control elements as shown in Fig. 4.3b, first fix the desired speed setting at some value N_{in}. Then for various speeds of rotation N_o plot the corresponding flow Q coming from the controller. In this manner, the family of curves of N_o versus Q for various constant values of N_{in} is obtained as shown in Fig. 4.3b.

By superimposing the characteristics of the control elements and the system to be controlled as shown in Fig. 4.4a, much information about the

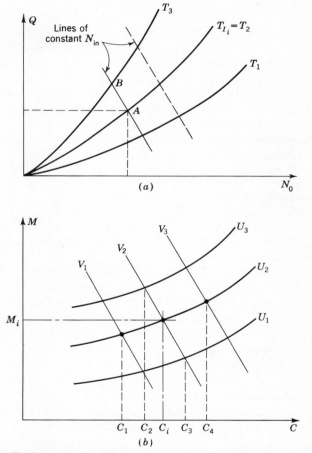

FIG. 4.4. (a) Engine and controller steady-state characteristics; (b) general representation of steady-state characteristics.

operation of the system may be obtained. For a given engine speed N_o the fuel flow being supplied by the controller is obtained from Fig. 4.4a by proceeding vertically up from N_o to the line of operation of the controller (e.g., line AB) and then proceeding horizontally to obtain the corresponding value of Q. Similarly, the fuel flow required to maintain the given flight condition ($T_L = T_1$, T_2, or T_3) is obtained by proceeding vertically up from N_o to the torque curve and then proceeding horizontally to obtain the corresponding value of Q. Steady-state operation exists at the intersection of the line of operation of the controller and the torque line for the given flight condition because at this intersection just enough flow is being supplied as is required to maintain the flight condition. For example, if the airplane is in level flight and the operating line for the desired speed setting is AB, then the intersection at point A of the line T_2 and the operating line AB is the steady-state operating point for the system. The speed-setting dial is calibrated by setting the value of speed N_{in} on the dial equal to the steady-state value of the output speed at the reference load T_2 (e.g., see Fig. 4.5). For a given speed setting, such as that indicated by the line AB, if the load is increased to T_3 while the desired speed is unchanged, then the new operating point must be on the line of T_3 at point B. Because AB is not a vertical line, variations in the load are seen to cause variations in the output speed. A proportional controller is sometimes called a droop controller, and the line AB is referred to as the droop line.

Coefficients of u and v. The characteristics of the system to be controlled are specified in Fig. 4.4a by the family of curves of Q (the manipulated variable) versus N_o (the controlled variable) with lines of constant T_L (the disturbance). The characteristics of the controller are represented by the lines of constant N_{in} (the command signal) which are superimposed upon this plot.

In general, one can plot M (the manipulated variable) versus C (the controlled variable) with lines of constant U (the disturbance) for the system to be controlled as shown in Fig. 4.4b. The characteristics of the controller may then be superimposed upon this plot, as illustrated by the lines of constant V (the command signal) in Fig. 4.4b. Thus, Fig. 4.4b is a general representation of the steady-state operating characteristics for a typical control system.

Equation (4.3) describes the steady-state characteristics about any reference point of operation. The constants in Eq. (4.3) may be evaluated from the operating curves of Fig. 4.4b. For example, the coefficient of the v term may be evaluated by maintaining U fixed so that $u = 0$. Thus, the u term in Eq. (4.3) vanishes. Solving the resultant expression for the coefficient of the v term gives

$$\frac{AK_{G_1}K_{G_2}}{1 + K_{G_1}K_{G_2}K_H} = \frac{c}{v}\bigg|_{u=0} = \frac{\Delta C}{\Delta V}\bigg|_{U=\text{constant}} = \frac{\partial C}{\partial V}\bigg|_{U=\text{constant}} \quad (4.8)$$

From Fig. 4.4b it is to be noticed that for operation about the point (C_i, M_i) the value of this coefficient is

$$\frac{AK_{G_1}K_{C_2}}{1 + K_{G_1}K_{G_2}K_H} = \frac{\Delta C}{\Delta V}\bigg|_{U_2} = \frac{C_4 - C_1}{V_3 - V_1} \quad (4.9)$$

Similarly, by maintaining a constant V so that $v = 0$, then from Eq. (4.3) the coefficient of the u term is found to be

$$\frac{BK_{G_2}}{1 + K_{G_1}K_{G_2}K_H} = \left.\frac{c}{u}\right|_{v=0} = \left.\frac{\Delta C}{\Delta U}\right|_{V=\text{constant}} = \left.\frac{\partial C}{\partial U}\right|_{V=\text{constant}} \quad (4.10)$$

For operation in the vicinity of the point (C_i, M_i) this coefficient is

$$\frac{BK_{G_2}}{1 + K_{G_1}K_{G_2}K_H} = \left.\frac{\Delta C}{\Delta U}\right|_{V_2} = \frac{C_3 - C_2}{U_1 - U_3} \quad (4.11)$$

When the droop line is vertical, $\Delta C = 0$. Thus, the coefficient of the u term vanishes. A vertical droop line is characteristic of an integral controller.

When the operating curves are all parallel and equidistant, then the value of each of the preceding steady-state constants remains the same over the entire range of operation.

ILLUSTRATIVE EXAMPLE 1. A typical family of steady-state operating curves for a speed control system for a diesel or turbine is shown in Fig. 4.5. Determine the steady-state equation for operation in the vicinity

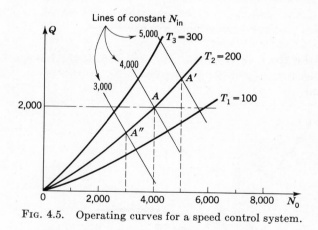

FIG. 4.5. Operating curves for a speed control system.

of point A. If this were an open-loop rather than a closed-loop system, what would be the equation for steady-state operation about point A?

SOLUTION. From Eq. (4.8) it follows that

$$\frac{AK_{G_1}K_{G_2}}{1 + K_{G_1}K_{G_2}K_H} = \left.\frac{\Delta N_o}{\Delta N_{\text{in}}}\right|_{T_2} = \frac{5,000 - 3,000}{5,000 - 3,000} = 1$$

Similarly from Eq. (4.10)

$$\frac{BK_{G_2}}{1 + K_{G_1}K_{G_2}K_H} = \left.\frac{\Delta N_o}{\Delta T_L}\right|_{N_{\text{in}}=4,000} = \frac{4,500 - 3,400}{100 - 300} = -5.5$$

Thus the equation for steady-state operation in the vicinity of point A is

$$n_o = n_{in} - 5.5\,t_L$$

For an open-loop control system there is but one set value of the flow Q for each desired speed. This value of Q must be the flow required to make N_o equal to N_{in} at the reference load torque $T_{L_i} = T_2$. For a desired speed of 4,000 rpm, it is to be noted from Fig. 4.5 that the value of Q is 2,000 lb/hr. Thus the horizontal line of Q equal to 2,000 is the open-loop operating line of the controller when $N_{in} = 4,000$. Similarly, when N_{in} is 5,000 the operating line is a horizontal line through A', and when N_{in} is 3,000 the operating line is a horizontal line through A''. Thus

$$\frac{AK_{G_1}K_{G_2}}{1 + K_{G_1}K_{G_2}K_H} = \frac{\Delta N_o}{\Delta N_{in}}\bigg|_{T_2} = \frac{5,000 - 3,000}{5,000 - 3,000} = 1$$

and

$$\frac{BK_{G_2}}{1 + K_{G_1}K_{G_2}K_H} = \frac{\Delta N_o}{\Delta T_L}\bigg|_{N_{in}=4,000} = \frac{5,800 - 2,700}{100 - 300} = -15.5$$

The resulting steady-state equation is

$$n_o = n_{in} - 15.5t_L$$

In effect, an open-loop system may be regarded as a proportional controller in which the droop lines are horizontal.

4.3 Integral Control Systems. By eliminating the linkage between x and y of Fig. 3.16 and using the hydraulic integrator shown in Fig. 4.6,

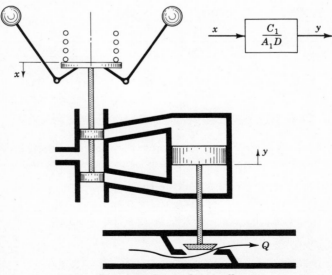

FIG. 4.6. Integral controller.

the proportional control system is converted to an integral control system. The block-diagram representation for the integrator is also shown in Fig. 4.6. The substitution of this diagram for that of the servomotor which it replaces in Fig. 3.20 yields the block-diagram representation shown in Fig. 4.7a.

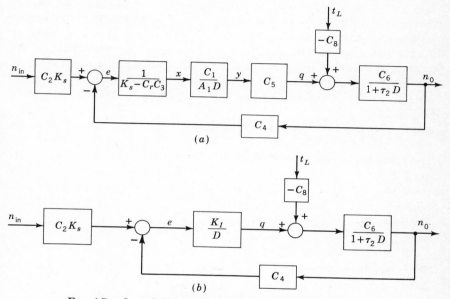

FIG. 4.7. Overall block diagram for integral control system.

The value of K_{G_1} is computed as follows,

$$K_{G_1} = \left[\frac{C_1 C_5}{(K_s - C_r C_3)A_1 D}\right]_{D=0} = \left(\frac{K_I}{D}\right)_{D=0} = \infty \qquad (4.12)$$

where $K_I = C_1 C_5/(K_s - C_r C_3)A_1$ is the constant associated with the integrating portion of the system, as is shown in Fig. 4.7b.

Because K_{G_1} is infinite, e must be zero for steady-state operation. Thus, subtracting the feedback signal from the reference input in Fig. 4.7b gives

$$C_2 K_s n_{in} - C_4 n_o = e = 0$$

or

$$n_o = \frac{C_2 K_s}{C_4} n_{in} \qquad (4.13)$$

The preceding expression shows that the speed is independent of the load torque for an integral control system. It is an easy matter to adjust the scale factor C_2 for the input speed dial so that $C_2 K_s/C_4 = 1$, in which case

$$n_o = n_{\text{in}} \tag{4.14}$$

The operation of an integral control system may be visualized as follows: From Fig. 4.6, it is to be seen that if x momentarily changes and then returns to its line-on-line position, the position of y has been changed permanently and so has the amount of flow going to the engine. Therefore, changing the amount of flow to account for a new operating torque does not change the steady-state position of x, which must be line on line. Because neither x nor the spring compression changes, the output speed must always be equal to the desired value in order that the flyweight force balances the spring force. (Note that, for the proportional control system, changing the fuel flow requires a permanent change in the position x.)

An integral control is easily recognized because *there must be an integrating component yielding a* $1/D$ *term in the block diagram between the comparator and the point where the external disturbance enters the system.* The line of operation of an integral controller is a vertical line. The operating characteristics of an integral control system are shown in Fig. 4.8.

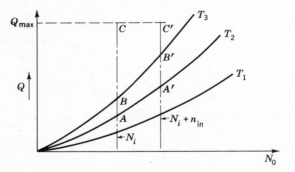

Fig. 4.8.   Operating characteristics for integral control system.

An integral controller is also called a floating controller because of the floating action of the position y of the flow setting valve. Two other terms used for an integral controller are reset controller and isochronous controller.

4.4 Proportional Plus Integral Control Systems. From a consideration of steady-state operation only, integral control systems seem preferable to proportional systems. However, it is generally easier to achieve good transient behavior with a proportional system rather than an integral system (techniques for determining the transient behavior of systems are presented in Chaps. 5 through 10). It is possible to combine the basic features of a proportional controller and an integral controller to form a proportional plus integral controller.

The action of a proportional plus integral controller to a change in the input or external disturbance is initially similar to that of a proportional controller, but as the new equilibrium point is reached, the control action becomes the same as that of an integral controller. (In effect, the slope of the droop line continually increases.)

A proportional plus integral controller combines the desirable transient characteristics of a proportional controller and the feature of no steady-state error of the integral controller.

A proportional plus integral controller is shown in Fig. 4.9. The proportional action is provided by unit 1, which is the same as that for the

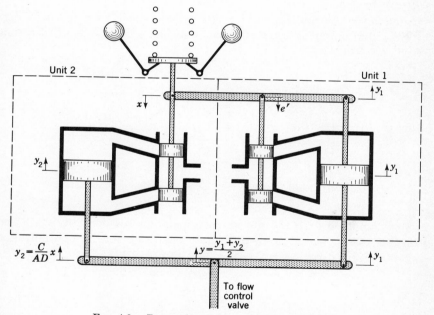

FIG. 4.9. Proportional plus integral controller.

proportional controller shown in Fig. 3.16. The equation for the proportional action is

$$y_1 = \frac{1}{1 + \tau_1 D} x \tag{4.15}$$

The integral action is provided by unit 2, which is the same as that for the integral controller shown in Fig. 4.6. The equation for this integral action is

$$y_2 = \frac{C}{AD} x \qquad (4.16)$$

The proportional and integral actions are added by a walking-beam linkage such that

$$y = \frac{y_1 + y_2}{2} \qquad (4.17)$$

The substitution of y_1 and y_2 into the preceding expression gives

$$y = \frac{1}{2}\left(\frac{1}{1 + \tau_1 D} + \frac{C}{AD}\right) x \qquad (4.18)$$

The individual block diagrams for Eqs. (4.15) to (4.17) are shown in Fig. 4.10a. The combined diagram is shown in Fig. 4.10b. The substitution

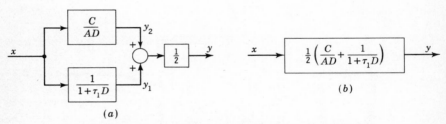

FIG. 4.10. Block diagram for proportional plus integral action.

of this combined diagram into its corresponding position between x and y of Fig. 4.7a yields the resulting representation for this proportional plus integral control system, as is shown in Fig. 4.11.

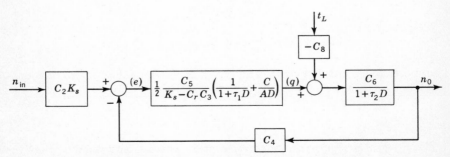

FIG. 4.11. Overall block diagram for proportional plus integral control system.

The value of K_{G_1} for this proportional plus integral control system is

$$K_{G_1} = \frac{C_5}{2(K_s - C_r C_3)} \left(\frac{1}{1 + \tau_1 D} + \frac{C}{AD} \right)_{D=0} = \infty \tag{4.19}$$

The proportional plus integral actions are clearly evidenced by Eq. (4.19). Because K_{G_1} is infinite for steady-state operation, it follows that e is zero during steady-state operation. Thus, from Fig. 4.11

$$C_2 K_s n_{\text{in}} - C_4 n_o = e = 0$$

or

$$n_o = \frac{C_2 K_s}{C_4} n_{\text{in}} \tag{4.20}$$

Comparison of Eqs. (4.20) and (4.13) shows that the steady-state operation of a proportional plus integral control system is the same as that of an integral control system alone. A proportional plus integral control is sometimes referred to as a compensated isochronous control. To better understand the action of this control, suppose that the throttle lever is moved to increase the speed. This causes the position x to move down as does e'. The time constant τ_1 of the proportional unit is small so that y_1 changes rapidly to increase the flow setting. The resulting motion of y_1 returns e' to its line-on-line position.

For the integrating unit, the quantity C/A is small so that y_2 continues to move at a slower rate to provide corrective action. As the speed increases, the position x moves up. The integrating unit continues to provide corrective action until x is returned to its line-on-line position (that is, $x = 0$). In summary, for proportional plus integral control, the initial effect is provided primarily by the proportional action, and the final effect is provided by the integrator.

4.5 Steady-state Constants. In Fig. 4.12a is shown the steady-state block diagram representation for a typical control system. The left portion enclosed by dotted lines is the controller. Similarly, the right portion is the system to be controlled. For the controller it follows that

$$(Av - K_H c)K_{G_1} = m \tag{4.21}$$

For $v = 0$, the preceding equation shows that

$$-K_H K_{G_1} = \frac{m}{c} \bigg|_{v=0} = \frac{\Delta M}{\Delta C} \bigg|_{v=0} = \frac{\partial M}{\partial C} \bigg|_V \tag{4.22}$$

For $v = 0$, then V must be a constant.

In Fig. 4.12b is shown the steady-state operating curves for a typical controller. It is to be noted that $\partial M / \partial C \big|_V$ is the slope of these curves.

Hence, the preceding equation relates the slope $\partial M / \partial C \big|_V$ and steady-state constants $-K_{G_1} K_H$.

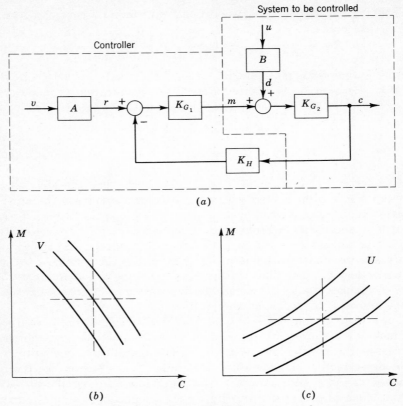

FIG. 4.12.   Steady-state characteristics of a control system.

For the case in which $c = 0$, Eq. (4.21) becomes

$$A K_{G_1} = \left. \frac{m}{v} \right|_{c=0} = \left. \frac{\Delta M}{\Delta V} \right|_{c=0} = \left. \frac{\partial M}{\partial V} \right|_C \qquad (4.23)$$

A line of constant C is a vertical line in Fig. 4.12b.   Furthermore, $\left. \partial M / \partial V \right|_C$ is the vertical spacing between lines of constant V.   Hence, the preceding result gives the vertical spacing $\left. \partial M / \partial V \right|_C$ in terms of steady-state constants $A K_{G_1}$.

Finally, for the case in which $m = 0$, Eq. (4.21) shows that

$$\frac{K_H}{A} = \left. \frac{v}{c} \right|_{m=0} = \left. \frac{\Delta V}{\Delta C} \right|_{m=0} = \left. \frac{\partial V}{\partial C} \right|_M \qquad (4.24)$$

A line of constant M is a horizontal line.   Hence, this result relates the horizontal spacing $\left. \partial V / \partial C \right|_M$ and steady-state constants K_H / A.

From Fig. 4.12a, the equation for steady-state operation of the system to be controlled is

$$(m + Bu)K_{G_2} = c \qquad (4.25)$$

By performing an analysis similar to that for the controller, it follows that

$$\left.\frac{\partial M}{\partial C}\right|_U = \frac{1}{K_{G_2}} \qquad \left.\frac{\partial M}{\partial U}\right|_C = -B \qquad \left.\frac{\partial C}{\partial U}\right|_M = BK_{G_2} \qquad (4.26)$$

The first partial $\left.\partial M/\partial C\right|_U$ is the slope of the steady-state operating curves shown in Fig. 4.12c, the second partial $\left.\partial M/\partial U\right|_C$ is the vertical spacing, and the last partial $\left.\partial C/\partial U\right|_M$ is the horizontal spacing. Hence, the individual constants in the block diagram of Fig. 4.12a may be evaluated from the steady-state operating curves and vice versa.

ILLUSTRATIVE EXAMPLE 1. The block diagram of a feedback control system for operation about a reference point is shown in Fig. 4.13.

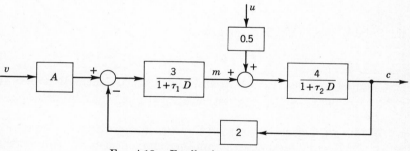

FIG. 4.13. Feedback control system.

Determine

1. The slope of the droop line
2. The slope of the operating line for the system being controlled
3. The value of A such that $\left.\partial C/\partial V\right|_U = 1$
4. The horizontal distance ΔC between lines of constant V for $\Delta V = 10$ units
5. The vertical distance ΔM between lines of constant V for $\Delta V = 10$ units

SOLUTION. From the block diagram it follows that $K_{G_1} = 3$, $K_{G_2} = 4$, $K_H = 2$, and $B = 0.5$.

1. The slope of the droop line is

$$\frac{\partial M}{\partial C}\bigg|_V = -K_H K_{G_1} = (-2)(3) = -6$$

2. The slope of the operating line for the system being controlled is

$$\frac{\partial M}{\partial C}\bigg|_U = \frac{1}{K_{G_2}} = \frac{1}{4} = 0.25$$

3. The value of A such that $\partial C/\partial V\big|_U = 1$ is

$$\frac{\partial C}{\partial V}\bigg|_U = \frac{A K_{G_1} K_{G_2}}{1 + K_{G_1} K_{G_2} K_H} = \frac{A(3)(4)}{1 + (3)(4)(2)} = \frac{12A}{25} = 1$$

Solving for A gives

$$A = {}^{25}\!/_{12}$$

4. Lines of constant V refer to the characteristics of the controller. Solving Eq. (4.24) for ΔC gives

$$\Delta C = \frac{A}{K_H} \Delta V = \frac{25}{(12)(2)} 10 = \frac{250}{24}$$

5. Solving Eq. (4.23) for ΔM gives

$$\Delta M = (A K_{G_1}) \Delta V = (25)(3)(10) = 750$$

In a similar manner, the horizontal and vertical spacing between the lines of constant U for the system being controlled may be determined.

4.6 Modes of Control.[1-3]   In addition to proportional, integral, and proportional plus integral control, another mode of control is derivative, or rate, action.   For a derivative controller, the steady-state expression for the control elements is

$$K_{G_1} = (KD)_{D=0} = 0 \tag{4.27}$$

The output of a derivative controller is proportional to the rate of change of error.   For any constant value of the actuating signal e, the output of the control elements is zero.   Thus, steady state may exist in a

---

[1] G. J. Murphy, "Basic Automatic Control Theory," Chap. 6, D. Van Nostrand Co., Inc., Princeton, N.J., 1957.

[2] D. P. Eckman, "Automatic Process Control," John Wiley & Sons, Inc., New York, 1958.

[3] G. K. Tucker and D. M. Wills, "A Simplified Technique of Control System Engineering," Minneapolis-Honeywell Regulator Co., Philadelphia, 1958.

derivative control system with any constant value of error signal. Because a derivative controller operates on the rate of change of error and not the error itself, the derivative mode of control is never used alone, but rather in combination with a proportional, or integral, or proportional plus integral controller.   The advantage of using derivative action is that the derivative is a measure of how fast the signal is changing and thus tends to give the effect of anticipation.   The addition of derivative action is limited primarily to systems which respond very slowly, such as large industrial processes.

The selection of the control elements $G_1(D)$ is seen to have a predominant effect upon the steady-state operation of a system.   For more complex control systems, it becomes increasingly difficult, if not impossible, to distinguish the individual modes of control.   However, regardless of the various modes that may be present, it is a relatively simple matter to determine whether K_{G_1} is finite or infinite.   For an infinite value, the integral action predominates and there is no steady-state error due to variations in the external disturbance.   For a finite value, the system behaves as a proportional control system.

A major problem in the design of control systems is the determination of the system parameters to obtain satisfactory transient performance. The transient behavior of a system is prescribed by the differential equation of operation for the system.   In the next chapter, it is shown how such differential equations may be solved algebraically by the use of Laplace transforms.   In Chap. 6, it is shown that the transient behavior is governed primarily by the roots of the characteristic equation for the system.   Thus, the transient characteristics of a system may be ascertained directly from a knowledge of the roots of the characteristic equation.

Problems

4.1 For the control system shown in Fig. P3.23, determine the steady-state equation relating v, u, and c for each of the following cases:

(a) $G_1(D) = \dfrac{K_1}{1 + \tau_1 D}$ (b) $G_1(D) = \dfrac{K_1}{D(1 + \tau_1 D)}$

(c) $G_1(D) = \dfrac{K_1}{D} + \dfrac{K_1}{1 + \tau_1 D}$

4.2 The steady-state operating curves for a proportional temperature control system are shown in Fig. P4.2.

(a) Determine the equation for steady-state operation about point A.

(b) If this were an open-loop rather than a closed-loop system, what would be the steady-state equation of operation?

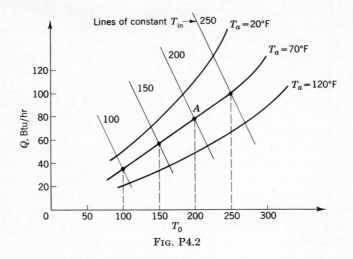

Fig. P4.2

4.3 For the illustrative example discussed in Sec. 4.2, determine the speed error when $N_{in} = 4,000$ and $T_L = 100$. If the slope of the droop line $\partial M/\partial C \big|_V = -K_H K_{G_1}$ is increased by a factor of 5, what is the new error?

4.4 The block diagram of a feedback control system for operation about a reference operating point is shown in Fig. P4.4. The steady-state equation of

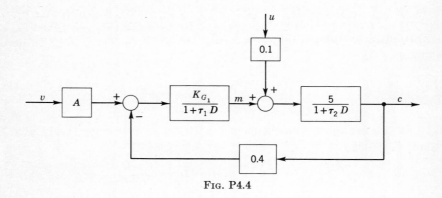

Fig. P4.4

operation is

$$c = \frac{\partial C}{\partial V}\bigg|_U v + \frac{\partial C}{\partial U}\bigg|_V u$$

(a) Determine the value of K_{G_1} such that $\partial C/\partial U \big|_V = 0.05$

(b) Determine the value of A such that $\partial C/\partial V \big|_U = 1$.

(c) For the system to be controlled, what is the slope of the lines of constant U?

(d) For the system to be controlled, determine the horizontal spacing ΔC between lines of constant U when $\Delta U = 10$ units.

4.5 For the system shown in Fig. P4.5,

(a) Determine K_{G_1} such that $\partial C/\partial U \big|_V = 0.1$.

(b) Determine A such that $\partial C/\partial V \big|_U = 1$.

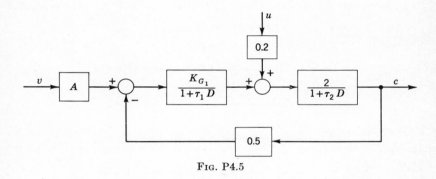

Fig. P4.5

4.6 The steady-state operating curves for a system to be controlled are shown in Fig. P4.6.

(a) Determine B and K_{G_2} at the reference operating point P.

(b) Determine the required slope of the droop lines $(-K_{G_1}K_H)$ such that the variation in C will not exceed 2 percent of its reference value $[c = 0.02(200) = 4$ units] when the external disturbance varies from its reference value to its maximum value $(u = U_{\max} - U_i = 20$ units).

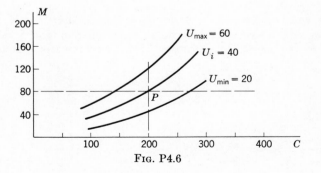

Fig. P4.6

4.7 At the reference operating point $C_i = 100$, $M_i = 5$, and $U_i = 10$, the characteristics of a system to be controlled are $B = 0.5$ and $K_{G_2} = 25$. Determine the slope of the load lines U and then:

(*a*) Draw the nominal load line $U = 10$ for the system to be controlled, and also draw the $U = 6$ and the $U = 14$ load lines. NOTE: Straight lines will suffice because we are working with linearized information about the reference operating point.

(*b*) Calculate the required slope of the droop line such that the output C will not change by more than 1 unit when the load is changed from the nominal value $U = 10$ to $U = 14$.

4.8 When the system to be controlled has an integrating element such as to make K_{G_2} infinite, the steady-state operating curves for the system become horizontal straight lines, as shown in Fig. P4.8. The steady-state operating curves for a remote-control positioning device are shown in Fig. P4.8. The controlled

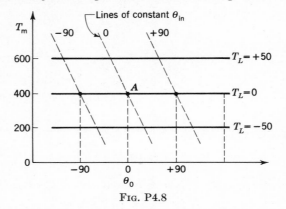

Fig. P4.8

shaft position is designated by θ_o and the set position by θ_{in}. Variations are to be indicated by $\Delta\theta$. For this remote-control positioning system, the external disturbance is a load torque T_L, and the manipulated variable is a motor torque T_m.

(*a*) Determine the steady-state equation of operation relating $\Delta\theta_o$, $\Delta\theta_{in}$, and t_L for operation about point A.

(*b*) To decrease the error caused by variations in the external disturbance by a factor of 5, what should be the new slope of the droop line?

4.9 In Fig. P4.9 is shown the steady-state block diagram for a system which is subjected to two external disturbances. Determine the steady-state equation

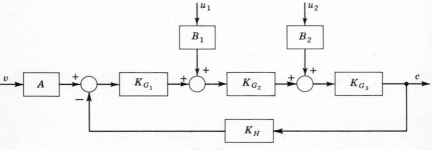

Fig. P4.9

relating c, v, u_1, and u_2. For which of the following cases will the steady-state operation be independent of variations in u_1? For which cases is it independent of variations in u_2? NOTE: Steady-state operation is independent of K_{G_3}.

(a) $K_{G_1} = \infty$ K_{G_2} and K_H are finite
(b) $K_{G_2} = \infty$ K_{G_1} and K_H are finite

4.10 Identify the mode of control for the control elements shown in units 1, 2, and 3 of Figs. P3.19 and P3.20a and b.

4.11 For each of the control elements shown in Fig. P4.11a and b, determine the operational form of the differential equation relating the actuating signal e and the output m. Identify the mode of control for each case.

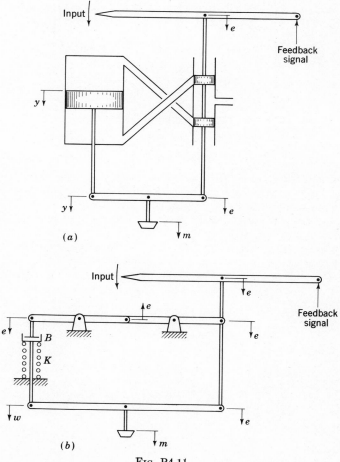

FIG. P4.11

4.12 A reproducing shaper is shown in Fig. P4.12. The position y of the duplicating cutter is seen to follow the position x of the master cutter. Determine the mode of operation of the shaper. What modifications would be necessary to convert this to a proportional plus integral controller?

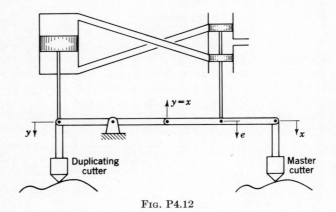

Fig. P4.12

5

Laplace transforms

By transient response is meant the manner in which a system changes from some initial operating condition to some final condition. For example, in Fig. 5.1 it is to be seen that at some arbitrary time $t = 0$

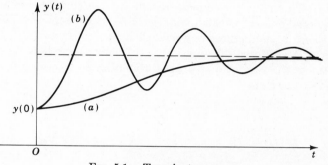

FIG. 5.1.   Transient response.

the output is $y(0)$. The curve marked (a) represents the transient response of a system in which the output $y(t)$ slowly approaches its new operating condition. The curve marked (b) shows a system which successively overshoots and undershoots, but these oscillations gradually die out as the new operating condition is obtained.

A linear control system or component is one in which the operation is described by a linear differential equation, usually with constant coefficients. For a known input, classical methods could be used for determining the output. However, considerable time is saved by using the Laplace transform method of solving linear differential equations. In addition, Laplace transform analysis is closely related to other methods for evaluating system performance, as is explained in later chapters.

A brief review of classical methods for solving differential equations with constant coefficients is first presented. This is done so that, when the Laplace transform method is explained, a clearer understanding of the similarities and the differences between the two methods results.

111

5.1 Classical Methods. The transient response of a control system may be obtained by solving differential equations of the general form

$$(D^n + b_{n-1}D^{n-1} + \cdots + b_1D + b_0)y(t)$$
$$= (a_mD^m + a_{m-1}D^{m-1} + \cdots + a_1D + a_0)f(t)$$

If the coefficient b_n of the $D^n y(t)$ term is not unity, it is an easy matter to divide each term by b_n to yield the preceding form. Solving for $y(t)$ gives

$$y(t) = \frac{a_mD^m + a_{m-1}D^{m-1} + \cdots + a_1D + a_0}{D^n + b_{n-1}D^{n-1} + \cdots + b_1D + b_0} f(t) \tag{5.1}$$

where $a_0, a_1, \ldots, a_m$ and $b_0, b_1, \ldots, b_n$ are constants. The term $f(t)$ represents the excitation to the system. This is called the forcing function because it forces or excites the system. The output $y(t)$ is called the response function because it responds to the forcing function $f(t)$. The denominator of Eq. (5.1) is the *characteristic function* of the differential equation. The equation which results by setting the characteristic function equal to zero is called the *characteristic equation*. The value of the exponent n, the highest power of D in the characteristic function, is the order of the differential equation. It is now shown how Eq. (5.1) may be written as the sum of first-order differential equations. First rewrite Eq. (5.1) in the form

$$y(t) = \frac{L_m(D)}{L_n(D)} f(t) \tag{5.2}$$

where
$$L_n(D) = D^n + b_{n-1}D^{n-1} + \cdots + b_1D + b_0$$
$$L_m(D) = a_mD^m + a_{m-1}D^{m-1} + \cdots + a_1D + a_0$$

The polynomial $L_n(D)$ may be factored into the form

$$L_n(D) = (D - r_1)(D - r_2) \cdots (D - r_n) \tag{5.3}$$

where $r_1, r_2, \ldots, r_n$ are the roots of the equation $L_n(D) = 0$. In factoring the polynomial $L_n(D)$ as shown in Eq. (5.3), it is to be noted that D may be treated as an algebraic quantity. For example, consider the function

$$L_n(D) = D^2 + 3D + 2 = (D - r_1)(D - r_2) \tag{5.4}$$

Setting $L_n(D)$ equal to zero yields

$$D^2 + 3D + 2 = 0 \tag{5.5}$$

The roots of the preceding equation are

$$r_{1,2} = \frac{-3 \pm \sqrt{9 - 8}}{2} = -1, -2 \tag{5.6}$$

Therefore, $L_n(D) = [D - (-1)][D - (-2)] = (D + 1)(D + 2)$.

Because $r_1, r_2, \ldots, r_n$ are the values of D for which $L_n(D) = 0$, then $r_1, r_2, \ldots, r_n$ are also called the zeros of the function $L_n(D)$. Thus, the roots of the equation $L_n(D) = 0$ are the zeros of the function $L_n(D)$. The zeros of $L_n(D)$ are said to be distinct if each zero has a different value (that is, $r_1 \neq r_2 \neq r_3 \neq \cdots \neq r_n$). When two or more zeros are equal, the characteristic function is said to have repeated zeros. The case in which $L_n(D)$ has distinct zeros is considered first.

From the theory of partial-fraction expansion, it follows that for distinct zeros $L_m(D)/L_n(D)$ in Eq. (5.2) may be written in the form

$$\frac{L_m(D)}{L_n(D)} = \frac{K_1}{D - r_1} + \frac{K_2}{D - r_2} + \cdots + \frac{K_i}{D - r_i} + \cdots + \frac{K_n}{D - r_n} \quad (5.7)$$

The procedure for obtaining any constant K_i is as follows: First multiply both sides of Eq. (5.7) by $D - r_i$, that is,

$$(D - r_i) \frac{L_m(D)}{L_n(D)} = \frac{D - r_i}{D - r_1} K_1 + \frac{D - r_i}{D - r_2} K_2$$
$$+ \cdots + K_i + \cdots + \frac{D - r_i}{D - r_n} K_n \quad (5.8)$$

The multiplication of the K_i term in Eq. (5.7) by $D - r_i$ is seen to cancel the denominator, thus leaving K_i alone as shown in Eq. (5.8). By letting $D = r_i$ in Eq. (5.8), each term of the right-hand side of Eq. (5.8) becomes zero except for K_i, which remains. Thus

$$K_i = \lim_{D \to r_i} \left[(D - r_i) \frac{L_m(D)}{L_n(D)} \right] \quad (5.9)$$

Successive application of Eq. (5.9), in which $i = 1, 2, \ldots, n$, yields each of the constants $K_1, K_2, \ldots, K_n$, respectively, in Eq. (5.7). As an example of the use of this partial-fraction-expansion technique, let it be desired to expand $L_m(D)/L_n(D)$, where

$$\frac{L_m(D)}{L_n(D)} = \frac{5D + 8}{D + 3D^2 + 2} = \frac{K_1}{D + 2} + \frac{K_2}{D + 1} \quad (5.10)$$

Application of Eq. (5.9) yields

$$K_1 = \lim_{D \to -2} \left[(D + 2) \frac{5D + 8}{(D + 2)(D + 1)} \right]$$
$$= \lim_{D \to -2} \frac{5D + 8}{D + 1} = \frac{-10 + 8}{-2 + 1} = 2$$

and
$$K_2 = \lim_{D \to -1} \frac{5D + 8}{D + 2} = \frac{-5 + 8}{-1 + 2} = 3$$

Thus
$$\frac{L_m(D)}{L_n(D)} = \frac{2}{D + 2} + \frac{3}{D + 1} \quad (5.11)$$

The general form for expressing a differential equation as a sum of first-order equations is obtained by substitution of $L_m(D)/L_n(D)$ from Eq. (5.7) into Eq. (5.2).   That is,

$$y(t) = \frac{K_1}{D - r_1} f(t) + \cdots + \frac{K_i}{D - r_i} f(t) + \cdots + \frac{K_n}{D - r_n} f(t)$$

$$= \sum_{i=1}^{n} \frac{K_i}{D - r_i} f(t) = \sum_{i=1}^{n} K_i y_i(t) \quad (5.12)$$

where

$$y_i(t) = \frac{1}{D - r_i} f(t) \quad (5.13)$$

Equation (5.13) is a linear differential equation of the first order.   Its solution is

$$y_i(t) = e^{r_i t}[\int e^{-r_i t} f(t) \, dt + c_i]$$

or

$$y_i(t) = c_i e^{r_i t} + e^{r_i t} \int e^{-r_i t} f(t) \, dt \quad (5.14)$$

where c_i is the constant of integration.   Because the constant of integration is displayed separately in Eq. (5.14), it suffices to evaluate the integral at time t only.   Substitution of Eq. (5.14) into Eq. (5.12) yields the following general solution,

$$y(t) = \sum_{i=1}^{n} k_i e^{r_i t} + \sum_{i=1}^{n} K_i e^{r_i t} \int e^{-r_i t} f(t) \, dt \quad (5.15)$$

where $k_i = c_i K_i$ is a constant.   The terms in the first summation of the right-hand side of Eq. (5.15) comprise the complementary solution, and the terms in the second summation comprise the particular solution.   That is,

$$y_c(t) = \sum_{i=1}^{n} k_i e^{r_i t} \quad (5.16)$$

and

$$y_p(t) = \sum_{i=1}^{n} K_i e^{r_i t} \int e^{-r_i t} f(t) \, dt \quad (5.17)$$

where $y_c(t)$ is the complementary solution and $y_p(t)$ is the particular solution.

ILLUSTRATIVE EXAMPLE 1.   Determine the solution for the following differential equation

$$(D^2 + 2D - 3)y(t) = t^2 \quad (5.18)$$

or

$$y(t) = \frac{1}{(D - 1)(D + 3)} t^2$$

Expanding the operator $L_m(D)/L_n(D)$ in a partial-fraction expansion gives

$$y(t) = \left(\frac{K_1}{D-1} + \frac{K_2}{D+3}\right) t^2 \qquad (5.19)$$

The constants K_1 and K_2 which arise from the partial-fraction expansion are

$$K_1 = \lim_{D \to 1}\left[(D-1)\frac{1}{(D-1)(D+3)}\right] = \frac{1}{4}$$

and $$K_2 = \lim_{D \to -3}\frac{1}{D-1} = -\frac{1}{4}$$

In Eq. (5.19), it is to be noted that $r_1 = 1$ and $r_2 = -3$; thus the complementary solution may be written directly from Eq. (5.16).

$$y_c(t) = k_1 e^{r_1 t} + k_2 e^{r_2 t} = k_1 e^t + k_2 e^{-3t} \qquad (5.20)$$

The particular solution is evaluated from Eq. (5.17) as follows:

$$\begin{aligned}
y_p(t) &= K_1 e^t \int e^{-t} t^2 \, dt + K_2 e^{-3t} \int e^{3t} t^2 \, dt \\
&= \frac{1}{4} e^t[-e^{-t}(t^2 + 2t + 2)] - \frac{1}{4} e^{-3t}\left[\frac{e^{3t}}{27}(9t^2 - 6t + 2)\right] \\
&= -\frac{t^2}{3} - \frac{4t}{9} - \frac{14}{27}
\end{aligned} \qquad (5.21)$$

The general solution is the sum of Eqs. (5.20) and (5.21). To evaluate the constants k_1 and k_2, two initial conditions are needed.

Repeated Zeros. Suppose that the characteristic function $L_n(D)$ has a multiple or repeated zero r which occurs q times, i.e.,

$$L_n(D) = (D - r)^q(D - r_1)(D - r_2) \cdots (D - r_{n-q}) \qquad (5.22)$$

For repeated zeros the partial-fraction expansion has the general form

$$\begin{aligned}
y(t) = \frac{L_m(D)}{L_n(D)} f(t) &= \frac{C_q f(t)}{(D-r)^q} + \frac{C_{q-1} f(t)}{(D-r)^{q-1}} + \cdots + \frac{C_1 f(t)}{D-r} \\
&+ \frac{K_1 f(t)}{D - r_1} + \frac{K_2 f(t)}{D - r_2} + \cdots + \frac{K_{n-q} f(t)}{D - r_{n-q}}
\end{aligned} \qquad (5.23)$$

The constants $K_1, K_2, \ldots, K_{n-q}$ are evaluated as before by application of Eq. (5.9); however, the constants $C_q, C_{q-1}, \ldots, C_1$, which arise from the partial-fraction expansion of the repeated zero, are evaluated as follows:

$$\begin{aligned}
C_q &= \lim_{D \to r}\left[(D - r)^q \frac{L_m(D)}{L_n(D)}\right] \\
C_{q-1} &= \lim_{D \to r}\left\{\frac{1}{1!}\frac{d}{dD}\left[(D - r)^q \frac{L_m(D)}{L_n(D)}\right]\right\} \\
C_{q-k} &= \lim_{D \to r}\left\{\frac{1}{k!}\frac{d^k}{dD^k}\left[(D - r)^q \frac{L_m(D)}{L_n(D)}\right]\right\}
\end{aligned} \qquad (5.24)$$

ILLUSTRATIVE EXAMPLE 2. Determine the partial-fraction expansion for

$$\frac{L_m(D)}{L_n(D)} = \frac{2D + 7}{(D + 3)^2} = \frac{C_2}{(D + 3)^2} + \frac{C_1}{D + 3} \tag{5.25}$$

For this example, q is equal to 2, so that

$$C_2 = \lim_{D \to -3} \left[(D + 3)^2 \frac{2D + 7}{(D + 3)^2} \right] = \lim_{D \to -3} (2D + 7) = 1$$

and

$$C_1 = \lim_{D \to -3} \left[\frac{d}{dD} (2D + 7) \right] = \lim_{D \to -3} 2 = 2$$

Thus

$$\frac{L_m(D)}{L_n(D)} = \frac{1}{(D + 3)^2} + \frac{2}{D + 3} \tag{5.26}$$

The portion of the response due to the term $C_i f(t)/(D - r)^i$ in Eq. (5.23) is

$$y_i(t) = \frac{C_i f(t)}{(D - r)^i} = (c_0 + c_1 t + \cdots + c_{i-1}t^{i-1})e^{rt}$$
$$+ C_i e^{rt} \int \cdots \int e^{-rt} f(t) \, (dt)^i \qquad i = 2, 3, \ldots, q \tag{5.27}$$

where $c_0, c_1, \ldots, c_{i-1}$ are constants which must be evaluated from the initial conditions. The first term containing the c constants is the complementary solution, whereas the second term on the right-hand side of the preceding expression is the particular solution. The response due to the distinct zeros in Eq. (5.23) and also the response due to the term $C_1 f(t)/(D - r)$ may be evaluated by application of Eq. (5.15).

ILLUSTRATIVE EXAMPLE 3. Let it be desired to solve the following equation, in which $f(t) = e^{-t}$, that is,

$$y(t) = \frac{2D + 7}{(D + 3)^2} e^{-t} = \frac{1}{(D + 3)^2} e^{-t} + \frac{2}{D + 3} e^{-t} \tag{5.28}$$

Application of Eq. (5.27) to the first term on the right-hand side of the preceding expression gives

$$y_2(t) = (c_0 + c_1 t)e^{-3t} + e^{-3t} \int\int e^{3t} e^{-t} \, dt \, dt$$
$$= (c_0 + c_1 t)e^{-3t} + \frac{e^{-t}}{4}$$

The response due to the second term is

$$y_1(t) = k_1 e^{-3t} + 2e^{-3t} \int e^{3t} e^{-t} \, dt$$
$$= k_1 e^{-3t} + e^{-t}$$

The total response $y(t)$ is the sum of the two preceding results, or

$$y(t) = [(c_0 + k_1) + c_1 t]e^{-3t} + \tfrac{5}{4}e^{-t} \tag{5.29}$$

Two initial conditions are required to evaluate the constant $c_0 + k_1$ and the constant c_1.

Numerous techniques such as the method of undetermined coefficients, variation of parameters, etc., have been developed for solving linear differential equations with constant coefficients. However, the method of Laplace transforms,[1-3] which is next described, is best suited for solving the type of problems which are of interest to control engineers. In many ways, the Laplace transform method is similar to the preceding method of using the partial-fraction expansion to reduce an nth order equation to the sum of n lower-order equations. A major difference is that, in the Laplace transform method, the response due to each term in the partial-fraction expansion is determined directly from the transform table. Thus, there is no need to perform the integrations indicated by either Eq. (5.15) or Eq. (5.27). Because initial conditions are automatically incorporated into the Laplace transforms, the resulting response expression yields directly the total solution (i.e., complementary plus particular solution). Thus, the constants arising from the initial conditions are automatically evaluated, so that the final desired result is obtained directly.

5.2 Laplace Transformation Method. This method of solving differential equations is somewhat analogous to the process of multiplying or dividing by use of logarithms. In the well-known transformation of logarithms, numbers are transformed into powers of the base 10 or some other base. This process in effect makes it possible to multiply and divide by use of the simpler operations of addition and subtraction. After obtaining the desired answer in logarithms, the transformation back to the real-number system is accomplished by finding antilogarithms.

In the method of Laplace transforms, transformation of the terms of the differential equation yields an algebraic equation in another variable s. Thereafter, the solution of the differential equation is effected by simple algebraic manipulations in the s domain (the new variable is s rather than time t). To obtain the desired time solution, it is necessary to invert the transform of the solution from the s domain back to the time domain. Actually, for much control work, information obtained in the s domain suffices so that it may be unnecessary to invert back to the time domain.

The Laplace transformation $F(s)$ of a function of time $f(t)$ is defined as follows,

$$F(s) = \mathcal{L}[f(t)] = \int_0^\infty f(t)e^{-st}\, dt \tag{5.30}$$

[1] F. H. Raven, "Mathematics of Engineering Systems," McGraw-Hill Book Co., New York, 1966.

[2] M. F. Gardner and J. L. Barnes, "Transients in Linear Systems," John Wiley & Sons, Inc., New York, 1942.

[3] R. V. Churchill, "Operational Mathematics," 2d ed., McGraw-Hill Book Company, New York, 1958.

where $\mathcal{L}$ is the symbol for taking the Laplace transform. The symbol $\mathcal{L}$ is read as "transform of" so that $\mathcal{L}[f(t)]$ means "transform of $f(t)$." For the integral on the right side of Eq. (5.30) the variable t vanishes after evaluation between the limits of integration. Thus, the resulting expression is a function of s only [that is, $F(s)$]. A verification for Eq. (5.30) is presented in Appendix I.

Transforming Functions from the Time Domain to the s Domain. Some input functions which are frequently used for investigating the characteristics of a control system are the step function, pulse function, impulse function, exponentially decaying function, and sinusoid.

Step Function. A graphical representation of a step function is shown in Fig. 5.2. A step function is designated by the symbol $hu(t)$, where h

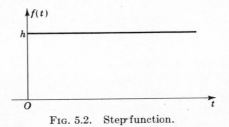

Fig. 5.2. Step function.

is the height and $u(t)$ is the symbol for a unit step function whose height is 1. Application of Eq. (5.30) gives

$$F(s) = \mathcal{L}[hu(t)] = \int_0^\infty he^{-st}\, dt = -\frac{he^{-st}}{s}\Big|_0^\infty = \frac{h(-e^{-s(\infty)} + e^{-s(0)})}{s} = \frac{h}{s} \tag{5.31}$$

In evaluating a transform, the term s is regarded as any constant which makes $F(s)$ convergent. As illustrated by Eq. (5.31), if s is any positive constant $(s > 0)$, then $e^{-s\infty} = 0$ and $e^{-s0} = e^{-0} = 1$ so that the result follows. However, it should be noted, for negative values of s, that $e^{-s\infty} = e^\infty = \infty$, in which case $F(s)$ would be divergent. As is discussed in Appendix I, the operator s must be taken as any constant such that $F(s)$ is convergent. Although there is a range of values of s over which $F(s)$ is convergent, there is but one transform $F(s)$ corresponding to each time function $f(t)$. In Table 5.1 is shown a list of time functions $f(t)$ and their corresponding transforms $F(s)$. In solving problems by Laplace transforms, the term s acts as a dummy operator, and thus there is no need for knowing the range of values over which $F(s)$ exists.

The listing of transform pairs [i.e., corresponding values of $F(s)$ and $f(t)$] given in Table 5.1 is adequate for the solution of most problems which

TABLE 5.1. LAPLACE TRANSFORM PAIRS

$f(t)$	$F(s)$
$u(t)$	$\dfrac{1}{s}$
$u_1(t)$	1
$e^{-\alpha t}$	$\dfrac{1}{s + \alpha}$
$e^{\alpha t}$	$\dfrac{1}{s - \alpha}$
$\sin \omega t$	$\dfrac{\omega}{s^2 + \omega^2}$
$\cos \omega t$	$\dfrac{s}{s^2 + \omega^2}$
$\dfrac{t^n}{n!}$	$\dfrac{1}{s^{n+1}}$
$\dfrac{t^n e^{\alpha t}}{n!}$	$\dfrac{1}{(s - \alpha)^{n+1}}$
$kf(t)$	$kF(s)$
$f_1(t) \pm f_2(t)$	$F_1(s) \pm F_2(s)$
$f'(t)$	$sF(s) - f(0)$
$f''(t)$	$s^2 F(s) - sf(0) - f'(0)$
$f'''(t)$	$s^3 F(s) - s^2 f(0) - sf'(0) - f''(0)$
$f^n(t)$	$s^n F(s) - s^{n-1}f(0) - \cdots - f^{n-1}(0)$
$f^{(-1)}(t)$	$\dfrac{F(s)}{s} + \dfrac{f^{(-1)}(0)}{s}$
$f^{(-n)}(t)$	$\dfrac{F(s)}{s^n} + \dfrac{f^{(-1)}(0)}{s^n}$ $+ \dfrac{f^{(-2)}(0)}{s^{n-1}} + \cdots + \dfrac{f^{(-n)}(0)}{s}$
$f(\tau) = f(t - t_0)$	$e^{-st_0}F(s)$

arise in control engineering. The derivation of most of these transform pairs is now explained.

Pulse Function. A pulse function is shown in Fig. 5.3. The height of the function is h and the width t_0 so that its area is ht_0. The Laplace transform is obtained by applying Eq. (5.30), in which $f(t) = h$ for $0 < t \leq t_0$ and $f(t) = 0$ for $t > t_0$.

$$F(s) = \int_0^{t_0} h e^{-st}\, dt = h \left[\frac{-e^{-st}}{s} \right]_0^{t_0} = \frac{h}{s} (1 - e^{-t_0 s}) \qquad (5.32)$$

A special case of a pulse function is an impulse function. By designating the height as $h = k/t_0$, it follows that the area is always equal to k. Now, as the width t_0 approaches zero, the height becomes infinite but the area

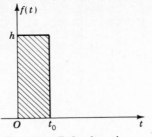

FIG. 5.3.   Pulse function.

remains equal to k.   This limiting case of a pulse function is called an impulse.   The symbol $ku_1(t)$ represents an impulse function whose area is k.   Substitution of $h = k/t_0$ into Eq. (5.32) and taking the limit as t_0 approaches zero gives the following transform for an impulse:

$$F(s) = \mathcal{L}[ku_1(t)] = \lim_{t_0 \to 0} \left[\frac{k}{t_0 s}(1 - e^{-t_0 s}) \right] = \frac{0}{0}$$

Application of Lhopital's rule for evaluating the preceding indeterminant gives

$$F(s) = \lim_{t_0 \to 0} \frac{d[k(1 - e^{-t_0 s})]/dt_0}{d(t_0 s)/dt_0} = \lim_{t_0 \to 0} \frac{kse^{-t_0 s}}{s} = k \qquad (5.33)$$

The transform of an impulse function is thus seen to be equal to the area of the function.   The impulse function whose area is unity, $u_1(t)$, is called a unit impulse.   Much information as to the transient behavior of a system may be obtained by determining the manner in which a system returns to its equilibrium state after the system has been excited by a momentary disturbance such as a pulse or an impulse.

Exponentially Decaying Function.   The function $f(t) = e^{-\alpha t}$ is shown in Fig. 5.4.   Applying Eq. (5.30) gives the transform of this exponentially decaying function.

$$F(s) = \mathcal{L}(e^{-\alpha t}) = \int_0^\infty e^{-(\alpha + s)t}\, dt = -\frac{e^{-(\alpha + s)t}}{s + \alpha}\Big|_0^\infty = \frac{1}{s + \alpha} \qquad (5.34)$$

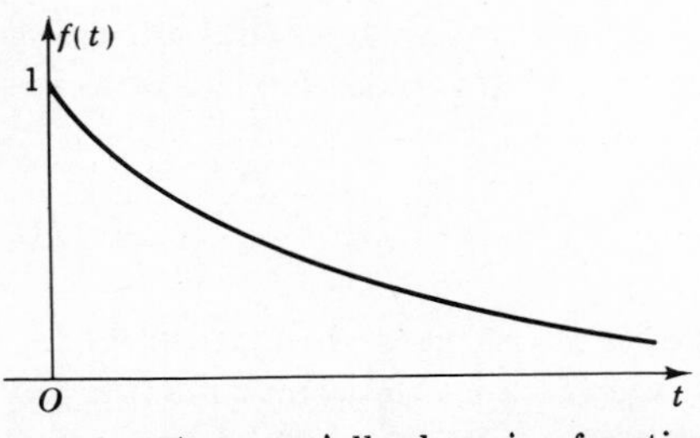

FIG. 5.4.   Exponentially decaying function.

Sinusoidal Function. A sinusoidal time function is shown in Fig. 5.5. The equation for this sinusoidal is $f(t) = \sin \omega t$. Thus

$$F(s) = \mathcal{L}(\sin \omega t) = \int_0^\infty e^{-st} \sin \omega t \, dt \qquad (5.35)$$

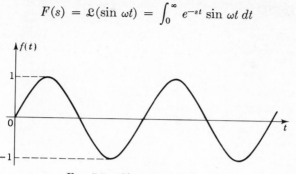

FIG. 5.5. Sinusoidal function.

The preceding integration is simplified by making use of Euler's equations.

$$e^{j\theta} = \cos \theta + j \sin \theta$$
$$e^{-j\theta} = \cos \theta - j \sin \theta \qquad (5.36)$$

Adding Euler's equations and dividing by 2 yields

$$\cos \theta = \frac{e^{j\theta} + e^{-j\theta}}{2} \qquad (5.37)$$

Subtracting the second of Euler's equations from the first and dividing by $2j$ yields

$$\sin \theta = \frac{e^{j\theta} - e^{-j\theta}}{2j} \qquad (5.38)$$

Substitution of the exponential form for $\sin \theta$ as given by Eq. (5.38) into Eq. (5.35) gives

$$F(s) = \int_0^\infty \frac{e^{j\omega t} - e^{-j\omega t}}{2j} e^{-st} \, dt$$
$$= \int_0^\infty \frac{e^{-(s-j\omega)t} - e^{-(s+j\omega)t}}{2j} \, dt$$
$$F(s) = \frac{1}{2j}\left(\frac{1}{s - j\omega} - \frac{1}{s + j\omega}\right) = \frac{\omega}{s^2 + \omega^2} \qquad (5.39)$$

The response of a system to a sinusoidal forcing function forms the basis for appraising the performance of systems by frequency-response techniques, as discussed in Chaps. 9 and 10.

5.3 Transform Properties. Significant characteristics and theorems pertaining to Laplace transformations are developed in this section.

With the aid of these properties, the usefulness of the Laplace transformation method is greatly extended.   In addition these theorems help us to obtain a much better understanding of the method.

   Real Translation.   The Laplace transform of a function $f(\tau)$ which begins at some time $t = t_0$, as shown in Fig. 5.6, rather than at $t = 0$ may

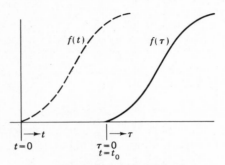

FIG. 5.6.   Delayed time function.

be obtained directly by application of the real-translation theorem. From Eq. (5.30), the Laplace transform for $f(\tau)$ is

$$\mathcal{L}[f(\tau)] = \int_0^\infty f(\tau)e^{-st}\,dt = \int_{t_0}^\infty f(\tau)e^{-st}\,dt \qquad (5.40)$$

   By noting that $t = t_0 + \tau$, $dt = d\tau$, and the lower limit of integration $t = t_0$ corresponds to $\tau = 0$, the preceding integral becomes

$$\mathcal{L}[f(\tau)] = \int_0^\infty f(\tau)e^{-s(t_0+\tau)}\,d\tau = e^{-t_0 s}\int_0^\infty f(\tau)e^{-s\tau}\,d\tau \qquad (5.41)$$

It is to be noted that

$$\int_0^\infty f(\tau)e^{-s\tau}\,d\tau = \int_0^\infty f(t)e^{-st}\,dt = F(s)$$

where $F(s)$ is the transform of the function if it is not delayed.   Substitution of the preceding result into Eq. (5.41) gives

$$\mathcal{L}[f(\tau)] = e^{-t_0 s}F(s) \qquad (5.42)$$

   An application of Eq. (5.42) is immediately evident by noting that the pulse function shown in Fig. 5.3 may be regarded as a step function of height h which begins at $t = 0$ minus a step function of height h which begins at $t = t_0$.   The transform for the first step function is h/s, while that for the delayed step function is $(h/s)e^{-t_0 s}$.   Subtracting the delayed step function from the first yields the following transform for the pulse:

$$\frac{h}{s}\,(1 - e^{-t_0 s})$$

This is the result given by Eq. (5.32).

Transform of a Derivative. Any linear differential equation will of course have derivatives of various orders. The order of each derivative is the same as the exponent of the operator D in the operational representation of the term. The general expression for transforming derivatives is obtained as follows:

Let $u = f(t)$ and $v = -e^{-st}/s$; then $du = (d/dt)[f(t)]\,dt$ and $dv = e^{-st}\,dt$. Integration by parts yields

$$\int u\,dv = uv - \int v\,du$$

Substitution of the preceding values for u and v and integration between the limits of zero and infinity gives

$$\int_0^\infty f(t)e^{-st}\,dt = -f(t)\,\frac{e^{-st}}{s}\,\Big|_0^\infty + \frac{1}{s}\int_0^\infty \frac{d}{dt} f(t)e^{-st}\,dt \qquad (5.43)$$

The left-hand member of the preceding expression is seen to be $F(s)$. For t equal to infinity, the upper limit of the first term on the right-hand side goes to zero. Thus

$$\begin{aligned}
F(s) &= \frac{f(0)}{s} + \frac{1}{s}\int_0^\infty \frac{d[f(t)]}{dt}\,e^{-st}\,dt \\
&= \frac{f(0)}{s} + \frac{1}{s}\,\mathcal{L}\left[\frac{df(t)}{dt}\right] \qquad (5.44)
\end{aligned}$$

where $f(0)$ is the initial value of $f(t)$. Solving Eq. (5.44) for the transform of the derivative gives

$$\mathcal{L}\left[\frac{df(t)}{dt}\right] = \mathcal{L}[f'(t)] = sF(s) - f(0) \qquad (5.45)$$

By the extension of the preceding techniques to higher-order derivatives, the following equations for transforms of higher-order derivatives are obtained,

$$\begin{aligned}
\mathcal{L}[f''(t)] &= s^2 F(s) - sf(0) - f'(0) \\
\mathcal{L}[f'''(t)] &= s^3 F(s) - s^2 f(0) - sf'(0) - f''(0) \qquad (5.46) \\
\mathcal{L}[f^n(t)] &= s^n F(s) - s^{n-1}f(0) - \cdots - f^{n-1}(0)
\end{aligned}$$

where $f'(t) = df(t)/dt$, $f''(t) = d^2 f(t)/dt^2$, ..., $f^n(t) = d^n f(t)/dt^n$, and $f'(0)$ is the initial value of $f'(t)$, etc. The initial conditions $f(0)$, $f'(0)$, $f''(0)$, . . . associated with a particular differential equation must, of course, be given.

An interesting result is obtained when Eq. (5.45) is applied to the function shown in Fig. 5.7. The initial value of this function is $f(0)$.

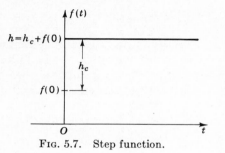

FIG. 5.7. Step function.

Because of the step change of height h_c, the value of the function for $t > 0$ is $h = h_c + f(0)$. The transform of this function is

$$F(s) = \mathcal{L}[f(t)] = \mathcal{L}\{[h_c + f(0)]u(t)\} = \frac{h_c + f(0)}{s}$$

Application of Eq. (5.45) to obtain the transform of the derivative of this function gives

$$\mathcal{L}\left[\frac{d}{dt}f(t)\right] = sF(s) - f(0) = \frac{s(h_c + f(0))}{s} - f(0) = h_c \quad (5.47)$$

The preceding transform is the same as that obtained for an impulse function. Thus, the derivative of a step change is an impulse function whose area is equal to the change in height h_c of the step.

Transform of an Integral. In using the Laplace transform method to solve integrodifferential equations, it is necessary to obtain the transform of an integral. The procedure for obtaining the equation for the transform of an integral is similar to that for a differential. In the general expression for integration by parts let $u = \int f(t)\,dt = f^{-1}(t)$ and $dv = e^{-st}\,dt$. Then application of the equation for integration by parts yields

$$\mathcal{L}[f^{(-1)}(t)] = \frac{F(s)}{s} + \frac{f^{(-1)}(0)}{s} \quad (5.48)$$

where $f^{(-1)}(t) = \int f(t)\,dt$ and $f^{(-1)}(0) = \int f(t)\,dt\Big|_{t=0}$ is the constant of integration which results from integrating $f(t)$.

By the repeated application of this procedure, it is found that

$$\mathcal{L}[f^{(-2)}(t)] = \frac{F(s)}{s^2} + \frac{f^{(-1)}(0)}{s^2} + \frac{f^{(-2)}(0)}{s}$$

$$\mathcal{L}[f^{(-n)}(t)] = \frac{F(s)}{s^n} + \frac{f^{(-1)}(0)}{s^n} + \frac{f^{(-2)}(0)}{s^{n-1}} + \cdots + \frac{f^{(-n)}(0)}{s} \qquad (5.49)$$

where $f^{(-n)}(t) = \int \cdots \int f(t)\, dt^n$, $f^{(-2)}(0) = \int\int f(t)\, dt^2 \big|_{t=0}$ is the second constant of integration which results from the double integration of $f(t)$, etc.

Linearity Theorem. The linearity characteristic of Laplace transformations is a very useful property. If k is a constant or a variable which is independent of both t and s, then it follows from Eq. (5.30) that

$$\mathcal{L}[kf(t)] = k\mathcal{L}[f(t)] = kF(s) \qquad (5.50)$$

Another important linearity property is

$$\mathcal{L}[f_1(t) \pm f_2(t)] = F_1(s) \pm F_2(s) \qquad (5.51)$$

Final-value Theorem. This theorem enables one to obtain the value $f(t)$ of a time function at $t = \infty$ directly from the Laplace transform $F(s)$. This is in effect the same type of information which is obtained from a steady-state analysis.

To develop the final-value theorem, first write the equation for the transform of a derivative in the form

$$\int_0^\infty f'(t)e^{-st}\, dt = sF(s) - f(0)$$

For s equal to zero, $e^{-st} = 1$, thus,

$$\int_0^\infty f'(t)\, dt = [sF(s)]_{s=0} - f(0) \qquad (5.52)$$

The preceding expression may be written as

$$\int_0^\infty f'(t)\, dt = f(t)\Big|_0^\infty = \lim_{t \to \infty} [f(t)] - f(0) \qquad (5.53)$$

The desired final-value theorem is obtained directly from Eqs. (5.52) and (5.53), i.e.,

$$\lim_{t \to \infty} f(t) = [sF(s)]_{s=0} \qquad (5.54)$$

The value of $y(t)$ at $t = \infty$ has no significance when $y(t)$ is a pure sinusoid or when $y(t)$ becomes infinite, and so in these cases the final-value theorem is meaningless.

As an application of the final-value theorem, consider the unity feedback system shown in Fig. 5.8. The error is $e = r - c = r - G(D)e$.

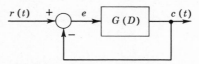

FIG. 5.8. Unity feedback system.

When all of the initial conditions are zero, the transformed equation is

$$E(s) = \frac{1}{1 + G(s)} R(s)$$

For a unit step-function input $[R(s) = 1/s]$, the steady-state error e_{ss} is

$$e_{ss} = \lim_{s \to 0} \frac{1}{1 + G(s)} = \frac{1}{1 + K_p}$$

where $K_p = \lim_{s \to 0} G(s)$ is called the positional error constant.   For a unit ramp input $[r(t) = t, R(s) = 1/s^2]$, the steady-state error is

$$e_{ss} = \lim_{s \to 0} \frac{1}{s + sG(s)} = \lim_{s \to 0} \frac{1}{sG(s)} = \frac{1}{K_v}$$

where $K_v = \lim_{s \to 0} sG(s)$ is called the velocity error constant.

For a unit parabolic input $[r(t) = t^2/2, R(s) = 1/s^3]$, the steady-state error is

$$e_{ss} = \lim_{s \to 0} \frac{1}{s^2 + s^2G(s)} = \lim_{s \to 0} \frac{1}{s^2G(s)} = \frac{1}{K_a}$$

where $K_a = \lim_{s \to 0} s^2G(s)$ is called the acceleration error constant.   The error constants provide a convenient method for determining the steady-state error to a unit step, unit ramp, or unit parabolic input for a unity feedback system.

Since the response due to initial conditions dies out as time approaches infinity, the preceding results are valid even if the initial conditions are not zero.

Initial-value Theorem.   With the aid of the initial-value theorem, the value $f(t)$ of a time function at $t = (0+)$ may be computed directly from the transform $F(s)$ for the function.   It is to be noted that $f(0+)$ is not the initial value $f(0)$ but rather the value of the function at a time slightly greater than zero.

The derivation of the initial-value theorem follows: For $t \approx 0$, then

$e^{-st} \approx 1$; thus the equation for the transform of a derivative can be written as

$$\mathcal{L}[f'(t)] = \int_0^{0+} f'(t)(1)\, dt + \int_{0+}^{\infty} f'(t)e^{-st}\, dt = sF(s) - f(0) \quad (5.55)$$

As s approaches infinity, $e^{-st} \approx 0$. Thus, as $s \to \infty$ in Eq. (5.55), the second integral vanishes. Hence,

$$f(0+) - f(0) = \lim_{s \to \infty} sF(s) - f(0)$$

or
$$f(0+) = \lim_{s \to \infty} sF(s) \quad (5.56)$$

This is the mathematical formulation of the initial-value theorem. Application of the initial-value theorem to the step function shown in Fig. 5.7 gives

$$f(0+) = [sF(s)]_{s=\infty} = \frac{s[h_c + f(0)]}{s}\bigg|_{s=\infty} = h_c + f(0) \quad (5.57)$$

Thus, a step change of height h_c is seen to occur at $t = 0$.

5.4 Initial Conditions. The initial state of the system is specified by the initial conditions. Because initial conditions are the state of the system as t approaches zero from a negative direction, then to be more precise these initial condition terms should be designated $f(0-)$, $f'(0-)$, $f''(0-)$, etc. However, for the sake of simplicity, initial conditions are designated as $f(0)$, $f'(0)$, $f''(0)$, etc., throughout this text.

The distinction between the initial condition and the value at $t = (0+)$ is further illustrated by the following examples. For a more rigorous presentation of this distinction, see Raven. [1]

ILLUSTRATIVE EXAMPLE 1. Use the Laplace transformation method to determine the solution of the following differential equation.

$$\frac{dy}{dt} + y = u_1(t)$$

The initial condition is $y(0) = 0$.

SOLUTION. The transform of each term is

$$\mathcal{L}\left(\frac{dy}{dt}\right) = sY(s) - y(0) = sY(s)$$
$$\mathcal{L}(y) = Y(s)$$
$$\mathcal{L}[u_1(t)] = 1$$

---

[1] F. H. Raven, "Mathematics of Engineering Systems," chap. 2, McGraw-Hill Book Company, New York, 1966.

Thus, the transformed equation is

$$sY(s) + Y(s) = 1$$

Solving for $Y(s)$ gives

$$Y(s) = \frac{1}{s+1} \tag{5.58}$$

To invert this equation from the s domain back to the time domain, it is to be noted that

$$\mathcal{L}[y(t)] = Y(s) \qquad \text{and} \qquad \mathcal{L}[e^{-t}] = \frac{1}{s+1}$$

The inverse transform of each term designated as $\mathcal{L}^{-1}$ is

$$\mathcal{L}^{-1}[Y(s)] = y(t) \qquad \mathcal{L}^{-1}\left(\frac{1}{s+1}\right) = e^{-t}$$

The inverse of a transform is thus seen to be the original function. That is

$$\mathcal{L}^{-1}[F(s)] = \mathcal{L}^{-1}\{\mathcal{L}[f(t)]\} = f(t)$$

The right-hand column of Table 5.1 is the transform of each corresponding function in the left-hand column. Similarly, the left-hand column is the inverse transform of each corresponding term in the right-hand column.

Thus, inverting Eq. (5.58) yields for the desired solution

$$y(t) = e^{-t} \qquad t > 0 \tag{5.59}$$

Solutions obtained by the Laplace transform method are valid for $t > 0$ only. In Fig. 5.9 is shown a plot of the preceding response. The initial value $y(0) = 0$ is indicated by an x.

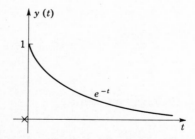

FIG. 5.9.   Response of a first-order system to a unit impulse.

Application of the initial-value theorem to Eq. (5.58) gives

$$y(0+) = \lim_{s \to \infty} sY(s) = \left.\frac{s}{s+1}\right|_{s=\infty} = \left.\frac{1}{1+1/s}\right|_{s=\infty} = 1$$

This result may also be verified by taking the limit of Eq. (5.59) as t approaches $(0+)$. As shown in this example, the initial-value theorem yields the value at $t = (0+)$ and not the initial value. The initial state of a system must be specified in order to solve a problem. Hence, all the initial values are known beforehand.

ILLUSTRATIVE EXAMPLE 2. In Fig. 5.10a is shown a spring and damper which is subjected to a suddenly applied force as shown in Fig. 5.10b.

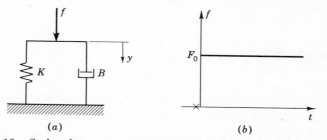

(a) $\qquad$ (b)

FIG. 5.10. Spring-damper system subjected to a suddenly applied force.

For the case in which $B = 1$, $K = 2$, and all the initial conditions are zero, determine

1. The equation for the motion y
2. The equation for the velocity v
3. The value of v at $t = (0+)$

SOLUTION. The differential equation of operation is

$$BDy + Ky = f$$

For $B = 1$ and $K = 2$, then

$$Dy + 2y = f \qquad (5.60)$$

1. The transform of the preceding equation is

$$sY(s) - y(0) + 2Y(s) = \frac{F_0}{s}$$

Because all initial conditions are zero, then $y(0) = 0$. Solving the preceding for $Y(s)$ and performing a partial-fraction expansion gives

$$Y(s) = \frac{F_0}{s(s + 2)} = \frac{F_0}{2s} - \frac{F_0}{2(s + 2)} \qquad (5.61)$$

To invert Eq. (5.61) from the s domain back to the time domain, it is to be noted that

$$\mathcal{L}[y(t)] = Y(s) \qquad \mathcal{L}[u(t)] = \frac{1}{s} \qquad \mathcal{L}(e^{-2t}) = \frac{1}{s + 2}$$

The inverse transform of each term designated $\mathcal{L}^{-1}$ is

$$\mathcal{L}^{-1}[Y(s)] = y(t) \qquad \mathcal{L}^{-1}\left(\frac{1}{s}\right) = u(t) \qquad \mathcal{L}^{-1}\left(\frac{1}{s+2}\right) = e^{-2t}$$

Thus, the inverse transform of Eq. (5.61) is

$$y(t) = (1 - e^{-2t})\frac{F_0}{2} \qquad t > 0 \tag{5.62}$$

2. Differentiation of Eq. (5.60) yields the following equation for the velocity, $v = Dy = \dot{y}$:

$$Dv + 2v = Df$$

Transforming gives

$$sV(s) - v(0) + 2V(s) = sF(s) - f(0)$$

Substituting the initial conditions $v(0) = f(0) = 0$ and the transform $F(s) = F_0/s$ into the preceding gives

$$V(s) = \frac{F_0}{s+2} \tag{5.63}$$

Inverting yields for the desired result

$$v(t) = F_0 e^{-2t} \qquad t > 0 \tag{5.64}$$

An alternate method for solving this problem is to note that

$$V(s) = \mathcal{L}(v) = \mathcal{L}\left(\frac{dy}{dt}\right) = sY(s) - y(0)$$

Substitution of $Y(s) = F_0/[s(s+2)]$ and $y(0) = 0$ into the preceding expression verifies Eq. (5.63), whence the result given by Eq. (5.64) follows. This result could also have been obtained by differentiating Eq. (5.62).

3. The substitution of $t = (0+)$ in Eq. (5.64) or the application of the initial-value theorem to Eq. (5.63) yields

$$v(0+) = F_0$$

The velocity v is discontinuous at the origin. That is, the initial value is $v(0) = 0$ and the value at time $t = (0+)$ is $v(0+) = F_0$.

As illustrated by the preceding examples, the initial state of a system is specified by the initial conditions [e.g., $y(0)$, $y'(0)$, $y''(0)$]. The time $t = (0+)$ occurs slightly later.

5.5 General Procedures. Let it be desired to determine the solution of the following differential equation

$$(\tau D + 1)y(t) = Kf(t) \tag{5.65}$$

When $K = 1$, this equation describes the operation of the servomotor shown in Fig. 3.5. For convenience in performing the partial fraction expansion, it is desirable to have the coefficient of the highest power of D in $L_n(D)$ unity. Thus

$$\left(D + \frac{1}{\tau}\right) y(t) = \frac{K}{\tau} f(t) \tag{5.66}$$

Transforming each term of this differential equation and solving for $Y(s)$ gives

$$Y(s) = \frac{(K/\tau)F(s) + y(0)}{s + 1/\tau} \tag{5.67}$$

The symbol $F(s)$ is the transform of the input. The nature of the expression $F(s)$ depends upon the particular input to the system, such as a step function, exponential, sinusoidal, etc.

All Initial Conditions Zero. Let it be desired to determine the response of this system to a step-function input $f(t)$ when all the initial conditions are zero. A plot of the input $f(t)$ is shown in Fig. 5.11a. The initial value is $f(0) = 0$, and then a step change h_c occurs so that the height of this function is $h = h_c$. The substitution of $F(s) = h_c/s$ and $y(0) = 0$ into Eq. (5.67) gives

$$Y(s) = \frac{Kh_c/\tau}{s(s + 1/\tau)} \tag{5.68}$$

The partial-fraction expansion is

$$Y(s) = Kh_c \left(\frac{1}{s} - \frac{1}{s + 1/\tau}\right)$$

Inverting yields for the response

$$y(t) = Kh_c(1 - e^{-t/\tau}) \qquad t > 0 \tag{5.69}$$

A graph of this response is also shown in Fig. 5.11a.

Initially at a Steady-state Operating Condition. A system is initially at a steady-state operating condition if the initial value of all the time derivatives is zero (that is, $D^n y = D^m f = 0$, $n = 1, 2, 3, \ldots$, and $m = 1, 2, 3, \ldots$). When this system is initially at a steady-state operating condition, then from Eq. (5.66) it follows that $y(0) = Kf(0)$.

Let us now determine the response for the case in which the initial value of the input is $f(0)$ as shown in Fig. 5.11b. The height h of the step

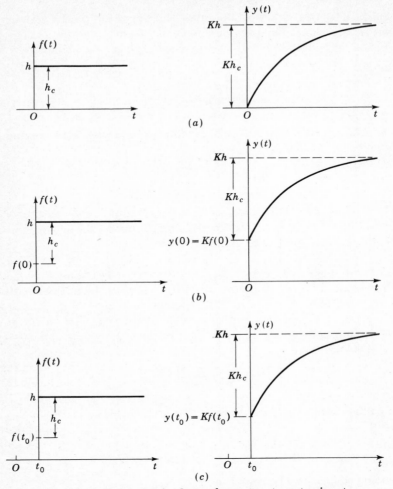

Fig. 5.11. Response of a first-order system to a step input.

input is the initial value $f(0)$ plus the change h_c. Thus

$$F(s) = \frac{h}{s} = \frac{h_c + f(0)}{s} = \frac{h_c + y(0)/K}{s} \tag{5.70}$$

The substitution of this value of $F(s)$ into Eq. (5.67) gives

$$Y(s) = \frac{Kh_c/\tau}{s(s + 1/\tau)} + \frac{y(0)}{s} \tag{5.71}$$

The partial-fraction expansion is

$$Y(s) = Kh_c \left(\frac{1}{s} - \frac{1}{s + 1/\tau} \right) + \frac{y(0)}{s} \tag{5.72}$$

Inverting yields

$$y(t) = Kh_c(1 - e^{-t/\tau}) + y(0) \qquad t > 0 \tag{5.73}$$

The first term on the right-hand side is seen to be the response due to the step change h_c alone when all of the initial conditions are zero [i.e., Eq. (5.69)]. A plot of this response is shown in Fig. 5.11b. This is the same response as Fig. 5.11a except that it is raised by the initial value $y(0)$.

In general, it may be shown that for a system which is initially at a steady-state operating condition, the response $y(t)$ is equal to the initial value $y(0)$ plus the response for the case in which all the initial conditions are zero.

Time Delay. To obtain the transform of the derivative of a delayed function, replace $f(\tau)$ by $df(\tau)/d\tau$ in Eq. (5.41). Thus

$$\mathfrak{L}\left[\frac{df(\tau)}{d\tau}\right] = e^{-t_0 s} \int_0^\infty \frac{df(\tau)}{d\tau} e^{-s\tau}\, d\tau = e^{-t_0 s}[sF(s) - f(\tau)]_{\tau=0}$$

$$= [sF(s) - f(t_0)]e^{-t_0 s} \tag{5.74}$$

where $f(\tau)\Big|_{\tau=0} = f(t)\Big|_{t=t_0} = f(t_0)$. In general, it follows that

$$\mathfrak{L}[f^n(\tau)] = [s^n F(s) - s^{n-1}f(t_0) - \cdots - f^{n-1}(t_0)]e^{-t_0 s} \tag{5.75}$$

Thus, to convert a transform to a delayed transform, multiply each term by $e^{-t_0 s}$ and evaluate the initial conditions at time t_0 which is the starting point for the delayed function.

Let it be desired to determine the response for the case in which the input of Fig. 5.11b is delayed by time t_0 as shown in Fig. 5.11c. Multiplying each term in Eq. (5.72) by $e^{-t_0 s}$ and evaluating the initial conditions at time t_0 gives for the transformed equation

$$Y(s)e^{-t_0 s} = Kh_c\left(\frac{1}{s} - \frac{1}{s + 1/\tau}\right)e^{-t_0 s} + \frac{y(t_0)}{s}e^{-t_0 s} \tag{5.76}$$

The operator $e^{-t_0 s}$ merely means that t should be replaced by $t - t_0$ in the regular transform. Thus, the inverse of Eq. (5.76) is

$$y(t - t_0) = Kh_c(1 - e^{-(t-t_0)/\tau}) + y(t_0) \qquad t > t_0 \tag{5.77}$$

This is the same as Eq. (5.75) except that t has been replaced by $t - t_0$, and the starting point is at time t_0 rather than at $t = 0$. The response shown in Fig. 5.11c is the same as that shown in Fig. 5.11b except that it is delayed a time t_0. It is not necessary that a system be initially at a steady-state operating condition to effect a time shift. For most problems in which a time shift occurs, it is more convenient to work the problem initially as though there were no time shift, and then replace t by $(t - t_0)$ to obtain the desired result.

The general procedure used to solve differential equations by Laplace transforms may be summarized as follows:

1. Transform each term of the differential equation from the time domain to the s domain, and then solve for $Y(s)$.
2. Substitute the value of the initial conditions and the transform of the input into the expression obtained in step 1.
3. Perform a partial fraction expansion.
4. Invert each term back to the time domain to obtain the desired time response.

Much simplification in carrying out the algebraic manipulations of a Laplace transform solution is afforded for the following special cases:

1. *All initial conditions zero.* When all the initial conditions are zero then the transform of a derivative is $\mathcal{L}[D^n f(t)] = s^n F(s)$. Thus, it follows that the transformed equation is obtained by substituting s for D, $Y(s)$ for $y(t)$, and $F(s)$ for $f(t)$ in the original differential equation.
2. *System initially at a steady-state operating condition.* When all of the initial derivatives are zero, then evaluating Eq. (5.1) at $t = 0$ shows that $ay(0) = bf(0)$ or $y(0) = (b/a)f(0)$. For this case, the response $y(t)$ is obtained by adding the initial value $y(0)$ to the response for the case in which all the initial conditions are zero (i.e., case 1).
3. *Time shift.* A time shift is effected by substituting $t - t_0$ for t. It is not necessary that all of the initial conditions be zero nor that the system be initially at a steady-state operating condition in order to effect a time shift.

ILLUSTRATIVE EXAMPLE 1. Determine the response of the following differential equation to a unit step function when all the initial conditions are zero:

$$(D^2 + 7D + 12)y(t) = (D + 2)f(t) \tag{5.78}$$

Because the initial conditions are zero, substitution of s for D, $Y(s)$ for $y(t)$, and $F(s)$ for $f(t)$ yields

$$Y(s) = \frac{(s + 2)F(s)}{s^2 + 7s + 12} = \frac{s + 2}{s(s^2 + 7s + 12)} \tag{5.79}$$

where $F(s) = 1/s$ for a unit step function. Performing a partial-fraction expansion gives

$$Y(s) = \frac{K_1}{s} + \frac{K_2}{s + 3} + \frac{K_3}{s + 4} \tag{5.80}$$

where
$$K_1 = \lim_{s \to 0} \frac{s + 2}{(s + 3)(s + 4)} = \frac{1}{6}$$

$$K_2 = \lim_{s \to -3} \frac{s + 2}{s(s + 4)} = \frac{1}{3}$$

$$K_3 = \lim_{s \to -4} \frac{s + 2}{s(s + 3)} = -\frac{1}{2}$$

Thus
$$Y(s) = \frac{1}{6s} + \frac{1}{3(s + 3)} - \frac{1}{2(s + 4)} \tag{5.81}$$

Inverting the preceding expression gives the desired time response

$$y(t) = \tfrac{1}{6} + \tfrac{1}{3}e^{-3t} - \tfrac{1}{2}e^{-4t} \tag{5.82}$$

If initially the system is at a steady-state operating condition so that $D^2y(0) = Dy(0) = Df(0) = 0$, then from Eq. (5.78) it is found that $12y(0) = 2f(0)$. The response is

$$y(t) = \tfrac{1}{6} + \tfrac{1}{3}e^{-3t} - \tfrac{1}{2}e^{-4t} + y(0) \tag{5.83}$$

A time shift by an amount t_0 can be effected by merely substituting $t - t_0$ for t.

5.6 Piecewise Continuous Functions. A piecewise continuous function is characterized by the fact that the equation for the function changes from interval to interval as is illustrated by the functions in Fig. 5.12. For example, in Fig. 5.12a, for $0 < t \le t_0$, $f(t) = at$; and for $t > t_0$, $f(t) = at_0$. For the first interval $0 < t \le t_0$, the input function is inclined

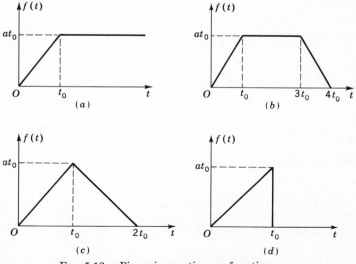

Fig. 5.12. Piecewise continuous functions.

at a slope a. Such an inclined straight line is called a ramp function. For $t > t_0$, the input is seen to be a step function. The solution of such problems is effected by starting with the first interval and successively solving for the response in each interval.

Let it be desired to solve Eq. (5.65) for the case in which the input is that shown in Fig. 5.12a. From the transform table, the transform for $t^n/n!$ is $1/s^{n+1}$; so for $n = 1$, it follows that $\mathcal{L}(at) = a/s^2$. Thus, the transform $F(s)$ for the input is

$$F(s) = \frac{a}{s^2} \qquad (5.84)$$

Substitution of the preceding result into Eq. (5.67) gives

$$Y(s) = \frac{Ka/\tau s^2 + y(0)}{s + 1/\tau} = \frac{Ka/\tau + s^2 y(0)}{s^2(s + 1/\tau)} \qquad (5.85)$$

A partial-fraction expansion of Eq. (5.85) gives

$$Y(s) = \frac{C_2}{s^2} + \frac{C_1}{s} + \frac{K_1}{s + 1/\tau} \qquad (5.86)$$

where from Eq. (5.24)

$$C_2 = \lim_{s \to 0} s^2 Y(s) = \lim_{s \to 0} \frac{Ka/\tau + s^2 y(0)}{s + 1/\tau} = Ka$$

$$C_1 = \lim_{s \to 0} \frac{d}{ds}[s^2 Y(s)] = \lim_{s \to 0} \frac{(s + 1/\tau)2sy(0) - [Ka/\tau + s^2 y(0)]}{(s + 1/\tau)^2}$$

$$= \frac{-Ka/\tau}{1/\tau^2} = -Ka\tau$$

$$K_1 = \lim_{s \to -1/\tau} \left[\left(s + \frac{1}{\tau} \right) Y(s) \right] = Ka\tau + y(0)$$

Substitution of these constants into Eq. (5.86) gives

$$Y(s) = \frac{Ka}{s^2} - \frac{Ka\tau}{s} + \frac{Ka\tau + y(0)}{s + 1/\tau} \qquad (5.87)$$

Inverting the preceding expression gives the desired response for $0 < t \le t_0$,

$$\begin{aligned} y(t) &= Kat - Ka\tau + [Ka\tau + y(0)]e^{-t/\tau} \\ &= Kat - Ka\tau(1 - e^{-t/\tau}) + y(0)e^{-t/\tau} \qquad 0 < t \le t_0 \quad (5.88) \end{aligned}$$

For the second interval the input is a step function. From Fig. 5.12a, it is to be seen that the initial value $f(t_0)$ is at_0. Because there is no change in the height of this function from its initial value, h_c equals zero. The step-function response for this system is determined by substituting $F(s) = (at_0/s)e^{-t_0 s}$ and $y(0) = y(t_0)e^{-t_0 s}$ into Eq. (5.67) and inverting. Thus,

$$y(t - t_0) = Kat_0 + [y(t_0) - Kat_0]e^{-(t-t_0)/\tau} \qquad t > t_0 \qquad (5.89)$$

The value of $y(t_0)$ is obtained by letting $t = t_0$ in Eq. (5.88)

$$y(t_0) = Kat_0 - Ka\tau(1 - e^{-t_0/\tau}) + y(0)e^{-t_0/\tau} \qquad (5.90)$$

Substitution of this result for $y(t_0)$ into Eq. (5.89) gives

$$\begin{aligned}
y(t - t_0) &= Kat_0 + [-Ka\tau(1 - e^{-t_0/\tau}) + y(0)e^{-t_0/\tau}]e^{-(t-t_0)/\tau} \\
&= Kat_0 - Ka\tau e^{-t/\tau}(e^{t_0/\tau} - 1) + y(0)e^{-t/\tau} \qquad t > t_0 \qquad (5.91)
\end{aligned}$$

In this method, the initial conditions for a new interval are obtained by evaluating the equation for the preceding interval at the value of time when the preceding interval ceases and the new one begins.

An alternate method for solving piecewise continuous problems is to regard the input as being the sum of separate functions as is illustrated in Fig. 5.13. The sum of the ramp function which begins at $t = 0$ and

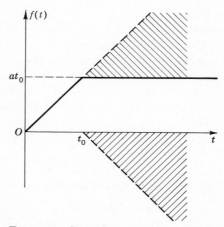

Fig. 5.13. Sum of two ramp functions.

the equal but opposite ramp function which begins at $t = t_0$ is seen to yield the function of Fig. 5.12a. Similarly, it is possible to represent any piecewise continuous function as the sum of other functions which are continuous.

The transform for the first ramp function of Fig. 5.13 is a/s^2, and that for the delayed ramp function is $-(a/s^2)e^{-t_0 s}$. Thus, the transform $F(s)$ for the input is

$$F(s) = \frac{a}{s^2} - \frac{a}{s^2}e^{-t_0 s} \qquad (5.92)$$

Substitution of the preceding result into Eq. (5.67) gives

$$Y(s) = \frac{Ka/\tau s^2 + y(0)}{s + 1/\tau} - \frac{(Ka/\tau s^2)e^{-t_0 s}}{s + 1/\tau} \qquad (5.93)$$

Because of the delaying factor $e^{-t_0 s}$ the second term on the right-hand side of Eq. (5.93) should be ignored for $t < t_0$. Thus, for $0 < t \le t_0$, the transform is the same as that given by Eq. (5.85). The corresponding response for $0 < t \le t_0$ is given by Eq. (5.88). For $t > t_0$, the response is the sum of that due to the second term of Eq. (5.93) plus that already obtained for the first term [Eq. (5.88)]. By noting that the second term of Eq. (5.93) is the same as the first with the exception of no initial-condition term $y(0)$, the response due to the second term is obtained by letting $y(0) = 0$ in Eq. (5.88) and substituting $t - t_0$ for t to take into account the time shift. Thus, for $t > t_0$ the total response is

$$y(t) = Kat - Ka\tau(1 - e^{-t/\tau}) + y(0)e^{-t/\tau}$$
$$- [Ka(t - t_0) - Ka\tau(1 - e^{-(t-t_0)/\tau})]$$

or $\qquad y(t) = Kat_0 - Ka\tau e^{-t/\tau}(e^{t_0/\tau} - 1) + y(0)e^{-t/\tau} \qquad (5.94)$

An advantage of this second method of solution is that initial conditions appear only in the transformed expression for the first interval. However, in this latter method, the amount of computational effort increases with the number of separate functions required to make up the overall piecewise continuous function. Thus, the choice of the first or second method depends on the particular problem to be solved. (In Appendix II, it is shown how the convolution integral may be used to determine the response to any arbitrary input function.)

Problems

5.1 Determine the general solution for the first-order differential equation

$$(D - r)y(t) = f(t)$$

5.2 Expand the following operators by use of partial-fraction expansion techniques:

(a) $\dfrac{L_m(D)}{L_n(D)} = \dfrac{6}{(D + 1)(D + 4)}$
(b) $\dfrac{L_m(D)}{L_n(D)} = \dfrac{2D + 3}{D(D + 3)}$

(c) $\dfrac{L_m(D)}{L_n(D)} = \dfrac{D^2 + 6D + 15}{(D + 1)(D + 3)(D + 6)}$
(d) $\dfrac{L_m(D)}{L_n(D)} = \dfrac{18D + 30}{D(D + 2)(D + 5)}$

5.3 Determine the partial-fraction expansion for the following operators:

(a) $\dfrac{L_m(D)}{L_n(D)} = \dfrac{D + 3}{D(D + 1)^2}$
(b) $\dfrac{L_m(D)}{L_n(D)} = \dfrac{3}{D^2(D + 3)^2}$

(c) $\dfrac{L_m(D)}{L_n(D)} = \dfrac{11D + 6}{D^3(D + 2)(D + 3)}$

5.4 Evaluate the unknown constants in the general solution of Eq. (5.18) for the case in which $y(0) = y'(0) = 0$. The complementary solution is given by Eq. (5.20) and the particular solution by Eq. (5.21).

5.5 Use the Laplace transform method to solve Eq. (5.18) for the case in which $y(0) = y'(0) = 0$.

5.6 Evaluate the unknown constants in the general solution of Eq. (5.28) for the case in which $y(0) = y'(0) = 0$. The general solution is given by Eq. (5.29).

5.7 Use the Laplace transform method to solve Eq. (5.28) for the case in which $y(0) = y'(0) = 0$.

5.8 Determine the Laplace transform for

(a) $f(t) = at$
(b) $f(t) = at^2$
(c) $f(t) = \cos \omega t$

5.9 By use of classical techniques, determine the solution of the following differential equations for the case in which the input $f(t)$ is a step function of height h. All initial conditions are zero.

(a) $y(t) = \dfrac{4}{(D + 1)(D + 3)} f(t)$

(b) $y(t) = \dfrac{4}{(D + 3)(D + 1)^2} f(t)$

5.10 Verify the solution of Prob. 5.9 by using the Laplace transform method.

5.11 Same as Prob. 5.9 except $f(t) = e^{-t}$.

5.12 Verify the solution of Prob. 5.11 by using the Laplace transform method.

5.13 For the system of Fig. P5.13, determine K_p, K_v, and K_a and then determine the steady-state error to a unit step, unit ramp, and unit parabolic input when $d(t) = 0$.

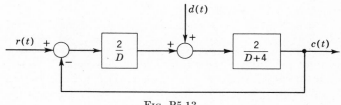

FIG. P5.13

5.14 For the feedback control system shown in Fig. P5.14 all of the initial conditions are zero and $K = 1.5$. Determine the response for each of the following cases.

(a) $r(t)$ is a unit step function and $d(t) = 0$.
(b) $d(t)$ is a unit step function and $r(t) = 0$.
(c) Both $r(t)$ and $d(t)$ are unit step functions.

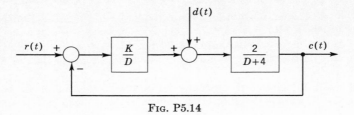

FIG. P5.14

5.15 Same as Prob. 5.14 except $K = 2$.

5.16 By use of Laplace transforms, determine the response $y(t)$ for the following differential equations for the case in which all the initial conditions are zero [i.e., the system is initially at a steady-state operating point and in addition $f(0) = y(0) = 0$]. The input $f(t)$ is an impulse of area k which occurs at time $t = 0$.

$$(a)\ \ y(t) = \frac{2D + 1}{(D + 2)(D + 5)} f(t) \qquad (b)\ \ y(t) = \frac{2D + 3}{D(D + 2)(D + 3)} f(t)$$

$$(c)\ \ y(t) = \frac{D^2 + 6D + 15}{(D + 1)(D + 3)(D + 6)} f(t)$$

5.17 Same as Prob. 5.16 except that $y(0) = 3$.

NOTE: The corresponding value of $f(0)$ may be determined from steady-state operating conditions.

5.18 Same as Prob. 5.16 except that the impulse excitation occurs at $t_0 = 4$.

5.19 Determine the final value $y(\infty)$ for each equation given in Prob. 5.16 by

(a) Application of the final-value theorem

(b) Substitution of $t = \infty$ into each of the resulting response equations of Prob. 5.16

5.20 Determine the initial value $y(0+)$ for each equation given in Prob. 5.16 by

(a) Application of the initial-value theorem

(b) Substitution of $t = 0+$ into each of the resulting response equations of Prob. 5.16

5.21 By using the Laplace transform method, determine the solution of the following differential equations for the case in which $f(t)$ is a step function of height h; all initial conditions are zero.

$$(a)\ \ y(t) = \frac{D + 5}{(D + 1)(D + 3)} f(t)$$

$$(b)\ \ y(t) = \frac{3D + 5}{(D + 1)^2(D + 3)} f(t)$$

5.22 Verify the solution of Prob. 5.21 by using the classical method.

5.23 Determine the solution of Eq. (5.65) for the case in which the input is that shown in Fig. 5.12b to d.

5.24 A mass-spring-damper system is shown in Fig. P5.24.

(*a*) Write the differential equation.

(*b*) Use Laplace transforms to solve this equation when $x(0) = 0$, $x'(0) = 15$, $f = 0$, $M = 1$, $B = 2$, and $K = 2$.

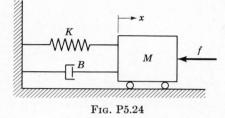

FIG. P5.24

6

The characteristic function

Because an actual system may be subjected to all types and varieties of input excitations $f(t)$, it becomes impractical to calculate the system response for every possible excitation. In this chapter, it is shown that a very good measure of the transient behavior may be obtained directly from the zeros of the characteristic function (i.e., roots of the characteristic equation). This criterion for evaluating transient performance is obtained by considering the essential characteristics of a general system of order n.

The general operational representation for a differential equation of order n is

$$y(t) = \frac{a_m D^m + a_{m-1} D^{m-1} + \cdots + a_1 D + a_0}{D^n + b_{n-1} D^{n-1} + \cdots + b_1 D + b_0} f(t) \qquad (6.1)$$

The transform of each term is

$$\mathcal{L}[D^n y(t)] = s^n Y(s) - I(s)_n$$
$$b_{n-1} \mathcal{L}[D^{n-1} y(t)] = b_{n-1} s^{n-1} Y(s) - I(s)_{n-1}$$
$$\cdots\cdots\cdots\cdots\cdots\cdots\cdots\cdots\cdots\cdots\cdots\cdots\cdots\cdots$$
$$a_m \mathcal{L}[D^m f(t)] = a_m s^m F(s) - I(s)_m$$
$$a_{m-1} \mathcal{L}[D^{m-1} f(t)] = a_{m-1} s^{m-1} F(s) - I(s)_{m-1}$$
$$\cdots\cdots\cdots\cdots\cdots\cdots\cdots\cdots\cdots\cdots\cdots\cdots\cdots\cdots$$

where I_n, I_{n-1}, $\ldots$ represent the initial conditions associated with each transform. Transforming each term of Eq. (6.1) accordingly and collecting terms yields

$$\begin{aligned}
Y(s) &= \frac{(a_m s^m + a_{m-1} s^{m-1} + \cdots + a_1 s + a_0) F(s) + I(s)}{s^n + b_{n-1} s^{n-1} + \cdots + b_1 s + b_0} \\
&= \frac{L_m(s) F(s) + I(s)}{L_n(s)}
\end{aligned} \qquad (6.2)$$

where $I(s) = I(s)_n + I(s)_{n-1} + \cdots - I(s)_m - I(s)_{m-1} - \cdots$ is the sum of all the initial conditions. By comparison of Eqs. (6.1) and (6.2), it is to be noted that the characteristic function in the s domain, $L_n(s)$, is

142

the same as that in the D domain $L_n(D)$. The numerator also has the same form with the exception that the initial conditions $I(s)$ are added in the s domain. Comparison of Eqs. (6.1) and (6.2) shows that, *when all the initial conditions are zero, the transform is obtained by merely substituting s for D, $Y(s)$ for $y(t)$, and $F(s)$ for $f(t)$ in the operational form of the differential equation.*

For this case

$$Y(s) = \frac{L_m(s)}{L_n(s)} F(s) \qquad (6.3)$$

where $L_m(s)/L_n(s)$ is called the *transfer function*. It is to be noted that $L_m(s)$ and $L_n(s)$ are obtained directly from the differential equation of operation for the system. Thus, *the transfer function contains basic information concerning the essential characteristics of a system* without regard to initial conditions or excitation.

The term $F(s)$ in Eq. (6.2) is the general representation for the transform of the input signal or forcing function. This term may be written as

$$F(s) = \frac{N_{F(s)}}{D_{F(s)}}$$

where $N_{F(s)}$ is the numerator of $F(s)$ and $D_{F(s)}$ is the denominator of $F(s)$. For example, for a unit step function, $F(s) = 1/s$ and thus $N_{F(s)} = 1$ and $D_{F(s)} = s$. Substitution of the preceding representation $F(s) = N_{F(s)}/D_{F(s)}$ into Eq. (6.2) yields the following general transformed form for $Y(s)$,

$$Y(s) = \frac{L_m(s)N_{F(s)} + I(s)D_{F(s)}}{L_n(s)D_{F(s)}} = \frac{A(s)}{B(s)} \qquad (6.4)$$

where $A(s)$ and $B(s)$ are polynomials in s.

6.1 Inverse Transformations. By an inverse transformation is meant the process of inverting a function from the s domain back to the time domain. The inverse transform $\mathcal{L}^{-1}$ of a function $F(s)$ is defined by the equation

$$\mathcal{L}^{-1}[F(s)] = \frac{1}{2\pi j} \int_C F(s)e^{ts}\, ds = f(t) \qquad (6.5)$$

where C is a suitably chosen contour in the s domain. This integral method of evaluating the inverse transform is not employed when the much simpler process of entering a transform table with the given $F(s)$ and reading directly the desired $f(t)$ can be utilized, as is the case for ordinary control analysis. A partial listing of commonly used transforms is given in Table 5.1.

The transform table may be used to obtain the Laplace transform $F(s)$

of a given function of time or to obtain the inverse transform $f(t)$ for a given function of s. This process is analogous to the use of a logarithmic table for obtaining the logarithm of a number or to the use of the same table for the opposite process of obtaining antilogarithms.

At first it would appear that the listing of transforms given in Table 5.1 would have to be extended considerably so that it would be applicable to the wide range of problems encountered in the design of systems. However, this is not the case. The listing given in Table 5.1 is adequate for the solution of most ordinary problems that arise in control engineering. The reason for this is that there are relatively few different types of terms which appear in the differential equation after it has been expanded by a partial-fraction expansion. In particular, the zeros of $B(s)$ are either distinct or repeated.

Distinct Zeros. The transformed function $B(s)$ is the denominator of Eq. (6.4). When the zeros of $B(s)$ are distinct, the denominator $B(s)$ can be factored in the form

$$B(s) = (s - r_1)(s - r_2) \cdots (s - r_n) \tag{6.6}$$

where $r_1, r_2, \ldots, r_n$ are n distinct zeros of $B(s)$.

The partial-fraction expansion of Eq. (6.4) is of the form

$$Y(s) = \frac{K_1}{s - r_1} + \frac{K_2}{s - r_2} + \cdots + \frac{K_i}{s - r_i} + \cdots + \frac{K_n}{s - r_n} \tag{6.7}$$

where $K_1, K_2, \ldots, K_n$ are n constants. Each constant K_i may be evaluated by the method used to obtain Eq. (5.9). That is, first multiply both sides of Eq. (6.7) by $s - r_i$; then take the limit as s approaches r_i. After performing these operations, the only term remaining on the right-hand side of Eq. (6.7) is K_i. Thus

$$K_i = \lim_{s \to r_i} [(s - r_i)Y(s)] \tag{6.8}$$

The inverse transform of Eq. (6.7) is obtained directly from the transform table and is

$$y(t) = K_1 e^{r_1 t} + K_2 e^{r_2 t} + \cdots + K_n e^{r_n t} \tag{6.9}$$

Equation (6.9) shows that *each distinct zero of* $B(s) = L_n(s)D_{F(s)}$ *yields an exponential-type term* $K_i e^{r_i t}$ *in the response function.* The exponent r_i is the corresponding zero of $B(s)$. Each zero $r_1, r_2, \ldots, r_n$ must be negative in order that each term $K_i e^{r_i t}$ in $y(t)$ be a decaying function. If any zero of $B(s)$ is positive, $y(t)$ will increase without bound as t increases to infinity. A constant term results if $r_i = 0$, because $K_i e^{(0)t} = K_i$.

Repeated Zeros. For the case in which $B(s)$ has a multiple or repeated zero r which occurs q times, $B(s)$ may be factored in the form

$$B(s) = (s - r)^q (s - r_1)(s - r_2) \cdots (s - r_{n-q}) \tag{6.10}$$

The corresponding partial-fraction expansion for $Y(s)$ is

$$Y(s) = \frac{C_q}{(s - r)^q} + \frac{C_{q-1}}{(s - r)^{q-1}} + \cdots + \frac{C_1}{s - r}$$
$$+ \frac{K_1}{s - r_1} + \frac{K_2}{s - r_2} + \cdots + \frac{K_{n-q}}{s - r_{n-q}} \tag{6.11}$$

The constant coefficients for the multiple terms are evaluated as follows:

$$C_q = \lim_{s \to r} [(s - r)^q Y(s)]$$
$$C_{q-1} = \lim_{s \to r} \left\{ \frac{d}{ds} [(s - r)^q Y(s)] \right\} \tag{6.12}$$
$$C_{q-k} = \lim_{s \to r} \left\{ \frac{1}{k!} \frac{d^k}{ds^k} [(s - r)^q Y(s)] \right\}$$

From the transform table, the inverse transform of Eq. (6.11) is found to be

$$y(t) = \left[\frac{C_q t^{q-1}}{(q - 1)!} + \frac{C_{q-1} t^{q-2}}{(q - 2)!} + \cdots + \frac{C_2 t}{1!} + C_1 \right] e^{rt}$$
$$+ K_1 e^{r_1 t} + K_2 e^{r_2 t} + \cdots + K_{n-q} e^{r_{n-q} t} \tag{6.13}$$

Each response term associated with the repeated zero $(s - r)^q$ is seen to be multiplied by the exponential factor e^{rt}. If the value of r is positive, $y(t)$ will become infinite as time increases. For negative values of r, a decreasing exponential results, and thus the response term due to the repeated zero eventually vanishes.

ILLUSTRATIVE EXAMPLE 1. Let it be desired to determine the time response $y(t)$ for the transformed equation

$$Y(s) = \frac{11s + 28}{(s + 2)^2 (s + 5)} = \frac{C_2}{(s + 2)^2} + \frac{C_1}{s + 2} + \frac{K_1}{s + 5} \tag{6.14}$$

The constants are evaluated as follows:

$$C_2 = \lim_{s \to -2} \frac{11s + 28}{s + 5} = 2$$
$$C_1 = \lim_{s \to -2} \left[\frac{d}{ds} \left(\frac{11s + 28}{s + 5} \right) \right] = \lim_{s \to -2} \frac{(s + 5)11 - (11s + 28)}{(s + 5)^2} = 3$$
$$K_1 = \lim_{s \to -5} \frac{11s + 28}{(s + 2)^2} = -3$$

Thus,
$$Y(s) = \frac{2}{(s + 2)^2} + \frac{3}{s + 2} - \frac{3}{s + 5}$$

By use of Table 5.1, the inverse transform of the preceding equation is found to be

$$y(t) = (2t + 3)e^{-2t} - 3e^{-5t} \qquad \text{*(6.15)}$$

6.2 Complex Conjugate Zeros. Complex zeros of $B(s)$ always occur in pairs, and furthermore these zeros are always conjugates of one another. That is, they have the same real part but equal and opposite imaginary parts. Thus, if the polynomial $B(s)$ has a complex zero $a + jb$, the complex conjugate $a - jb$ will also be a zero of $B(s)$. Although the preceding discussion of distinct zeros is also applicable to complex conjugate zeros, the following analysis brings out more clearly the fact that a pair of complex conjugate zeros in $B(s)$ combine to introduce an exponentially damped sinusoidal term in $y(t)$.

A pair of complex conjugate zeros when multiplied together yield the following quadratic:

$$(s - a - jb)(s - a + jb) = s^2 - 2as + (a^2 + b^2) \qquad (6.16)$$

For any given quadratic term, the values of a and b may be computed by equating coefficients of like terms as follows: Consider the expression

$$s^2 + 4s + 9$$

The coefficient 4 of the s term is equal to $-2a$ so that $-2a = 4$ or $a = -2$. Similarly equating the constant terms gives $a^2 + b^2 = 9$ or $b = \sqrt{9 - 4} = \sqrt{5}$. Thus, the complex conjugate zeros are $a \pm jb = -2 \pm j\sqrt{5}$. If in the determination of b it is found that b is an imaginary number, the two zeros are real and unequal rather than complex conjugates. For example consider the quadratic

$$s^2 + 8s + 12$$

The value of a is equal to -4 so that $b = \sqrt{12 - 16} = j\sqrt{4} = j2$. For this case, the zeros are $a \pm jb = -4 \pm (j^2 2) = -4 \mp 2 = -6, -2$. Because the case of real zeros has been previously discussed, it is assumed in the following analysis that b is real so that the zeros are complex conjugates.

For complex conjugate zeros $B(s)$ may be factored in the form

$$B(s) = (s - a - jb)(s - a + jb)(s - r_1) \cdots (s - r_{n-2}) \qquad (6.17)$$

The partial-fraction expansion for $Y(s) = A(s)/B(s)$ is of the form

$$Y(s) = \frac{K_c}{s - a - jb} + \frac{K_{-c}}{s - a + jb} + \frac{K_1}{s - r_1} + \cdots + \frac{K_{n-2}}{s - r_{n-2}} \qquad (6.18)$$

The inverse transform of Eq. (6.18) is

$$y(t) = K_c e^{(a+jb)t} + K_{-c} e^{(a-jb)t} + K_1 e^{r_1 t} + \cdots + K_{n-2} e^{r_{n-2} t} \qquad (6.19)$$

The constants K_c and K_{-c} associated with the complex conjugate zeros are evaluated as usual for distinct zeros by the application of Eq. (6.8). That is,

$$K_c = \lim_{s \to a+jb}$$
$$\left[(s - a - jb) \frac{A(s)}{(s - a - jb)(s - a + jb)(s - r_1) \cdots (s - r_{n-2})} \right]$$
$$= \lim_{s \to a+jb} \left[\frac{1}{2jb} \frac{A(s)}{(s - r_1) \cdots (s - r_{n-2})} \right] = \frac{1}{2jb} K(a + jb) \qquad (6.20)$$

where

$$K(a + jb) = \lim_{s \to a+jb} \frac{A(s)}{(s - r_1) \cdots (s - r_{n-2})}$$
$$= \left[(s^2 - 2as + a^2 + b^2) \frac{A(s)}{B(s)} \right]_{s=a+jb}$$

Similarly, the constant K_{-c} is obtained as follows:

$$K_{-c} = \lim_{s \to a-jb}$$
$$\left[(s - a + jb) \frac{A(s)}{(s - a - jb)(s - a + jb)(s - r_1) \cdots (s - r_{n-2})} \right]$$
$$= \lim_{s \to a-jb} \frac{1}{(-2jb)} \frac{A(s)}{(s - r_1) \cdots (s - r_{n-2})} = -\frac{1}{2jb} K(a - jb) \qquad (6.21)$$

where $K(a - jb) = \lim_{s \to a-jb} \dfrac{A(s)}{(s - r_1) \cdots (s - r_{n-2})}$

$$= \left[(s^2 - 2as + a^2 + b^2) \frac{A(s)}{B(s)} \right]_{s=a-jb}$$

The constants $K(a + jb)$ and $K(a - jb)$ are complex conjugate numbers. These complex numbers may be represented as shown graphically in Fig. 6.1, whence

$$K(a + jb) = |K(a + jb)| e^{j\alpha}$$
$$K(a - jb) = |K(a + jb)| e^{-j\alpha} \qquad (6.22)$$

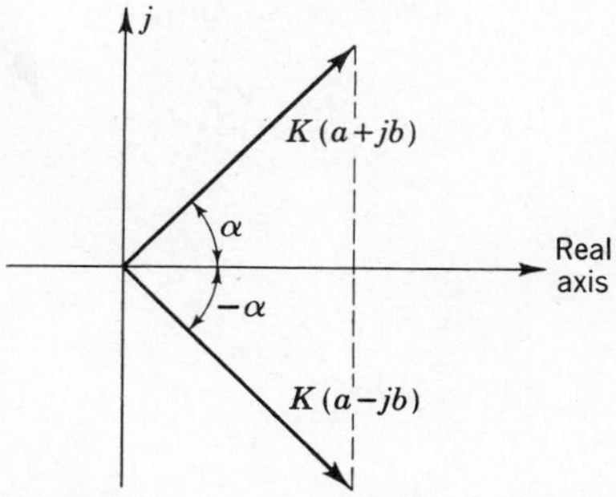

Fig. 6.1. Vector representation for $K(a + jb)$ and $K(a - jb)$.

where $|K(a + jb)| = |K(a - jb)|$ is the length of either vector, α is the angle of the vector $K(a + jb)$, and $-\alpha$ is the angle of the vector $K(a - jb)$.

The constants K_c and K_{-c}, which are also complex conjugate numbers, may be written in the form

$$K_c = \frac{1}{2jb} |K(a + jb)|e^{j\alpha}$$

$$K_{-c} = -\frac{1}{2jb} |K(a + jb)|e^{-j\alpha}$$

(6.23)

Substitution of K_c and K_{-c} from Eq. (6.23) into Eq. (6.19) gives

$$y(t) = \frac{1}{b} |K(a + jb)|e^{at} \frac{e^{j(bt+\alpha)} - e^{-j(bt+\alpha)}}{2j} + K_1 e^{r_1 t} + \cdots + K_{n-2} e^{r_{n-2} t}$$

or

$$y(t) = \frac{1}{b} |K(a + jb)|e^{at} \sin(bt + \alpha) + K_1 e^{r_1 t} + \cdots + K_{n-2} e^{r_{n-2} t} \quad (6.24)$$

ILLUSTRATIVE EXAMPLE 1.   Determine the inverse transformation of the following transformed equation:

$$Y(s) = \frac{20}{(s^2 + 4s + 13)(s + 6)}$$

SOLUTION.   Equating coefficients to obtain the value of a and b for the quadratic yields $-2a = 4$, or $a = -2$, and $a^2 + b^2 = 13$, or $b = \sqrt{13 - 4} = 3$.   Evaluation of $K(a + jb)$ gives

$$K(a + jb) = \left[(s^2 - 2as + a^2 + b^2) \frac{A(s)}{B(s)} \right]_{s=a+jb}$$

$$= \left(\frac{20}{s + 6} \right)_{s=-2+j3} = \frac{20}{4 + j3}$$

(6.25)

As shown in Fig. 6.2, the vector whose real part is 4 and imaginary part is 3 may be expressed in the polar form

$$4 + j3 = 5\underline{/36.8°}$$

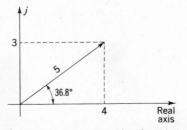

FIG. 6.2.   Vector representation for $(4 + j3)$.

Hence, Eq. (6.25) becomes

$$K(a + jb) = \frac{20}{5/36.8°} = 4/\underline{-36.8°}$$

Thus $$|K(a + jb)| = 4$$
and $$\alpha = \measuredangle K(a + jb) = -36.8°$$

The general form of the inverse transformation is

$$y(t) = \frac{1}{b}|K(a + jb)|e^{at}\sin(bt + \alpha) + K_1 e^{r_1 t}$$

Evaluation of K_1 gives

$$K_1 = \lim_{s \to -6} \frac{20}{s^2 + 4s + 13} = \frac{20}{25} = 0.8$$

Thus the desired result is

$$y(t) = \tfrac{4}{3}e^{-2t}\sin(3t - 36.8°) + 0.8e^{-6t} \tag{6.26}$$

Equation (6.24) shows the exponentially damped sinusoidal term which results from complex conjugate zeros of $B(s)$. The exponential factor a is the real part of the complex conjugate zeros. The imaginary part b is the frequency of oscillation of the exponentially damped sinusoid. Thus, b is referred to as the damped frequency of oscillation or damped natural frequency. The period of each oscillation is $2\pi/b$. The envelope of this sinusoid is $(1/b)|K(a + jb)|e^{at}$. To have the exponential term decreasing with time, it is necessary that a be negative. For the case in which $a = 0$, a sinusoid of constant amplitude $(1/b)|K(a + jb)|$ results. For $a = 0$, Eq. (6.24) becomes

$$y(t) = \frac{1}{b}|K(a + jb)|\sin(bt + \alpha) + K_1 e^{r_1 t} + \cdots + K_{n-2}e^{r_{n-2}t} \tag{6.27}$$

In Fig. 6.3 is graphically illustrated the type of time-response terms that result from complex conjugate zeros. When the zeros lie to the left of the imaginary axis ($a < 0$), a decreasing sinusoid results; when the zeros are on the imaginary axis ($a = 0$), a sinusoid of constant amplitude results; and when the zeros are to the right of the imaginary axis ($a > 0$), an increasing sinusoid results.

In Fig. 6.4 is shown a plot of the type of response terms that result from real zeros. These results follow directly from Eq. (6.9). Because the exponential factor is the value of the zero, a negative zero ($r_i < 0$) yields an exponentially decreasing term, while a positive zero ($r_i > 0$) yields an exponentially increasing term. A zero at the origin ($r_i = 0$) results in a constant term. Even though a zero may be repeated, the exponential term dominates the response.

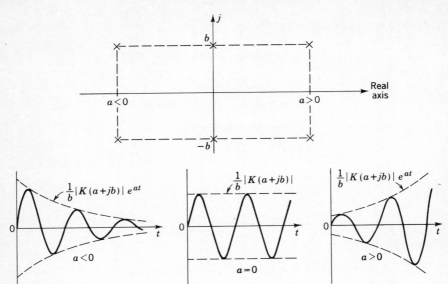

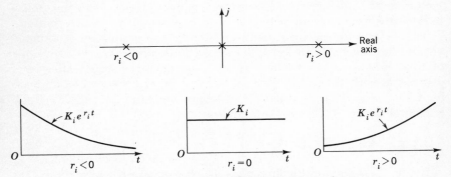

FIG. 6.3.   Response terms that result from complex conjugate zeros.

FIG. 6.4.   Response terms that result from real zeros.

6.3 Damping Ratio and Natural Frequency. In Fig. 6.5 is shown a pair of complex conjugate zeros. The distance from the origin to each zero is

$$\omega_n = \sqrt{a^2 + b^2}$$

The angle β is such that

$$\cos (\pi - \beta) = -\cos \beta = \frac{a}{\omega_n}$$

In terms of the polar coordinates β and ω_n the quadratic form is

$$s^2 - 2as + a^2 + b^2 = s^2 + 2\omega_n \cos \beta \, s + \omega_n^2 \qquad 0 < \beta < \pi \qquad (6.28)$$

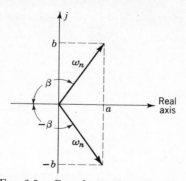

Fig. 6.5. Complex conjugate zeros.

The coefficient of the s term $(2\omega_n \cos \beta)$ is a measure of the amount of damping in the system.   The response ceases to be sinusoidal when $\beta = 0$. For this critically damped case, the quadratic form is

$$s^2 + 2\omega_n s + \omega_n{}^2 = (s + \omega_n)^2 \tag{6.29}$$

Thus, the roots are repeated.   The damping ratio ζ is defined as the ratio of the actual amount of damping $(2\omega_n \cos \beta)$ to the critical amount of damping $(2\omega_n)$.   That is,

$$\zeta = \frac{2\omega_n \cos \beta}{2\omega_n} = \cos \beta$$

As β goes from 0 to π, then the damping ratio ζ goes from 1 to -1.   Thus for $0 \leq \beta \leq \pi$, then $1 \geq \zeta \geq -1$.

In terms of ζ, the quadratic form becomes

$$s^2 + 2\zeta\omega_n s + \omega_n{}^2 \tag{6.30}$$

The zeros are

$$r_{1,2} = -\zeta\omega_n \pm j\omega_n \sqrt{1 - \zeta^2} \tag{6.31}$$

For any given quadratic expression, the numerical values of ζ and ω_n are computed by equating coefficients.   For example, consider the expression $s^2 + 4s + 9$.   The constant term is $\omega_n{}^2 = 9$ or $\omega_n = 3$. The reason for using only the positive value when mathematically

$$\omega_n = \sqrt{9} = \pm 3$$

is that ω_n is the distance from the origin to the zero and must be positive. The coefficients for the s term give $2\zeta\omega_n = 4$, or $\zeta = 4/2\omega_n = \frac{2}{3}$.   If so desired, the values of a and b are readily computed; that is,

$$a = -\omega_n\zeta = -3(\tfrac{2}{3}) = -2$$

and $b = \omega_n \sqrt{1 - \zeta^2} = 3 \sqrt{1 - \tfrac{4}{9}} = 3 \sqrt{\tfrac{5}{9}} = \sqrt{5}$.

The time response due to complex conjugate zeros of $B(s)$ [Eq. (6.24)] may be written in terms of the damping ratio and natural frequency as follows:

$$y(t) = \frac{1}{b} |K(a + jb)| e^{-\zeta \omega_n t} \sin [(\omega_n \sqrt{1 - \zeta^2})t + \alpha]$$
$$+ K_1 e^{r_1 t} + \cdots + K_{n-2} e^{r_{n-2} t} \qquad -1 < \zeta < 1 \quad (6.32)$$

For the case in which $\zeta = 0$, Eq. (6.29) becomes

$$y(t) = \frac{1}{b} |K(a + jb)| \sin (\omega_n t + \alpha) + K_1 e^{r_1 t} + \cdots + K_{n-2} e^{r_{n-2} t} \quad (6.33)$$

Thus, a sinusoidal term of constant amplitude $(1/b)|K(a + jb)|$ and natural frequency of oscillation ω_n is seen to result.

In Fig. 6.6 is shown a more general plot of a pair of complex conjugate zeros. When a is negative so that a decreasing exponential results, the

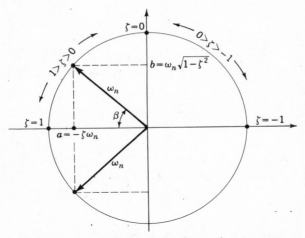

FIG. 6.6. General plot of complex conjugate zeros.

zeros are to the left of the imaginary axis so that $\beta < 90°$, in which case $1 > \zeta > 0$. For positive values of a, the zeros are to the right of the imaginary axis so that $\beta > 90°$ and $0 > \zeta > -1$. A positive value of ζ yields a decreasing sinusoid, while a negative value results in an increasing sinusoid. For ζ equal to zero ($\beta = 90°$) a sinusoid of constant amplitude is obtained. When the magnitude of ζ is greater than 1, two real zeros result rather than complex conjugate zeros. The case of real zeros has previously been discussed.

ILLUSTRATIVE EXAMPLE 1. Let it be desired to determine the general equation for the transient response of a second-order system to a unit-step-function change which occurs at $t = 0$. The operational form of the differential equation is

$$y(t) = \frac{\omega_n^2}{D^2 + 2\zeta\omega_n D + \omega_n^2} f(t) \tag{6.34}$$

Assume that all the initial conditions are zero.

SOLUTION. The transform for this differential equation is

$$Y(s) = \frac{\omega_n^2 F(s)}{s^2 + 2\zeta\omega_n s + \omega_n^2} = \frac{\omega_n^2}{(s^2 + 2\zeta\omega_n s + \omega_n^2)s} \tag{6.35}$$

where $F(s) = 1/s$ is the transform for the step input.

For complex conjugate zeros (that is, $-1 < \zeta < 1$), the response has the general form

$$y(t) = \frac{1}{b} |K(a + jb)| e^{at} \sin(bt + \alpha) + K_1 \tag{6.36}$$

Evaluation of $K(a + jb)$ gives

$$K(a + jb) = \frac{\omega_n^2}{s} \bigg|_{s = a+jb} = \frac{\omega_n^2}{a + jb} = \frac{\omega_n^2}{\sqrt{a^2 + b^2}/\tan^{-1} b/a}$$

Thus,

$$|K(a + jb)| = \frac{\omega_n^2}{\sqrt{a^2 + b^2}} = \omega_n \tag{6.37}$$

and

$$\alpha = \angle K(a + jb) = -\tan^{-1}\frac{b}{a} = \tan^{-1}-\frac{b}{a}$$

$$= \tan^{-1}\frac{-\sqrt{1 - \zeta^2}}{-\zeta} \tag{6.38}$$

where $\sqrt{a^2 + b^2} = \omega_n$

$$a = -\zeta\omega_n$$
$$b = \omega_n\sqrt{1 - \zeta^2}$$

The constant K_1 is evaluated as follows:

$$K_1 = \lim_{s \to 0} \frac{\omega_n^2}{s^2 + 2\zeta\omega_n s + \omega_n^2} = 1$$

Thus, the desired transient response is

$$y(t) = \frac{1}{\sqrt{1 - \zeta^2}} e^{-\zeta\omega_n t} \sin[(\omega_n\sqrt{1 - \zeta^2})t + \alpha] + 1 \qquad -1 < \zeta < 1 \tag{6.39}$$

For the case in which $\zeta = 1$, the quadratic term in Eq. (6.35) is

$$s^2 + 2\omega_n s + \omega_n^2 = (s + \omega_n)^2$$

Thus the partial-fraction expansion for $Y(s)$ is

$$Y(s) = \frac{C_2}{(s + \omega_n)^2} + \frac{C_1}{s + \omega_n} + \frac{K_1}{s} \tag{6.40}$$

The constants C_2, C_1, and K_1 are evaluated as follows:

$$C_2 = \lim_{s \to -\omega_n} \frac{\omega_n{}^2}{s} = -\omega_n$$

$$C_1 = \lim_{s \to -\omega_n} \left[\frac{d}{ds} \left(\frac{\omega_n{}^2}{s} \right) \right] = \left. \frac{-\omega_n{}^2}{s^2} \right|_{s = -\omega_n} = -1$$

$$K_1 = \lim_{s \to 0} \frac{\omega_n{}^2}{s^2 + 2\omega_n s + \omega_n{}^2} = 1$$

Thus $\qquad\qquad\qquad y(t) = (C_2 t + C_1)e^{-\omega_n t} + K_1$

or $\qquad\qquad\qquad y(t) = 1 - (\omega_n t + 1)e^{-\omega_n t} \tag{6.41}$

In a similar manner, the equation of the time response for $\zeta > 1$ or $\zeta \le -1$ may also be derived. For these cases the zeros are real and thus exponential terms are contributed to the response.

In Fig. 6.7 is shown the response $y(t)$ to a step change in the input for various values of the damping ratio ζ. It is to be noted that, for $\zeta < 0.4$,

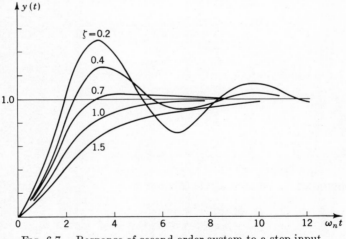

Fig. 6.7. Response of second-order system to a step input.

there is an excessive amount of overshooting and oscillations. For $\zeta > 1$, an excessive amount of time is required to reach the new operating condition. Thus, for most control work, it is desired to have $0.4 < \zeta < 1$.

As shown in Fig. 6.5, the form $a \pm jb$ is the rectangular representation for complex conjugate roots. That is, in rectangular coordinates, the real part a is the horizontal component and the imaginary part b is the vertical component. Similarly, the polar form for complex conjugate roots is specified by the radius $\omega_n = \sqrt{a^2 + b^2}$ and the angle $\beta = \cos^{-1} \zeta$. For computational purposes, the response is usually obtained most readily by using the rectangular form. It is then an easy matter to obtain the polar quantities ω_n and ζ. The polar form has the advantage of providing a more general insight into the actual behavior of the system. For example, Fig. 6.7 shows that the form of the response is determined by ζ. The speed of response is governed by ω_n. That is, Fig. 6.7 shows that for $\zeta = 0.2$ the response $y(t)$ first crosses the value $y(t) = 1$ when $\omega_n t = 2$. Thus, if $\omega_n = 0.1$, the time is $t = 2/\omega_n = 2/0.1 = 20$ sec. For $\omega_n = 10$, the time is $t = 2/\omega_n = 2/10 = 0.2$ sec. Hence, the larger the value of ω_n, the faster is the speed of response.

Logarithmic Decrement. For an exponentially damped sinusoid as shown in Fig. 6.8, the amplitude of the sinusoid after each oscillation

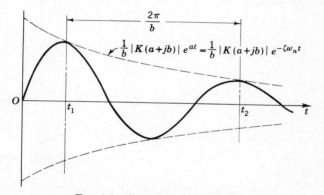

Fig. 6.8. Logarithmic decrement.

changes in a geometric series. At time t_1, the amplitude is $(1/b)|K(a + jb)|e^{at_1}$. The time required to complete one period is $T = 2\pi/b$, and thus the time t_2 after one oscillation is completed is $t_2 = t_1 + T = t_1 + 2\pi/b$. The new amplitude is $(1/b)|K(a + jb)|e^{a(t_1+2\pi/b)}$, and the ratio of amplitudes is

$$\frac{(1/b)|K(a + jb)|e^{at_1}}{(1/b)|K(a + jb)|e^{at_1}e^{2\pi a/b}} = e^{-2\pi a/b} = e^{2\pi\zeta/\sqrt{(1-\zeta^2)}} \qquad (6.42)$$

The ln of this amplitude ratio is $-2\pi a/b = 2\pi\zeta/\sqrt{1 - \zeta^2}$, which is called the logarithmic decrement. The amplitude ratio after one oscillation is thus seen to be a function of the damping ratio only.

6.4 Transient Response. The general form of the transient response can be ascertained directly from the zeros of the transformed function

$B(s)$. For example, suppose that the zeros of $B(s)$ are those plotted in Fig. 6.9. It follows that $B(s)$ may be factored in the form

$$B(s) = (s - a_1 - jb_1)(s - a_1 + jb_1)(s - jb_2)$$
$$(s + jb_2)(s - 0)(s - r_2)(s - r)^2 \quad (6.43)$$

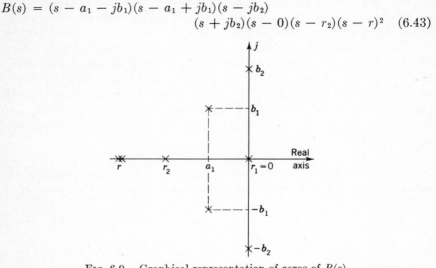

FIG. 6.9. Graphical representation of zeros of $B(s)$.

Performing a partial-fraction expansion on $Y(s) = A(s)/B(s)$ yields

$$Y(s) = \frac{K_{c1}}{s - a_1 - jb_1} + \frac{K_{-c1}}{s - a_1 + jb_1} + \frac{K_{c2}}{s - jb_2} + \frac{K_{-c2}}{s + jb_2} + \frac{K_1}{s}$$
$$+ \frac{K_2}{s - r_2} + \frac{C_2}{(s - r)^2} + \frac{C_1}{s - r} \quad (6.44)$$

Taking the inverse transform of the preceding expression yields

$$y(t) = \frac{1}{b_1} |K(a_1 + jb_1)| e^{a_1 t} \sin (b_1 t + \alpha_1) + \frac{1}{b_2} |K(jb_2)| \sin (b_2 t + \alpha_2)$$
$$+ K_1 + K_2 e^{r_2 t} + (C_2 t + C_1) e^{rt} \quad (6.45)$$

It is to be noted that a pair of complex conjugate zeros yields an exponentially varying sinusoidal term. A pair of complex conjugate zeros on the imaginary axis yields a sinusoid with a constant amplitude. The zero at the origin contributes a constant term. Distinct or multiple zeros on the real axis yield exponential terms.

The term $B(s) = L_n(s)D_{F(s)}$ consists of the zeros of $L_n(s)$ of the characteristic function for the system plus the zeros $D_{F(s)}$ corresponding to the denominator of the transform of the input excitation. If any zero of the characteristic function for the system $L_n(s)$ lies to the right of the imaginary axis, the response contains an increasing time function and will increase without bound. *Thus, if any zero of $L_n(s)$ lies in the right half* *plane (i.e., to the right of the imaginary axis), then the system is basically unstable.* Whether a system is stable or unstable is a basic property of the system $L_n(s)$ itself and not the particular input, or excitation, to the system.

The zeros of $D_{F(s)}$ yield response terms associated with the particular excitation to the system. Take, for example, a ramp function $D_{F(s)} = s^2$ which gives a response term of the form $C_1 t$. It should be noted that the input which is a ramp function eventually becomes infinite, and thus the output of the system has been forced to infinity because of the particular input. As is illustrated by this example, the *zeros of $D_{F(s)}$ do not affect the basic stability of a system* but merely yield response terms appropriate to the particular excitation.

ILLUSTRATIVE EXAMPLE 1. The differential equation of operation for a control system is given by Eq. (6.46). Determine the general form of the response equation when the input excitation $f(t)$ is a unit step function.

$$y(t) = \frac{360(D^2 + D + 1)}{(D^2 + 2D + 5)(D^2 + 6D + 9)(D^2 + 6D + 8)} f(t) \quad (6.46)$$

SOLUTION. Because of the unit-step-function input $N_{F(s)} = 1$, $D_{F(s)} = s$ so that $B(s) = L_n(s)D_{F(s)} = L_n(s)s$. Thus

$$Y(s) = \frac{360(s^2 + s + 1)(1) + sI(s)}{(s^2 + 2s + 5)(s^2 + 6s + 9)(s^2 + 6s + 8)s} = \frac{A(s)}{B(s)}$$

The partial-fraction expansion for $Y(s)$ gives

$$Y(s) = \frac{K_c}{s + 1 + j2} + \frac{K_{-c}}{s + 1 - j2} + \frac{C_2}{(s + 3)^2} + \frac{C_1}{s + 3} + \frac{K_1}{s + 2}$$
$$+ \frac{K_2}{s + 4} + \frac{K_3}{s}$$

Thus, the general form of the time solution is

$$y(t) = \tfrac{1}{2}|K(a + jb)|e^{-t} \sin(2t + \alpha) + (C_2 t + C_1)e^{-3t}$$
$$+ K_1 e^{-2t} + K_2 e^{-4t} + K_3 \quad (6.47)$$

It should be noted in all cases that the exponent of each exponential term is equal to the horizontal distance from the imaginary axis to the zero of interest. That is, the exponential factor is equal to the numerical value of the real part of the zero. The terms due to zeros which are located far to the left of the imaginary axis have large exponential decaying factors and tend to decrease very rapidly to negligible quantities. Thus, zeros closer to the imaginary axis usually have a more predominant effect upon the transient behavior. Accordingly, the analysis of complicated control systems is often approximated by omitting from the characteristic function zeros which do not affect substantially the performance of the system.

6.5 Response to an External Disturbance.   In this section, it is shown that the characteristic function for the differential equation which relates the output of a system to a change in the external disturbance is the same as that for the differential equation which relates the output to a change in the desired input.   In Fig. 6.10 is shown the general representation

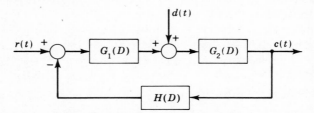

FIG. 6.10.   General representation for a feedback control system.

for a feedback control system in which $d(t)$ represents the external disturbance.

As previously discussed, the effect of the input $r(t)$ and external disturbance $d(t)$ on the output or controlled variable $c(t)$ may be considered individually and then each result added by superposition to obtain the total variation in $c(t)$.   The block diagram which relates the input $r(t)$ to the output $c(t)$ without regard to the external disturbance is shown in Fig. 6.11.   The equation relating $r(t)$ and $c(t)$ is obtained as follows:

$$[r(t) - H(D)c(t)]G_1(D)G_2(D) = c(t) \tag{6.48}$$

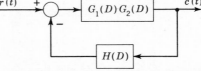

FIG. 6.11.   Block diagram for consideration of the input $r(t)$.

Solving for $c(t)$ gives

$$c(t) = \frac{G_1(D)G_2(D)}{1 + G_1(D)G_2(D)H(D)} \, r(t)$$

By using N_{G_1} to designate the numerator of $G_1(D)$ and D_{G_1} to designate the denominator of $G_1(D)$, etc., the preceding expression may be written in the form

$$c(t) = \frac{N_{G_1}N_{G_2}/D_{G_1}D_{G_2}}{1 + N_{G_1}N_{G_2}N_H/D_{G_1}D_{G_2}D_H} \, r(t)$$

$$= \frac{N_{G_1}N_{G_2}D_H}{D_{G_1}D_{G_2}D_H + N_{G_1}N_{G_2}N_H} \, r(t) \tag{6.49}$$

The characteristic function $L_n(D)$ for the system is $D_{G_1}D_{G_2}D_H + N_{G_1}N_{G_2}N_H$.

The block diagram which relates the external disturbance $d(t)$ to the output when $r(t)$ is considered zero is shown in Fig. 6.12. The equation

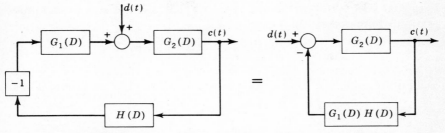

FIG. 6.12. Block diagram for consideration of effect of an external disturbance $d(t)$.

relating $d(t)$ and $c(t)$ is

$$[d(t) - G_1(D)H(D)c(t)]G_2(D) = c(t) \qquad (6.50)$$

$$\text{or} \quad c(t) = \frac{G_2(D)}{1 + G_1(D)G_2(D)H(D)} d(t) = \frac{N_{G_2}/D_{G_2}}{1 + N_{G_1}N_{G_2}N_H/D_{G_1}D_{G_2}D_H} d(t)$$

$$= \frac{N_{G_2}D_{G_1}D_H}{D_{G_1}D_{G_2}D_H + N_{G_1}N_{G_2}N_H} d(t) \qquad (6.51)$$

It can be shown that, if an excitation enters any place in the loop, the differential equation relating the disturbance and the output will always have the same characteristic function $L_n(D)$ which is the product of all the denominator terms plus the product of all the numerators. However, the constant terms which appear in the partial-fraction expansion depend upon where the disturbance enters the system. Thus, there is but one characteristic function for a system, and this function gives basic information as to the transient behavior of a system.

6.6 Impulse Response. The response of a system to a unit impulse excitation provides a good indication or measure of the general transient behavior of the system. The unit impulse is in effect a momentary disturbance which upsets the initial state of equilibrium of the system. In time, a stable system will return again to its equilibrium position.

Substitution of $F(s) = 1$ into Eq. (6.2) yields the transformed equation for a unit impulse excitation.

$$Y(s) = \frac{L_m(s) + I(s)}{L_n(s)} \qquad (6.52)$$

It is to be noted that the basic form of the response of a system to a unit impulse is determined entirely by the zeros of the characteristic function, $L_n(s)$. If any zero lies to the right of the imaginary axis the output increases without bound. Thus the system is basically unstable. For an unstable system, it is impossible to achieve any equilibrium state, because as soon as the power is turned on, the output continually increases with time.

In Fig. 6.13 is shown the response to a unit impulse of a second-order system whose operational equation is

$$(D^2 + 2\zeta\omega_n D + \omega_n^2)y(t) = \omega_n^2 f(t) \tag{6.53}$$

It is to be seen from Fig. 6.13 that for $\zeta < 0.4$ there is a considerable amount of oscillation before the system again reaches equilibrium opera-

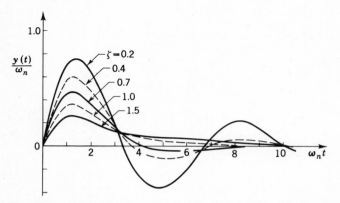

Fig. 6.13.   Response of a second-order system to a unit impulse.

tion.   Also, for $\zeta > 1.0$ a considerable amount of time is required for the system to return to its initial state.   Thus, it seems desirable to have $0.4 < \zeta < 1.0$.   This is the result that was obtained from a consideration of the step-function response.   Because the scale of the horizontal axis is $\omega_n t$, then the speed of response is governed by the natural frequency ω_n as is described in Sec. 6.3.

6.7 Stability Criteria.   A major difficulty in using the Laplace transform method for determining the transient response of a feedback control system is that it necessitates determining the zeros of the characteristic function.   The general form for the characteristic function has previously been shown to be

$$D_{G_1}D_{G_2}D_H + N_{G_1}N_{G_2}N_H \tag{6.54}$$

In determining the block diagram for a system, the terms N_{G_1}, N_{G_2}, N_H, D_{G_1}, D_{G_2}, and D_H are usually obtained in factored form.   Because of the plus sign in Eq. (6.54), the zeros of N_{G_1}, N_{G_2}, etc., are not the zeros of this characteristic function.   Thus, it becomes necessary to determine the zeros of the general polynomial represented by Eq. (6.54).   This presents no difficulty for first- and second-order systems. The zero of a first-order system is immediately obvious, and the two zeros of a quadratic equation are readily solved. However, a third-order system requires determining the three zeros of a cubic, and a fourth-order system necessitates solving a quartic, etc.

Routh's Criterion.[1] Routh's criterion is a method for determining whether or not any of the zeros of the characteristic function are in the right half plane. The application of this criterion is as follows: First write the characteristic function in the general form

$$b_n s^n + b_{n-1} s^{n-1} + b_{n-2} s^{n-2} + \cdots + b_2 s^2 + b_1 s + b_0 \qquad (6.55)$$

Next arrange the coefficients of the characteristic function according to the following schedule

$$
\begin{array}{lllll}
b_n & b_{n-2} & b_{n-4} & b_{n-6} & \cdots \\
b_{n-1} & b_{n-3} & b_{n-5} & b_{n-7} & \cdots \\
c_1 & c_2 & c_3 & c_4 & \cdots \\
d_1 & d_2 & d_3 & \cdots \\
\cdots \cdots \cdots \cdots \cdots \cdots \\
e_1 & e_2 & 0 \\
f_1 & f_2 & 0 \\
g_1 & 0 \\
h_1 & 0
\end{array}
\qquad (6.56)
$$

After first arranging the b coefficients as shown, the row of c terms is evaluated as follows:

$$c_1 = \frac{b_{n-1}b_{n-2} - b_n b_{n-3}}{b_{n-1}}$$

$$c_2 = \frac{b_{n-1}b_{n-4} - b_n b_{n-5}}{b_{n-1}} \qquad (6.57)$$

$$c_3 = \frac{b_{n-1}b_{n-6} - b_n b_{n-7}}{b_{n-1}}$$

The arrows in Eq. (6.56) show the schedule of cross multiplication that is used to evaluate c_2. This same general schedule is used for each successive term. By dropping down a row, the same schedule is used for evaluating each d term. That is,

$$d_1 = \frac{c_1 b_{n-3} - b_{n-1} c_2}{c_1}$$

$$d_2 = \frac{c_1 b_{n-5} - b_{n-1} c_3}{c_1} \qquad (6.58)$$

[1] E. J. Routh, "Dynamics of a System of Rigid Bodies," 3d ed., The Macmillan Company, New York, 1877.

This process is continued until one more row is obtained than the order of the differential equation. Thus, a third-order equation has four rows, a fourth-order equation has five rows, etc. To illustrate, consider the function

$$s^4 + 3s^3 + s^2 + 6s + 2 \tag{6.59}$$

The first two rows of the following array are obtained directly from the coefficients of Eq. (6.59), and the remaining rows are computed as just described:

$$
\begin{array}{c|cccc}
1 & 1 & 1 & 2 & 0 \\
2 & 3 & 6 & 0 & \\
3 & -1 & 2 & 0 & \\
4 & 12 & 0 & & \\
5 & 2 & 0 & &
\end{array}
\tag{6.60}
$$

The numbering scheme to the left of the line indicates the number of rows which in this case is 5 because Eq. (6.59) is a fourth-order polynomial.

Routh's criterion states that the number of changes of sign of the coefficients in the left-hand column is equal to the number of zeros of the characteristic function that are located to the right of the imaginary axis. For the preceding example, the signs of the numbers in the left-hand column are seen to go from plus to minus and then back to plus again so that there are two changes of sign. Thus, there are two zeros located to the right of the imaginary axis.

It is not necessary to use Routh's criterion if any of the coefficients of the characteristic function are zero or negative, because when this is so, it can be shown that there is at least one zero located on, or to the right of, the imaginary axis.

To determine how many zeros of the characteristic function lie to the right of some vertical line, a distance σ from the imaginary axis (i.e., the number of zeros that have a real part greater than σ), transform the characteristic function by substituting $s + \sigma$ for s, and apply Routh's criterion as just described. The number of changes of sign in the first column for this new function is equal to the number of zeros which are located to the right of the vertical line through σ.

If a 0 appears in the left-hand column and the sign of the term above the 0 is opposite of that below the 0, then there is but one sign change. However, when the sign of the term above the 0 is the same as that below it, a pair of zeros on the imaginary axis is indicated. For example, consider the function

$$s^3 + 3s^2 + 4s + 12 = (s + 3)(s^2 + 4) \tag{6.61}$$

The array of coefficients is

$$
\begin{array}{c|ccc}
1 & 1 & 4 & 0 \\
2 & 3 & 12 & 0 \\
3 & 0 & 0 & \\
4 & 0 - 0 & & \\
\hline
 & 0 & &
\end{array}
\tag{6.62}
$$

To evaluate the fourth coefficient in the left-hand column, replace the 0 obtained for the third coefficient by ϵ, which is a very small number. Thus

$$
\begin{array}{c|ccc}
1 & 1 & 4 & 0 \\
2 & 3 & 12 & 0 \\
3 & \epsilon \approx 0 & 0 & \\
4 & 12 & 0 &
\end{array}
\tag{6.63}
$$

The value of the fourth coefficient is $(12\epsilon - 0)/\epsilon = 12$. The factored form of Eq. (6.61) shows the imaginary zeros indicated by the preceding array.

The number of coefficients in the left-hand column is $n + 1$, where n is the order of the characteristic function. If the Routh's array is continued past the last row, it is found that only zeros result. The reason that it is necessary to keep track of the number of pertinent rows is that if the coefficient of the last row is zero, then the characteristic equation has a root at the origin. If the coefficients of the last two pertinent rows are zero, then the characteristic equation has a double root at the origin, etc.

Hurwitz Criterion.[1] This criterion determines the conditions which must be satisfied by the coefficients of the characteristic function so that the system is stable (i.e., all the zeros lie in the left half plane). In the Hurwitz criterion, the coefficients of the characteristic function [Eq. (6.55)] are arranged in the following array:

$$
\begin{array}{ccccccc}
D_1 & b_1 & b_0 & 0 & 0 & 0 & \cdots \\
D_2 & b_3 & b_2 & b_1 & b_0 & 0 & \cdots \\
D_3 & b_5 & b_4 & b_3 & b_2 & b_1 & \cdots \\
D_4 & b_7 & b_6 & b_5 & b_4 & b_3 & \cdots \\
\end{array}
\tag{6.64}
$$

[1] E. A. Guillemin, "The Mathematics of Circuit Analysis," pp. 395–409, John Wiley & Sons, Inc., New York, 1949.

whence the determinants D_1, D_2, D_3, . . . are found to be

$$D_1 = b_1 \qquad D_2 = \begin{vmatrix} b_1 & b_0 \\ b_3 & b_2 \end{vmatrix}$$

$$D_3 = \begin{vmatrix} b_1 & b_0 & 0 \\ b_3 & b_2 & b_1 \\ b_5 & b_4 & b_3 \end{vmatrix} \tag{6.65}$$

For stability, it is necessary that all the determinants be positive. That is, $D_1 > 0$, $D_2 > 0$, $D_3 > 0$, etc.

For a general cubic expression

$$b_3 s^3 + b_2 s^2 + b_1 s + b_0 \tag{6.66}$$

the application of the Hurwitz criterion gives

$$D_1 = b_1 > 0$$

$$D_2 = \begin{vmatrix} b_1 & b_0 \\ b_3 & b_2 \end{vmatrix} = b_1 b_2 - b_0 b_3 > 0 \tag{6.67}$$

$$D_3 = b_3 D_2 > 0 \text{ or } b_3 > 0$$

Thus for stability

$$b_1 b_2 > b_0 b_3 \tag{6.68}$$

With the Hurwitz criterion, similar conditions necessary for the stability of higher-order systems may also be derived. The preceding techniques of Routh and Hurwitz can be extended to yield information regarding the location of the zeros as the coefficients are varied.[1-4]

6.8 Summary. In this chapter it is shown that the transient response of a system is governed primarily by the location of the zeros of $B(s) = L_n(s)D_{F(s)}$. The zeros of $D_{F(s)}$ yield response terms appropriate to the particular excitation to the system. The function $L_n(s)$ is a basic property of the system itself. When all the zeros of $L_n(s)$ are located in the left half plane, the system is stable (i.e., for any bounded input the response is also bounded). If any zero of $L_n(s)$ is located in the right half plane, the system is unstable (i.e., the response is always unbounded). The imaginary axis is the border line between stable and unstable systems. Complex imaginary zeros are undesirable because they yield constant

[1] E. Sponder, On the Representation of the Stability Region in Oscillation Problems with the Aid of Hurwitz Determinants, *NACA Tech. Mem.* 1348, August, 1952.

[2] J. F. Koenig, On the Zeros of Polynomials and the Degree of Stability of Linear Systems, *J. Appl. Phys.*, **24**: 476 (1953).

[3] T. J. Higgins and J. G. Levinthal, Stability Limits for Third Order Servomechanisms, *Trans. AIEE*, **71**: (2) 459 (1952).

[4] H. A. Hogan and T. J. Higgins, Stability Boundaries for Fifth Order Servomechanisms, *Proc. Natl. Electronics Conf.*, **11**: 1001–1011 (1955).

sinusoids. A zero of $L_n(s)$ at the origin is also undesirable because it indicates an integration of the input. Note that an integrator in the feedforward elements (which integrates the error signal) does not yield a zero of $L_n(s)$ at the origin because the zeros of $D_{G(s)}$ are not the zeros of $L_n(s)$. When the characteristic function $L_n(s)$ has a zero at the origin, a constant input (i.e., a step function) yields an unbounded time term $C_1 t$ in the output which is the integral of the input.

The basic form of the response due to repeated zeros is the same as that for distinct zeros, with the exception that repeated zeros on the imaginary axis yield increasing time terms rather than time terms with constant amplitudes. Because $B(s) = L_n(s)D_{F(s)}$, the zeros of $L_n(s)$ and $D_{F(s)}$ act independently to yield the time response unless one or more of the zeros of $L_n(s)$ and $D_{F(s)}$ are the same. This introduces repeated zeros in $B(s)$, which affects the basic form of the response equation only if the zeros are on the imaginary axis. For example, a repeated complex imaginary zero results in an increasing sinusoid rather than a constant sinusoid. Similarly, a repeated zero at the origin yields an increasing time function rather than a constant. To ensure stability, zeros of $L_n(s)$ should be excluded not only from the right half plane but also from the imaginary axis.

Table 6.1 summarizes the type of response terms associated with the zeros of $B(s)$.

TABLE 6.1. LOCATION OF ZEROS AND CORRESPONDING RESPONSE FUNCTIONS

Zeros of $B(s) = L_n(s)D_{F(s)}$	Type of response
Left half plane (distinct or repeated)	Decaying exponential and/or decaying sinusoid
Right half plane (distinct or repeated)	Increasing exponential and/or increasing sinusoid

Imaginary axis:
  Distinct
  Repeated
	
	Constant and/or constant sinusoid
	Increasing time function and/or increasing sinusoid

Problems

6.1 Determine the time response $y(t)$ for each of the following transformed equations:

(a) $Y(s) = \dfrac{2s + 12}{s(s + 3)(s + 4)}$

(b) $Y(s) = \dfrac{s^2 + 3s + 8}{(s + 2)(s^2 + 5s + 4)}$

(c) $Y(s) = \dfrac{2s + 3}{s^3(s + 3)}$

6.2 Determine the time response $y(t)$ for each of the following transformed equations:

(a) $Y(s) = \dfrac{10}{s(s^2 + 2s + 5)}$

(b) $Y(s) = \dfrac{2s^2 + 3s + 4}{(s + 3)(s^2 + 2s + 10)}$

(c) $Y(s) = \dfrac{2s + 8}{(s + 2)(s^2 + 4)}$

(d) $Y(s) = \dfrac{20(s + 5)}{s(s^2 + 4)(s^2 + 6s + 25)}$

6.3 Use the Laplace transformation method to solve the following second-order differential equation for the case in which the roots are complex conjugates. The input $f(t)$ is a unit impulse and all the initial conditions are zero.

$$y(t) = \frac{\omega_n{}^2}{D^2 + 2\zeta\omega_n D + \omega_n{}^2} f(t)$$

6.4 For the system shown in Fig. P6.4 show that

$$J\ddot{\theta} + L^2 B\dot{\theta} + (K_1 L_1{}^2 + K_2 L_2{}^2)\theta = T$$

where $J = ML^2$. Determine

(a) The damping ratio ζ and natural frequency ω_n.
(b) The value of B such that the system is critically damped.
(c) The damped natural frequency.

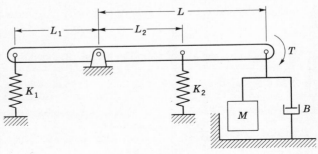

FIG. P6.4

6.5 Same as Prob. 5.14 except $K = 4$.

6.6 The characteristic function for a control system is known to be

$$L_n(D) = (D + 5)(D^2 + 4D + 13)$$

Determine the general form of the equation for the response $y(t)$ of this system when the input excitation $f(t)$ is

(a) An impulse
(b) A step function

Is the general form of these response expressions affected by the initial conditions?

6.7 The zeros of the characteristic function $L_n(D)$ for a control system are plotted in Fig. P6.7. Determine the general form of the equation describing the response $y(t)$ of this system when the input excitation $f(t)$ is

(a) An impulse
(b) A step function

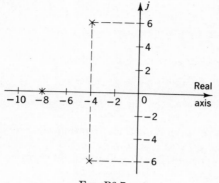

FIG. P6.7

6.8 Determine the characteristic function for the control system shown in Fig. P6.8. Use block-diagram algebra to move the constants A and B into the main loop. Does this affect the characteristic function?

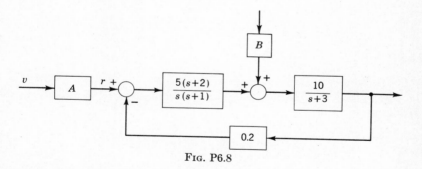

FIG. P6.8

6.9 For each of the characteristic functions given below:

(a) Determine the number of zeros that lie on or to the right of the imaginary axis.

$$s^3 + 2s^2 + 5s + 24 \qquad s^4 + 2s^3 + 6s^2 + 2s + 5$$
$$s^4 + 3s^3 + 4s^2 + 6s$$

(b) Determine the number of zeros that have a real part greater than or equal to -4.

6.10 (a) Apply Routh's criterion to determine an equation for K in terms of a, b, and c such that the cubic equation given below will have no roots with positive real parts.

$$as^3 + bs^2 + cs + K$$

(b) Same as part (a) except for the equation

$$as^3 + bs^2 + Ks + c$$

6.11 The characteristic equation for a feedback control system is

$$(s + 2)(s^2 + 4s + 8) + K = 0$$

Use Routh's criterion to determine the range of values of K for which the system is stable.

6.12 The characteristic equation for a control system is

$$s(s^2 + 8s + a) + 4(s + 8) = 0$$

Use Routh's criterion to obtain the range of values of a for which the system is stable.

6.13 Equation (6.68) is the functional relationship which must be satisfied to have all the roots of a cubic equation lie to the left of the imaginary axis (i.e., have a real part less than 0). Derive a similar relationship to determine whether or not all the roots have a real part less than -2.

6.14 For the quartic expression given below, determine the functional relationships which must be satisfied to have all the roots lie to the left of the imaginary axis.

$$b_4s^4 + b_3s^3 + b_2s^2 + b_1s + b_0$$

7

The root-locus method

The root-locus method was developed by W. R. Evans.[1-4] This method enables one to determine the roots of the characteristic equation (i.e., the zeros of the characteristic function) by knowing the factored form of the feedforward and feedback elements of a control system. As is discussed in Chap. 6, the transient behavior of a system is governed primarily by the roots of the characteristic equation for the system. Neither the initial conditions nor the particular excitation affects the basic operation of a system.

7.1 Significance of Root Loci. Consider the control system represented by Fig. 7.1a. The general form for the characteristic equation is

$$D_G D_H + N_G N_H = 0 \qquad (7.1)$$

From Fig. 7.1a it follows that $N_G = K$, $D_G = s(s + 4)$, $N_H = 1$, and $D_H = 1$. Thus, the characteristic function for this system is

$$s(s + 4) + K = s^2 + 4s + K \qquad (7.2)$$

The roots of the characteristic equation depend upon the value of K, which is the *static loop sensitivity*. As is shown in Fig. 7.1a, the static loop sensitivity K is the product of all the constant terms in the control loop when the coefficient of each s term is unity.

Because Eq. (7.2) is a quadratic, the roots are $r_{1,2} = a \pm jb$, in which $-2a = 4$ or $a = -2$ and $b = \sqrt{K - a^2} = \sqrt{K - 4}$. Thus

$$
\begin{array}{lll}
\text{For } K > 4 & r_{1,2} = -2 \pm j\sqrt{K - 4} & \\
\text{For } K = 4 & r_1 = r_2 = -2 & \qquad (7.3) \\
\text{For } K < 4 & r_{1,2} = -2 \pm j\sqrt{K - 4} = -2 \mp \sqrt{4 - K} &
\end{array}
$$

[1] W. R. Evans, Graphical Analysis of Control Systems, *Trans. AIEE*, **67**: 547–551 (1948).

[2] W. R. Evans, "Control-system Dynamics," McGraw-Hill Book Company, New York, 1954.

[3] J. J. D'azzo and C. H. Houpis, "Control System Analysis and Synthesis," McGraw-Hill Book Company, New York, 1960.

[4] C. J. Savant, Jr., "Basic Feedback Control System Design," McGraw-Hill Book Company, New York, 1958.

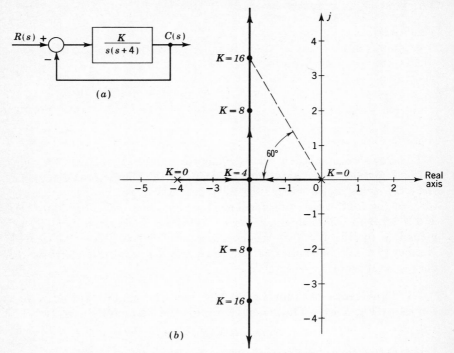

FIG. 7.1.   (a) Second-order system; (b) root-locus plot for $s(s + 4) + K = 0$.

In this last case, the roots are real and unequal.   The heavy lines in Fig. 7.1b are a plot of the roots of this characteristic equation for various values of K.   When $K = 0$, the roots are $r_{1,2} = 0, -4$; when $K = 4$, the roots are $r_1 = r_2 = -2$; when $K = 16$, the roots are $r_{1,2} = -2 \pm j \sqrt{12}$; etc.

Such a plot of the roots of the characteristic equation for each value of K as K varies from 0 to ∞ is a root-locus plot.   From such a root-locus plot, it is an easy matter to select the value of K to yield the desired roots of the characteristic equation.   For example, let it be desired to have a damping ratio $\zeta = 0.5$.   As discussed in the preceding chapter, $\beta = \cos^{-1} \zeta = \cos^{-1} 0.5 = 60°$.   As is shown in Fig. 7.1b, the line inclined at the angle $\beta = 60°$ intersects the root-locus plot at a value of $K = 16$.   From this plot, the corresponding roots are

$$r_{1,2} = -2 \pm j \sqrt{12}$$

Thus, the factored form of the characteristic function is

$$(s - r_1)(s - r_2) = (s + 2 - j2 \sqrt{3})(s + 2 + j2 \sqrt{3})$$
$$= s^2 + 4s + 16 \quad (7.4)$$

From the preceding expression, it follows that $\omega_n{}^2 = 16$ or $\omega_n = 4$, and equating $2\zeta\omega_n$ to the coefficient 4 of the s term gives $\zeta = 4/2\omega_n = \frac{1}{2}$, which verifies the preceding results.

A plot of the roots of the characteristic equation as K varies from 0 to ∞ yields very valuable information. For example, consider the feedback control system shown in Fig. 7.2a. It is to be noted that

$$N_G = K \qquad D_G = s(s + 4)(s + 6) \qquad N_H = 1 \qquad D_H = 1 \qquad (7.5)$$

Thus the characteristic function is

$$s(s + 4)(s + 6) + K = (s - r_1)(s - r_2)(s - r_3) \qquad (7.6)$$

The right-hand side of Eq. (7.6) is the factored form of the characteristic function. Because the number of roots $r_1, r_2, \ldots, r_n$ is equal to the order of the equation, the number of loci is also equal to the order of the equation, which in this case is 3. For each value of K, there corre-

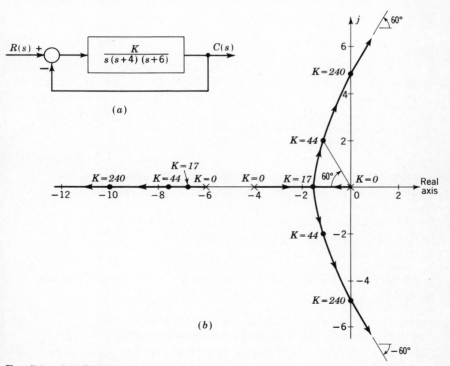

Fig. 7.2. (a) Third-order system; (b) root-locus plot for $s(s + 4)(s + 6) + K = 0$.

sponds a particular value of r_1, r_2, and r_3. Thus, for each value of K from 0 to ∞ one may plot the loci of corresponding values of r_1, r_2, and r_3. The three loci for Eq. (7.6) are drawn in Fig. 7.2b. One locus starts at $r_1 = -6$ for $K = 0$ and proceeds out the negative real axis as K increases. Another locus starts at $r_2 = -4$ and goes to the right along the real axis to the point $r_2 = -1.57$ and then leaves the real axis and proceeds out along a 60° asymptote toward infinity. The third locus starts at $r_3 = 0$ and moves along the negative real axis to $r_3 = -1.57$. This locus then leaves the real axis and proceeds toward infinity along a $-60°$ asymptote. In the construction of the loci, the three loci are determined without regard to which is considered the r_1, the r_2, or the r_3 locus. That is, from the similarity of the terms on the right-hand side of Eq. (7.6), it is seen that the particular subscripts 1, 2, and 3 may be used interchangeably.

From Fig. 7.2b it is to be noted that, if K is 240, then the three roots of the characteristic equation are

$$r_1 = -10 \qquad r_2 = j4.9 \qquad r_3 = -j4.9$$

Thus, the characteristic function may be written in the following factored form:

$$s(s + 4)(s + 6) + 240 = (s + 10)(s - j4.9)(s + j4.9) \qquad (7.7)$$

For $K = 240$, a pair of roots lie on the imaginary axis which would yield a sinusoidal response term of constant amplitude. From the root-locus plot, it is to be noted that, for $K > 240$, a pair of roots will always lie in the right half plane, thus making the system unstable.

For each value of K the corresponding roots of the characteristic equation may be determined directly from the root-locus plot. These roots in turn govern the transient behavior. From the root-locus plot, the designer may select the value of K such that the system will have a desired transient behavior. For example, let it be desired to have a damping ratio of 0.5. The intersection of the line drawn at the angle $\beta = 60°$ with the loci determines the value of $K = 44$. It is to be noted that the loci are always symmetrical with respect to the real axis because complex roots always occur as conjugate pairs.

ILLUSTRATIVE EXAMPLE 1.   For the control system shown in Fig. 7.2, determine

1.   The differential equation relating $c(t)$ and $r(t)$.
2.   The transformed equation relating $C(s)$ and $R(s)$.
3.   The response $c(t)$ of this system for the case in which $K = 44$, the input $r(t)$ is a unit impulse, and all of the initial conditions are zero.

SOLUTION

1. Replacing s by D in the block diagram and then applying Eq. (3.53) gives for the differential equation

$$c(t) = \frac{Kr(t)}{D(D+4)(D+6)+K} = \frac{Kr(t)}{D^3 + 6D^2 + 24D + K}$$

2. The transform is

$$C(s) = \frac{KR(s) + [s^2 c(0) + sc'(0) + c''(0)] + 6[sc(0) + c'(0)] + 24c(0)}{s^3 + 6s^2 + 24s + K}$$

3. For $K = 44$, the root-locus plot shows that the roots of the characteristic equation are $a \pm jb = -1.2 \pm j2.1$ and $r = -7.6$. Hence, the factored form of the characteristic equation is

$$s^3 + 6s^2 + 24s + K = (s^2 + 2.4s + 5.85)(s + 7.6)$$

For $R(s) = 1$ and all the initial conditions zero, then the transformed equation becomes

$$C(s) = \frac{44}{(s + 7.6)(s^2 + 2.4s + 5.85)}$$

The general form of the response is

$$c(t) = K_1 e^{-7.6t} + \frac{|K(a + jb)|}{b} e^{at} \sin(bt + \alpha)$$

The value of K_1 is

$$K_1 = \lim_{s \to -7.6} \frac{44}{s^2 + 2.4s + 5.85} = \frac{44}{81.85} = 0.54$$

The value of $K(a + jb)$ is

$$K(a + jb) = \lim_{s \to -1.2 + j2.1} \frac{44}{s + 7.6} = \frac{44}{6.4 + j2.1} = \frac{44}{6.74 / 18.2°}$$
$$= 6.53 / -18.2$$

Thus, the desired solution is

$$c(t) = 0.54 e^{-7.6t} + 3.11 e^{-1.2t} \sin(2.1t - 18.2°)$$

It is to be noted that regardless of the particular problem being solved, the general form of the transient response is determined by the roots of the characteristic equation. For a given value of K these roots are ascertained directly from the root-locus plot.

7.2 Construction of Loci. By determining certain points and asymptotes, the loci may be sketched in quite readily. The loci always originate, or begin, at $K = 0$, in which case the value of the roots is obtained

directly from the characteristic equation.   For example, from Eq. (7.6)
when $K = 0$, the roots are 0, -4, and -6.

The roots $r_1, r_2, \ldots, r_n$ of a characteristic equation are those values
of s which make the characteristic function equal to zero, i.e.,

$$s(s + 4)(s + 6) + K = (s - r_1)(s - r_2)(s - r_3) = 0 \qquad (7.8)$$

Thus, a root $r_1, r_2, \ldots, r_n$ of a characteristic equation is a value of s
such that

$$s(s + 4)(s + 6) + K = 0$$

or $\qquad\qquad\qquad s(s + 4)(s + 6) = -K \qquad\qquad\qquad (7.9)$

In Fig. 7.3, it is to be noted that the term s in Eq. (7.9) may be represented as a vector drawn from the origin to any point $s = a + jb$ in

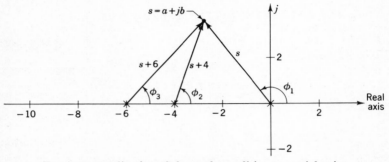

FIG. 7.3.   Application of the angle condition to a trial point.

the s plane.   The term $s + 4$ is the vector sum of the vector drawn from
the -4 point to the origin plus the vector from the origin to the point s.
This vector sum is equal to the vector drawn directly from the -4 point
to s.   Similarly, $s + 6$ is the vector drawn from -6 to s.   Thus, Eq.
(7.9) may be regarded as a vector equation.   The length or magnitude
of each vector satisfies the magnitude condition

$$|s|\,|s + 4|\,|s + 6| = |-K| = K \qquad (7.10)$$

where $|s|$ is the length of the s vector in Fig. 7.3, $|s + 4|$ is the length of
the $s + 4$ vector, etc.   In addition, the angle of each vector must satisfy
the angle condition

$$\angle s + \angle(s + 4) + \angle(s + 6) = \angle(-K) = 180° \pm k360° \quad (7.11)$$

where $k = 0, 1, 2, 3, \ldots$

$$\angle s = \phi_1$$
$$\angle(s + 4) = \phi_2$$
$$\angle(s + 6) = \phi_3$$

The angles ϕ_1, ϕ_2, and ϕ_3 are illustrated in Fig. 7.3.

The term $-K$ is a negative number which may be represented as being at the point $-K$ on the negative real axis so that $\measuredangle(-K)$ is $180° \pm k360°$.

In order that a point in the s plane be a root of the characteristic equation and thus lie on a locus of the roots, it is necessary that the point be located so that Eq. (7.11) is satisfied. Thus, the paths of the loci are determined from Eq. (7.11). After the root-locus plot has been obtained by application of Eq. (7.11), then the value of K at any point on a locus may be computed by means of Eq. (7.10).

The first place to start investigating the location of loci is along the real axis. For a trial point s that lies to the right of the origin on the real axis,

$$\measuredangle s = \measuredangle(s + 4) = \measuredangle(s + 6) = 0° \qquad (7.12)$$

Thus, $\phi_1 + \phi_2 + \phi_3 = 0°$, in which case the angle condition is not satisfied. Therefore, there is no locus on the positive real axis.

For a trial point s that lies on the real axis between 0 and -4,

$$\measuredangle s = 180° \qquad \measuredangle(s + 4) = 0° \qquad \measuredangle(s + 6) = 0° \qquad (7.13)$$

Because $\phi_1 + \phi_2 + \phi_3 = 180°$ satisfies the angle condition, there is a locus on the real axis between 0 and -4.

For the region from -4 to -6, it follows that

$$\measuredangle s = 180° \qquad \measuredangle(s + 4) = 180° \qquad \measuredangle(s + 6) = 0° \qquad (7.14)$$

Thus, $\phi_1 + \phi_2 + \phi_3 = 360°$ does not satisfy the angle condition. Finally for the region from -6 to $-\infty$ on the negative real axis,

$$\phi_1 + \phi_2 + \phi_3 = 180° + 180° + 180° = 540°$$

so that Eq. (7.11) is again satisfied, which signifies a locus in this region.

The next step in the construction of the loci is to determine the asymptotes as s approaches infinity. For very large values of s, the terms 0, 4, 6 in Eq. (7.9) become negligible compared with the value of s, so that Eq. (7.9) becomes

$$s(s + 4)(s + 6) \approx s(s)(s) = s^3 = -K \qquad (7.15)$$

The angle condition is

$$\measuredangle s^3 = 3\measuredangle s = 180° \pm k360°$$

or

$$\measuredangle s = \frac{180° \pm k360°}{3} = 60° \pm k120° \qquad (7.16)$$

Only three distinct angles, $60°, -60°, 180°$, are obtained from Eq. (7.16).

In order to locate the asymptotes, it is necessary to know where they intersect the real axis. The point σ_c where the asymptotes cross the real axis is determined from the general equation.

$$\sigma_c = \frac{\Sigma \text{ zeros of } D_G D_H - \Sigma \text{ zeros of } N_G N_H}{(\text{no. of zeros of } D_G D_H) - (\text{no. of zeros of } N_G N_H)} \qquad (7.17)$$

To verify Eq. (7.17), first write the characteristic equation [i.e., Eq. (7.1)] in the form

$$(s - p_1)(s - p_2) \cdots (s - p_n) + K(s - z_1)(s - z_2) \cdots (s - z_m) = 0$$

where $p_1, p_2, \ldots, p_n$ are the roots of $D_G D_H$ and $z_1, z_2, \ldots, z_m$ are the roots of $N_G N_H$. Solving for $-K$ gives

$$-K = \frac{(s - p_1) \cdots (s - p_n)}{(s - z_1) \cdots (s - z_m)} = \frac{s^n - (p_1 + \cdots + p_n)s^{n-1} + \cdots}{s^m - (z_1 + \cdots + z_m)s^{m-1} + \cdots}$$
$$(7.18)$$

It is to be noted that the coefficient of the second term in a polynomial is the negative of the sum of the roots.

Each numerator factor and each denominator factor may be written in the following form

$$s - p_i = (s - \sigma_c) - (p_i - \sigma_c)$$
$$s - z_i = (s - \sigma_c) - (z_i - \sigma_c)$$

In Fig. 7.4, the point s is indicated by a dot, p_i by an x, z_i by a circle, and σ_c by a $+$. The various vector quantities are indicated on this dia-

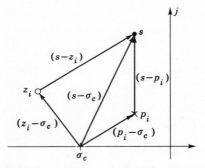

FIG. 7.4.   Trial point s, pole p_i, zero z_i, and asymptote crossing σ_c.

gram.   For a given value of p_i the vector $p_i - \sigma_c$ remains constant. Hence, as s becomes infinite $s - \sigma_c \gg p_i - \sigma_c$. Thus, for very large s

$$s - p_i \approx s - \sigma_c$$

Similarly, as s becomes infinite it follows that

$$s - z_i \approx s - \sigma_c$$

Thus

$$-K \approx \frac{(s - \sigma_c)^n}{(s - \sigma_c)^m} = (s - \sigma_c)^{n-m} = s^{n-m} - \sigma_c(n - m)s^{n-m-1} + \cdots$$

Performing the division indicated in Eq. (7.18) gives

$$-K = s^{n-m} - [(p_1 + p_2 + \cdots + p_n)$$
$$- (z_1 + z_2 + \cdots + z_m)]s^{n-m-1} + \cdots$$

Equating the coefficients of the second terms in the two preceding equations for $-K$ and solving for σ_c verifies the result given by Eq. (7.17). For the system under consideration Eq. (7.17) becomes

$$\sigma_c = \frac{[(0) + (-4) + (-6)] - 0}{3 - 0} = \frac{-10}{3} = -3\frac{1}{3} \qquad (7.19)$$

The information thus far obtained concerning the location of the roots is shown graphically in Fig. 7.5. By knowing the point at which the

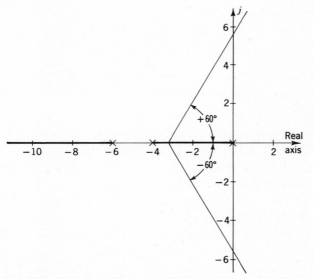

FIG. 7.5. Location of loci on real axis and the asymptotes.

locus between 0 and -4 breaks away from the real axis, one can construct a reasonably good sketch of the locus. This breakaway point σ_b is determined as follows: Consider in Fig. 7.6 a point s which is a small vertical distance Δ above the real axis. The equation for each angle is

$$\phi_1 = \pi - \tan^{-1}\frac{\Delta}{0 - \sigma_b}$$
$$\phi_2 = \tan^{-1}\frac{\Delta}{\sigma_b - (-4)} \qquad (7.20)$$
$$\phi_3 = \tan^{-1}\frac{\Delta}{\sigma_b - (-6)}$$

For small values of Δ, $\tan^{-1} (\Delta/-\sigma_b) \approx -\Delta/\sigma_b$, etc.   From Fig. 7.6, it is to be seen that, as Δ approaches zero, $\phi_1 + \phi_2 + \phi_3 \approx \pi + 0 + 0 = \pi$.

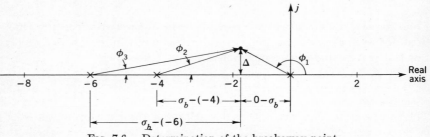

Fɪɢ. 7.6.   Determination of the breakaway point.

Thus

$$\phi_1 + \phi_2 + \phi_3 = \pi + \frac{\Delta}{\sigma_b} + \frac{\Delta}{4 + \sigma_b} + \frac{\Delta}{6 + \sigma_b} = \pi$$

or

$$\frac{\Delta}{\sigma_b} + \frac{\Delta}{\sigma_b + 4} + \frac{\Delta}{\sigma_b + 6} = 0 \qquad (7.21)$$

After eliminating Δ and obtaining a common denominator, the preceding expression becomes

$$3\sigma_b{}^2 + 20\sigma_b + 24 = 0$$

whence

$$\sigma_b = -1.57 \qquad (7.22)$$

The value of K at the point where the locus breaks away from the real axis is the maximum value that K attains between the points 0 and -4. Thus, an alternate method for determining σ_b is first to solve the characteristic equation for K:

$$K = -s(s + 4)(s + 6) = -(s^3 + 10s^2 + 24s) \qquad (7.23)$$

Differentiation to obtain the value of $s = \sigma_b$ at which K is a maximum gives

$$\frac{dK}{ds} = -\frac{d}{ds} (s^3 + 10s^2 + 24s) = -(3s^2 + 20s + 24) = 0 \quad (7.24)$$

Equation (7.24) is the result that was obtained by the preceding geometric evaluation.   The occurrence of a breakaway point is ascertained by the fact that *there is always a breakaway point between any two adjacent $\times$'s on the real axis which are connected by a locus.*   An $\times$ is used to designate a zero of $D_G D_H$.

With the information obtained thus far, the root-locus plot may be sketched in quite accurately, as is shown in Fig. 7.7.   For better accuracy in constructing the path of the loci from the breakaway point to the asymptote, it is necessary by trial and error to select trial points in this region and apply the angle condition. Trial points which satisfy the angle condition are points on the locus. It is a good idea to start by choosing all trial points on the same horizontal line until the point on the loci is obtained. For a trial point on one side of the loci, the angle condition will yield an angle greater than 180°, and for a trial point on the other side, an angle less than 180° is indicated. This information indicates in what direction a new trial point should be taken. The use of a spirule, which is a commercially available device, saves much effort in finding the angle of a trial point.

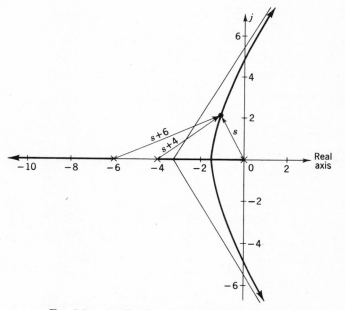

FIG. 7.7. Application of magnitude condition.

To illustrate the application of the magnitude condition, consider the point shown on the locus in Fig. 7.7. The value of s at this point is

$$s = -1.2 + j2.1$$

From Eq. (7.10), it follows that

$$K = |s| \, |s + 4| \, |s + 6|$$
$$= \sqrt{-1.2^2 + 2.1^2} \, \sqrt{2.8^2 + 2.1^2} \, \sqrt{4.8^2 + 2.1^2} = 44$$

In summary, the path of the locus plots is obtained entirely from the angle condition [Eq. (7.11)], and the values of K along the loci are determined from the magnitude condition [Eq. (7.10)].

The value of K at which the locus crosses the imaginary axis may be computed by Routh's method if so desired. That is, application of Routh's criterion to the characteristic function $s^3 + 10s^2 + 24s + K$ gives the following array:

$$
\begin{array}{ccc}
1 & 24 & 0 \\
10 & K & 0 \\
\dfrac{240 - K}{10} = \epsilon & 0 & \\
\dfrac{K\epsilon}{\epsilon} = K & &
\end{array}
$$

The value of K which makes the third coefficient vanish is $K = 240$.

Complex Conjugate Terms. The application of the root-locus method is now illustrated for the system shown in Fig. 7.8. The characteristic equation for this system is

$$(s + 1)(s^2 + 6s + 13) + K(s + 4) = (s - r_1)(s - r_2)(s - r_3) = 0 \tag{7.25}$$

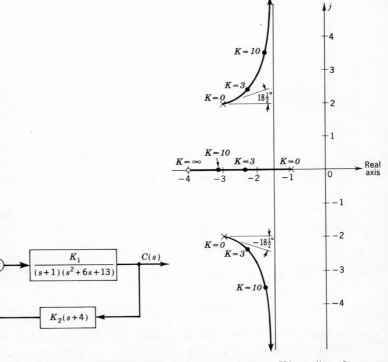

FIG. 7.8. Root-locus plot for $(s + 1)(s^2 + 6s + 13) + K(s + 4) = 0$.

where $K = K_1K_2$. The characteristic equation is now written in the form

$$\frac{(s+1)(s+3+j2)(s+3-j2)}{s+4} = -K \qquad (7.26)$$

The zeros of D_GD_H are -1, $-3 - j2$, and $-3 + j2$. The zero of N_GN_H is -4. To begin to construct a locus, first plot the zeros of D_GD_H and the zeros of N_GN_H. As is shown in Fig. 7.9, the location of the zeros of

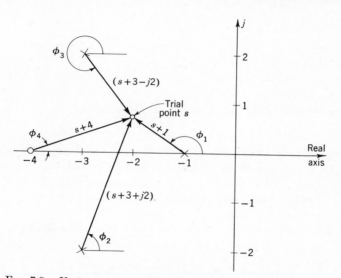

Fig. 7.9. Vector representation of D_GD_H terms and N_GN_H.

D_GD_H are indicated by crosses ($\times$), and the zeros of N_GN_H are indicated by circles ($\odot$). Also, it is to be noted that the vector drawn from each $\times$ to a point s is the corresponding term in the numerator of Eq. (7.26). Similarly, the vector drawn from the circle ($\odot$) to the point s is the corresponding term in the denominator of Eq. (7.26). The angle condition is

$$\angle(s+1) + \angle(s+3+j2) + \angle(s+3-j2) - \angle(s+4)$$
$$= 180° \pm k360° \qquad (7.27)$$

or
$$\phi_1 + \phi_2 + \phi_3 - \phi_4 = 180° \pm k360°$$

where
$$\phi_1 = \angle(s+1)$$
$$\phi_2 = \angle(s+3+j2)$$
$$\phi_3 = \angle(s+3-j2)$$
$$\phi_4 = \angle(s+4)$$

As usual, the first place to investigate the possible location of loci is along the real axis. As is illustrated in Fig. 7.10, the value of $\phi_2 + \phi_3$

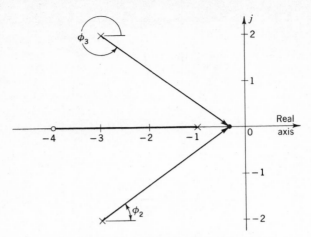

FIG. 7.10.   Location of loci on real axis.

will always be 360° when s is on the real axis.   For any trial point s on the real axis, the sum of the angular contribution $\phi_2 + \phi_3$ for any complex conjugate ×'s (zeros of $D_G D_H$) or ⊙'s (zeros of $N_G N_H$) will always be 360°.   Thus, *the location of the loci along the real axis is determined only by the ×'s and ⊙'s which lie on the real axis.*   When s is to the right of the -1 point, $\phi_1 = \phi_4 = 0°$.   Thus, there is no locus located to the right of the -1 point.   When s is between -1 and -4,

$$\phi_1 - \phi_4 = 180° - 0° = 180°$$

so that a locus is located in this region.   Similarly, it can be established that there is no locus to the left of the -4 point.

The next step in the construction of the loci is to determine the asymptotes for very large values of s.   In Eq. (7.27), the terms 1, $3 + j2$, $3 - j2$, and 4 become negligible compared with the value of s, so that Eq. (7.27) becomes

$$\angle s + \angle s + \angle s - \angle s = 180° \pm k360° \qquad k = 0, 1, 2, \ldots \quad (7.28)$$

or
$$3\angle s - \angle s = 2\angle s = 180° \pm k360°$$

$$\angle s = \frac{180° \pm k360°}{2} = 90° \pm k180° = \pm 90° \qquad (7.29)$$

In general, it follows that the angle of the asymptotes is

$$\angle s = \frac{180° \pm k360°}{n - m} \qquad k = 0, 1, 2, \ldots \qquad (7.30)$$

where n = highest power of s in $D_G D_H$ = no. of ×'s
$\quad\quad\; m$ = highest power of s in $N_G N_H$ = no. of ⊙'s

The number of distinct asymptotes is equal to $n - m$. Although it would appear from Eq. (7.30) that there are more asymptotes, the angles repeat for other values of k after $n - m$ distinct angles have been determined. In Fig. (7.11) is shown a plot of the asymptotes for the cases in

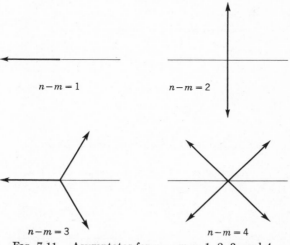

$$n - m = 1 \qquad n - m = 2$$

$$n - m = 3 \qquad n - m = 4$$

FIG. 7.11.   Asymptotes for $n - m = 1, 2, 3,$ and 4.

which $n - m = 1, 2, 3,$ and 4. For $n - m = 1$ the angle is $-180°$, for $n - m = 2$ the angles are $\pm 90°$, for $n - m = 3$ the angles are $-180°$ and $\pm 60°$, and for $n - m = 4$ the angles are $\pm 45°$ and $\pm 135°$.

For the system under consideration, the intersection of the asymptotes with the real axis is found as follows by application of Eq. (7.17):

$$\sigma_c = \frac{[(-1) + (-3 - j2) + (-3 + j2)] - (-4)}{3 - 1} = -1.5 \quad (7.31)$$

The information thus far obtained is sketched in Fig. 7.12. The next step is to determine the angle of departure of the loci from the complex conjugate zeros of $D_G D_H$. To do this, a trial point s is taken which is located very close to the point $(-3 - j2)$. From Fig. 7.12, the following values for ϕ_1, ϕ_3, and ϕ_4 are obtained:

$$\phi_1 = \tan^{-1} \frac{(-2) - 0}{(-3) - (-1)} = \tan^{-1} \frac{-2}{-2} = 225°$$

$$\phi_3 = \tan^{-1} \frac{(-2) - 2}{(-3) - (-3)} = \tan^{-1} \frac{-4}{0} = 270° \qquad (7.32)$$

$$\phi_4 = \tan^{-1} \frac{(-2) - 0}{(-3) - (-4)} = \tan^{-1} \frac{-2}{1} = 296.5°$$

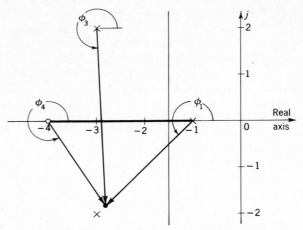

FIG. 7.12. Determination of angle of departure.

The angle ϕ_2 of departure of the loci from the point $(-3 - j2)$ is determined from the angle condition as follows:

$$\phi_1 + \phi_2 + \phi_3 - \phi_4 = 225° + \phi_2 + 270° - 296.5° = 180° \pm k360°$$

(7.33)

Thus $\phi_2 + 198.5° = 180° \pm k360°$

or $\phi_2 = -18.5° \pm k360° = -18.5°$ (7.34)

Because the loci are symmetrical about the real axis, the angle of departure from the other conjugate zero will be $+18.5°$. The complete root-locus plot may now be sketched in as shown in Fig. 7.8. The value of K at any place along the loci is determined by application of the magnitude condition.

From Eq. (7.26), it is to be noted that for $s = -1$, $-3 - j2$, or $-3 + j2$, the value of K is 0. These values of s are the zeros of $D_G D_H$. Thus, in general, one locus begins at each zero of $D_G D_H$ (that is, each ×). Similarly, for $s = -4$, $K = \infty$. The value $s = -4$ is a zero of $N_G N_H$, and thus one locus will terminate at each zero of $N_G N_H$ (that is, each ⊙). If n is the number of ×'s and m the number of ⊙'s, then the remaining $n - m$ loci terminate along asymptotes at infinity.

7.3 General Procedure. In the preceding section, it was shown that the loci could be sketched in quite accurately by knowing a few critical points, asymptotes, and the angle of departure from complex zeros, etc. The general procedure for constructing root loci is summarized as follows.

1. *Origin.* When K is zero, the zeros of the characteristic function are the zeros of $D_G D_H$. Thus, *each locus originates at a zero of $D_G D_H$ (desig-*

nated by ×'s) and the number of individual loci is equal to n, the number of zeros of $D_G D_H$.

2. *Terminus.* As K becomes very large, m loci (m is the number of zeros of $N_G N_H$) will approach the m zeros of $N_G N_H$. That is, *one locus will terminate at each of the m zeros of $N_G N_H$. The remaining $n - m$ loci will approach infinity along asymptotes.*

3. *Asymptotes.* The angles at which each of the $n - m$ loci approaches infinity is determined from Eq. (7.30); i.e.,

$$\angle s = \frac{180° \pm k360°}{n - m}$$

The point σ_c at which the asymptotes intersect or cross the real axis is computed by Eq. (7.17); i.e.,

$$\sigma_c = \frac{\Sigma \ (\text{zeros of } D_G D_H) - \Sigma \ (\text{zeros of } N_G N_H)}{n - m}$$

4. *Loci on real axis.* Complex zeros of $D_G D_H$ or $N_G N_H$ have no effect on the location of loci on the real axis. The place at which the loci are located along the real axis is determined by considering only zeros of $D_G D_H$ and $N_G N_H$ which lie on the real axis. As is illustrated in Fig. 7.13,

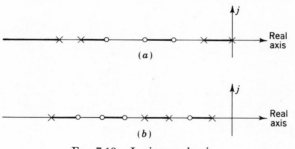

Fig. 7.13. Loci on real axis.

there is never a locus to the right of the first ⊙ or × on the real axis, but there is always a locus to the left of the first ⊙ or ×, there is never a locus to the left of the second ⊙ or ×, there is always a locus to the left of the third ⊙ or ×, never left of fourth, always left of fifth, and so on, alternating.

5. *Angle of departure.* The angle of departure of a locus from a complex zero of $D_G D_H$ is obtained by selecting a trial point very close to this zero and applying the angle condition.

6. *Angle of arrival.* The angle at which a locus will terminate at a complex zero of $N_G N_H$ is determined by taking a trial point which is close to this zero and applying the angle condition. This process is similar to that used to obtain the angle of departure from a zero of $D_G D_H$.

7. *Breakaway or break-in points.* The point σ_b at which the locus breaks away from or breaks into the real axis is obtained by applying the angle condition to an arbitrarily chosen point which is a small vertical distance Δ from the real axis and then solving this resultant equation for the only unknown term σ_b. This may also be determined by finding the real value $s = \sigma_b$ at which $dK/ds = 0$.

A breakaway point is located where K is a maximum, and a break-in point is located where K is a minimum. A break-in point is similar to a breakaway point with the exception that a pair of loci comes into the real axis rather than leaving it. A break-in point is illustrated in Fig. 7.14.

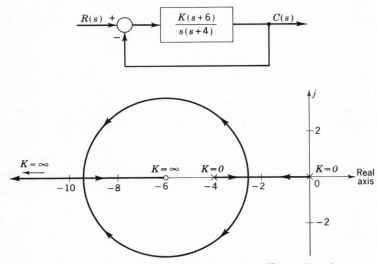

FIG. 7.14.　Root-locus plot for $s(s + 4) + K(s + 6) = 0$.

This is the system shown in Fig. 7.1, with the addition of the $s + 6$ term in N_G. The characteristic equation for the system of Fig. 7.14 is

$$s(s + 4) + K(s + 6) = 0 \qquad (7.35)$$

Application of rule 4 to determine the loci on the real axis yields the location of loci along the real axis as shown in Fig. 7.14.

The breakaway and break-in points are evaluated as follows:

$$\frac{dK}{ds} = -\frac{d}{ds}\frac{s(s + 4)}{s + 6} = -\left[\frac{(s + 6)(2s + 4) - s(s + 4)}{(s + 6)^2}\right] = 0 \qquad (7.36)$$

Thus,
$$s^2 + 12s + 24 = 0$$
whence
$$s = -6 \pm 2\sqrt{3} = -2.54, \ -9.46 \qquad (7.37)$$

Further investigation shows that the value -2.54 makes K a maximum in the region $-4 < s < 0$; thus this is the breakaway point. The value -9.46 makes K a minimum in the range $-\infty < s < -6$; thus this is a break-in point as illustrated in Fig. 7.14. These breakaway and break-in points could also be computed by the geometrical technique previously discussed of assuming a trial point s which is a small distance Δ above the real axis.

The occurrence of a breakaway or break-in point can be recognized from a consideration of the ×'s and ⊙'s which lie on the real axis. Every locus begins at an × and terminates at a ⊙ or along an asymptote at ∞. Thus, *there must be a breakaway point between any two adjacent ×'s on the real axis which are connected by a locus. Similarly, a break-in point is required if a ⊙ on the real axis is not connected to an adjacent × on the real axis by a locus.* Thus, if the locus is not located entirely on the real axis between an adjacent ⊙ and ×, it is necessary that it come into the real axis from elsewhere. The preceding rules may be verified for the root-locus plots shown in Fig. 7.15.

When the equation for dK/ds is a cubic, quartic, or higher-degree polynomial, then it is a very laborious process to solve for the break-in or breakaway point. A plot of dK/ds versus s would yield the desired breakaway or break-in point as the value of s at which $dK/ds = 0$. However, construction of such a plot is quite time consuming. For this type of situation, the method of taking a point a small vertical distance Δ from the real axis also results in a cubic, quartic, or higher-degree equation.

A technique for obtaining a close approximation to the break-in or breakaway point for such cases is explained in the following.

Newton's Method and the Remainder Theorem. Let $P(s)$ be the numerator of dK/ds. Thus when $P(s) = 0$, then $dK/ds = 0$. In Fig. 7.16 is shown a plot of $P(s)$ versus s. The tangent to this curve at $s = s_1$ is

$$P'(s_1) = \frac{P(s_1)}{s_1 - s_2}$$

Solving for s_2 gives

$$s_2 = s_1 - \frac{P(s_1)}{P'(s_1)} \tag{7.38}$$

The point s_2 which is the intersection of the tangent and the horizontal axis is a closer approximation to σ_b than is s_1. After evaluating s_2, then applying the same process yields a closer approximation s_3, etc. Usually one trial yields sufficient accuracy for constructing the root-locus plot.

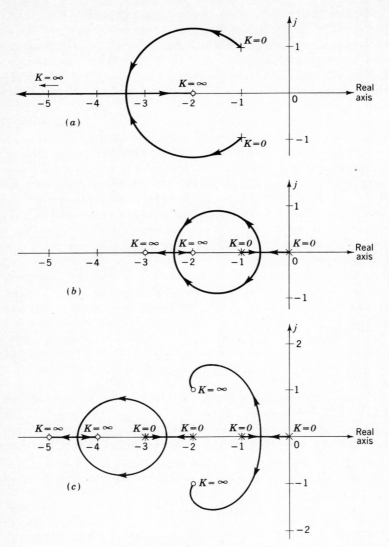

FIG. 7.15.   Root-locus plots.

It is now shown how $P(s_1)/P'(s_1)$ may be obtained by use of the remainder theorem.

Dividing $P(s)$ by $(s - s_1)$ gives

$$s - s_1 \overline{)P(s)}^{\displaystyle Q(s) \,+\, R_1/(s - s_1)}$$

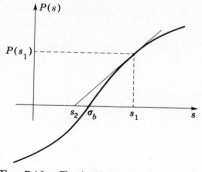

FIG. 7.16.   Typical plot of $P(s)$ versus s.

An alternate form for this division is

$$\frac{P(s)}{s - s_1} = Q(s) + \frac{R_1}{s - s_1}$$

where R_1 is the remainder that results when $P(s)$ is divided by $s - s_1$. Multiplying through by $s - s_1$ gives

$$P(s) = (s - s_1)Q(s) + R_1 \tag{7.39}$$

Taking the limit as s approaches s_1 shows that

$$P(s_1) = R_1 \tag{7.40}$$

By similarly dividing $Q(s)$ by $s - s_1$, it follows that

$$s - s_1 \overline{\big/ Q(s)} \; \frac{T(s) + R_2/(s - s_1)}{}$$

or

$$\frac{Q(s)}{s - s_1} = T(s) + \frac{R_2}{s - s_1} \tag{7.41}$$

where R_2 is the remainder that results when $Q(s)$ is divided by $s - s_1$. Multiplying through Eq. (7.41) by $(s - s_1)$ and then taking the limit as s approaches s_1 shows that

$$Q(s_1) = R_2 \tag{7.42}$$

To show that $Q(s_1) = P'(s_1)$, first differentiate Eq. (7.39) with respect to s

$$P'(s) = (s - s_1)Q'(s) + Q(s)$$

Taking the limit as s approaches s_1 verifies the fact that

$$P'(s_1) = Q(s_1) = R_2 \tag{7.43}$$

Equation (7.38) may now be expressed in the form

$$s_2 = s_1 - \frac{R_1}{R_2} \tag{7.44}$$

To illustrate the application of this method, let us assume as a first trial that the breakaway point for Fig. 7.7 occurs at $s_1 = -2.0$. From Eq. (7.24), the polynomial $P(s)$ is

$$P(s) = 3s^2 + 20s + 24$$

Division by $s - s_1 = s + 2$ yields

$$
\begin{array}{r}
3s + 14 \\
s + 2\overline{\smash{)}3s^2 + 20s + 24} \\
\underline{3s^2 + 6s} \\
14s + 24 \\
\underline{14s + 28} \\
-4
\end{array}
$$

Hence, $Q(s) = 3s + 14$ and $R_1 = -4$. Dividing $Q(s)$ by $s - s_1$ gives

$$
\begin{array}{r}
3 \\
s + 2\overline{\smash{)}3s + 14} \\
\underline{3s + 6} \\
8
\end{array}
$$

Hence, $T(s) = 3$ and $R_2 = 8$. Application of Eq. (7.44) yields the closer approximation

$$s_2 = -2 - \frac{-4}{8} = -1.5$$

The preceding divisions are simplified by the use of synthetic division as is illustrated below.

$$
\begin{array}{ccc|c}
3 & 20 & 24 & \underline{/-2} \\
 & -6 & -28 & \\
\hline
3 & 14 & -4 &
\end{array}
$$

The first row consists of the coefficients of the polynomial $P(s)$ and the root -2. The first coefficient 3 is brought below the line, then multiplying 3 by -2 yields -6 as shown. Adding 20 and -6 gives 14 as shown. Multiplying 14 by -2 yields the -28 term. Finally, adding 24 and -28 yields the remainder $R_1 = -4$ which is circled. It is to be noted that the coefficients of $Q(s)$ appear to the left of the circled remainder. The remainder R_2 is now obtained by similarly applying synthetic division to the $Q(s)$ polynomial. That is

$$
\begin{array}{cc|c}
3 & 14 & \underline{/-2} \\
 & -6 & \\
\hline
3 & 8 &
\end{array}
$$

Thus, the remainder R_2 is 8 and $T(s)$ is simply 3.

Let us now take -1.5 as the new trial root, and then employ synthetic division to obtain the next closer approximation. Thus

$$
\begin{array}{cccc}
3.00 & 20.00 & 24.00 & \underline{/\,-1.50} \\
 & -4.50 & -23.25 & \\
\hline
3.00 & 15.50 & 0.75 & \\
 & -4.50 & & \\
\hline
3.00 & 11.00 & &
\end{array}
$$

Thus, $R_1 = 0.75$, $R_2 = 11.00$, $Q(s) = 3s + 15.50$, and $T(s) = 2$. The closer approximation is

$$
s_3 = s_2 - \frac{R_1}{R_2} = -1.50 - \frac{0.75}{11.00} = -1.57
$$

7.4 Loci Equations. In studying control systems, one frequently encounters the case in which there are two $\times$'s and one $\odot$ as shown in Fig. 7.17. It is now shown that when a locus leaves the real axis, it follows a circular path. The characteristic equation for this case is

$$(s - p_1)(s - p_2) + K(s - z) = 0 \tag{7.45}$$

As shown in Fig. 7.17a, a trial point s may be expressed in the form

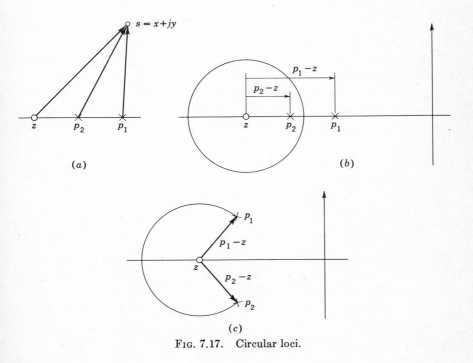

(a)

(b)

(c)

Fig. 7.17.   Circular loci.

$s = x + jy$. The substitution of $s = x + jy$ in the preceding equation gives

$$(x^2 + 2jxy - y^2) - (p_1 + p_2 - K)(x + jy) + p_1p_2 - Kz = 0$$

In order that this equation equal zero, it is necessary that both the real parts and the imaginary parts (i.e., j components) be zero. Thus,

$$x^2 - y^2 - (p_1 + p_2 - K)x + p_1p_2 - Kz = 0$$
$$2xy - (p_1 + p_2 - K)y = 0$$

To eliminate K between the two preceding equations, first solve each for K. That is

$$K = \frac{(x^2 - y^2) - (p_1 + p_2)x + p_1p_2}{z - x} \tag{7.46}$$

$$K = (p_1 + p_2) - 2x \tag{7.47}$$

The term K is now eliminated by equating the right-hand sides of the preceding expressions. Thus

$$x^2 + y^2 = p_1p_2 + [2x - (p_1 + p_2)]z \tag{7.48}$$

Completing the square gives

$$(x - z)^2 + y^2 = (p_1 - z)(p_2 - z) \tag{7.49}$$

This is recognized as the equation of a circle with center at z. The radius is the square root of the product of the distance from z to p_1 and the distance z to p_2. That is

$$R = \sqrt{(p_1 - z)(p_2 - z)} \tag{7.50}$$

A typical root-locus plot for the case in which p_1 and p_2 are real is shown in Fig. 7.17b. For the case in which p_1 and p_2 are complex conjugate roots, then the distance from z to p_1 equals the distance from z to p_2. Thus, the radius is simply the distance from z to either of the complex conjugate roots as is shown in Fig. 7.17c.

Equation (7.47) may be used to determine the gain K for points on the loci in the complex plane (i.e., off the real axis). For loci on the real axis, then $y = 0$. Thus, letting $y = 0$ in Eq. (7.46) yields an equation for evaluating the gain K for loci points on the real axis.

ILLUSTRATIVE EXAMPLE 1. Construct the root-locus plot for the system shown in Fig. 7.18a, and then determine the gain K at $x = -4$ and at $x = -8$.

SOLUTION. The characteristic equation for this system is

$$s(s + 2) + K(s + 4) = 0$$

Thus, $z = -4$, $p_1 = 0$, and $p_2 = -2$.

The location of the loci on the real axis may be drawn as shown in Fig. 7.18b. Because there are two ×'s and a ⊙, then in the complex

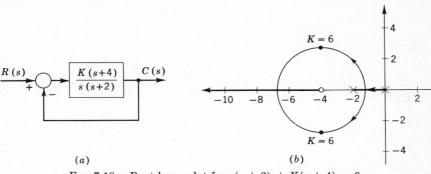

(a)   (b)

FIG. 7.18.   Root-locus plot for $s(s + 2) + K(s + 4) = 0$.

plane (i.e., off the real axis) the loci form a circle with center at $z = -4$ and radius

$$R = \sqrt{(p_1 - z)(p_2 - z)} = \sqrt{(4)(2)} = \sqrt{8}$$

The application of Eq. (7.47) to determine the gain K at $x = -4$ gives

$$K = (p_1 + p_2) - 2x = (0 - 2) - 2(-4) = 6$$

For the loci on the real axis at $x = -8$, then application of Eq. (7.46) in which $y = 0$ gives

$$K = \frac{x^2 - (p_1 + p_2)x + p_1 p_2}{z - x} = \frac{64 - (-2)(-8)}{-4 - (-8)} = \frac{48}{4} = 12$$

The preceding method for obtaining the equation for a circular locus may be applied to any locus. The method is to replace s by $x + jy$ in the characteristic equation. Because both the real and imaginary parts must be zero, then two equations are obtained. One equation gives values of gain K for loci on the real axis and the other equation gives values of gain K for loci in the complex plane. Eliminating K between these two equations yields a general equation in x and y for the loci. Corresponding values of x and y that satisfy this equation are points on the loci. In the preceding example the equation was recognized as that of a circle. However, for more complex systems, it may be necessary to use a digital computer to ascertain the corresponding values of x and y

that satisfy the equation, and thus are points on the locus. For most engineering work, the spirule provides sufficient accuracy for sketching the loci in the complex plane. Thus, there is seldom need for the additional refinement provided by a computer solution.

7.5 Variation of Parameters. Thus far the discussion of root locus has been concerned with the case in which the gain K is the variable parameter. By algebraically rearranging the characteristic equation, the effect of the change of any parameter can be investigated.

To illustrate this procedure, consider the system shown in Fig. 7.19a. The characteristic equation for this system is

$$s(s + 4) + K = 0$$

The basic root-locus plot is shown in Fig. 7.19b. For $K = 20$, it is to be

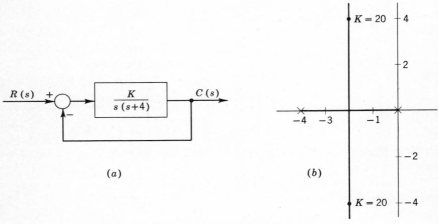

(a) (b)

FIG. 7.19.   Root-locus plot for $s(s + 4) + K = 0$.

noted that the roots of the characteristic equation are $-2 \pm j4$. Thus

$$s(s + 4) + 20 = [s - (-2 - j4)][s - (-2 + j4)] = 0$$

Let it now be desired to investigate the effect of varying the parameter 4 when $K = 20$. Replacing the parameter 4 by $4 + \Delta$, where Δ is the change in the parameter, yields for the new characteristic equation

$$
\begin{aligned}
s[s + (4 + \Delta)] + 20 &= [s(s + 4) + 20] + s\Delta \\
&= [s - (-2 - j4)][s - (-2 + j4)] + s\Delta = 0
\end{aligned}
$$
$$(7.51)$$

This equation has the familiar form except that Δ is now the variable rather than K. The new root-locus plot begins at the value of the roots on the basic plot for $K = 20$. Equation (7.51) shows that the ×'s for the new plot are at $s = -2 \pm j4$ and there is a ⊙ at the origin. The corresponding root-locus plot for positive values of Δ is shown in Fig. 7.20a.

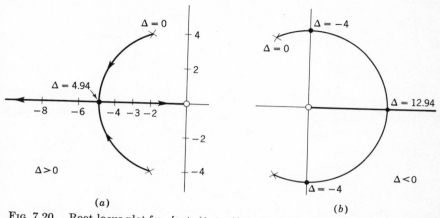

Fig. 7.20.   Root-locus plot for $s[s + (4 + \Delta)] + 20 = [s(s + 4) + 20] + s\Delta = 0$.

In investigating the effect of a change in a parameter, it is desired to know the effect of decreasing as well as increasing the parameter. Thus far, root-locus plots have been constructed for positive values of K only. From Eq. (7.11), it follows that when K (or Δ) is positive then the summation of the angles is $180° \pm k360°$. When K (or Δ) is a negative number, then $(-K)$ is a positive number which may be represented by a point on the positive real axis. For negative K the angle is

$$\angle(-K) = 0° \pm k360°$$

The following rules for constructing a root-locus plot for negative values of K (or Δ) are very similar to those given in Sec. 7.3 for positive values of K.

1. *Origin.*   One locus begins at each × as was the case for positive K.
2. *Terminus.*   One locus ends at each ⊙ as was the case for positive K. The remaining $n - m$ loci terminate at asymptotes.
3. *Asymptotes.*   The angles at which each $n - m$ locus approaches infinity is

$$\angle s = \frac{0° \pm k360°}{n - m}$$

The corresponding asymptotes for $n - m = 1, 2, 3,$ and 4 are shown in Fig. 7.21. For $n - m = 1$ the angle is $0°$, for $n - m = 2$ the angles

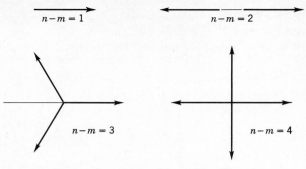

FIG. 7.21.   Asymptotes for negative K or Δ.

are 0° and 180°, for $n - m = 3$ the angles are 0° and $\pm 120°$, and for $n - m = 4$ the angles are 0°, $\pm 90°$, and 180°.

The point σ_c at which the asymptotes intersect the real axis is obtained by Eq. (7.17) in the same manner as for positive K.

4.   *Loci on the real axis.*   The location of loci on the real axis is determined by the ×'s and ⊙'s that lie on the real axis.   The summation of angles at any point on the real axis is either 0° or 180°.   For positive K the loci are regions on the real axis where the angle is 180°.   The remaining regions on the real axis must be places where the angle is 0°, and thus these are the regions of the loci for negative values of K.   In Fig. 7.22

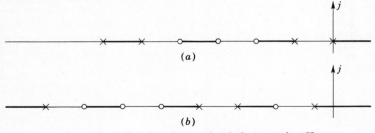

FIG. 7.22.   Location of loci on real axis for negative K or Δ.

is shown the location of loci on the real axis for negative K for the same × and ⊙ pattern of Fig. 7.14.   The loci now appear at all regions on the real axis that did not have loci in Fig. 7.14.   For the case of negative K, a locus always appears to the right of the first ⊙ or × on the real axis, there is never a locus to the left of the first ⊙ or ×, there is always a locus to the left of the second ⊙ or ×, there is never a locus to the left of the third ⊙ or ×, and so on alternating.

5.   *Angle of departure.*   Because the summation of angles is now 0° rather than 180°, then the angle of departure for negative K is always 180° different from that obtained for positive K.

6. *Angle of arrival.* The angle of arrival for negative K is always 180° different from that obtained for positive K.

7. *Breakaway or break-in points.* These are determined in the same way as for positive K. In determining the breakaway or break-in points for positive K, oftentimes extra or extraneous values were obtained. Actually, these values are the ones for the case of negative K.

In Fig. 7.20b is shown the root-locus plot for negative values of Δ. Because there are two ×'s and one ⊙, the loci is a circle in the complex plane. The system becomes unstable when the locus crosses the imaginary axis which occurs at $\Delta = -4$. The preceding concepts are further illustrated in the following example.

ILLUSTRATIVE EXAMPLE 1. Suppose that for the system shown in Fig. 7.2 the gain K must be maintained at 240 to achieve satisfactory steady-state operation. For $K = 240$ the roots of the characteristic equation are $s = \pm j \sqrt{24}$ and $s = -10$. Hence, the factored form of the characteristic equation is

$$s(s + 4)(s + 6) + 240 = (s + 10)(s^2 + 24)$$

Determine whether or not this system can be stabilized and good dynamic behavior achieved by changing the parameter 4 in the term $s + 4$.

SOLUTION. Replacing 4 by $4 + \Delta$ yields, for the new characteristic equation,

$$s[(s + 4) + \Delta](s + 6) + 240 = [s(s + 4)(s + 6) + 240] + s(s + 6)\Delta = 0$$
$$= (s + 10)(s^2 + 24) + s(s + 6)\Delta = 0$$

To construct the root-locus plot for positive values of Δ, first draw the loci on the real axis as shown in Fig. 7.23a. Next the angle of departure from the × at $s = j \sqrt{24}$ is

$$\left(\phi_d + 90° + \tan^{-1} \frac{\sqrt{24}}{10} \right) - \left(90° + \tan^{-1} \frac{\sqrt{24}}{6} \right) = 180°$$

Solving for ϕ_d gives $\phi_d = 193.1°$.

A break-in point is seen to occur between 0 and -6 on the real axis. As a first trial, let s_1 be the midpoint -3. To apply Newton's method, first solve the characteristic equation for Δ.

$$\Delta = \frac{(s + 10)(s^2 + 24)}{s(s + 6)}$$

Differentiation to obtain $d\Delta/ds$ gives

$$\frac{d\Delta}{ds} = - \frac{s^4 + 12s^3 + 36s^2 - 480s - 1440}{(s^2 + 6s)^2} = 0$$

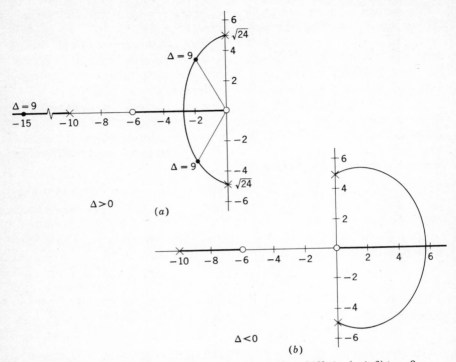

FIG. 7.23.   Root-locus plot for $[s(s + 4)(s + 6) + 240] + s(s + 6)\Delta = 0$.

The polynomial $P(s)$ is taken as the numerator of $d\Delta/ds$. Thus, application of double synthetic division to obtain the remainders yields

$$
\begin{array}{rrrrr}
1 & 12 & 36 & -480 & -1,440 \qquad \underline{/-3} \\
  & -3 & -27 & -27 & 1,521 \\
\hline
1 & 9 & 9 & -507 & 81 \\
  & -3 & -18 & 27 & \\
\hline
1 & 6 & -9 & -480 &
\end{array}
$$

Thus, $R_1 = 81$, $R_2 = -480$, $Q(s) = s^3 + 9s^2 + 9s - 507$, and $T(s) = s^2 + 6s - 9$. The value of s_2 is

$$
s_2 = -3 - \frac{81}{-480} = -2.83
$$

The remaining portion of the root-locus plot for positive values of Δ may now be sketched in as shown in Fig. 7.23a.

To construct the root-locus plot for negative Δ, first draw the loci on the real axis as is shown in Fig. 7.23b. The angle of departure for negative values of Δ is 180° different from that for positive Δ, hence

$$\phi_d = 193.1° - 180.0° = 13.1°$$

It is seen that a break-in point must occur on the positive real axis. Taking $s_1 = 5$ as the first trial and then applying double synthetic division gives

$$
\begin{array}{rrrrr}
1 & 12 & 36 & -480 & -1{,}440 \quad \underline{/5} \\
  & 5 & 85 & 605 & 625 \\
\hline
1 & 17 & 121 & 125 & -815 \\
  & 5 & 110 & 1{,}155 \\
\hline
1 & 22 & 231 & 1{,}280 \\
\end{array}
$$

Thus, $R_1 = -815$, $R_2 = 1{,}280$, $Q(s) = s^3 + 17s^2 + 121s + 125$, and $T(s) = s^2 + 22s + 231$. Application of Eq. (7.24) to obtain the closer approximation to the break-in point gives

$$s_2 = 5.0 - \frac{-815}{1{,}280} = 5.64$$

From the root-locus plot it is seen that good dynamic behavior is obtained for $\Delta = 9$ in which case the three roots are $-2 \pm j\sqrt{12}$ and -15. For the complex conjugate roots $\zeta = 0.5$ and $\omega_n = 4$.

7.6 Sensitivity. The parameters used in the design of control systems vary due to factors such as wear, aging, variations in the operating point, temperature, etc. It is thus desired to know the effect of small variations in these parameters upon the dynamic response of the system. In Sec. 7.5, it was shown how to determine the effect of such variations upon the location of the roots of the characteristic equation. The sensitivity method is described in the following.

The sensitivity S is defined as the percentage change in the system transmittance T to the percentage change in the parameter K. That is

$$S_K^T = \frac{dT/T}{dK/K} = \frac{K}{T}\frac{dT}{dK} = \frac{d \ln T}{d \ln K}$$

where $T(s) = C(s)/R(s)$ is the closed-loop transfer function for the system. The term K may represent any parameter such as gain, time constant, damping ratio, natural frequency, etc. To have the transmittance T which represents the system dynamics insensitive to variations in a parameter, then the sensitivity S should be zero, or as small as possible.

The transfer function for the system of Fig. 7.19 may be expressed in the general form

$$G(s) = \frac{K}{s(s + a)} = \frac{K}{s(s + 1/\tau)}$$

where $a = 1/\tau$ in which τ is the time constant. As indicated in the following, for computational purposes it is easier to work with a. It is an easy matter to convert the resulting answer from a to τ if so desired.

The transmittance T is

$$T(s) = C(s)/R(s) = \frac{G(s)}{1 + G(s)} = \frac{K}{s(s + a) + K}$$

The sensitivity with respect to the gain K is

$$S_K^T = \frac{K}{T}\frac{dT}{dK} = \frac{K[s(s + a) + K]}{K}\frac{[s(s + a) + K] - K}{[s(s + a) + K]^2}$$

$$= \frac{s(s + a)}{s(s + a) + K} \tag{7.52}$$

The sensitivity with respect to the parameter a is

$$S_a^T = \frac{a}{T}\frac{dT}{da} = \frac{a[s(s + a) + K]}{K}\frac{-sK}{[s(s + a) + K]^2}$$

$$= \frac{-as}{s(s + a) + K} \tag{7.53}$$

For both Eqs. (7.52) and (7.53), the steady-state sensitivity obtained by letting $s = 0$ is $S_K^T = S_a^T = 0$. The dynamic sensitivity is obtained by replacing s by $j\omega$ in the sensitivity equations, and then making plots of the sensitivity as a function of the frequency ω. The significance of replacing s by $j\omega$ is explained in Chaps. 9 and 10. Actually, the steady-state sensitivity $s = 0$ and the dynamic sensitivity $s = j\omega$ are somewhat misleading in that the designer is more interested in the values of s that are the roots of the characteristic equation.

By defining sensitivity in a slightly different manner, it is possible to determine the change in the roots of the characteristic equation for small variations of a parameter. Thus, sensitivity is now defined as the rate of change of the root location with respect to the parameter. That is

$$S_K^s = \frac{ds}{dK} \tag{7.54}$$

where ds/dK is the rate of change of the root location s in the characteristic equation with respect to K. For the system of Fig. 7.19, the characteristic equation is

$$s(s + a) + K = (s - r_1)(s - r_2) = 0$$

The derivative with respect to K is

$$2s \frac{ds}{dK} + a \frac{ds}{dK} + 1 = 0$$

Thus, the sensitivity with respect to the parameter K is

$$S_K^s = \frac{ds}{dK} = \frac{-1}{a + 2s}$$

At the reference operating condition $a = 4$ and $K = 20$, the roots are $r_1 = -2 + j4$ and $r_2 = -2 - j4$. The sensitivity of the location of the root r_1 is obtained by evaluating S_K^s at $s = r_1$. Thus,

$$S_K^{r_1} = \frac{dr_1}{dK} = \frac{-1}{4 + 2(-2 + j4)} = \frac{-1}{j8} = \frac{j}{8}$$

Because $dr_1 = (dr_1/dK) \, dK = S_K^{r_1} \, dK$, then

$$\Delta r_1 \approx S_K^{r_1} \Delta K = \frac{j}{8} \Delta K \tag{7.55}$$

If ΔK is 4, then $\Delta r_1 \approx 0.5j$. Hence, for $K = 20 + \Delta K = 24$, then $r_1 \approx (-2 + j4) + 0.5j = -2 + j4.50$. From the characteristic equation, the exact value of r_1 is found to be $-2 + j \sqrt{20} = -2 + j4.47$. In a similar manner, the change in the location of the root r_2 may also be found.

The sensitivity of the location of the roots with respect to the parameter a is

$$S_a^s = \frac{ds}{da}$$

The derivative of the characteristic equation with respect to a is

$$2s \frac{ds}{da} + a \frac{ds}{da} + s \frac{da}{da} = 0$$

Thus, the sensitivity ds/da is

$$S_a^s = \frac{ds}{da} = \frac{-s}{a + 2s}$$

The root sensitivity at $s = r_1$ is

$$S_a^{r_1} = \frac{dr_1}{da} = \frac{-(-2 + j4)}{4 + 2(-2 + j4)} = -\frac{2 + j}{4}$$

Thus

$$\Delta r_1 \approx -\frac{2 + j}{4} \Delta a \tag{7.56}$$

Because $a = 1/\tau$, then if the time constant τ is changed from $\frac{1}{4}$ to $\frac{1}{2}$, then $\Delta a = 1/(\frac{1}{4}) - 1/(\frac{1}{2}) = 4 - 2 = 2$. Thus

$$r_1 \approx \frac{(-2 + j4) - 2(2 + j)}{4} = -3 + j3.50$$

From the characteristic equation (for $a = 4 + 2 = 6$ and $K = 20$) the exact value of r_1 is found to be $-3 + j \sqrt{11} = -3 + j3.32$.

By expressing the sensitivity in the polar form, then Eqs. (7.55) and (7.56) become

$$\Delta r_1 \approx 0.125 \, \Delta K \underline{/90°}$$

$$\Delta r_1 \approx -\sqrt{5} \, \frac{\Delta a}{4} \, \underline{/206.6°}$$

The angles indicate the direction that the roots leave the reference value for positive variations in ΔK or Δa. The direction is reversed by 180° for negative variations.

If both K and a change simultaneously, then

$$\Delta s \approx \frac{\partial s}{\partial K} \, \Delta K + \frac{\partial s}{\partial a} \, \Delta a = S_K^s \, \Delta K + S_a^s \, \Delta a$$

Thus, the effects add when more than one parameter varies. For example, if $\Delta K = 4$ and $\Delta a = 2$, then the change Δr_1 is

$$\Delta r_1 \approx \frac{j}{8} \, 4 - \frac{2 + j}{4} \, 2 = -1$$

The new value of r_1 is $(-2 + j4) - 1 = -3 + j4$. From the characteristic equation for $K = 20 + 4 = 24$ and $a = 4 + 2 = 6$, the exact value is found to be $-3 + j \sqrt{15} = -3 + j3.87$.

7.7 Series Compensation. A very versatile technique for improving the performance of a system is to insert a compensator in series with the feedforward elements as is illustrated in Fig. 7.24. The block $G_c(s)$ represents the compensating elements. These components are usually such that the output of the compensator either leads or lags the input.

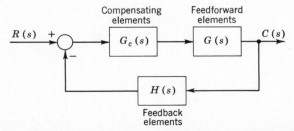

FIG. 7.24. Compensator $G_c(s)$ in series with feedforward elements $G(s)$.

Lead compensators and lag compensators are discussed separately in the following.

Lead Compensation. In Fig. 7.25 is shown both an electrical and a mechanical circuit used to provide lead compensation.

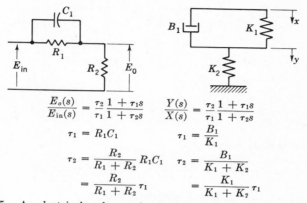

$$\frac{E_o(s)}{E_{in}(s)} = \frac{\tau_2}{\tau_1} \frac{1 + \tau_1 s}{1 + \tau_2 s} \qquad \frac{Y(s)}{X(s)} = \frac{\tau_2}{\tau_1} \frac{1 + \tau_1 s}{1 + \tau_2 s}$$

$$\tau_1 = R_1 C_1 \qquad\qquad \tau_1 = \frac{B_1}{K_1}$$

$$\tau_2 = \frac{R_2}{R_1 + R_2} R_1 C_1 \qquad \tau_2 = \frac{B_1}{K_1 + K_2}$$

$$\quad = \frac{R_2}{R_1 + R_2} \tau_1 \qquad\qquad = \frac{K_1}{K_1 + K_2} \tau_1$$

FIG. 7.25. An electrical and a mechanical circuit used to obtain phase lead.

The transfer function for these compensators is

$$\frac{E_o(s)}{E_{in}(s)} = \frac{Y(s)}{X(s)} = \frac{\tau_2}{\tau_1} \frac{1 + \tau_1 s}{1 + \tau_2 s} \qquad \tau_1 > \tau_2$$

Because of the τ_2/τ_1 factor introduced by these components, additional amplification equal to τ_1/τ_2 must be provided to maintain the original system gain. The resulting transfer function for series lead compensation is

$$\frac{1 + \tau_1 s}{1 + \tau_2 s} \qquad \tau_1 > \tau_2 \tag{7.57}$$

For steady-state operation the gain is one. Hence, lead compensation does not affect the steady-state operation of a system.

When lead compensation is inserted in series as shown in Fig. 7.24, the characteristic equation has the form

$$D_G D_H (1 + \tau_2 s) + N_G N_H (1 + \tau_1 s) = 0$$

or
$$D_G D_H \left(s + \frac{1}{\tau_2} \right) + \frac{\tau_1}{\tau_2} N_G N_H \left(s + \frac{1}{\tau_1} \right) = 0 \tag{7.58}$$

Thus, an $\times$ is added to the root-locus plot at $-1/\tau_2$ and a circle at $-1/\tau_1$. Because $\tau_1 > \tau_2$, then $1/\tau_1 < 1/\tau_2$. Thus, the $\times$ and $\odot$ are located as shown in Fig. 7.26 in which the $\odot$ is to the right of the $\times$.

When lead compensation is added to the system of Fig. 7.19, the

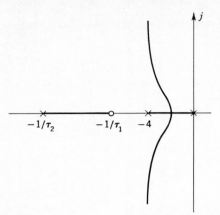

FIG. 7.26. The × at $-1/\tau_2$ and ⊙ at $-1/\tau_1$ introduced by a series lead compensator.

characteristic equation becomes

$$s(s + 4)\left(s + \frac{1}{\tau_2}\right) + \frac{\tau_1}{\tau_2} K\left(s + \frac{1}{\tau_1}\right) = 0$$

The resultant root-locus plot is shown in Fig. 7.26.

With the preceding method, it is necessary to construct a new root-locus plot for every different value of τ_1 or τ_2. A more general procedure for investigating the effect of lead compensation is obtained by rewriting Eq. (7.58) in the form

$$s\left(D_G D_H + \frac{\tau_1}{\tau_2} N_G N_H\right) + \frac{1}{\tau_2}(D_G D_H + N_G N_H) = 0 \qquad (7.59)$$

The circles are the roots of the characteristic equation $(D_G D_H + N_G N_H)$, and the ×'s are the roots of the characteristic equation when the gain is increased by the factor τ_1/τ_2 plus an additional × at the origin due to the s factor. A good indication of the effect of the ratio τ_1/τ_2 may usually be obtained by constructing the root-locus plot for a small ratio such as $\tau_1/\tau_2 = 4$ and for a large ratio such as $\tau_1/\tau_2 = 10$.

Let us now investigate the effect of adding series lead compensation to the system shown in Fig. 7.19 for the case in which $K = 20$. The characteristic equation for the basic system (i.e., the system without compensation) is

$$s(s + 4) + K = 0 \qquad (7.60)$$

The corresponding root-locus plot for the uncompensated, or basic, system is shown in Fig. 7.27a.

The characteristic equation for the compensated system is obtained by substituting $D_G D_H = s(s + 4)$ and $N_G N_H = K = 20$ in Eq. (7.59). Thus,

$$s\left[s(s + 4) + 20\frac{\tau_1}{\tau_2}\right] + \frac{1}{\tau_2}[s(s + 4) + 20] = 0 \qquad (7.61)$$

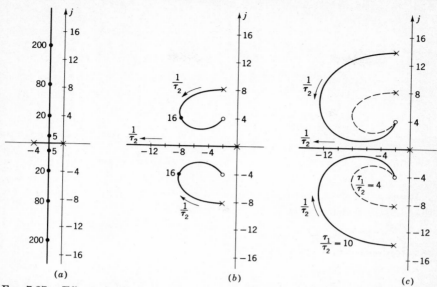

FIG. 7.27. Effect of adding series lead compensation to system of Fig. 7.19: (a) uncompensated system; (b) compensated system with $\tau_1/\tau_2 = 4$; (c) compensated system with $\tau_1/\tau_2 = 10$.

In Fig. 7.27b is shown the root-locus plot of this compensated system for $\tau_1/\tau_2 = 4$. Equation (7.61) shows that the $\odot$'s are obtained from the basic root-locus plot at $K = 20$. The $\times$'s are obtained from the basic root-locus plot at a gain of $20(\tau_1/\tau_2) = 80$ plus the one at the origin. Values of $1/\tau_2$ are indicated along this root-locus plot shown in Fig. 7.27b. For example, when $1/\tau_2 = 16$ then the roots of the characteristic equation are -4 and $-8 \pm j4$. Thus

$$s[s(s + 4) + 20(4)] + 16[s(s + 4) + 20] = (s + 4)(s^2 + 16s + 80)$$

In Fig. 7.27c the root-locus plot for $\tau_1/\tau_2 = 10$ is superimposed upon that for $\tau_1/\tau_2 = 4$. The $\odot$'s for this plot for $\tau_1/\tau_2 = 10$ are the same as those for $\tau_1/\tau_2 = 4$. The $\times$'s are obtained from the basic root-locus plot at a gain of $20(\tau_1/\tau_2) = 200$ plus the one at the origin. As is illustrated in Fig. 7.27c, for $\tau_1/\tau_2 = 10$ the effect of compensation is more pronounced then for $\tau_1/\tau_2 = 4$.

Lag Compensation. Both an electrical and a mechanical circuit used to provide lag compensation are shown in Fig. 7.28. The transfer function for these compensators is

$$\frac{E_o(s)}{E_{\text{in}}(s)} = \frac{Y(s)}{X(s)} = \frac{1 + \tau_2 s}{1 + \tau_1 s} \qquad \tau_1 > \tau_2 \qquad (7.62)$$

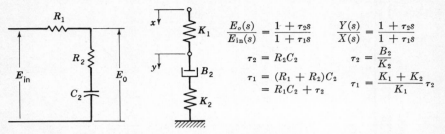

$$\frac{E_o(s)}{E_{in}(s)} = \frac{1 + \tau_2 s}{1 + \tau_1 s} \qquad \frac{Y(s)}{X(s)} = \frac{1 + \tau_2 s}{1 + \tau_1 s}$$

$$\tau_2 = R_2 C_2 \qquad \tau_2 = \frac{B_2}{K_2}$$

$$\tau_1 = (R_1 + R_2)C_2 \qquad \tau_1 = \frac{K_1 + K_2}{K_1} \tau_2$$
$$= R_1 C_2 + \tau_2$$

FIG. 7.28. An electrical and a mechanical circuit used to obtain phase lag.

When a lag compensator is placed in series as shown in Fig. 7.24, then the characteristic equation is

$$D_G D_H (1 + \tau_1 s) + N_G N_H (1 + \tau_2 s) = 0$$

or

$$D_G D_H \left(s + \frac{1}{\tau_1} \right) + \frac{\tau_2}{\tau_1} N_G N_H \left(s + \frac{1}{\tau_2} \right) = 0 \qquad (7.63)$$

Thus, lag compensation is seen to add a $\times$ to the root-locus plot at $-1/\tau_1$ and a $\odot$ at $-1/\tau_2$. Because $\tau_1 > \tau_2$, then the $\times$ is to the right of the $\odot$ as illustrated in Fig. 7.29.

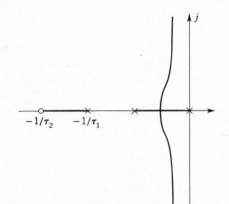

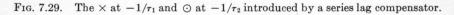

FIG. 7.29. The $\times$ at $-1/\tau_1$ and $\odot$ at $-1/\tau_2$ introduced by a series lag compensator.

When lag compensation is added to the system of Fig. 7.19, the characteristic equation becomes

$$s(s + 4) \left(s + \frac{1}{\tau_1} \right) + \frac{\tau_2}{\tau_1} K \left(s + \frac{1}{\tau_2} \right) = 0$$

The corresponding root-locus plot is shown in Fig. 7.29.

A more general procedure for analyzing the effect of lag compensation is obtained by rewriting Eq. (7.63) in the form

$$s\left(D_G D_H + \frac{N_G N_H}{\tau_1/\tau_2}\right) + \frac{1}{\tau_1}(D_G D_H + N_G N_H) = 0 \qquad (7.64)$$

The $\odot$'s are the roots of the uncompensated system $(D_G D_H + N_G N_H)$, and the $\times$'s are the roots of the characteristic equation when the gain is changed by the factor $1/(\tau_1/\tau_2)$ plus the $\times$ at the origin due to the s factor. The effect of the ratio τ_1/τ_2 may be ascertained by constructing the root-locus plot for a small ratio such as $\tau_1/\tau_2 = 4$ and for a large ratio such as $\tau_1/\tau_2 = 10$.

Let us now investigate the effect of adding series lag compensation to the system shown in Fig. 7.19 when $K = 20$. This is the same system which was just analyzed with respect to lead compensation. The characteristic equation for the uncompensated, or basic, system is given by Eq. (7.60), and the corresponding root-locus plot is shown in Fig. 7.30a.

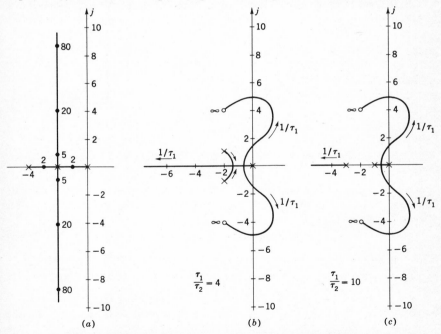

(a)   (b)   (c)

FIG. 7.30. Effect of adding series lag compensation to system of Fig. 7.19: (a) uncompensated system; (b) compensated system with $\tau_1/\tau_2 = 4$; (c) compensated system with $\tau_1/\tau_2 = 10$.

The characteristic equation for the compensated system is

$$s\left[s(s + 4) + \frac{20}{\tau_1/\tau_2}\right] + \frac{1}{\tau_1}[s(s + 4) + 20] = 0 \qquad (7.65)$$

The root-locus plot for $\tau_1/\tau_2 = 4$ is shown in Fig. 7.30b. It is to be noted that the circles are obtained from the basic root-locus plot (Fig. 7.30a) at $K = 20$, and the ×'s are obtained from the basic root-locus plot at the gain $20/(\tau_1/\tau_2) = 5$ plus the one at the origin. The arrows indicate increasing values of $1/\tau_1$.

The root-locus plot for $\tau_1/\tau_2 = 10$ is shown in Fig. 7.30c. The circles for this $\tau_1/\tau_2 = 10$ plot are the same as those for the $\tau_1/\tau_2 = 4$ plot. The ×'s are obtained from the basic plot at the gain $20/(\tau_1/\tau_2) = 2$ plus the one at the origin.

Figure 7.30b and c shows that depending on the value of τ_1 it is possible to have the system become unstable when lag compensation is employed. Comparison of Figs. 7.27 and 7.30 shows that lead compensation is better than lag compensation for this particular system. For other systems, lag compensation may give better results than lead.

7.8 Internal Feedback. By internal feedback is meant a feedback loop within the main loop. In Fig. 7.31a is shown a basic feedback con-

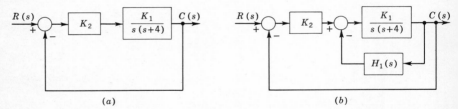

(a)   *(b)*

Fig. 7.31.   (a) Basic feedback control system; (b) system with internal feedback.

trol system and in Fig. 7.31b is shown the system with an internal feedback loop about the element $K_1/s(s + 4)$. The characteristic equation for the basic system is

$$s(s + 4) + K_1 K_2 = 0 \tag{7.66}$$

The corresponding root-locus plot is shown in Fig. 7.32a.

The characteristic equation for the system with internal feedback is

$$[s(s + 4) + K_1 K_2] + K_1 H_1(s) = 0$$
or $$D_{H_1}[s(s + 4) + K_1 K_2] + K_1 N_{H_1}(s) = 0 \tag{7.67}$$

where $H_1(s) = N_{H_1}/D_{H_1}$. This characteristic equation shows that $\odot$'s are added to the root-locus plot at the roots of N_{H_1} and ×'s are added at roots of D_{H_1}. Derivative action of the form $H_1(s) = \beta s$ is commonly used as the internal feedback element.

ILLUSTRATIVE EXAMPLE 1.   Suppose that the internal feedback element for the system of Fig. 7.31b is $H_1(s) = \beta s$. Determine the value of β

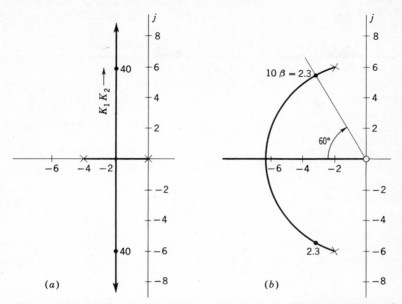

FIG. 7.32. (a) Root-locus plot for basic system shown in Fig. 7.31a; (b) root-locus plot for system with internal feedback shown in Fig. 7.31b.

such that the characteristic equation has a pair of complex conjugate roots in which $\zeta = 0.5$. The value of K_1 is 10 and K_2 is 4.

SOLUTION. The characteristic equation is

$$[s(s + 4) + (10)(4)] + 10\beta s = 0$$

or $$[s - (-2 - j6)][s - (-2 + j6)] + 10\beta s = 0 \qquad (7.68)$$

The corresponding root-locus plot in which $K = 10\beta$ is shown in Fig. 7.32b. At $\zeta = 0.5$, then $s = -3.33 + j5.66$. Substituting this value into the characteristic equation and solving for β yields $\beta = 0.23$.

A comparison of the root-locus plot given in Fig. 7.15 with that of Fig. 7.1 shows that a zero of $N_G N_H$ (that is a ⊙) has the effect of pulling the locus to the left. For large values of K the system of Fig. 7.1 would have a small damping ratio and would thus exhibit a very oscillatory type of response. For the system of Fig. 7.15, large values of K would result in negative real roots and thus a damped exponential type of response. In general, the addition of a ⊙ in the left half plane tends to make the system more stable. On the other hand, adding an × in the left half plane tends to push the root-locus plot to the right and thus decrease stability.

Problems

7.1 The root-locus plot for the system of Fig. 7.1a is given in Fig. 7.1b. Determine the response equation $c(t)$ for the case in which $r(t)$ is a unit step function and $K = 8$. All the initial conditions are zero.

7.2 The root-locus plot for the system of Fig. 7.2a is given in Fig. 7.2b. Determine the response $c(t)$ for the case in which $r(t)$ is a unit impulse and $K = 17$. All the initial conditions are zero.

7.3 Sketch the root-locus plot for the system shown in Fig. P7.3. Determine the value K to yield a damping ratio of 0.5.

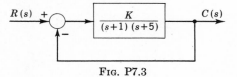

$$R(s) \xrightarrow{+} \bigcirc \xrightarrow{} \boxed{\frac{K}{(s+1)(s+5)}} \xrightarrow{} C(s)$$

FIG. P7.3

7.4 The block diagram and corresponding root-locus plot for a control system are shown in Fig. P7.4.

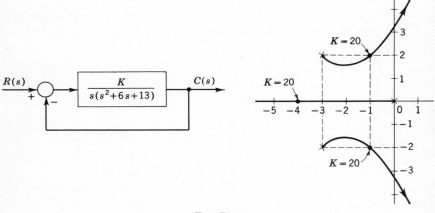

FIG. P7.4

(a) Determine the differential equation relating the output $c(t)$ and the input $r(t)$.

(b) Determine the response $c(t)$ for the case in which all of the initial conditions are zero, $K = 20$, and the input excitation $r(t)$ is a unit impulse.

(c) Use Routh's criterion to determine the value of the gain K at which the system becomes unstable.

7.5 The block diagram for a control system is shown in Fig. P7.5. The controller is represented by the block $G_c(s)$. Determine the characteristic equation, and then sketch the corresponding root-locus plot for each of the following cases.

(a) Proportional controller, $G_c(s) = K_1$ and $H(s) = 1$.

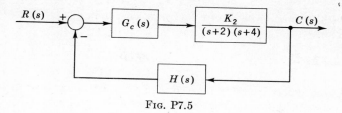

FIG. P7.5

(b) Integral controller, $G_c(s) = K_1/s$ and $H(s) = 1$.
(c) Proportional plus integral controller, $G_c(s) = K_1(1 + 1/s)$ and $H(s) = 1$.
(d) Proportional plus rate feedback, $G_c(s) = K_1$ and $H(s) = K_3(1 + s)$.

7.6 Sketch the root-locus plot for each of the systems shown in Fig. P7.6.

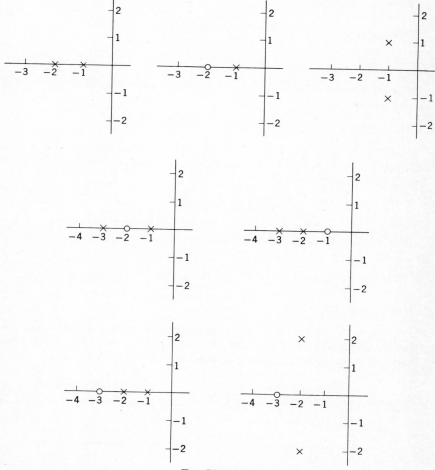

FIG. P7.6

7.7 Sketch the root-locus plot for the system shown in Fig. P7.7 for each of the following cases:

(a) $G_1(s) = \dfrac{K_1}{s}$ (b) $G_1(s) = \dfrac{K_1}{s+4}$

For each case, determine the value of $K_1 K_2 K_3$ to yield a damping ratio of 0.5 for the dominant roots (i.e., the ones located nearest the imaginary axis).

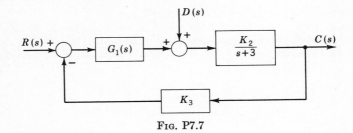

FIG. P7.7

7.8 Sketch the root-locus plot for the system shown in Fig. P7.8 for each of the following cases:

(a) $H(s) = 1$ (b) $H(s) = s + 1$

For each case, determine the value of K to yield a damping ratio of 0.5 for the dominant roots. Comment on the effect of adding derivative action in the feedback path (i.e., case b).

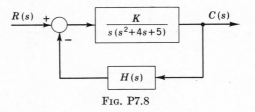

FIG. P7.8

7.9 Sketch the root-locus plot for each of the two systems shown in Fig. P7.9. Determine the value of K at which each system becomes unstable. Comment on the effect of adding an integrating element as is done in case b.

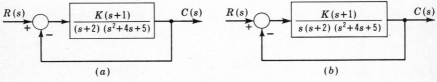

FIG. P7.9

7.10 The block diagram and root-locus plot for a control system are shown in Fig. P7.10. Repeated roots occur at $s = -6$.

(a) Determine the value of the gain K such that the characteristic equation has repeated roots.

(b) For the case in which the characteristic equation has repeated roots, determine the response $c(t)$ when $r(t)$ is a unit impulse and all the initial conditions are zero.

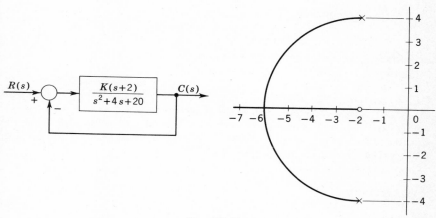

$$\frac{K(s+2)}{s^2+4s+20}$$

Fɪɢ. P7.10

7.11 Sketch the root-locus plot for each of the following characteristic equations:

(a) $s(s^2 + 8s + 25) + K = 0$ (b) $s(s^2 + 8s + 25) + K(s + 2) = 0$
(c) $s(s^2 + 8s + 25) + K(s + 2)(s + 4) = 0$

7.12 Sketch the root-locus plot for each of the following characteristic equations:

(a) $s(s + 2) + K(s + 4) = 0$ (b) $s^2(s + 2) + K(s + 4) = 0$
(c) $(s^2 + 8s + 20) + K(s + 2) = 0$ (d) $s(s^2 + 8s + 20) + K = 0$

7.13 The characteristic equation for Fig. 7.2 is given by Eq. (7.6). If a zero is added to the system, the characteristic equation becomes

$$s(s + 4)(s + 6) + (s + 2)K = 0$$

Sketch the root-locus plot for this new system.

7.14 Sketch the root-locus plot for each of the characteristic equations given below:

(a) $s^2(s + 8) + K = 0$ (b) $s^2(s + 8) + (s + 2)K = 0$

7.15 The root locus plot for the system whose characteristic equation is $s(s + 2) + K(s + 4) = 0$ is shown in Fig. 7.18. When $K = 6$, the roots are

$-4 \pm j \sqrt{8}$. Hence, for $K = 6$, the factored form of the characteristic equation is

$$s(s + 2) + 6(s + 4) = s^2 + 8s + 24 = (s + 4 + j\sqrt{8})(s + 4 - j\sqrt{8})$$

To investigate the effect of changing the parameter 4, the term $s + 4$ may be written in the form $s + 4 + \Delta$. Thus, the new characteristic equation to be investigated is

$$s(s + 2) + 6(s + 4 + \Delta) = [s(s + 2) + 6(s + 4)] + 6\Delta$$
$$= (s^2 + 8s + 24) + 6\Delta$$

    (*a*) Sketch the root locus plot for positive Δ.
    (*b*) Sketch the root locus plot for negative Δ.

7.16 Same as Prob. 7.15 except vary the parameter 2 instead of 4.

7.17 The root-locus plot for a unity feedback control system is shown in Fig. P7.17. When the gain K is 4 the roots are $-2 + j2$, $-2 - j2$, and -4. For a gain $K = 4$, investigate the effect of varying the parameter 20 in the transfer function $G(s) = K/s(s^2 + 8s + 20)$. Sketch the resulting loci for both positive and negative values of Δ.

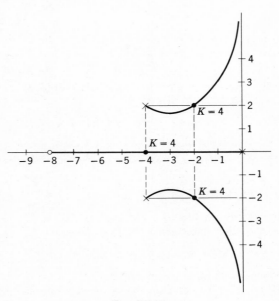

FIG. P7.17

7.18 Determine the response of the system of Prob. 7.17 to a unit impulse $u_1(t)$ for the case in which all of the initial conditions are zero ($K = 4$ and $\Delta = 0$).

7.19 The transfer function for a unity feedback control system is

$$G(s) = \frac{K}{s^2 + 2\zeta\omega_n s + \omega_n{}^2} = \frac{15}{s^2 + 4s + 5}$$

The roots of the characteristic equation are $r_{1,2} = -2 \pm j4$. Determine the equation for the change Δr_1 in the root r_1 due to a change in (a) K, (b) ω_n, and (c) ζ.

7.20 The transfer function for a unity feedback control system is $G(s) = 100/s^2$. To achieve satisfactory dynamic behavior a series lead compensator is added to the system. Sketch the resulting root-locus plot for

(a) $\tau_1/\tau_2 = 4$ (b) $\tau_1/\tau_2 = 10$

7.21 The characteristic equation for a feedback control system is

$$(s + 10)(s^2 + 8s + 25) + 1{,}000 = 0$$

The root-locus plot for this system is shown in Fig. P7.21.

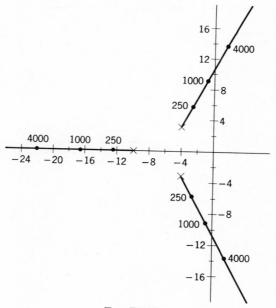

Fig. P7.21

(a) Determine the characteristic equation for series lead compensation and then sketch the resulting root-locus plot for $\tau_1/\tau_2 = 4$.

(b) Same as part (a) except use lag compensation.

7.22 The block diagram for a control system is shown in Fig. P7.22. For $K = 8$, sketch the resulting root-locus plot when using a lag compensator in which $\tau_1/\tau_2 = 4$.

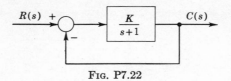

FIG. P7.22

7.23 In Fig. P7.23 is shown a feedback control system with internal feedback. Construct the root-locus plot for the basic system without the internal feedback ($\beta = 0$), and then construct the root-locus plot for the modified system in which β is the variable parameter, $K_1 = 2$, and $K_2 = 5$.

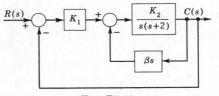

FIG. P7.23

8

Analog computers

The use of computers has played a major role in the recent advances in the design of automatic control systems. These computers may be divided into two types, analog computers[1-3] and digital computers.[4,5]

An analog computer is one in which the equation describing the operation of the computer is analogous to that for the actual system. The most commonly used analog computer is the electronic analog computer, in which voltages at various places within the computer are proportional to the variable terms in the actual system. As is shown in this chapter, the operation of a control system can be simulated by the use of an analog computer.

Basically a digital computer can only add and subtract. Thus it is necessary to reduce all problems to rather elementary mathematical manipulations. This process is called programming. The programming of a problem for solution on a digital computer makes extensive use of the methods of "numerical analysis" to convert the problem to the numerical operations which the computer can perform. It may require weeks or even months to program a problem for a computer, which in turn completes the solution in a few minutes or seconds. A digital computer has been referred to as an "energetic moron" in that it is capable of performing thousands of simple additions and subtractions in a second. A digital computer must store information for use in later computations. This is usually done by means of a magnetic drum, which acts as a memory device.

[1] G. A. Korn and T. M. Korn, "Electronic Analog Computers," 2d ed., McGraw-Hill Book Company, New York, 1956.

[2] A. S. Jackson, "Analog Computation," McGraw-Hill Book Company, New York, 1960.

[3] G. W. Smith and R. C. Wood, "Principles of Analog Computation," McGraw-Hill Book Company, New York, 1959.

[4] N. R. Scott, "Analog and Digital Computer Technology," McGraw-Hill Book Company, New York, 1960.

[5] R. S. Ledley, "Digital Computer and Control Engineering," McGraw-Hill Book Company, New York, 1960.

The input to a digital computer consists of numbers and instructions for the operation of the machine on these numbers. These numbers and instructions may be fed into the machine by various methods such as punched cards, tape, typewriter, etc.

Because of the ability of both digital and analog computers to solve complicated mathematical equations almost instantaneously, they are often incorporated as part of control systems to compute desired information. This information may then be used immediately to improve the control of the particular system. For example, in an inertial guidance system, the output of three mutually perpendicular accelerometers is fed into a computer, which in turn calculates the position of the vehicle. Thus, the output of this computer is the actual position of the vehicle, which is compared with the desired position to yield an error signal for actuating the steering mechanism.

The electronic analog computer is a very powerful tool for investigating the performance of control systems. For more complex systems, the advantages of the analog computer become more apparent. Analog computers are used for many purposes besides that of investigating linear and nonlinear control systems. For example, they are used to solve nonlinear differential equations, partial differential equations, systems of differential or partial differential equations, matrix and eigenvalue problems, operational research problems, etc. New applications and uses for this versatile computing device are continually being discovered.

This chapter is primarily concerned with the use of these computers for simulating control systems. For this purpose, the equation describing the operation of the analog computer is analogous to that which represents the actual physical system. The variable quantities of the actual system such as the output, input, error, etc., are represented by voltages at various places within the analog computer. Permanent records of these voltages may be obtained by using recording equipment. By using potentiometers or variable capacitors to vary the resistance or capacitance at various places within the computer, the effect upon system performance of changing the corresponding parameters in the actual system (e.g., gain, time constants, damping ratio, etc.) may be determined immediately.

8.1 Computer Operations. To solve any linear differential equation with constant coefficients, it is necessary only to make use of the processes of integration, summation, and multiplication by a constant. This is illustrated by the block diagram of Fig. 8.1 for the equation

$$M\ddot{y} + B\dot{y} + Ky = f(t) \tag{8.1}$$

To set up the block-diagram representation for a differential equation,

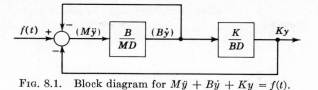

FIG. 8.1. Block diagram for $M\ddot{y} + B\dot{y} + Ky = f(t)$.

first solve for the highest-order differential appearing in the original equation. The highest-order term appearing in Eq. (8.1) is $M\ddot{y}$. Solving Eq. (8.1) for $M\ddot{y}$ yields

$$M\ddot{y} = f(t) - B\dot{y} - Ky \tag{8.2}$$

Successive integration of the highest-order differential and multiplication by appropriate constants yields the other lower-order terms. That is,

$$\frac{B/M}{D}(M\ddot{y}) = B\dot{y}$$
$$\frac{K/B}{D}(B\dot{y}) = Ky \tag{8.3}$$

Each term on the right-hand side of Eq. (8.2) goes into the summer of Fig. 8.1, so that the output of the summer is proportional to the acceleration. Successive integration of this acceleration yields the velocity and displacement.

The heart of the electronic analog computer is the operational amplifier, which is a very-high-gain dc amplifier. This device may be used as an integrator, summer, or multiplier. The particular mathematical operation depends upon the particular network of resistors and capacitors which are placed around it.

In Fig. 8.2 is shown the schematic representation of an operational

FIG. 8.2. Schematic representation for an operational amplifier.

amplifier. The input voltage is e_i, the output is e_2, and the amplification is $-A$. Thus

$$e_2 = -Ae_i \tag{8.4}$$

The reason for the minus sign is that the amplifier reverses the phase of the input. For most operational amplifiers, the value of A is very large. Values of A may range from 100×10^3 to 100×10^6.

Multiplication by a Constant. By feeding the input voltage through a resistor R_1 and by putting a resistor R_2 in parallel with the amplifier as shown in Fig. 8.3, a circuit for multiplication by a constant is obtained.

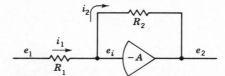

FIG. 8.3. Operational amplifier circuit for multiplying by a constant.

Because the input grid of the amplifier draws little or no current (a typical value is 10^{-9} amp), then

$$i_1 \approx i_2 \tag{8.5}$$

The values of i_1 and i_2 are

$$i_1 = \frac{e_1 - e_i}{R_1} \qquad i_2 = \frac{e_i - e_2}{R_2} \tag{8.6}$$

Equating i_1 and i_2 yields

$$\frac{e_1 - e_i}{R_1} = \frac{e_i - e_2}{R_2} \tag{8.7}$$

Usually e_2 is less than 100 volts; so for very large values of A, it follows from Eq. (8.4) that $e_i = -e_2/A \approx 0$. The substitution of $e_i \approx 0$ into Eq. (8.7) gives

$$e_2 = -\frac{R_2}{R_1} e_1 \tag{8.8}$$

The value of the multiplication constant is $-R_2/R_1$. When $R_2 = R_1$, the constant is -1, which means simply that the phase of the input signal has been inverted.

Integration. By replacing the resistor R_2 of Fig. 8.3 by a capacitor as shown in Fig. 8.4, then an integrating circuit is obtained. The current

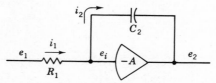

FIG. 8.4. Operational amplifier circuit for integrating.

i_2 flowing through this capacitor is

$$i_2 = C_2 D(e_i - e_2) \tag{8.9}$$

By equating i_1 and i_2 as before, it follows that

$$\frac{e_1 - e_i}{R_1} = C_2 D(e_i - e_2) \tag{8.10}$$

Because $e_i \approx 0$, the preceding expression reduces to

$$e_2 = \frac{-e_1}{R_1 C_2 D} = \frac{-1}{R_1 C_2} \int_0^t e_1 \, dt + e_2(0) \tag{8.11}$$

where $e_2(0)$ is the value of e_2 when $t = 0$. In addition to integration, the circuit of Fig. 8.4 also multiplies by the constant $-1/R_1 C_2$.

Summation. The effect of summation is obtained by placing the desired quantities to be added in parallel at the input to the computer circuit. The output will then be the summation of the effect due to each individual input. A general summing circuit is shown in Fig. 8.5a, and

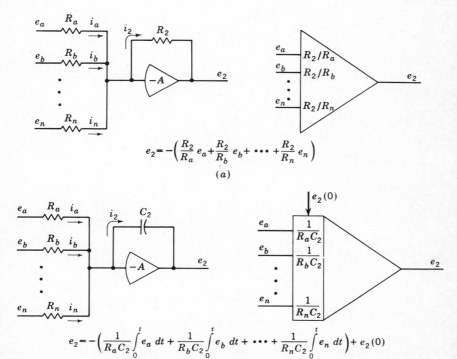

$$e_2 = -\left(\frac{R_2}{R_a} e_a + \frac{R_2}{R_b} e_b + \cdots + \frac{R_2}{R_n} e_n \right)$$

(a)

$$e_2 = -\left(\frac{1}{R_a C_2} \int_0^t e_a \, dt + \frac{1}{R_b C_2} \int_0^t e_b \, dt + \cdots + \frac{1}{R_n C_2} \int_0^t e_n \, dt \right) + e_2(0)$$

(b)

FIG. 8.5. General summing circuits.

a circuit to integrate more than one quantity is shown in Fig. 8.5b. A simplified notation for these various computer elements is also shown in Fig. 8.5a and b. This schematic notation saves much effort in drawing the computer diagram for a circuit.

8.2 Direct Programming. Let it be desired to determine the computer diagram for solving the following equation:

$$\ddot{y} + 8\dot{y} + 2y = f(t) \tag{8.12}$$

The initial conditions are $y(0) = 2$ ft and $\dot{y}(0) = 5$ ft/sec. The expected maximum values are $y_m = 5$ ft, $\dot{y}_m = 10$ ft/sec, $\ddot{y}_m = 20$ ft/sec², and $f(t)_m = 20$ lb. Solving Eq. (8.12) for the highest-order derivative yields

$$\ddot{y} = f(t) - 8\dot{y} - 2y \tag{8.13}$$

The general computer diagram for Eq. (8.13) is shown in Fig. 8.6a.

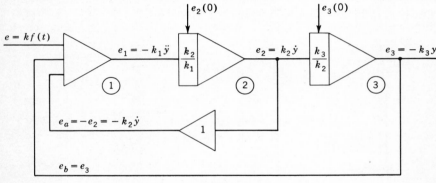

(a)

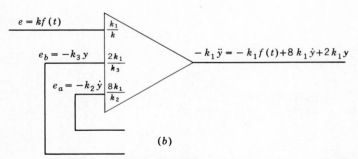

(b)

FIG. 8.6.   Computer diagram for $\ddot{y} = f(t) - 8\dot{y} - 2y$.

Because an amplifier reverses the sign from the input to the output, the sign in front of each scale factor alternates in going from one amplifier to the next. As shown in Fig. 8.6a, the output of the first amplifier is

$e_1 = -k_1\ddot{y}$, the output of the second is $e_2 = k_2\dot{y}$, and the output of the third is $e_3 = -k_3 y$. A more detailed diagram of the first amplifier is shown in Fig. 8.6b. This first amplifier yields the highest order derivative. The remaining amplifiers integrate to yield lower-order derivates.

The voltage relationship for the first amplifier is

$$e_1 = -\frac{R_2}{R} e - \frac{R_2}{R_a} e_a - \frac{R_2}{R_b} e_b \tag{8.14}$$

Multiplying through Eq. (8.13) by $-k_1$ gives

$$-k_1 \ddot{y} = -k_1 f(t) + 8k_1 \dot{y} + 2k_1 y$$

This may be written in the form

$$-k_1 \ddot{y} = -\frac{k_1}{k} [kf(t)] - \frac{8k_1}{k_2} (-k_2 \dot{y}) - \frac{2k_1}{k_3} (-k_3 y) \tag{8.15}$$

Equation (8.14) is the voltage relationship for the amplifier, and Eq. (8.15) is the corresponding physical relationship.

Termwise comparison of Eqs. (8.14) and (8.15) shows that to have the voltage relationships $e_1 = -k_1\ddot{y}, e = kf(t), e_a = -k_2\dot{y} = -e_2, e_b = -k_3 y = e_3$, then the following relationships must hold:

$$\frac{R_2}{R} = \frac{k_1}{k} \qquad \frac{R_2}{R_a} = \frac{8k_1}{k_2} \qquad \frac{R_2}{R_b} = \frac{2k_1}{k_3}$$

Because the output of the second amplifier is $e_2 = k_2\dot{y}$, it is necessary to use a sign changer to obtain $e_a = -k_2\dot{y}$. The voltage $e_3 = -k_3 y$ may be fed back directly.

The voltage relationship for the second amplifier, which is an integrator, is

$$e_2 = \frac{-1}{(R_1 C_2)_2} \int_0^t e_1 \, dt + e_2(0)$$

where $(R_1 C_2)_2$ is the product of the resistance and capacitance for amplifier 2. Substitution of $e_1 = -k_1\ddot{y}$ into the preceding expression gives

$$e_2 = \frac{k_1}{(R_1 C_2)_2} \int_0^t \ddot{y} \, dt + e_2(0) \tag{8.16}$$

Because the integral of acceleration is velocity, it follows that

$$\dot{y} = \int_0^t \ddot{y} \, dt + \dot{y}(0)$$

Multiplication of the preceding expression by k_2 yields

$$k_2\dot{y} = k_2 \int_0^t \ddot{y} \, dt + k_2\dot{y}(0) \tag{8.17}$$

Equation (8.16) is the voltage relationship for the amplifier, and Eq. (8.17) is the corresponding physical relationship. It is desired to have

e_2 equal to $k_2\dot{y}$. This is accomplished by equating the right-hand sides of Eqs. (8.16) and (8.17); thus

$$\frac{k_1}{(R_1C_2)_2} \int_0^t \ddot{y} \, dt + e_2(0) = k_2 \int_0^t \ddot{y} \, dt + k_2\dot{y}(0)$$

Because corresponding terms in the preceding expression are equal, the following relationships must hold:

$$\frac{1}{(R_1C_2)_2} = \frac{k_2}{k_1} \qquad \text{and} \qquad e_2(0) = k_2\dot{y}(0) \tag{8.18}$$

Each integrator may be initially biased by a dc voltage to give the effect of initial conditions, as is represented diagrammatically at the top of each integrator in Fig. 8.6a. In practice, the initial condition is obtained by placing a source of constant potential such as a battery of potential $e_2(0)$ in parallel with the capacitor, as is shown in Fig. 8.7. For $t < 0$,

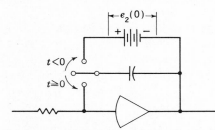

Fig. 8.7. Circuit for obtaining initial conditions.

the switch is up so that the battery can charge the capacitor to the desired initial value. At $t = 0$, the switch moves down to disconnect the battery so that the integrator circuit functions as previously discussed.

The voltage equation for the third amplifier circuit is

$$e_3 = \frac{-1}{(R_1C_2)_3} \int_0^t e_2 \, dt + e_3(0) = \frac{-k_2}{(R_1C_2)_3} \int_0^t \dot{y} \, dt + e_3(0) \tag{8.19}$$

Because the integral of velocity is displacement,

$$y = \int_0^t \dot{y} \, dt + y(0) \tag{8.20}$$

Multiplication of the preceding expression by $-k_3$ gives

$$-k_3 y = -k_3 \int_0^t \dot{y} \, dt - k_3 y(0) \tag{8.21}$$

To have $e_3 = -k_3 y$, then equating the right-hand sides of Eqs. (8.19) and (8.21) shows that

$$\frac{1}{(R_1C_2)_3} = \frac{k_3}{k_2} \qquad \text{and} \qquad e_3(0) = -k_3 y(0) \tag{8.22}$$

The voltage equation for the amplifier which changes the sign of e_2 is

$$e_a = -\frac{R_2}{R_1} e_2 = \frac{-R_2}{R_1} k_2 \dot{y} \qquad (8.23)$$

The desired relationship for this amplifier is

$$e_a = -k_2 \dot{y} \qquad (8.24)$$

Thus it follows from Eqs. (8.23) and (8.24) that

$$\frac{R_2}{R_1} = \frac{k_2}{k_2} = 1 \qquad (8.25)$$

There is never any need to apply an initial voltage $e(0)$ to account for initial conditions when an amplifier is used to multiply by a constant. Only integration requires initial conditions.

Scale Factors. Because the voltages e, e_1, e_2, and e_3 correspond to values of quantities in the physical system $[e = kf(t)$, $e_1 = -k_1\ddot{y}$, $e_2 = k_2\dot{y}$, $e_3 = -k_3y]$, it is necessary to select the value of the scale factors k, k_1, k_2, and k_3 in order to interpret the results. For many computers, the voltages e, e_1, e_2, and e_3 should be limited to within 100 volts. Thus, the scale factor may be obtained from the equation

$$\text{Scale factor} = \frac{100}{\text{maximum value of parameter}} \qquad (8.26)$$

From the originally given information, the scale factors are computed as follows:

$$
\begin{aligned}
k &= \frac{100}{f(t)_m} = \frac{100}{20} = 5 \text{ volts/lb} \\
k_1 &= \frac{100}{\ddot{y}_m} = \frac{100}{20} = 5 \text{ volts/(ft)(sec}^2) \\
k_2 &= \frac{100}{\dot{y}_m} = \frac{100}{10} = 10 \text{ volts/(ft)(sec)} \\
k_3 &= \frac{100}{y_m} = \frac{100}{5} = 20 \text{ volts/ft}
\end{aligned}
\qquad (8.27)
$$

Substitution of the preceding results into Fig. 8.6a and b yields the final scaled computer diagram shown in Fig. 8.8a, where the values of the initial voltages $e_2(0)$ and $e_3(0)$ are computed as follows:

$$
\begin{aligned}
e_2(0) &= k_2\dot{y}(0) = 10(5) = 50 \text{ volts} \\
e_3(0) &= -k_3y(0) = -20(2) = -40 \text{ volts}
\end{aligned}
$$

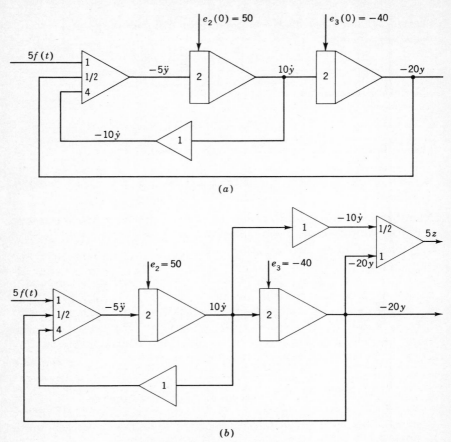

Fig. 8.8.   Final scaled computer diagram.

The general procedure for setting up an electronic analog computer to solve a differential equation of order n may be summarized as follows.

1.   Solve the differential equation for the highest order derivative. For example,

$$\dddot{y} = f(t) - C_2\ddot{y} - C_3\dot{y} - C_4y$$

2.   The output of the first amplifier is $e_1 = -k_1\dddot{y}$. The outputs for the successive integrators are $e_2 = k_2\ddot{y}$, $e_3 = -k_3\dot{y}$, and $e_4 = k_4y$. Multiply through the preceding equation by $-k_1$, and then express it in the form

$$-k_1\dddot{y} = -\frac{k_1}{k}[kf(t)] + C_2\frac{k_1}{k_2}[k_2\ddot{y}] + C_3\frac{k_1}{k_3}[k_3\dot{y}] + C_4\frac{k_1}{k_4}[k_4y] \quad (8.28)$$

Because an amplifier reverses sign, the input to the first amplifier should be the negative of the right-hand side of the preceding expression. That is,

$$\frac{k_1}{k}\,[kf(t)] + C_2\,\frac{k_1}{k_2}\,[-k_2\ddot{y}] + C_3\,\frac{k_1}{k_3}\,[-k_3\dot{y}] + C_4\,\frac{k_1}{k_4}\,[-k_4y] \qquad (8.29)$$

The coefficients in front of the brackets are the ratio of resistors (i.e., $R_2/R_a, R_2/R_b, \ldots, R_2/R_n$) to be used at the input to the first amplifier. When the sign of the term in the computer is opposite to that of the corresponding term in the brackets (for example, $e_2 = k_2\ddot{y}$ and $e_4 = k_4y$), a sign changer must be inserted to multiply the feedback sign by -1.

3. The value of $1/R_1C_2$ for each integrator is equal to the ratio of the scale factor for the output voltage term to that for the input [for example $1/(R_1C_2)_2 = k_2/k_1,\ 1/(R_1C_2)_3 = k_3/k_2,\ \ldots$].

In accordance with Eq. (8.26), the value of each scale factor is seen to depend on the maximum value of the corresponding parameter. For most systems being studied, there is usually sufficient information available to make a reasonable estimate of the maximum value of each term. If an error is made in predicting the maximum value of a term, then the maximum value of the voltage corresponding to that term will not be 100 volts. Such a situation is easily detected and is corrected as follows: Suppose that the maximum value of the voltage e_1 is found to be 50 volts rather than 100 volts. The original scale factor was $k_1 = 5$, so that the maximum value of $\ddot{y}$ is now found to be $\ddot{y}_m = e_{1m}/k_1 = {}^{50}\!/_5 = 10$ ft/sec^2 rather than 20 ft/sec^2. Thus, the value of k_1 should be $k_1 = {}^{100}\!/_{10} = 10$ rather than 5. It is an easy matter to revise the computer diagram using $k_1 = 10$ so that the maximum value of the voltage e_1 will be 100 volts. It should be noticed that the original solution with $k_1 = 5$ is correct. The reason for revising the computer diagram is to obtain better accuracy by using the full range of 100 volts rather than 50 volts.

Consider now the differential equation

$$Z = \frac{(D + 4)f(t)}{D^2 + 8D + 2}$$

This may be expressed in the form

$$Z = (D + 4)y = \dot{y} + 4y$$

where

$$y = \frac{f(t)}{D^2 + 8D + 2}$$

The differential equation for y is the same as Eq. (8.12) and the corresponding computer diagram is shown in Fig. 8.8a. In Fig. 8.8b is shown the modified computer diagram for the case in which $Z_m = 20$ and thus the output is $5Z = 5(\dot{y} + 4y)$. When the initial conditions are given in terms of Z, it is necessary to convert them to y in order to obtain the computer diagram for y. Equations relating y and $\dot{y}$ to Z and $\dot{Z}$ are obtained from the original equation for the system as follows:

$$Z = \dot{y} + 4y$$
$$\dot{Z} = \ddot{y} + 4\dot{y} = [-8\dot{y} - 2y + f(t)] + 4\dot{y}$$
$$= -4\dot{y} - 2y + f(t)$$

Solving for y and $\dot{y}$ in terms of Z and $\dot{Z}$ gives

$$y = \frac{\dot{Z} + 4Z - f(t)}{14}$$

$$\dot{y} = -\frac{2\dot{Z} + Z - 2f(t)}{7}$$

8.3 Time Scale. For many problems, it is desired that the speed at which the analog computer solves the problem be different from the speed at which the phenomena actually occur. For example, various phenomena of astronomy require years; so obviously it is desirable to increase the speed at which such problems are solved on the computer. For other phenomena which take place very rapidly, it is necessary to slow down the speed at which such problems are simulated by the computer. By letting t represent the time at which a phenomenon actually occurs and the term τ represent the time required for this phenomenon to occur on the computer, $\tau = at$ relates the actual time t to the computer or machine time τ. For $a < 1$ the phenomenon occurs faster in the computer than it does in nature. For example, if $a = 0.1$, something which requires 10 sec actually to complete is completed by the computer in $\tau = 0.1t = 0.1 \times 10 = 1$ sec. Similarly, if $a > 1$, the phenomenon is slowed down by the computer.

ILLUSTRATIVE EXAMPLE 1. Let it be desired to slow down the computer solution of Eq. (8.12) by a factor of 5. The first step in the solution of this problem is to transform the original equation from a function of actual time t to a function of machine time τ. This is accomplished by noting that

$$\tau = at \tag{8.30}$$

and

$$\frac{d\tau}{dt} = a \tag{8.31}$$

Thus

$$\dot{y} = \frac{dy}{dt} = \frac{d\tau}{dt}\frac{dy}{d\tau} = a\frac{dy}{d\tau}$$

$$\ddot{y} = \frac{d^2y}{dt^2} = \frac{d}{dt}\left(\frac{dy}{dt}\right) = \frac{d\tau}{dt}\frac{d}{d\tau}\left(a\frac{dy}{d\tau}\right) = a^2\frac{d^2y}{d\tau^2} \tag{8.32}$$

Similarly, it may be shown that in general

$$\frac{d^n y}{dt^n} = a^n \frac{d^n y}{d\tau^n} \tag{8.33}$$

Application of the preceding rules to convert the original time expression given by Eq. (8.12) from a function of t to a function of τ gives

$$a^2 \frac{d^2 y}{d\tau^2} + 8a \frac{dy}{d\tau} + 2y = f\left(\frac{\tau}{a}\right) \tag{8.34}$$

where $f(\tau/a)$ is obtained by substitution of τ/a for t in the original function $f(t)$. Because of the change of variable, the term y in Eq. (8.34) is now a function of τ rather than t. To slow down the solution by a factor of 5, the value of a is 5 so that Eq. (8.34) becomes

$$25 \frac{d^2 y}{d\tau^2} + 40 \frac{dy}{d\tau} + 2y = f\left(\frac{\tau}{5}\right) \tag{8.35}$$

The transformed initial conditions are

$$\frac{dy}{d\tau}\bigg|_{\tau=0} = \frac{1}{a} \frac{dy}{dt}\bigg|_{t=0} = \frac{1}{5}(5) = 1 \text{ ft/sec} \tag{8.36}$$

Similarly, the transformed maximum values are

$$\left(\frac{d^2 y}{d\tau^2}\right)_m = \frac{1}{a^2}\left(\frac{d^2 y}{dt^2}\right)_m = \frac{20}{25} = 0.8 \text{ ft/sec}^2$$
$$\left(\frac{dy}{d\tau}\right)_m = \frac{1}{a}\left(\frac{dy}{dt}\right)_m = \frac{10}{5} = 2.0 \text{ ft/sec} \tag{8.37}$$

As is shown in Fig. 8.9, the function $f(\tau/5)$ is obtained by multiplying the original time scale by the factor $a = 5$. Thus, a time-scale change

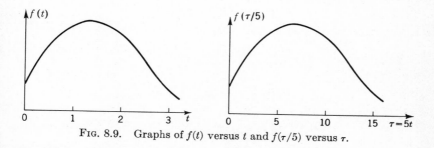

Fig. 8.9. Graphs of $f(t)$ versus t and $f(\tau/5)$ versus τ.

does not affect the initial and maximum values of $f(\tau/a)$. Similarly, the initial and maximum values for y are unaffected by a change in the time scale.

The new scale factors are computed as follows:

$$k = \frac{100}{f(\tau/a)_m} = \frac{100}{20} = 5 \text{ volts/lb}$$

$$k_1 = \frac{100}{(d^2y/d\tau^2)_m} = \frac{100}{0.8} = 125 \text{ volts/(ft)(sec}^2)$$

$$k_2 = \frac{100}{(dy/d\tau)_m} = \frac{100}{2} = 50 \text{ volts/(ft)(sec)}$$

$$k_3 = \frac{100}{y_m} = \frac{100}{5} = 20 \text{ volts/ft}$$

(8.38)

The computer diagram is now obtained by application of the general procedure given in the preceding section. Solving Eq. (8.35) for $d^2y/d\tau^2$ and multiplying by $-k_1 = -125$ gives

$$-k_1 \frac{d^2y}{d\tau^2} = -125 \frac{d^2y}{d\tau^2} = -5f\left(\frac{\tau}{5}\right) + 200 \frac{dy}{d\tau} + 10y \qquad (8.39)$$

This is now written in the form

$$-125 \frac{d^2y}{d\tau^2} = -\frac{5}{k} kf\left(\frac{\tau}{5}\right) - \frac{200}{k_2}\left(-k_2 \frac{dy}{d\tau}\right) - \frac{10}{k_3}(-k_3\dot{y})$$

The negative of the right-hand side is

$$5f\left(\frac{\tau}{5}\right) + 4\left(-50 \frac{dy}{d\tau}\right) + 0.5 (-20y) \qquad (8.40)$$

The resulting computer diagram is shown in Fig. 8.10a.

The coefficients of the terms of Eq. (8.40) are the effective input multipliers at the first amplifier. The multiplication factors for the second and third amplifiers are obtained as follows:

$$\left(\frac{1}{R_1C_2}\right)_2 = \frac{k_2}{k_1} = \frac{50}{125} = 0.4 \qquad (8.41)$$

$$\left(\frac{1}{R_1C_2}\right)_3 = \frac{k_3}{k_2} = \frac{20}{50} = 0.4 \qquad (8.42)$$

The values of the initial voltages $e_2(0)$ and $e_3(0)$ are computed in the following manner:

$$e_2(0) = k_2 \frac{dy}{d\tau}\bigg|_{\tau=0} = 50(1) = 50 \text{ volts}$$

$$e_3(0) = -k_3y\bigg|_{\tau=0} = -20(2) = -40 \text{ volts}$$

(8.43)

Comparison of Figs. 8.8a and 8.10a shows that the gains in the operational amplifiers which multiply by a constant are unaffected by a time scale change. Only the gains of the integrating amplifiers are affected. It is to be noted that the value of the gain in the integrators of Fig. 8.10a

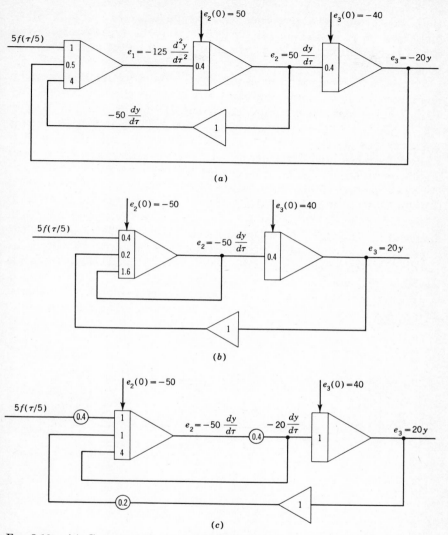

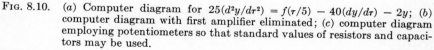

FIG. 8.10. (a) Computer diagram for $25(d^2y/d\tau^2) = f(\tau/5) - 40(dy/d\tau) - 2y$; (b) computer diagram with first amplifier eliminated; (c) computer diagram employing potentiometers so that standard values of resistors and capacitors may be used.

is equal to that in Fig. 8.8a divided by the scale constant a (i.e., $2/a = \frac{2}{5} = 0.4$). Thus, the easiest way to obtain the computer diagram for a time scale change is to first of all obtain the diagram for the case of no time change and then divide the gain in each integrator by a. The scale factors are most readily obtained by first noting that the scale factor for the y term is unaffected by a time scale change (i.e., $e_3 = -20y$). Thus, dividing $k_3 = 20$ by the amplifier gain 0.4 yields the scale factor $k_2 = 50$ shown in Fig. 8.10a. Similarly, dividing $k_2 = 50$ by 0.4 yields the scale factor $k_1 = 125$.

If it is not necessary to measure $d^2y/d\tau^2$, the first amplifier may be eliminated by multiplying the input constants of the first summer by the factor 0.4 for the next amplifier [that is, $(1)(0.4) = 0.4$, $(0.5)(0.4) = 0.2$, $(4)(0.4) = 1.6$], as shown in Fig. 8.10b. The elimination of this amplifier changes the signs of the resulting voltages, and thus the sign of each feedback quantity must be reversed. Similarly the sign of each initial condition voltage must be changed.

Some operational amplifiers use standard resistors of 1×10^6, 0.25×10^6, and 0.10×10^6 ohms and a standard capacitor of 1×10^{-6} farad. Thus, only gains of $1/RC$ equal to 1, 4, or 10 are readily available for each integrator. It is possible to put two resistors in parallel or series at the input to obtain some other effective value of resistance. For example, two 1×10^6 ohm resistors in series yield a 2×10^6 ohm resistance, while two 1×10^6 ohm resistors in parallel yield a 0.5×10^6 ohm resistance.

In general, it is necessary to use a potentiometer to obtain the desired effective resistance. Figure 8.11 shows a schematic diagram of a poten-

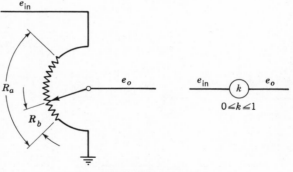

FIG. 8.11.   Potentiometer.

tiometer. The voltage relationship is

$$e_o = \frac{R_b}{R_a} e_{\text{in}} = ke_{\text{in}}$$

$$k = \frac{R_b}{R_a} \leq 1$$
(8.44)

where

The computer diagram of Fig. 8.10b may be modified by the addition of three potentiometers as shown in Fig. 8.10c such that only gains of 1, 4, or 10 are necessary at each amplifier. By comparison of Fig. 8.10b and c, it is to be noted that the effective gain of an amplifier is the product of the gain of the amplifier and the value of k for the potentiometer in front of the amplifier.

8.4 Simulation. A very important application of the analog computer is the simulation of automatic control systems. One method that could be used to simulate a control system would be to determine the overall differential equation and solve this on the computer. Usually though, one is interested in determining the effect on the system performance when certain parameters are varied. Using the preceding technique would mean solving a new differential equation for each change.

Because of the similarity between a block diagram and a computer diagram, it is customary to simulate each portion of the system and then interconnect each of these elements. Thus, the effect of changing one of the terms in the original block diagram may be accomplished by changing the corresponding quantity in the computer diagram.

In Fig. 8.12 is shown a schematic representation of an operational amplifier in which the input impedance is Z_1 and the parallel impedance is

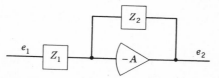

FIG. 8.12. General schematic representation of an operational amplifier.

Z_2. The equation of operation for this amplifier is

$$\frac{e_2}{e_1} = - \frac{Z_2}{Z_1} \tag{8.45}$$

When the input impedance is a resistor R_1 and the parallel impedance is a resistor R_2, the preceding expression reduces to the result given by Eq. (8.8). For the case in which $Z_1 = R_1$ and $Z_2 = 1/C_2D$ the result given by Eq. (8.11) is verified.

In Table 8.1 is shown a number of computer circuits for simulating various transfer functions. For the first circuit $Z_1 = R_1$ and $Z_2 = 1/(1/R_2 + C_2D) = R_2/(1 + R_2C_2D)$. Substitution of the values of these impedances into Eq. (8.45) gives the equation of operation for this computer circuit, i.e.,

$$e_2 = - \frac{R_2}{R_1(1 + R_2C_2D)} e_1 \tag{8.46}$$

In Fig. 8.13a is shown a typical block diagram, and the corresponding computer diagram is shown in Fig. 8.13b.

TABLE 8.1

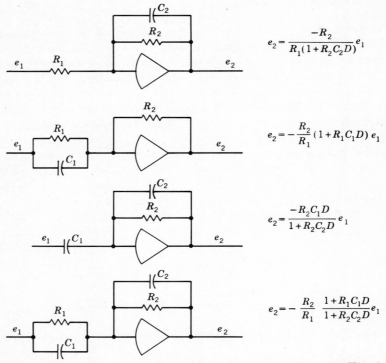

$$e_2 = \frac{-R_2}{R_1(1+R_2C_2D)}e_1$$

$$e_2 = -\frac{R_2}{R_1}(1+R_1C_1D)e_1$$

$$e_2 = \frac{-R_2C_1D}{1+R_2C_2D}e_1$$

$$e_2 = -\frac{R_2}{R_1}\frac{1+R_1C_1D}{1+R_2C_2D}e_1$$

ILLUSTRATIVE EXAMPLE 1. Suppose that the system shown in Fig. 8.13*a* is used to control the angular position of a shaft. For this system, it is known that $K_1 = 10$, $K_2 = 5$, and $\tau = 1.0$. The maximum values have been estimated to be $c(t)_m = 20$ radians, $r(t)_m = 10$ radians, $m_m = 50$ in.-lb, and $d(t)_m = 100$ in.-lb. Determine the values of the resistors and capacitors for the computer diagram of Fig. 8.13*b*.

SOLUTION. The voltage equation for the first amplifier is

$$e_m = \frac{-1}{R_r C_e}\int_0^t e_r\,dt - \frac{1}{R_c C_e}\int_0^t e_b\,dt + e_m(0) \qquad (8.47)$$

The equation which describes the operation of the corresponding portion of the actual system is

$$m(t) = K_1\int_0^t [r(t) - c(t)]\,dt + m(0)$$

$$= K_1\int_0^t r(t)\,dt - K_1\int c(t)\,dt + m(0) \qquad (8.48)$$

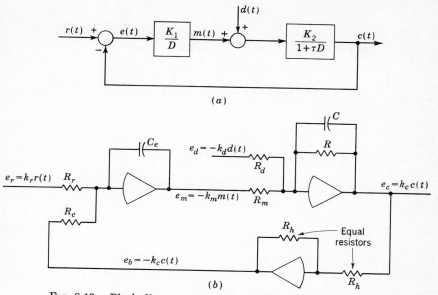

Fig. 8.13. Block diagram and corresponding computer diagram.

Multiplication of Eq. (8.48) by $-k_m$ gives

$$-k_m m(t) = -\frac{k_m K_1}{k_r} \int_0^t k_r r(t)\, dt + \frac{k_m K_1}{k_c} \int_0^t k_c c(t)\, dt - k_m m(0) \quad (8.49)$$

In order that $e_m = -k_m m(t)$, $e_r = k_r r(t)$, and $e_b = -k_c c(t)$, comparison of corresponding terms in Eqs. (8.47) and (8.49) shows that

$$\frac{1}{R_r C_e} = \frac{k_m K_1}{k_r} \qquad \frac{1}{R_c C_e} = \frac{k_m K_1}{k_c} \qquad e_m(0) = -k_m m(0) \quad (8.50)$$

For any system, k_m, k_r, k_c, R_r, and R_c are constant, and thus the gain K_1 may be changed independently by varying the capacitance C_e.

Numerical values are obtained by first computing the scale factors. Thus,

$$\begin{aligned}
k_r &= {}^{100}\!/_{10} = 10 \text{ volts/radian} \\
k_c &= {}^{100}\!/_{20} = 5 \text{ volts/radian} \\
k_m &= {}^{100}\!/_{50} = 2 \text{ volts/(in.)(lb)} \\
k_d &= {}^{100}\!/_{100} = 1 \text{ volt/(in.)(lb)}
\end{aligned} \quad (8.51)$$

From Eq. (8.50), it follows that

$$\frac{1}{R_r C_e} = \frac{(2)K_1}{10} = 2 \qquad \frac{1}{R_c C_e} = \frac{(2)K_1}{5} = 4 \qquad e_m(0) = -2m(0) \quad (8.52)$$

If a 1-μf capacitor is used for C_e, then

$$R_r = \frac{1}{2C_e} = \frac{1}{2 \times 10^{-6}} = 500,000 \text{ ohms} \tag{8.53}$$

$$R_c = \frac{1}{4C_e} = 250,000 \text{ ohms} \tag{8.54}$$

From Table 8.1, it follows that the voltage equation for the second amplifier is

$$e_c = -\frac{R}{R_m(1 + RCD)} e_m - \frac{R}{R_d(1 + RCD)} e_d \tag{8.55}$$

The equation for the corresponding portion of the actual system is

$$c(t) = \frac{K_2}{1 + \tau D} [m(t) + d(t)] \tag{8.56}$$

Multiplication by k_c gives

$$k_c c(t) = \frac{k_c K_2}{k_m(1 + \tau D)} k_m m(t) + \frac{k_c K_2}{k_d(1 + \tau D)} k_d d(t) \tag{8.57}$$

By comparison of corresponding terms in Eqs. (8.55) and (8.57), it follows that, to have $e_c = k_c c(t)$, $e_m = -k_m m(t)$, and $e_d = -k_d d(t)$, the following relationships must hold:

$$\frac{Rk_m}{R_m} = k_c K_2 \qquad \frac{Rk_d}{R_d} = k_c K_2 \qquad \tau = RC \tag{8.58}$$

The substitution of numerical values gives

$$RC = \tau = 1 \tag{8.59}$$

$$\frac{R}{R_m} = \frac{k_c K_2}{k_m} = \frac{(5)(5)}{2} = 12.5 \tag{8.60}$$

$$\frac{R}{R_d} = \frac{k_c K_2}{k_d} = \frac{(5)(5)}{1} = 25 \tag{8.61}$$

If a 1-μf capacitor is used for C, then

$$R = \frac{1}{C} = 1,000,000 \text{ ohms}$$

$$R_m = \frac{R}{12.5} = 80,000 \text{ ohms} \tag{8.62}$$

$$R_d = \frac{R}{25} = 40,000 \text{ ohms}$$

Because C appears only in Eq. (8.59), τ may be varied independently by varying C. A variable capacitor provides a convenient means for varying C. From Eqs. (8.60) and (8.61) it follows that to change the value of K_2 both R_m and R_d must be changed accordingly. A variable resistance is provided by a potentiometer.

Because the output e_c is to be subtracted from the input e_r, it is necessary to multiply the output by -1, as shown in the feedback path of Fig. 8.13b.

If, in testing, it is found that $e_{c_m} \neq 100$ volts, this is evidence that the originally estimated value for $c(t)_m$ is not correct. Because $e_c = k_c c(t)$, the actual value of $c(t)_m$ is now easily found to be

$$c(t)_m = \frac{e_{c_m}}{k_c} \tag{8.63}$$

When the maximum value of $c(t)$ is near 100 volts, there is no need to change the value of k_c. However, if the maximum voltage is quite small, then it is desirable to increase the accuracy with which the output voltage can be read by using a new value of k_c based on the value of $c(t)_m$ obtained from Eq. (8.63). Similarly, if e_{c_m} was sufficiently greater than 100 volts to cause overloading, then it would be necessary to decrease the value of k_c. For most amplifiers, an overload light turns on when the maximum voltage is high enough to overload an amplifier.

A time-scale change $\tau = at$ is readily effected by substituting aD for D in the block diagram of Fig. 8.13a.

A major application of analog computers is in the design of systems with nonlinear components. Standard electronic circuits are available for simulating commonly encountered nonlinear effects such as coulomb friction, backlash, dead zone, saturation, continuous nonlinear functions, etc.

8.5 Parallel Programming. In this method each term of the partial-fraction expansion is simulated. The desired result is then obtained by adding all the individual terms. Simplicity is afforded by the fact that only three types of terms arise in partial-fraction expansions (i.e., distinct factors, repeated factors, and complex conjugate factors).

Distinct Factors. A distinct factor has the form

$$y = \frac{1}{D - a} f(t) \tag{8.64}$$

The block-diagram representation for this factor is shown in Fig. 8.14a. The computer circuit diagram is shown in Fig. 8.14b, and the corresponding schematic representation is shown in Fig. 8.14c. From Fig. 8.14a, the physical relationship may be expressed in the form

$$y = \frac{1}{D} [f(t) + ay]$$

Multiplying through by $-k_y$, and rearranging gives

$$-k_y y = -\frac{1}{D} \left[\frac{k_y}{k} kf(t) - a(-k_y y) \right] \tag{8.65}$$

From Fig. 8.14b, the voltage relationship for the computer circuit is

$$e_y = -\frac{1}{D} \left(\frac{1}{RC} e + \frac{1}{R_a C} e_y \right) \tag{8.66}$$

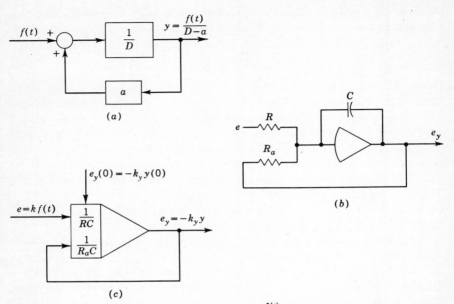

FIG. 8.14. Simulation of distinct factor, $y = \dfrac{f(t)}{(D-a)}$: (a) block diagram; (b) computer diagram; (c) schematic representation.

In order that $e = kf(t)$ and $e_y = -k_y y$, then termwise comparison of Eqs. (8.65) and (8.66) reveals the following scale-factor relationships:

$$\frac{k_y}{k} = \frac{1}{RC}$$
$$a = -\frac{1}{R_a C} \tag{8.67}$$

Because $e_y = -k_y y$, the initial-condition relationship is

$$e_y(0) = -k_y y(0)$$

The relationship $a = -1/R_a C$ shows that this analysis is appropriate for negative values of a (i.e., stable systems). For positive values of a it is necessary to put a sign changer in each of the feedback paths of Fig. 8.14a, b, and c. Thus, the new scale-factor relationship is $a = 1/R_a C$.

Repeated Factors. A repeated factor has the form

$$y = \frac{1}{(D-a)^n} f(t) \tag{8.68}$$

where n is the number of times the factor is repeated. The block diagram representation for a root which is repeated three times is shown in Fig. 8.15a. The corresponding computer diagram is shown in Fig. 8.15b.

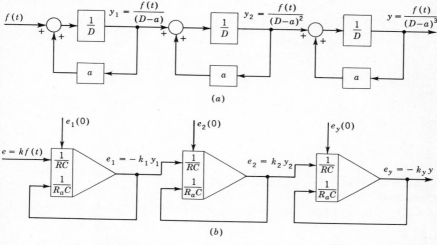

(a)

(b)

FIG. 8.15. Simulation of repeated factor, $y = \dfrac{f(t)}{(D-a)^3}$.

It is to be noted that the block diagram and the computer diagram consist of three distinct factors in series. For the first factor

$$y_1 = \frac{f(t)}{D-a}$$

For the second factor

$$y_2 = \frac{y_1}{D-a} = \frac{f(t)}{(D-a)^2}$$

For the third factor

$$y = \frac{y_2}{D-a} = \frac{f(t)}{(D-a)^3}$$

Thus, the scale-factor relationships are

$$a = -\frac{1}{R_a C}$$

$$k_1 = \frac{1}{RC}\,k$$

$$k_2 = \frac{k_2}{k_1}k_1 = \left(\frac{1}{RC}\right)^2 k$$

$$k_y = \frac{k_y}{k_2}\frac{k_2}{k_1}k_1 = \left(\frac{1}{RC}\right)^3 k$$

(8.69)

The initial biasing voltages are obtained by first noting that

$$y_2 = (D - a)y$$
$$y_1 = (D - a)^2 y$$

Thus,

$$e_y(0) = -k_y y(0)$$
$$e_2(0) = k_2 y_2(0) = k_2[\dot{y}(0) - ay(0)]$$
$$e_1(0) = -k_1 y_1(0) = -k_1[\ddot{y}(0) - 2a\dot{y}(0) + a^2 y(0)]$$

Complex Conjugate Factors. Complex conjugate factors may be expressed in the form

$$y = \frac{b}{D^2 - 2aD + a^2 + b^2} f(t) \qquad (8.70)$$

The constant b is introduced in the numerator because it results in a simplified computer diagram. The block diagram representation for Eq. (8.70) is shown in Fig. 8.16*a*. The corresponding computer diagram

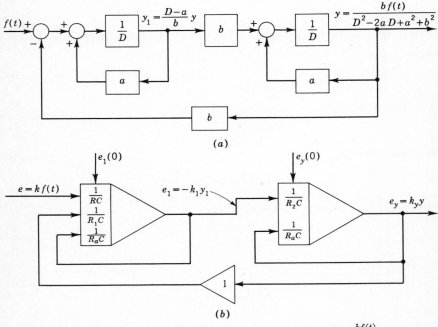

FIG. 8.16. Simulation of complex conjugate factor, $y = \dfrac{bf(t)}{D^2 - 2aD + a^2 + b^2}$.

is shown in Fig. 8.16b. The scale-factor relationships are

$$a = -\frac{1}{R_a C} \qquad \frac{k_1}{k} = \frac{1}{RC}$$

$$\frac{k_1 b}{k_y} = \frac{1}{R_1 C} \qquad \frac{k_y b}{k_1} = \frac{1}{R_2 C} \qquad (8.71)$$

Again, this analysis is applicable for negative values of a. For positive values of a, a sign changer must be inserted in the feedback path around each of the two integrators of Fig. 8.16b. The voltage signal after each integrator is indicated in Fig. 8.16b. Thus, the initial biasing voltages are

$$e_y(0) = k_y y(0)$$

$$e_1(0) = -k_1 y_1(0) = -k_1 \frac{\dot{y}(0) - a y(0)}{b}$$

ILLUSTRATIVE EXAMPLE 1. Determine the computer diagram for the differential equation

$$y = \frac{3D + 4}{(D + 1)(D + 2)^2} f(t) \qquad (8.72)$$

The initial conditions are $y(0) = f(0) = 1$ and $y'(0) = y''(0) = 0$. The maximum expected values are $f(t)_m = 4$ and $y_m = 4$.

SOLUTION. The partial-fraction expansion is

$$y = \left[\frac{1}{D + 1} - \frac{1}{(D + 2)} + \frac{2}{(D + 2)^2} \right] f(t) \qquad (8.73)$$

The block-diagram representation for the distinct factor and the repeated factor is shown in Fig. 8.17a. It is to be noted that

$$q_1 = \frac{f(t)}{D + 1} \qquad (8.74)$$

$$q_2 = \frac{f(t)}{(D + 2)} \qquad (8.75)$$

$$q_3 = \frac{q_2}{D + 2} = \frac{f(t)}{(D + 2)^2} \qquad (8.76)$$

where q with appropriate subscript is used to distinguish that the term is a component of the partial-fraction expansion.

In terms of the components q_1, q_2, and q_3, Eq. (8.73) is

$$y = q_1 - q_2 + 2q_3 \qquad (8.77)$$

The addition of these components to obtain y is shown to the right of the dotted line of Fig. 8.17a.

The final computer diagram is shown in Fig. 8.17b.

To determine $e_1(0)$, $e_2(0)$, and $e_3(0)$, it is necessary to know $q_1(0)$, $q_2(0)$,

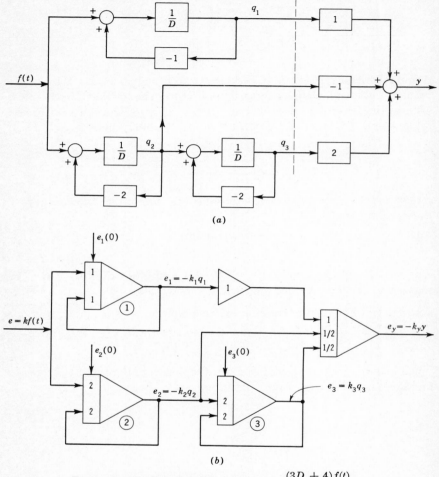

Fig. 8.17. Computer diagram for $y = \dfrac{(3D + 4)f(t)}{(D + 1)(D + 2)^2}$.

and $q_3(0)$. The initial value $q_1(0)$ is obtained by writing Eq. (8.72) in the form

$$(D + 2)^2 y = \frac{3D + 4}{D + 1} f(t) = \left(3 + \frac{1}{D + 1}\right) f(t) = 3f(t) + q_1 \quad (8.78)$$

Evaluating at $t = 0$ and solving for $q_1(0)$ gives

$$q_1(0) = \ddot{y}(0) + 4\dot{y}(0) + 4y(0) - 3f(0) = 1$$

To obtain $q_2(0)$, Eq. (8.72) is written in the form

$$(D + 1)(D + 2)y = \frac{3D + 4}{D + 2} f(t) = \left(3 - \frac{2}{D + 2}\right) f(t) = 3f(t) - 2q_2$$

$$(8.79)$$

Hence, $q_2(0) = -0.5$. To obtain $q_3(0)$, Eq. (8.72) is written in the form

$$(D + 1)y = \frac{3D + 4}{(D + 2)^2} f(t) = \left[\frac{3}{D + 2} - \frac{2}{(D + 2)^2}\right] f(t) = 3q_2 - 2q_3$$

$$(8.80)$$

Hence $q_3(0) = 1.25$. To determine the scale factors k_1, k_2, and k_3, it is necessary to know the maximum values of q_1, q_2, and q_3. Substitution of $D = 0$ into Eqs. (8.74), (8.75), and (8.76) yields the steady-state relationships $q_1 = f$, $q_2 = f/2$, and $q_3 = f/4$. These steady-state relationships may be used to obtain an estimate of the maximum values; thus $q_{1_m} = f_m = 4$, $q_{2_m} = f_m/2 = 2$, and $q_{3_m} = f_m/4 = 1$. The corresponding scale factors are $k = 100/f_m = 25$, $k_1 = 100/q_{1_m} = 25$, $k_2 = 100/q_{2_m} = 50$, $k_3 = 100/q_{3_m} = 100$, and $k_y = 100/y_m = 25$. For amplifier 1, $1/RC = k_1/k = 1$ and $1/R_aC = -a = 1$. For amplifier 2, $1/RC = k_2/k = 2$ and $1/R_aC = 2$. For amplifier 3, $1/RC = k_3/k_2 = 2$ and $1/R_aC = 2$.

The physical relationship for the final summing amplifier, Eq. (8.77), may be written in the form

$$-k_y y = -\frac{k_y}{k_1}(k_1 q_1) - \frac{k_y}{k_2}(-k_2 q_2) - \frac{2k_y}{k_3}(k_3 q_3)$$

$$= -(k_1 q_1) - \tfrac{1}{2}(-k_2 q_2) - \tfrac{1}{2}(k_3 q_3)$$

The voltage equation for the final summer is

$$e_y = -\frac{R_2}{R_a} e_1 - \frac{R_2}{R_b} e_2 - \frac{R_2}{R_c} e_3$$

Thus, $R_2/R_a = 1$, $R_2/R_b = \tfrac{1}{2}$, and $R_2/R_c = \tfrac{1}{2}$. The computer diagram shows that $e_1 = -k_1 q_1$, $e_2 = -k_2 q_2$, and $e_3 = k_3 q_3$. The e_1 voltage must go through a sign changer to make the two preceding equations identical.

ILLUSTRATIVE EXAMPLE 2. Determine the computer diagram for the differential equation

$$y = \frac{D + 5}{(D + 1)(D^2 + 4D + 5)} f(t) \qquad (8.81)$$

The initial conditions are $y(0) = f(0) = 1$ and $\dot{y}(0) = \ddot{y}(0) = 0$. The maximum expected values are $f_m = 5$ and $y_m = 5$.

SOLUTION. The partial-fraction expansion may be written in the form

$$\frac{D + 5}{(D + 1)(D^2 + 4D + 5)} = \frac{K}{D + 1} + \frac{AD + B}{D^2 + 4D + 5}$$

where

$$K = \frac{D + 5}{D^2 + 4D + 5}\bigg|_{D = -1} = 2$$

The constants A and B are evaluated by multiplying through by the quadratic $D^2 + 4D + 5$, and then taking the limit as D approaches the root $a + jb = -2 + j$. Thus

$$\frac{D + 5}{D + 1}\bigg|_{D = -2+j} = \frac{3 + j}{-1 + j} = -1 - j2$$

$$AD + B\bigg|_{D = -2+j} = (-2A + B) + jA$$

Equating imaginary parts shows that $A = -2$. Similarly, from the real parts, $4 + B = -1$, or $B = -5$. The resulting form of the differential equation is

$$y = \left(\frac{2}{D + 1} - \frac{2D + 5}{D^2 + 4D + 5}\right)f(t) \tag{8.82}$$

The block-diagram representation for obtaining the linear factor and the quadratic factor is shown to the left of the dotted line in Fig. 8.18a. It is to be noted that

$$q_1 = \frac{f(t)}{D + 1} \tag{8.83}$$

$$q_2 = \frac{bf(t)}{D^2 + 4D + 5} \tag{8.84}$$

$$q_3 = \frac{D - a}{b} q_2 = \frac{(D + 2)f(t)}{D^2 + 4D + 5} \tag{8.85}$$

In terms of the components q_1, q_2, and q_3, the differential equation is

$$y = 2q_1 - q_2 - 2q_3 \tag{8.86}$$

The final addition of these components to obtain y is shown to the right of the dotted line in Fig. 8.18a. The final computer diagram is shown in Fig. 8.18b. To obtain the initial value $q_1(0)$, Eq. (8.81) is written in the form

$$(D^2 + 4D + 5)y = \frac{D + 5}{D + 1}f(t) = 1 + \frac{4}{D + 1}f(t) = f(t) + 4q_1 \tag{8.87}$$

Evaluating at $t = 0$, and solving for $q_1(0)$ gives

$$q_1(0) = \frac{\ddot{y}(0) + 4\dot{y}(0) + 5y(0) - f(0)}{4} = \frac{5 - 1}{4} = 1$$

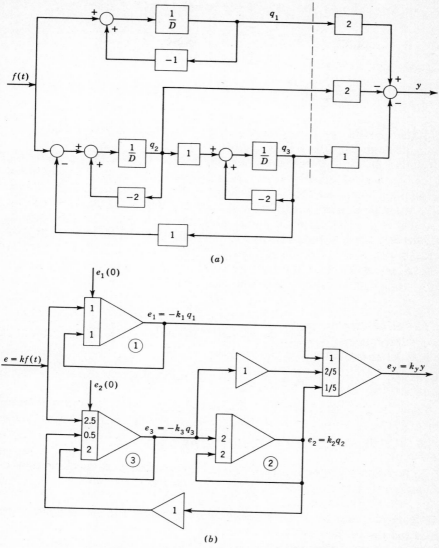

(a)

(b)

Fig. 8.18. Computer diagram for $y = \dfrac{(D + 5)f(t)}{(D + 1)(D^2 + 4D + 5)}$.

To obtain $q_2(0)$ and $q_3(0)$, Eq. (8.81) is written in the form

$$(D + 1)y = \frac{D + 5}{D^2 + 4D + 5} f(t) = 3q_2 + q_3 \qquad (8.88)$$

Multiplying through by D shows that

$$(D^2 + D)y = \frac{D^2 + 5D}{D^2 + 4D + 5} f(t) = \left(1 + \frac{D - 5}{D^2 + 4D + 5}\right) f(t)$$
$$= f(t) - 7q_2 + q_3 \qquad (8.89)$$

Evaluating the two preceding equations at $t = 0$ and then solving simultaneously gives $q_2(0) = \frac{1}{5}$ and $q_3(0) = \frac{2}{5}$.

Substitution of $D = 0$ into Eqs. (8.83), (8.84), and (8.85) yields the steady-state relationships $q_1 = f$, $q_2 = f/5$, and $q_3 = 2f/5$. The estimated maximum values are $q_{1_m} = f_m = 5$, $q_{2_m} = f_m/5 = 1$, and $q_{3_m} = 2$. Thus, the scale factors are $k = 100/f_m = 20$, $k_1 = 100/q_{1_m} = 20$, $k_2 = 100/q_{2_m} = 100$, $k_3 = 100/q_{3_m} = 50$, and $k_y = 100/y_m = 20$. For amplifier 1, $1/RC = k_1/k = 1$ and $1/R_aC = 1$. For amplifier 2, $1/R_2C = (k_2/k_3)b = 2$ and $1/R_aC = 2$. For amplifier 3, $1/RC = k_3/k = 2.5$ and $1/R_3C = (k_3/k_2)b = 0.5$. The physical relationship for the final summing amplifier, Eq. (8.86), may be written in the form

$$k_y y = \frac{2k_y}{k_1}(k_1 q_1) - \frac{k_y}{k_2}(k_2 q_2) - \frac{2k_y}{k_3}(k_3 q_3)$$
$$= -2(-k_1 q_1) - \tfrac{1}{5}(k_2 q_2) - \tfrac{4}{5}(k_3 q_3)$$

The voltage equation for the final summer is

$$e_y = -\frac{R_2}{R_a} e_1 - \frac{R_2}{R_b} e_2 - \frac{R_2}{R_c} e_3$$

Thus, $R_2/R_a = 2$, $R_2/R_b = \frac{1}{5}$, and $R_2/R_c = \frac{4}{5}$. The computer diagram shows that $e_1 = -k_1 q_1$, $e_2 = k_2 q_2$, and $e_3 = -k_3 q_3$. The e_3 voltage must go through a sign changer before entering the final summer.

8.6 Matrix Method. Matrix algebra provides a convenient mathematical notation for performing the mathematical manipulations involved in parallel programming.

Consider now the differential equation given by Eq. (8.72) which may be written in the form

$$(D^3 + 5D^2 + 8D + 4)y = (3D + 4)f(t)$$

or
$$\dddot{y} = -4y - 8\dot{y} - 5\ddot{y} + 4f(t) + 3f'(t)$$

By letting $y = y_1$, $\dot{y} = \dot{y}_1 = y_2$, and $\ddot{y} = \ddot{y}_1 = \dot{y}_2 = y_3$, then this third-order differential equation may be expressed as three first-order equations.

$$\dot{y}_1 = 0 + y_2 + 0$$
$$\dot{y}_2 = 0 + 0 + y_3$$
$$\dot{y}_3 = -4y_1 - 8y_2 - 5y_3 + 4f(t) + 3f'(t)$$

This is referred to as the state-space representation for the system. The terms y_1, y_2, and y_3 are called the state variables. The state-space equations may be written in the following matrix form.

$$\begin{bmatrix} \dot{y}_1 \\ \dot{y}_2 \\ \dot{y}_3 \end{bmatrix} = \begin{bmatrix} 0 & 1 & 0 \\ 0 & 0 & 1 \\ -4 & -8 & -5 \end{bmatrix} \begin{bmatrix} y_1 \\ y_2 \\ y_3 \end{bmatrix} + \begin{bmatrix} 0 \\ 0 \\ 4 \end{bmatrix} f(t) + \begin{bmatrix} 0 \\ 0 \\ 3 \end{bmatrix} f'(t)$$

or
$$\dot{\mathbf{y}} = A\mathbf{y} + \mathbf{b}_0 f(t) + \mathbf{b}_1 f'(t) \tag{8.90}$$

Boldface lowercase letters $\dot{\mathbf{y}}$, $\mathbf{y}$, $\mathbf{b}_0$, and $\mathbf{b}_1$ are used to represent column matrices, or column vectors. Capital letters such as A are used to represent coefficient matrices.

To solve differential equations by the matrix method, the equations are first expressed in canonical form. To write the canonical form, it is only necessary to know the roots of the characteristic equation. For example, if the characteristic equation has two distinct roots λ_1 and λ_2, the canonical form is

$$\begin{bmatrix} \dot{q}_1 \\ \dot{q}_2 \end{bmatrix} = \begin{bmatrix} \lambda_1 & 0 \\ 0 & \lambda_2 \end{bmatrix} \begin{bmatrix} q_1 \\ q_2 \end{bmatrix} + \begin{bmatrix} 1 \\ 1 \end{bmatrix} f(t)$$

The corresponding equations are

$$(D - \lambda_1)q_1 = f(t)$$
$$(D - \lambda_2)q_2 = f(t)$$

For a root λ which is repeated twice the canonical form is

$$\begin{bmatrix} \dot{q}_1 \\ \dot{q}_2 \end{bmatrix} = \begin{bmatrix} \lambda & 0 \\ 1 & \lambda \end{bmatrix} \begin{bmatrix} q_1 \\ q_2 \end{bmatrix} + \begin{bmatrix} 1 \\ 0 \end{bmatrix} f(t)$$

The corresponding equations are

$$(D - \lambda)q_1 = f(t)$$
$$(D - \lambda)q_2 = q_1$$

Eliminating q_1 from the last expression yields the following equation for the canonical variable q_2

$$(D - \lambda)^2 q_2 = f(t)$$

For complex conjugate roots $a \pm jb$, the canonical form is

$$\begin{bmatrix} \dot{q}_1 \\ \dot{q}_2 \end{bmatrix} = \begin{bmatrix} a & b \\ -b & a \end{bmatrix} \begin{bmatrix} q_1 \\ q_2 \end{bmatrix} + \begin{bmatrix} 0 \\ 1 \end{bmatrix} f(t)$$

The corresponding equations are

$$(D - a)q_1 = bq_2$$
$$(D - a)q_2 = -bq_1 + f(t)$$

Solving simultaneously yields the following equations for the canonical variables q_1 and q_2

$$(D^2 - 2aD + a^2 + b^2)q_1 = bf(t)$$
$$(D^2 - 2aD + a^2 + b^2)q_2 = (D - a)f(t)$$

The canonical form reduces the solution of a differential equation to the solution of a sum of differential equations having distinct, repeated, or complex conjugate roots.

For the case of Eq. (8.72), the characteristic equation has a distinct root $\lambda_1 = -1$, and a root which is repeated twice, $\lambda = -2$. The matrix representation for the canonical form is

$$\begin{bmatrix} \dot{q}_1 \\ \dot{q}_2 \\ \dot{q}_3 \end{bmatrix} = \begin{bmatrix} -1 & 0 & 0 \\ 0 & -2 & 0 \\ 0 & 1 & -2 \end{bmatrix} \begin{bmatrix} q_1 \\ q_2 \\ q_3 \end{bmatrix} + \begin{bmatrix} 1 \\ 1 \\ 0 \end{bmatrix} f(t) \qquad (8.91)$$

The dotted partitioning distinguishes the contribution due to the distinct root and that due to the repeated root. The corresponding differential equations are

$$(D + 1)q_1 = f(t)$$
$$(D + 2)q_2 = f(t)$$
$$(D + 2)^2 q_3 = f(t)$$

Solving these differential equations yields the canonical variables q_1, q_2, and q_3.

The general canonical form for any differential equation is

$$\dot{\mathbf{q}} = X^{-1}AX\mathbf{q} + X^{-1}\mathbf{b}f(t)$$
$$= \Lambda\mathbf{q} + X^{-1}\mathbf{b}f(t) \qquad (8.92)$$

where A = coefficient matrix as illustrated in Eq. (8.90)
$\quad\ X$ = the modal matrix
$\ X^{-1}$ = its inverse

The matrix $\Lambda = X^{-1}AX$ is called the lambda matrix. Such a matrix which has the form $X^{-1}AX$ is called a similarity matrix. The form of Λ and $X^{-1}\mathbf{b}$ for distinct, repeated and complex conjugate roots has previously been described.

The relationship for transforming from the canonical variables q_1, q_2, and q_3 to the state variables y_1, y_2, and y_3 is ascertained as follows. Multiplying through Eq. (8.92) by the modal matrix X and subtracting this result from Eq. (8.90) gives

$$\dot{\mathbf{y}} - X\dot{\mathbf{q}} - \mathbf{b}_1 f'(t) = A\{(\mathbf{y} - X\mathbf{q}) - A^{-1}(\mathbf{b} - \mathbf{b}_0)f(t)]$$

For $\mathbf{b}_1 = A^{-1}(\mathbf{b} - \mathbf{b}_0)$ or $\mathbf{b} = \mathbf{b}_0 + A\mathbf{b}_1$, the left-hand side is seen to be the derivative of the term in brackets on the right-hand side. Thus, the preceding equation can be satisfied only if

$$\mathbf{y} = X\mathbf{q} + \mathbf{b}_1 f(t) \tag{8.93}$$

This is the desired transformation relationship.

To evaluate Eq. (8.93), it is necessary to know the modal matrix X. The partial-fraction expansion for $y = y_1$, Eq. (8.77), is

$$y_1 = q_1 - q_2 + 2q_3$$

Differentiation to obtain $\dot{y} = \dot{y}_1 = y_2$ gives

$$y_2 = \dot{q}_1 - \dot{q}_2 + 2\dot{q}_3$$

From the canonical form, Eq. (8.91), it is seen that $\dot{q}_1 = -q_1 + f(t)$, $\dot{q}_2 = 2q_2 + f(t)$, and $\dot{q}_3 = q_2 - 2q_3$. Thus, the preceding equation becomes

$$y_2 = -q_1 + 4q_2 - 4q_3$$

Similarly, differentiating y_2 to obtain y_3, and then eliminating $\dot{q}_1$, $\dot{q}_2$, and $\dot{q}_3$ by means of Eq. (8.91), it follows that

$$y_3 = q_1 - 12q_2 + 8q_3 + 3f(t)$$

The equations for y_1, y_2, and y_3 may be written in the matrix form

$$\begin{bmatrix} y_1 \\ y_2 \\ y_3 \end{bmatrix} = \begin{bmatrix} 1 & -1 & 2 \\ -1 & 4 & -4 \\ 1 & -12 & -8 \end{bmatrix} \begin{bmatrix} q_1 \\ q_2 \\ q_3 \end{bmatrix} + \begin{bmatrix} 0 \\ 0 \\ 3 \end{bmatrix} f(t)$$

This is the transformation whose general form is given by Eq. (8.92). The transformation matrix not only gives the relationship for obtaining the solution $y = y_1$, but also the equations for the other state variables y_2 and y_3.

In order to solve the canonical equations, it is necessary to know the initial conditions in terms of the canonical variables [that is, $q_1(0)$, $q_2(0)$, and $q_3(0)$]. Usually, the initial conditions for a system are given in terms of the state variables [that is, $y_1(0)$, $y_2(0)$, and $y_3(0)$]. The equation for transforming from the state variables to the canonical variables is obtained by multiplying Eq. (8.92) by X^{-1}. Thus

$$\mathbf{q} = X^{-1}\mathbf{y} - X^{-1}\mathbf{b}_1 f(t) \tag{8.94}$$

Since the modal matrix X has previously been ascertained, then its inverse X^{-1} may be calculated by matrix algebra. Thus, the preceding equation may be evaluated. An alternate and simpler method for evaluating Eq. (8.94) is to note that Eqs. (8.78) to (8.80) may be written in the corresponding matrix form.

$$
\begin{bmatrix} q_1 \\ q_2 \\ q_3 \end{bmatrix} = \begin{bmatrix} 4 & 4 & 1 \\ -1 & -\frac{3}{2} & -\frac{1}{2} \\ -2 & -11\frac{1}{4} & -\frac{3}{4} \end{bmatrix} \begin{bmatrix} y_1 \\ y_2 \\ y_3 \end{bmatrix} + \begin{bmatrix} -3 \\ \frac{3}{2} \\ \frac{9}{2} \end{bmatrix} f(t)
$$

Evaluation at $t = 0$ yields the desired transformation equations. When all of the initial conditions are zero, then all the initial values of the canonical variables are also zero.

It is interesting to note that Eqs. (8.78) to (8.80) provide an independent technique for ascertaining the inverse X^{-1}, whence the modal matrix X may be obtained by matrix algebra. This eliminates the need for obtaining X from the partial fraction expansion for $y = y_1$.

ILLUSTRATIVE EXAMPLE 1. Let it be desired to determine the matrix representation for the control system shown in Fig. 8.19. The differ-

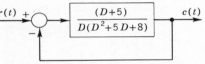

FIG. 8.19.   Feedback control system.

ential equation of operation for this system is

$$
c = \frac{(D + 5)r(t)}{D(D^2 + 5D + 8) + (D + 5)} = \frac{(D + 5)r(t)}{D^3 + 5D^2 + 9D + 5}
$$
$$
= \frac{(D + 5)r(t)}{(D + 1)(D^2 + 4D + 5)}
$$

This differential equation is the same as Eq. (8.81). By letting $c = y_1$, $\dot{c} = \dot{y}_1 = y_2$, $\ddot{c} = \ddot{y}_1 = \dot{y}_2 = y_3$, and $r(t) = f(t)$, then the corresponding state-space representation is

$$
\begin{bmatrix} \dot{y}_1 \\ \dot{y}_2 \\ \dot{y}_3 \end{bmatrix} = \begin{bmatrix} 0 & 1 & 0 \\ 0 & 0 & 1 \\ -5 & -9 & -5 \end{bmatrix} \begin{bmatrix} y_1 \\ y_2 \\ y_3 \end{bmatrix} + \begin{bmatrix} 0 \\ 0 \\ 5 \end{bmatrix} f(t) + \begin{bmatrix} 0 \\ 0 \\ 1 \end{bmatrix} f'(t)
$$

or $\qquad \dot{\mathbf{y}} = A\mathbf{y} + \mathbf{b}_0 f(t) + \mathbf{b}_1 f'(t)$

The characteristic equation has a distinct root $\lambda = -1$ and a complex conjugate pair $a \pm jb = -2 \pm j$. Thus, the canonical form is

$$
\begin{bmatrix} \dot{q}_1 \\ \dot{q}_2 \\ \dot{q}_3 \end{bmatrix} = \begin{bmatrix} -1 & 0 & 0 \\ 0 & -2 & 1 \\ 0 & -1 & -2 \end{bmatrix} \begin{bmatrix} q_1 \\ q_2 \\ q_3 \end{bmatrix} + \begin{bmatrix} 1 \\ 0 \\ 1 \end{bmatrix} f(t) \qquad (8.95)
$$

or $\qquad \dot{\mathbf{q}} = \Lambda\mathbf{q} + X^{-1}\mathbf{b}f(t)$

Solving Eqs. (8.87) to (8.89) for q_1, q_2, and q_3 gives

$$\begin{bmatrix} q_1 \\ q_2 \\ q_3 \end{bmatrix} = \begin{bmatrix} 5/4 & 1 & 1/4 \\ 1/10 & 0 & -1/10 \\ 7/10 & 1 & 3/10 \end{bmatrix} \begin{bmatrix} y_1 \\ y_2 \\ y_3 \end{bmatrix} + \begin{bmatrix} -1/4 \\ 1/10 \\ -3/10 \end{bmatrix} f(t)$$

or
$$\mathbf{q} = X^{-1}\mathbf{y} - X^{-1}\mathbf{b}_1 f(t)$$

Evaluating these equations at $t = 0$ yields $q_1(0)$, $q_2(0)$, and $q_3(0)$, whence the canonical equations may be solved for q_1, q_2, and q_3. Multiplying through the preceding equation by X shows that the solution $\mathbf{y}$ is

$$\mathbf{y} = X\mathbf{q} + \mathbf{b}_1 f(t)$$

Using matrix algebra to obtain the modal matrix X from the known inverse X^{-1} gives

$$\begin{bmatrix} y_1 \\ y_2 \\ y_3 \end{bmatrix} = \begin{bmatrix} 2 & -1 & -2 \\ -2 & 4 & 3 \\ 2 & -11 & -2 \end{bmatrix} \begin{bmatrix} q_1 \\ q_2 \\ q_3 \end{bmatrix} + \begin{bmatrix} 0 \\ 0 \\ 1 \end{bmatrix} f(t)$$

The preceding matrix could also have been ascertained from the known partial-fraction expansion for $y = y_1$, and then differentiating to obtain the relations for y_2 and y_3.

ILLUSTRATIVE EXAMPLE 2. Determine the response of the system of Fig. 8.19 for the case in which the input $r(t) = f(t)$ is a unit impulse and all of the initial conditions are zero.

The differential equations for the canonical variables are obtained directly from Eq. (8.95). Thus,

$$(D + 1)q_1 = f(t)$$
$$(D^2 + 4D + 5)q_2 = f(t)$$
$$(D^2 + 4d + 5)q_3 = (D + 2)f(t)$$

Taking the Laplace transform of each equation and then solving for q_1, q_2, and q_3 respectively gives

$$q_1 = e^{-t}$$
$$q_2 = e^{-2t} \sin t$$
$$q_3 = e^{-2t} \sin (t + 90°)$$

The desired solution $c = y = y_1$ is the linear combination given by Eq. (8.86).

8.7 Digital Computers. As is discussed at the beginning of this chapter, a problem must be reduced to elementary mathematical operations before being submitted to a digital computer. For example, consider the problem discussed in Sec. 8.2, that is,

$$\ddot{y} + 8\dot{y} + 2y = f(t)$$

where the initial values $y(0)$ and $\dot{y}(0)$ are known, as is the function $f(t)$. The initial value of $\ddot{y}(0)$ is obtained by solving the above equation for $\ddot{y}$ and substituting the given initial conditions into this expression, i.e.,

$$\ddot{y}(0) = x(0) - 8\dot{y}(0) - 2y(0)$$

By choosing a small increment Δt such that the slope $\dot{y}(0)$ of the curve of y versus t may be considered to remain constant in the interval $0 \leq t \leq \Delta t$, it follows that

$$y(\Delta t) = y(0) + \dot{y}(0)\,\Delta t \qquad (8.96)$$

Similarly, if Δt is small enough so that the slope $\ddot{y}(0)$ of the graph of velocity vs. time does not vary appreciably,

$$\dot{y}(\Delta t) = \dot{y}(0) + \ddot{y}(0)\,\Delta t \qquad (8.97)$$

The value of $\ddot{y}(\Delta t)$ may now be computed from the original differential equation, i.e.,

$$\ddot{y}(\Delta t) = f(\Delta t) - 8\dot{y}(\Delta t) - 2y(\Delta t) \qquad (8.98)$$

Similarly, the evaluation of each term at time $t = 2\,\Delta t$ is accomplished as follows:

$$y(2\,\Delta t) = y(\Delta t) + \dot{y}(\Delta t)\,\Delta t$$
$$\dot{y}(2\,\Delta t) = \dot{y}(\Delta t) + \ddot{y}(\Delta t)\,\Delta t$$
$$\ddot{y}(2\,\Delta t) = f(2\,\Delta t) - 8\dot{y}(2\,\Delta t) - 2y(2\,\Delta t)$$

Thus, in general, it follows that, at time $t = n\,\Delta t$,

$$y(n\,\Delta t) = y[(n-1)\,\Delta t] + \dot{y}[(n-1)\,\Delta t]\,\Delta t$$
$$\dot{y}(n\,\Delta t) = \dot{y}[(n-1)\,\Delta t] + \ddot{y}[(n-1)\,\Delta t]\,\Delta t$$
$$\ddot{y}(n\,\Delta t) = f(n\,\Delta t) - 8\dot{y}(n\,\Delta t) - 2y(n\,\Delta t)$$

By continuing this process, values for y, $\dot{y}$, and $\ddot{y}$ may be obtained for any time $n\,\Delta t$. Accuracy is increased by using smaller increments for Δt. The preceding method for reducing a linear differential equation to a sequence of simple mathematical operations is known as the straight-line approximation method. Although more accurate techniques of numerical analysis could have been employed, the preceding method suffices to illustrate the fundamental concepts. It should be noticed that it is necessary to store the initial conditions and values of $f(t)$ at $t = 0, \Delta t, 2\,\Delta t, 3\,\Delta t, \ldots, n\,\Delta t$ in the machine so that they are available for computation when needed. Similarly, the answers to Eqs. (8.96) and (8.97) must be stored in the machine so that $\ddot{y}(\Delta t)$ in Eq. (8.98) may be computed, etc. Such storage devices in a digital computer are referred to as memory units. In essence, then, numbers and directions are the input to a digital computer, and the output is in the form of numbers.

Parallel programming and matrix methods lend themselves to solution on the digital computer where there is no need to introduce scale factors to relate voltages and corresponding system parameters. As there is no need for a circuit diagram, the block diagram suffices as the basis for programming the digital computer.

Usually an analog computer can be set up to simulate a control system much faster than it can be programmed for solution on a digital computer. In addition, an analog computer tends to be more versatile and convenient to use for most problems encountered in control work.

Problems

8.1 (a) Derive the equation of operation for each circuit shown in Fig. 8.5.
 (b) Determine the computer diagram for the following first-order equation:

$$(0.5D + 1)y = f(t)$$

The initial condition is $y(0) = 2$ ft, and the maximum expected values are $f(t)_m = 10$ lb, $y_m = 5$ ft, and $\dot{y}_m = 20$ ft/sec.

8.2 Determine the computer diagram to solve the following differential equation:

$$\ddot{y} + 2y = 5f(t)$$

The initial conditions are $y(0) = 3$ and $\dot{y}(0) = 2$. The maximum expected values are $y_m = 10$, $\dot{y}_m = 20$, $\ddot{y}_m = 50$, $f(t)_m = 2$.

8.3 (a) Determine the computer diagram to solve the following differential equation:

$$\dddot{y} + 8\ddot{y} + 25\dot{y} + 20y = f(t)$$

The initial conditions are $\ddot{y}(0) = 3$, $\dot{y}(0) = 1$, $y(0) = 1$. The maximum expected values are $\dddot{y}_m = 10$, $\ddot{y}_m = 5$, $\dot{y}_m = 2$, $y_m = 1$, $f(t)_m = 40$.

 (b) Determine the computer diagram which will speed up solution of part (a) by a factor of 2.

8.4 (a) Determine the computer diagram for the following third-order differential equation:

$$(D^3 + 2D^2 + 5D + 10)y = f(t)$$

The initial conditions are $y(0) = 5$ ft, $\dot{y}(0) = 0$, and $\ddot{y}(0) = 10$ ft/sec². The maximum expected values are $f(t)_m = 25$ lb, $y_m = 10$ ft, $\dot{y}_m = 20$ ft/sec, $\ddot{y}_m = 50$ ft/sec², and $\dddot{y}_m = 100$ ft/sec³.

(*b*) Suppose that in part (*a*) it is found that $e_{3m} = k_3 \dot{y}_m = 25$ volts rather than 100 volts. What is the actual value of $\dot{y}_m$? Revise the computer diagram so that e_{3m} will be 100 volts.

8.5 Determine the differential equation that is being solved by the computer diagram shown in Fig. P8.5.

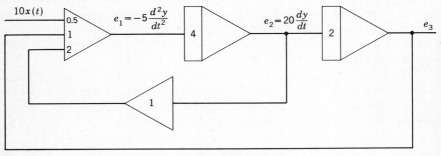

FIG. P8.5

8.6 (*a*) Determine the differential equation that is being solved by the analog computer shown in Fig. P8.6.

(*b*) For the first amplifier

$$\frac{bk_1}{k_3} = \frac{R_2}{R_b} \qquad \frac{ak_1}{k_2} = \frac{R_2}{R_a}$$

Let $a = 2\zeta\omega_n$ and $b = \omega_n{}^2$. Solve for ζ and ω_n in terms of these electrical constants and scale factors. Can either ζ or ω_n be varied independently?

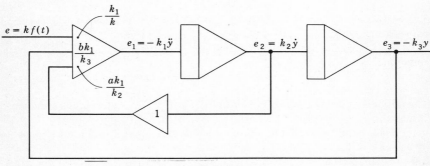

FIG. P8.6

8.7 Let it be desired to speed up the computer solution for Prob. 8.1 by a factor of 5. Determine the computer diagram for this case.

8.8 Let it be desired to slow down the computer solution for Prob. 8.4 by a factor of 2. Determine the computer diagram for this case.

8.9 Derive the equation of operation for each of the amplifier circuits shown in Fig. P8.9.

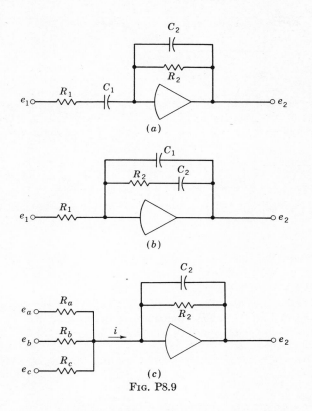

Fig. P8.9

8.10 Set up the computer diagram for simulating the system shown in Fig. P8.10 for the case in which $r(t)_m = 20$, $c(t)_m = 10$, $K = 20$, and $\tau = 0.5$. (Use a 1-μf capacitor.)

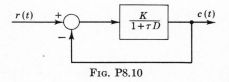

Fig. P8.10

8.11 Determine the computer diagram for simulating the control system shown in Fig. P8.11. The maximum expected values are $r(t)_m = 5$, $c(t)_m = 10$, $d(t)_m = 25$, and $m(t)_m = 20$. The values of the constants are $K_1 = 10$, $K_2 = 20$, $\tau_1 = 0.2$, and $\tau_2 = 1.0$. (Use 1-μf capacitors.)

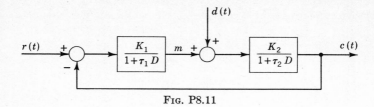

FIG. P8.11

8.12 Construct the computer diagram for simulating the control system shown in Fig. P8.12. For this system $K_1 = 5$, $K_2 = 2$, and $\tau_1 = 1$. The maximum expected values are $r(t)_m = 10$ and $c(t)_m = 20$. (Use a value off C_2 or 1-μf.)

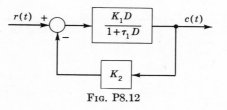

FIG. P8.12

8.13 Determine the block-diagram representation for the control system which is being simulated by the analog computer shown in Fig. P8.13.

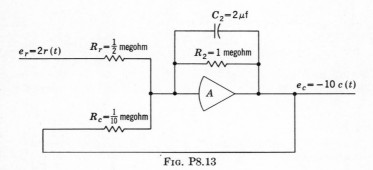

FIG. P8.13

8.14 (a) Determine the block diagram for the system which is being simulated by the analog computer diagram shown in Fig. P8.14. HINT: First obtain block diagram for portion of circuit enclosed by dashed lines, that is, the block diagram relating the input x to output c.

(b) Draw directly the new computer diagram for speeding up the solution of the above problem by a factor of 2.

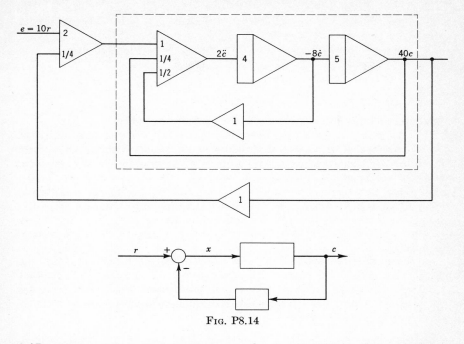

F<small>IG</small>. P8.14

8.15 Construct the computer diagram for solving the two simultaneous differential equations

$$\dot{x} + 5x = y + f(t)$$
$$\ddot{y} + 10y = 2x$$

The initial conditions are $x(0) = 1$, $\dot{y}(0) = 0$, and $y(0) = 2$. The maximum expected values are $x_m = 4$, $\dot{x}_m = 10$, $y_m = 1$, $\dot{y}_m = 2$, $\ddot{y}_m = 4$, and $f(t)_m = 10$.

8.16 Use the partial-fraction method to determine the computer diagram for the equation

$$y = \frac{D + 6}{(D + 2)(D + 3)} f(t)$$

The initial conditions are $y(0) = f(0) = 1$ and $\dot{y}(0) = 0$. The maximum expected values are $y_m = f_m = 6$.

8.17 Use parallel programming to determine the computer diagram for simulating the differential equation

$$y = \frac{2D + 9}{(D + 3)^2} f(t)$$

The initial conditions are $y(0) = f(0) = 1$ and $\dot{y}(0) = 0$. The maximum expected values are $y_m = f_m = 9$.

8.18 Use parallel programming to determine the computer diagram for simulating the differential equation

$$y = \frac{3D + 25}{D^2 + 6D + 25} f(t)$$

The initial conditions are $y(0) = f(0) = 1$ and $\dot{y}(0) = 0$. The maximum expected values are $y_m = f_m = 25$.

8.19 For a root λ which is repeated three times, the canonical form is

$$\begin{bmatrix} \dot{q}_1 \\ \dot{q}_2 \\ \dot{q}_3 \end{bmatrix} = \begin{bmatrix} \lambda & 0 & 0 \\ 1 & \lambda & 0 \\ 0 & 1 & \lambda \end{bmatrix} \begin{bmatrix} q_1 \\ q_2 \\ q_3 \end{bmatrix} + \begin{bmatrix} 1 \\ 0 \\ 0 \end{bmatrix} f(t)$$

What are the differential equations for the canonical variables q_1, q_2, and q_3?

8.20 (a) When the state-space form is $\dot{\mathbf{y}} = A\mathbf{y} + \mathbf{b}_0 f(t)$, the transformation $\mathbf{y} = X\mathbf{q}$ transforms the canonical variables to the state variables. Show that substitution of the transformation matrix $\mathbf{y} = X\mathbf{q}$ into the state-space form yields the canonical form $\dot{\mathbf{q}} = \Lambda\mathbf{q} + X^{-1}\mathbf{b}f(t)$ where $\mathbf{b} = \mathbf{b}_0$.

(b) When the state-space form is $\dot{\mathbf{y}} = A\mathbf{y} + \mathbf{b}_0 f(t) + \mathbf{b}_1 f'(t)$, the transformation $\mathbf{y} = X\mathbf{q} + \mathbf{b}_1 f(t)$ transforms the canonical variables to the state variables. Show that substitution of the transformation matrix $\mathbf{y} = X\mathbf{q} + \mathbf{b}_1 f(t)$ into the state-space form yields the canonical form $\dot{\mathbf{q}} = \Lambda\mathbf{q} + X^{-1}\mathbf{b}f(t)$ where $\mathbf{b} = \mathbf{b}_0 + A\mathbf{b}_1$.

(c) When the state-space form is $\dot{\mathbf{y}} = A\mathbf{y} + \mathbf{b}_0 f(t) + \mathbf{b}_1 f'(t) + \mathbf{b}_2 f''(t)$, the transformation $\mathbf{y} = X\mathbf{q} + (\mathbf{b}_1 + A\mathbf{b}_2)f(t) + \mathbf{b}_2 f'(t)$ transforms the canonical variables to the state variables. Show that substitution of the transformation matrix into the state-space form yields the canonical form $\dot{\mathbf{q}} = \Lambda\mathbf{q} + X^{-1}\mathbf{b}f(t)$ where $\mathbf{b} = \mathbf{b}_0 + A\mathbf{b}_1 + A^2\mathbf{b}_2$.

9

Frequency-response methods

Frequency-response methods provide a convenient means for investigating the dynamic behavior of control systems. By frequency response is meant the response of a system to a sinusoidal input $f = f_0 \sin \omega t$. A characteristic of linear systems is that after the effect of the initial transients has "died out," the response also becomes a sinusoid with the same angular velocity ω of the input. As is illustrated in Fig. 9.1, the response $y = y_0 \sin (\omega t + \phi)$ is displaced some phase

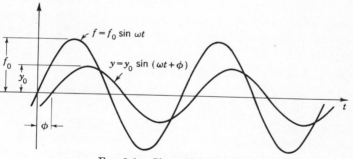

FIG. 9.1. Sinusoidal response.

angle ϕ from the input, and the amplitude y_0 is different from that of the input f_0. Both the phase angle ϕ and the amplitude ratio y_0/f_0 are functions of the angular velocity ω of the input signal. Graphs of ϕ versus ω and of amplitude ratio y_0/f_0 versus ω form the basis for frequency-response methods.

9.1 Frequency Response. Because frequency-response methods are based on a knowledge of ϕ versus ω and y_0/f_0 versus ω, it is now shown how these quantities may be determined directly by substitution of $j\omega$ for D in the operational form of the differential equation for the system.

The general operational form of a differential equation is

$$y(t) = \frac{(a_m D^m + a_{m-1}D^{m-1} + \cdots + a_1 D + a_0)f(t)}{D^n + b_{n-1}D^{n-1} + \cdots + b_1 D + b_0} = \frac{L_m(D)f(t)}{L_n(D)} \quad (9.1)$$

The transform of the preceding expression is

$$Y(s) = \frac{L_m(s)F(s) + I(s)}{L_n(s)} = \frac{L_m(s)N_{F(s)}}{L_n(s)D_{F(s)}} + \frac{I(s)}{L_n(s)} \quad (9.2)$$

The transform for the input is

$$F(s) = \mathfrak{L}(f_0 \sin \omega t) = \frac{\omega f_0}{s^2 + \omega^2} = \frac{N_{F(s)}}{D_{F(s)}} \quad (9.3)$$

Expanding Eq. (9.2) in a partial-fraction expansion and noting that $D_{F(s)} = s^2 + \omega^2 = (s - j\omega)(s + j\omega)$ gives

$$Y(s) = \frac{K_1}{s - r_1} + \cdots + \frac{K_n}{s - r_n} + \frac{K_C}{s - j\omega} + \frac{K_{-C}}{s + j\omega}$$
$$+ \frac{I_1}{s - r_1} + \cdots + \frac{I_n}{s - r_n} \quad (9.4)$$

where $r_1, r_2, \ldots, r_n$ are the zeros of $L_n(s)$ and $K_1, K_2, \ldots, K_n, K_C$ and K_{-C} are the constants which arise from the partial-fraction expansion of $L_m(s)N_{F(s)}/L_n(s)D_{F(s)}$ and $I_1, I_2, \ldots, I_n$ are the constants which arise from the partial-fraction expansion of $I(s)/L_n(s)$. Inverting Eq. (9.4) gives

$$y(t) = (K_1 + I_1)e^{r_1 t} + \cdots + (K_n + I_n)e^{r_n t}$$
$$+ \frac{1}{b}|K(a + jb)|e^{at} \sin(bt + \phi) \quad (9.5)$$

For a stable system $r_1, r_2, \ldots, r_n$ must have negative real parts, so that after sufficient time the effect of these terms becomes negligible. Thus, for stable systems, the steady-state sinusoidal response $y(t)_{ss}$ is determined by the last term of Eq. (9.5). For the quadratic $s^2 + \omega^2$, it follows that $a = 0$ and $b = \omega$.

Thus
$$y(t)_{ss} = \frac{1}{\omega}|K(j\omega)| \sin(\omega t + \phi) \quad (9.6)$$

The terms $|K(j\omega)|$ and $\phi = \angle K(j\omega)$ are evaluated as follows:

$$K(j\omega) = \lim_{s \to j\omega}\left[(s^2 + \omega^2)\frac{L_m(s)N_F(s)}{L_n(s)D_F(s)}\right] \quad (9.7)$$
$$= \lim_{s \to j\omega}\left[\frac{(s^2 + \omega^2)L_m(s)\omega f_0}{L_n(s)(s^2 + \omega^2)}\right]$$
$$= \frac{L_m(j\omega)\omega f_0}{L_n(j\omega)} \quad (9.8)$$

The terms $L_m(j\omega)$ and $L_n(j\omega)$ are obtained by substituting $j\omega$ for D in $L_m(D)$ and $L_n(D)$. From Eq. (9.8) it follows that

$$|K(j\omega)| = \left|\frac{L_m(j\omega)}{L_n(j\omega)}\right| \omega f_0 \tag{9.9}$$

and

$$\phi = \angle \left[\frac{L_m(j\omega)}{L_n(j\omega)}\right] \omega f_0 = \angle \frac{L_m(j\omega)}{L_n(j\omega)} \tag{9.10}$$

Substitution of Eq. (9.9) into Eq. (9.6) yields

$$y(t)_{ss} = \left|\frac{L_m(j\omega)}{L_n(j\omega)}\right| f_0 \sin(\omega t + \phi) = y_0 \sin(\omega t + \phi) \tag{9.11}$$

From Eq. (9.11), the amplitude y_0 of the steady-state response $y(t)_{ss}$ is seen to be

$$y_0 = \left|\frac{L_m(j\omega)}{L_n(j\omega)}\right| f_0 \tag{9.12}$$

The amplitude ratio is

$$\frac{y_0}{f_0} = \left|\frac{L_m(j\omega)}{L_n(j\omega)}\right| \tag{9.13}$$

It is now shown how to obtain plots of the amplitude ratio y_0/f_0 versus ω and also phase angle ϕ versus ω. Consider the first-order linear differential equation

$$y(t) = \frac{1}{1 + \tau D} f(t) \tag{9.14}$$

The substitution of $j\omega$ for D in the differential operator gives

$$\frac{L_m(j\omega)}{L_n(j\omega)} = \frac{1}{1 + j\tau\omega} \tag{9.15}$$

The ratio of the amplitude of the output to that of the input is

$$\frac{y_0}{f_0} = \left|\frac{L_m(j\omega)}{L_n(j\omega)}\right| = \frac{1}{\sqrt{1 + (\tau\omega)^2}} \tag{9.16}$$

The phase angle ϕ is

$$\phi = \angle \frac{1}{1 + j\tau\omega} \tag{9.17}$$

The angle of the numerator is $\angle(1 + j0) = \tan^{-1} 0 = 0$. Thus, subtracting the angle of the denominator from the angle of the numerator gives

$$\phi = 0 - \angle(1 + j\tau\omega) = -\tan^{-1} \tau\omega \tag{9.18}$$

In Fig. 9.2 is shown a graph of the amplitude ratio y_0/f_0 versus ω and a graph of the phase angle ϕ as a function of the angular velocity ω of the forcing function. When ω is small, the amplitude of the output is almost equal to that of the input and the phase angle ϕ is quite small.   The output cannot keep up with the input at higher frequencies, and it begins to lag behind the input.   For $\omega > 1/\tau$ this effect becomes very pronounced.

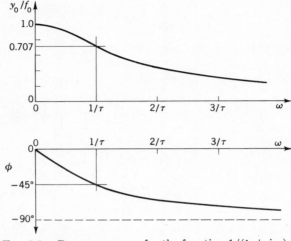

FIG. 9.2.   Response curves for the function $1/(1 + j\tau\omega)$.

From Fig. 9.2, it is to be noticed that, for a given ω, the amplitude ratio has a given value and also there is a certain phase angle ϕ between the input and the output.   This amplitude ratio $|L_m(j\omega)/L_n(j\omega)|$ and phase angle $\angle L_m(j\omega)/L_n(j\omega)$ determine a vector $L_m(j\omega)/L_n(j\omega)$.   The path of the tip of this vector (vector loci) for values of ω from zero to ∞ is shown in Fig. 9.3.   This is called a polar plot.   The polar plot shown in Fig. 9.3

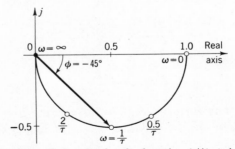

FIG. 9.3.   Polar plot for the function $1/(1 + j\tau\omega)$.

is seen to convey the same information as the two separate curves shown in Fig. 9.2.   The polar plot for this first-order system is a semicircle as shown in Fig. 9.3.   At $\omega = 0$, the length of the vector is 1, and the phase angle zero.   At $\omega = 1/\tau$ the phase angle $\phi = -45°$, and the length of the vector is 0.707.

The operation of the feedforward part of a control system is given by the equation

$$c(t) = G(D)e(t) \tag{9.19}$$

When the actuating signal $e(t)$ is a sinusoid $[e(t) = e_0 \sin \omega t]$, then the controlled variable $c(t)$ is also a sinusoid $[c(t) = c_0 \sin (\omega t + \phi)]$.   The amplitude ratio c_0/e_0 and the phase angle ϕ are

$$\frac{c_0}{e_0} = |G(j\omega)|$$

$$\phi = \angle G(j\omega) \tag{9.20}$$

Thus $G(j\omega)$ completely describes the frequency response of the feedforward elements.   Similarly, the response of the feedback elements is determined by $H(j\omega)$.

The transfer function is the same as the differential operator except that D is replaced by s.   Thus either the substitution of $j\omega$ for D in the differential operator or the substitution of $j\omega$ for s in the transfer function gives the vector equation for evaluating the frequency response.

9.2 Logarithmic Representation.   Frequency-response methods are based on the response $G(j\omega)$ of the feedforward elements and $H(j\omega)$ of the feedback elements.   The transfer functions for these quantities are $G(s)$ and $H(s)$, respectively.   These quantities are usually obtained in factored form and are composed of multiples or ratios of one or more of the following types of terms: s, $1 + \tau s$, $(s^2 + 2\zeta\omega_n s + \omega_n{}^2)/\omega_n{}^2$.   The substitution of $j\omega$ for s means that $G(j\omega)$ or $H(j\omega)$ will be composed of terms such as $j\omega$, $1 + j\tau\omega$, or $(\omega_n{}^2 - \omega^2 + j2\zeta\omega_n\omega)/\omega_n{}^2$.   To obtain the resulting frequency response, the multiplication of such terms is simplified by the use of logarithms.   For example, let the value of $G(s)$ be given by the equation

$$G(s) = \frac{K}{s(1 + \tau s)} \tag{9.21}$$

Substituting $j\omega$ for s yields

$$G(j\omega) = \frac{K}{j\omega(1 + j\tau\omega)} \tag{9.22}$$

The magnitude of Eq. (9.22) is

$$|G(j\omega)| = \frac{K}{|j\omega|\,|1 + j\tau\omega|} = \frac{K}{\omega\,\sqrt{1 + \tau^2\omega^2}} \tag{9.23}$$

Taking the logarithm of the preceding expression gives

$$\log \left| \frac{G(j\omega)}{K} \right| = - \log \omega - \tfrac{1}{2} \log (1 + \tau^2\omega^2) \qquad (9.24)$$

The angle ϕ is

$$\phi = \measuredangle G(j\omega) = - \measuredangle j\omega - \measuredangle (1 + j\tau\omega)$$
$$= -90° - \tan^{-1} \tau\omega \qquad (9.25)$$

The contribution due to the $1/j\omega$ term is shown in Fig. 9.4. The equation for the amplitude is $\log |1/j\omega| = - \log \omega$. When ω is 1, the value of

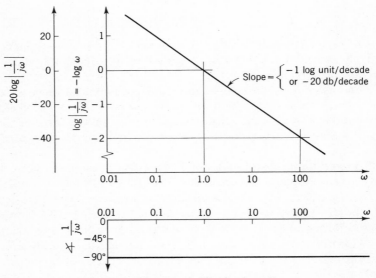

FIG. 9.4.   Log-magnitude plot for $1/j\omega$.

$- \log \omega$ is 0, and when ω changes by multiples of 10, the value of $- \log \omega$ changes in increments of 1. The slope of this straight-line logarithmic response shown in Fig. 9.4 is -1 log unit/decade. A decade is the horizontal distance on the frequency scale from any value of ω to ten times ω. Thus, the distance from $\omega = 1$ to $\omega = 10$ or from $\omega = 3$ to $\omega = 30$, etc., is a decade.

The vertical log-magnitude scale is sometimes expressed in decibel units. To convert the vertical log-magnitude scale of Fig. 9.4 to decibel units, it is necessary only to multiply by a factor of 20. In using decibel units the slope is -20 db/decade rather than -1 log unit/decade. In this text, the log-magnitude scale is expressed directly in logarithmic units rather than decibels.

The contribution due to $\log |1/(1 + j\tau\omega)|$ is shown in Fig. 9.5. For small values of ω such that $\omega \ll 1/\tau$,

$$-\tfrac{1}{2} \log (1 + \tau^2\omega^2) \approx -\tfrac{1}{2} \log 1 = 0 \qquad (9.26)$$

This is the equation for the low-frequency asymptote to the exact curve as is shown in Fig. 9.5. For $\omega \gg 1/\tau$,

$$-\tfrac{1}{2} \log (1 + \tau^2\omega^2) \approx -\tfrac{1}{2} \log \tau^2\omega^2 = -\log \tau\omega \qquad (9.27)$$

This is the high-frequency asymptote. When $\omega = 1/\tau$, the value of $-\log \tau\omega$ is zero, and for $\omega = 10/\tau$, the function is -1, etc. The slope of

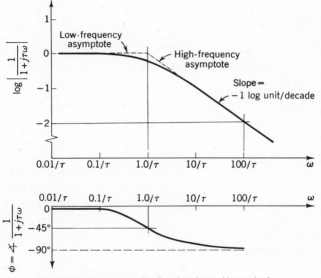

Fig. 9.5. Log-magnitude plot for $1/(1 + j\tau\omega)$.

this high-frequency asymptote is thus seen to be -1 log unit/decade. The break frequency ($\omega = 1/\tau$) is located directly under the intersection of the two asymptotes. For most preliminary design work, the asymptotes are sufficiently close to the exact curve so that the extra effort, involved in using the exact curve is generally not warranted. The maximum error occurs at the "break frequency" and is $0 - \tfrac{1}{2} \log (1 + 1) = -0.303/2 = -0.1515$. It should be noticed that Fig. 9.5 is applicable for any value of τ. Thus, by using a separate scale for each break frequency as shown in Fig. 9.6, then the same curve may be used to represent various functions of the form $(1 + \tau_1 s)$, $(1 + \tau_2 s)$, etc.

The phase-angle curve is obtained by solving the equation

$$\phi = -\tan^{-1} \tau\omega \qquad (9.28)$$

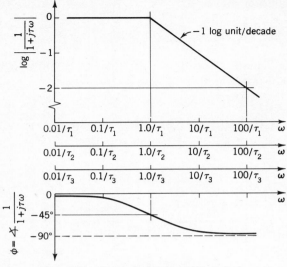

FIG. 9.6.   General plot for $1/(1 + j\tau\omega)$.

In Fig. 9.7, it is shown graphically how Figs. 9.4 and 9.5 may be added to solve Eqs. (9.24) and (9.25).   For numerical purposes, it is assumed that the value of τ is 0.1 sec.   For $\omega > 1/\tau = 10$, the slope is the sum of that due to the $1/j\omega$ term plus that due to the high-frequency asymptote of $1/(1 + j\tau\omega)$, that is, -2 log units/decade.   Such graphs of the log magnitude and angle vs. log frequency are called log-magnitude or Bode diagrams.   H. W. Bode made many contributions to the development of frequency-response techniques.

A feature of the logarithmic method is that, if the term appears in the numerator rather than the denominator, it is necessary merely to change the sign of the amplitude and phase-angle scales in tabulating the result. For example, if Eq. (9.22) were of the form

$$G(j\omega) = \frac{K(1 + j\tau\omega)}{j\omega} \tag{9.29}$$

then $$\log \frac{|G(j\omega)|}{K} = -\log \omega + \tfrac{1}{2} \log (1 + \tau^2\omega^2) \tag{9.30}$$

and $$\measuredangle G(j\omega) = -90° + \tan^{-1} \tau\omega \tag{9.31}$$

By comparing Eqs. (9.30) and (9.31) with Eqs. (9.24) and (9.25), it is seen that only the sign of the term which went from the denominator to the numerator has changed.   In Fig. 9.8 is shown the log-magnitude diagram for $G(j\omega)/K = (1 + j\tau\omega)/j\omega$, in which the value of τ is assumed to be 0.1 sec.   Comparison of the log-magnitude diagram for $1 + j\tau\omega$ of

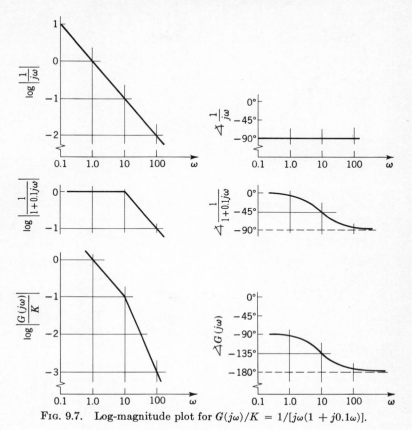

FIG. 9.7.   Log-magnitude plot for $G(j\omega)/K = 1/[j\omega(1 + j0.1\omega)]$.

Fig. 9.8 with that for $1/(1 + j\tau\omega)$ of Fig. 9.7 shows that the sign of the logarithm of the amplitude ratio and the sign of the phase angle have been changed.

The third type of term which occurs is of the form $(\omega_n{}^2 - \omega^2 + j2\zeta\omega_n\omega)/\omega_n{}^2$. By using a generalized graph, this term may be treated in a manner analogous to that described for using Fig. 9.6 to evaluate terms of the form $1 + j\tau\omega$. Consider the function

$$G(j\omega) = \frac{K_1}{(1 + j\tau\omega)(\omega_n{}^2 - \omega^2 + j2\zeta\omega_n\omega)} \tag{9.32}$$

This may be rewritten in the form

$$G(j\omega) = \frac{K}{(1 + j\tau\omega)\left[\dfrac{(\omega_n{}^2 - \omega^2) + j2\zeta\omega_n\omega}{\omega_n{}^2}\right]} \tag{9.33}$$

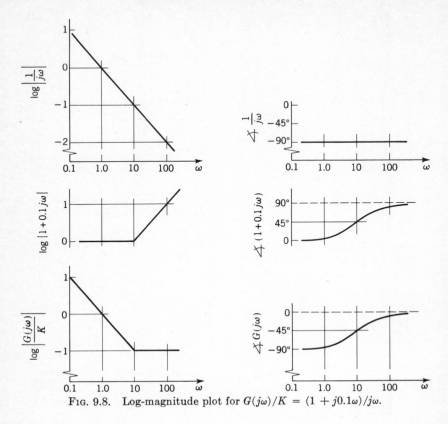

Fig. 9.8.   Log-magnitude plot for $G(j\omega)/K = (1 + j0.1\omega)/j\omega$.

where $K = K_1/\omega_n^2$.

The logarithm of the magnitude of the quadratic term is

$$\log \left| \frac{1}{[1 - (\omega/\omega_n)^2] + j2\zeta(\omega/\omega_n)} \right| = \log \frac{1}{\sqrt{[1 - (\omega/\omega_n)^2]^2 + [2\zeta(\omega/\omega_n)]^2}}$$

$$= -\frac{1}{2} \log \left\{ \left[1 - \left(\frac{\omega}{\omega_n} \right)^2 \right]^2 + \left(2\zeta \frac{\omega}{\omega_n} \right)^2 \right\} \quad (9.34)$$

For small values of ω/ω_n such that $\omega/\omega_n \ll 1$, Eq. (9.34) becomes

$$-\tfrac{1}{2} \log 1 = 0 \quad (9.35)$$

This is the equation for the low-frequency asymptote which is a horizontal straight line like that obtained for a $1 + j\tau\omega$ term.

The equation for the high-frequency asymptote is obtained by noting that, for $\omega/\omega_n \gg 1$, it follows that

$$\left[1 - \left(\frac{\omega}{\omega_n} \right)^2 \right]^2 \approx \left(\frac{\omega}{\omega_n} \right)^4 \gg \left(2\zeta \frac{\omega}{\omega_n} \right)^2$$

Thus, for $\omega/\omega_n \gg 1$, Eq. (9.34) becomes

$$-\frac{1}{2} \log \left(\frac{\omega}{\omega_n}\right)^4 = -2 \log \frac{\omega}{\omega_n} \qquad (9.36)$$

The slope of the high-frequency asymptote is -2 log units/decade, and this asymptote intersects the low-frequency asymptote at $\omega/\omega_n = 1$.

The value of the phase angle is

$$\phi = - \tan^{-1} \frac{2\zeta(\omega/\omega_n)}{1 - (\omega/\omega_n)^2} \qquad (9.37)$$

The nondimensional curves for the logarithm of the amplitude and the phase angle as given by Eqs. (9.34) and (9.37), respectively, are shown in Fig. 9.9. The curves for the reciprocal of this function are obtained by merely changing the sign of the amplitude and phase-angle scales.

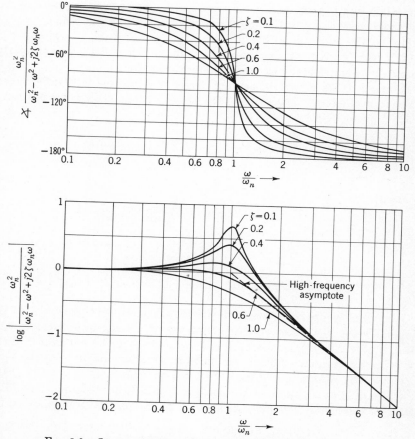

FIG. 9.9. Log-magnitude plot for $1/[1 - (\omega/\omega_n)^2 + j2\zeta(\omega/\omega_n)]$.

In summary, for any function which is composed of multiples of terms such as $j\omega$, $1 + j\tau\omega$, and $(\omega_n{}^2 - \omega^2 + j2\zeta\omega_n\omega)/\omega_n{}^2$ the value of the log $|G(j\omega)|$ and the $\angle G(j\omega)$ at any given angular velocity ω of the driving sine wave is the sum of the contribution due to each term which is obtained from Fig. 9.4, 9.6, or 9.9. Thus, having the $|G(j\omega)|$ and the $\angle G(j\omega)$, one may construct a polar plot of $G(j\omega)$, as was demonstrated by Fig. 9.3. Tables of the log-magnitude and angle for the functions $j\omega$, $1/(1 + j\tau\omega)$, and $1/[1 - (\omega/\omega_n)^2 + j2\zeta(\omega/\omega_n)]$ shown in Figs. 9.4, 9.6, and 9.9 respectively are given in Appendix VI.

Experimental Determination of Frequency Response.[1] A feature of frequency-response methods is that the response $G(j\omega)$ and $H(j\omega)$ may be determined experimentally. For example, at a given frequency ω, the value of $G(j\omega)$ is obtained by exciting the feedforward elements with a sinusoidal input of angular velocity ω and then measuring the ratio of the amplitude of the output to that of the input and also measuring the phase angle ϕ. By repeating this process for a wide range of values of ω the frequency response is obtained. The response $H(j\omega)$ is similarly obtained by sinusoidally exciting the feedback elements.

In Fig. 9.10 are shown the asymptotes of an experimentally determined log-magnitude plot. Because of the change of slope at ω_1, there is a term

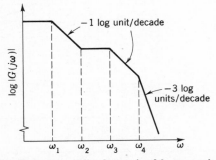

FIG. 9.10. Experimentally determined log-magnitude plot.

$1/(1 + j\tau_1\omega)$ where $\tau_1 = 1/\omega_1$ in the frequency-response equation. At the angular velocity ω_2 there is a net increase of $+1$ log units/decade, and thus the term $1 + j\tau_2\omega$, where $\tau_2 = 1/\omega_2$ appears in the numerator of the response expression. The change in slope at ω_3 is indicative of the term $1/(1 + j\tau_3\omega)$, where $\tau_3 = 1/\omega_3$. Because the slope changes by -2 log units/decade at ω_4, there is a quadratic term in the denominator. The value of the break frequency ω_4 is equal to the natural frequency ω_n for

[1] R. A. Bruns and R. M. Saunders, "Analysis of Feedback Control Systems," chap. 14, McGraw-Hill Book Company, New York, 1955.

the quadratic. That is, from Fig. 9.9, it follows that at the break point for a quadratic $\omega/\omega_n = \omega_4/\omega_n = 1$ or $\omega_n = \omega_4$. To determine the damping ratio ζ, it is necessary to compare the exact response curve for the component which causes this quadratic term in $G(j\omega)$ to the general response curves of Fig. 9.9. From the preceding, it follows that the frequency response for $G(j\omega)$ is

$$G(j\omega) = \frac{K(1 + j\tau_2\omega)}{(1 + j\tau_1\omega)(1 + j\tau_3\omega)[(\omega_4{}^2 - \omega^2 + j2\zeta\omega_4\omega)/\omega_4{}^2]} \qquad (9.38)$$

In the next section, it is shown how the value of K can be determined directly from the low-frequency portion of the log-magnitude diagram.

It is a rather lengthy process to excite control elements at various frequencies in order to obtain experimentally the frequency response. An alternate procedure is to determine the transient response to some known input and then use the method presented in Appendix III for calculating the frequency response from the transient response.

After the equation for the frequency response has been experimentally determined, it is a simple matter to substitute s for $j\omega$ to obtain the transfer function. The substitution of s for $j\omega$ in Eq. (9.38) gives

$$G(s) = \frac{K(1 + \tau_2 s)}{(1 + \tau_1 s)(1 + \tau_3 s)[(s^2 + 2\zeta\omega_4 s + \omega_4{}^2)/\omega_4{}^2]} \qquad (9.39)$$

The substitution of D for s gives the differential equation of operation.

The magnitude of $1 + j\tau\omega$ is the same as that of $1 - j\tau\omega$. However, as the phase angle for $1 + j\tau\omega$ goes from 0 to $+90°$, the phase angle for $1 - j\tau\omega$ goes from 0 to $-90°$. Most systems are minimum-phase systems;[1] i.e., all factors are of the form $j\omega$, $1 + j\tau\omega$, or $(\omega_n{}^2 - \omega^2 + j2\zeta\,\omega_n\omega)/\omega_n{}^2$. For minimum-phase systems, as ω becomes infinite, the phase angle is $\phi = -90°(n - m)$, where n is the order of the denominator and m that of the numerator. Non-minimum-phase systems may be detected from the phase-angle plot, because as ω becomes infinite $\phi \neq -90°(n - m)$. For either minimum- or non-minimum-phase systems the slope of the log-magnitude diagram at high frequencies is $-(n - m)$ log units/decade.

9.3 Evaluating the Gain K. In general a transfer function may be expressed in the form

$$G(s) = \frac{K_n\{(1 + \tau_a s) \cdots [(s^2 + 2\zeta_a\omega_{n_a}s + \omega_{n_a}{}^2)/\omega_{n_a}{}^2] \cdots\}}{s^n\{(1 + \tau_1 s) \cdots [(s^2 + 2\zeta_1\omega_{n_1}s + \omega_{n_1}{}^2)/\omega_{n_1}{}^2] \cdots\}} \qquad (9.40)$$

where K_n is the overall gain of the transfer function $G(s)$, and n is the power to which the s term in the denominator is raised. Usually the

[1] J. L. Bower and P. M. Schultheiss, "Introduction to the Design of Servomechanisms," John Wiley & Sons, Inc., New York, 1958.

value of n is 0, 1, or 2. The first time constant in the numerator is τ_a, the second τ_b, etc. The natural frequency for the first quadratic term in the numerator is ω_{n_a}, and the damping ratio is ζ_a. Similarly, τ_1 is the first time constant which appears in the denominator, the second τ_2, etc. The natural frequency for the first quadratic term in the denominator is ω_{n_1}, and its damping ratio is ζ_1.

The substitution of $j\omega$ for s in Eq. (9.40) gives

$$G(j\omega) = \frac{K_n\{(1 + j\tau_a\omega) \cdots [(\omega_{n_a}^2 - \omega^2 + j2\zeta_a\omega_{n_a}\omega)/\omega_{n_a}^2] \cdots\}}{(j\omega)^n\{(1 + j\tau_1\omega) \cdots [(\omega_{n_1}^2 - \omega^2 + j2\zeta_1\omega_{n_1}\omega)/\omega_{n_1}^2] \cdots\}} \tag{9.41}$$

For small values of ω all the terms inside the braces of the preceding expression approach 1, so that

$$G(j\omega) = \frac{K_n}{(j\omega)^n} \qquad \omega \approx 0 \tag{9.42}$$

As is indicated from the preceding expression, the gain K_n can be determined from the low-frequency portion of a log-magnitude plot. Equation (9.42) is valid for minimum- as well as non-minimum-phase systems. All the frequency-response techniques to be discussed in this text are equally valid for minimum- or non-minimum-phase systems. The techniques for evaluating K_n for $n = 0$, 1, or 2 are described in the following.

$n = 0$. When n is zero, there is no $j\omega$ term in $G(j\omega)$. Thus, Eq. (9.42) becomes

$$G(j\omega) = K_0 \qquad \omega \approx 0 \tag{9.43}$$

A typical log-magnitude plot for this case is shown in Fig. 9.11a. For small values of ω the low-frequency asymptote has a constant value $G(j\omega) = K_0$.

$n = 1$. For small values of ω and for n equal to 1, it follows from Eq. (9.42) that

$$G(j\omega) = \frac{K_1}{j\omega} \qquad \omega \approx 0 \tag{9.44}$$

The logarithm of the magnitude of $G(j\omega)$ is

$$\log |G(j\omega)| = \log K_1 - \log \omega \qquad \omega \approx 0 \tag{9.45}$$

From Eq. (9.45), it follows that, as ω changes by a factor of 10, then $\log |G(j\omega)|$ changes by -1. Thus for $\omega \approx 0$ the slope of the curve of $\log |G(j\omega)|$ versus ω is -1 log unit/decade. A typical log-magnitude diagram for the case in which $n = 1$ is shown in Fig. 9.11b. It is to be noted that the low-frequency slope of -1 log unit/decade or its extension intersects the horizontal axis $\log |G(j\omega)| = 0$ at the point where

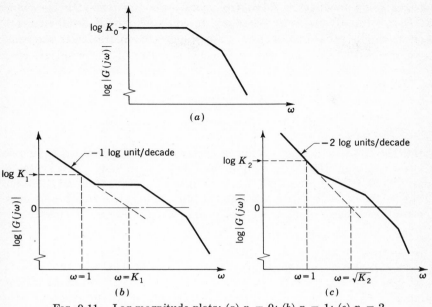

Fig. 9.11. Log-magnitude plots: (a) $n = 0$; (b) $n = 1$; (c) $n = 2$.

$\omega = K_1$. This fact follows directly from Eq. (9.45) by noting that, when $\log |G(j\omega)| = 0$, then $\log \omega = \log K_1$ or simply $\omega = K_1$. In addition, for ω equal to 1, Eq. (9.45) becomes $\log |G(j\omega)| = \log K_1$. Thus, as is shown in Fig. 9.11b, a vertical line through $\omega = 1$ intersects the low-frequency asymptote or its extension at the value $\log K_1$.

$n = 2$. The low-frequency equation for this case is

$$G(j\omega) = \frac{K_2}{(j\omega)^2} = -\frac{K_2}{\omega^2} \qquad (9.46)$$

The logarithm of the magnitude of $G(j\omega)$ is

$$\log |G(j\omega)| = \log K_2 - 2 \log \omega \qquad (9.47)$$

A typical log-magnitude diagram for $n = 2$ is illustrated in Fig. 9.11c. The slope at low frequencies is $-2 \log$ units/decade. From Eq. (9.47), it follows that, when $\log |G(j\omega)| = 0$, then $\log \omega = \frac{1}{2} \log K_2$ or $\omega = \sqrt{K_2}$. Thus, the low-frequency asymptote or its extension intersects the horizontal line $\log |G(j\omega)| = 0$ at the frequency $\omega = \sqrt{K_2}$. When $\omega = 1$, then Eq. (9.47) becomes $\log |G(j\omega)| = \log K_2$. Thus, a vertical line through $\omega = 1$ intersects the low-frequency asymptote or its extension at $\log K_2$.

9.4 Equivalent Unity-feedback System. Much simplification is afforded in the application of frequency-response methods to systems having unity feedback. A control system having feedback elements $H(D)$ can usually be represented by an equivalent unity-feedback system, as is illustrated in Fig. 9.12. For the case in which $H(D)$ is a con-

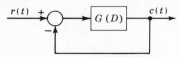

FIG. 9.12. Unity-feedback system.

stant, the equivalent unity-feedback system is readily obtained by moving the constant $H(D)$ to the input side of the main loop. The systems represented by Figs. 3.21, 4.7b, and 4.11 have a constant term $H(D) = C_4$ in the feedback path. Moving C_4 to the input side of the main loop yields the unity-feedback systems shown in Fig. 9.13a, b, and c, respectively.

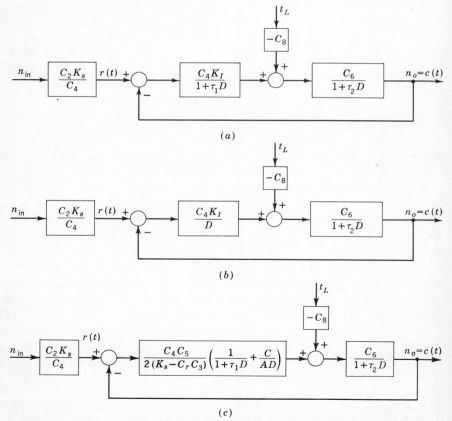

FIG. 9.13. Equivalent unity-feedback systems when $H(D)$ is a constant.

To obtain the equivalent unity-feedback system when $H(D)$ is not a constant, first write $H(D)$ in the form $H(D) = C[1 + H_1(D)]$. The constant C may now be taken out of the feedback path, and the remaining term $1 + H_1(D)$ may be represented as shown in Fig. 9.14 by two separate

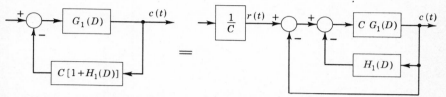

FIG. 9.14.   Equivalent unity-feedback system when $H(D)$ is not a constant.

paths.   The design of such systems in which there is an inner, or minor, feedback path is often facilitated by the use of inverse polar plots, as is discussed in Sec. 10.7.

In obtaining the equivalent unity-feedback system, only constant terms are to be taken outside the main loop.   The fact that $r(t)$ is equal to some constant times the command signal does not affect the basic dynamic behavior of the system.

System Type.   When a system is represented in its equivalent unity-feedback form, the value of n in $G(s)$ as indicated by Eq. (9.40) has a predominant effect upon the behavior of the system.   When $n = 0$, the system is designated as a type 0 system.   A type 1 system is one for which $n = 1$, a type 2 system is one for which $n = 2$, etc.

A type 0 system results when there is no integration as in a proportional control.   For an integral control in which there is one integrator in the feedforward elements, n is equal to 1.   A type 2 system has two integrations in the feedforward elements, etc.

9.5 Polar Plots.   Vector loci or polar plots are better suited for the solution of certain control problems than are log-magnitude diagrams, and vice versa.   As is later explained, other methods of representing frequency-response information are the log-modulus, or Nichols, plot and the inverse polar plot.   A control engineer must be familiar with all these means of plotting frequency-response data so that he can select the method which is best suited to his particular problem.

The polar plots for a number of commonly encountered functions are shown in Fig. 9.15.   Polar plots may often be roughly sketched by knowing the location at low frequencies ($\omega \to 0$) and at high frequencies

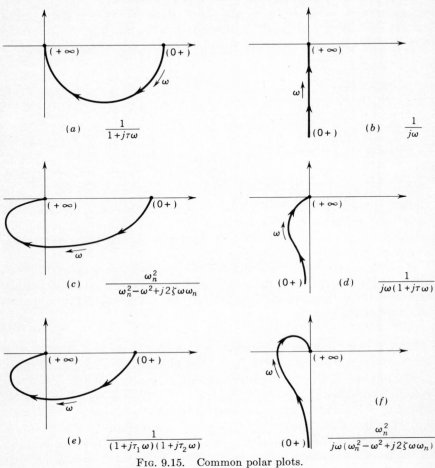

FIG. 9.15.   Common polar plots.

($\omega \to \infty$).   For example, in Fig. 9.15a

$$\frac{1}{1+j\tau\omega}\bigg|_{\omega=0+} = 1$$

$$\frac{1}{1+j\tau\omega}\bigg|_{\omega=+\infty} \approx \frac{1}{j\tau\omega}\bigg|_{\omega=+\infty} = \frac{e^{-j90°}}{\tau\omega}\bigg|_{\omega=+\infty} = (0+)e^{-j90°} \quad (9.48)$$

Thus, the locus of Fig. 9.15a begins at the $+1$ point on the positive real axis, and as ω approaches ∞, the locus approaches 0 along the $-90°$ axis.

The low- and high-frequency values for Fig. 9.15b are

$$\frac{1}{j\omega}\bigg|_{\omega=0+} = \frac{1}{\omega}e^{-j90°}\bigg|_{\omega=0+} = (+\infty)e^{-j90°}$$

$$\frac{1}{j\omega}\bigg|_{\omega=+\infty} = \frac{1}{\omega}e^{-j90°}\bigg|_{\omega=+\infty} = (0+)e^{-j90°}$$

(9.49)

For Fig. 9.15c

$$\frac{1}{1 - (\omega/\omega_n)^2 + j2\zeta(\omega/\omega_n)}\bigg|_{\omega=0+} = 1$$

$$\frac{1}{1 - (\omega/\omega_n)^2 + j2\zeta(\omega/\omega_n)}\bigg|_{\omega=+\infty} \approx \frac{1}{-(\omega/\omega_n)^2}\bigg|_{\omega=+\infty} = -\left(\frac{\omega_n}{\omega}\right)^2\bigg|_{\omega=+\infty}$$

$$= (0+)e^{-j180°} \quad (9.50)$$

The limiting value for a function composed of multiples of the preceding terms is equal to the product of the contribution of each term. For example, in Fig. 9.15d

$$\frac{1}{j\omega(1 + j\tau\omega)}\bigg|_{\omega=0+} = \frac{1}{j\omega}\bigg|_{\omega=0+} \times \frac{1}{1 + j\tau\omega}\bigg|_{\omega=0+} = (+\infty)e^{-j90°}$$

$$\frac{1}{j\omega(1 + j\tau\omega)}\bigg|_{\omega=+\infty} = \frac{1}{j\omega}\bigg|_{\omega=+\infty} \times \frac{1}{1 + j\tau\omega}\bigg|_{\omega=+\infty} = (0+)e^{-j90°}(0+)e^{-j90°}$$

$$= (0+)e^{-j180°} \quad (9.51)$$

Application of this technique will verify the results shown in Fig. 9.15e and f.

The low- and high-frequency locations are summarized in Table 9.1. The reciprocal of any term in Table 9.1 is obtained by changing the sign of

TABLE 9.1

ω	$\dfrac{1}{j\omega}$	$\dfrac{1}{1 + j\tau\omega}$	$\dfrac{\omega_n{}^2}{\omega_n{}^2 - \omega^2 + j2\zeta\omega\omega_n}$
$0+$	$\infty\underline{/-90°}$	$1\underline{/0°}$	$1\underline{/0°}$
$+\infty$	$0\underline{/-90°}$	$0\underline{/-90°}$	$0\underline{/-180°}$

the phase angle and taking the reciprocal of the magnitude. At low frequencies, there is a phase shift with the $1/j\omega$ term only. Thus, for a type 0 system, the polar plot originates on the positive real axis, where ϕ is zero. Typical polar plots for type 0, 1, 2, and 3 systems are shown in Fig. 9.16. A type 1 system begins at infinity on the negative 90° axis, a type 2 system begins at infinity on the negative 180° axis, etc. For most systems, the polar plot terminates at the origin when $\omega = \infty$.

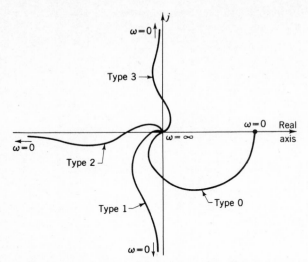

Fig. 9.16.   Polar plots for type 0, 1, 2, and 3 systems.

9.6 *M* and *α* Circles.   Frequency-response methods make extensive use of the open-loop frequency response $G(j\omega)$.   The open-loop response is the response that would be obtained if the feedback path were disconnected at the comparator (i.e., opened).

For unity-feedback systems, the closed-loop frequency response

$$C(j\omega)/R(j\omega)$$

is related to the open-loop response $G(j\omega)$ by the equation

$$\frac{C(j\omega)}{R(j\omega)} = \frac{G(j\omega)}{1 + G(j\omega)} \tag{9.52}$$

In Fig. 9.17 is shown a typical $G(j\omega)$ plot.   The vector from the origin to a point on the curve is $G(j\omega)$, and the vector from the point $-1 + j0$ to the

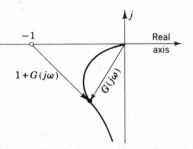

Fig. 9.17.   Determination of closed-loop frequency response from the open-loop response.

same point on this curve is $1 + G(j\omega)$. The ratio of these two vectors is the closed-loop frequency response for the value of ω at that point. This shows that every point on the $G(j\omega)$ plane corresponds to a certain value of $C(j\omega)/R(j\omega)$. The magnitude of the ratio of the amplitude of the output sinusoid to the input is designated by the symbol $M = |C(j\omega)/R(j\omega)|$.

In Fig. 9.18, it is to be seen that the locus of lines of constant M are circles on the $G(j\omega)$ plane. The proof of this follows: Consider any point

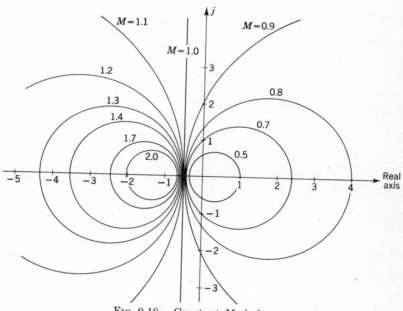

FIG. 9.18. Constant M circles.

$G(j\omega) = x + jy$ in the $G(j\omega)$ plane of Fig. 9.18. The closed-loop frequency response is

$$\frac{C(j\omega)}{R(j\omega)} = \frac{x + jy}{1 + x + jy} \tag{9.53}$$

The magnitude of the preceding equation is

$$M = \left|\frac{C(j\omega)}{R(j\omega)}\right| = \left(\frac{x^2 + y^2}{1 + 2x + x^2 + y^2}\right)^{\frac{1}{2}} \tag{9.54}$$

Squaring and cross multiplying gives

$$x^2(M^2 - 1) + 2xM^2 + y^2(M^2 - 1) = -M^2 \tag{9.55}$$

Dividing by $M^2 - 1$ and completing the square by adding $M^4/(M^2 - 1)^2$

to both sides yields

$$x^2 + \frac{2xM^2}{M^2 - 1} + \frac{M^4}{(M^2 - 1)^2} + y^2 = \frac{M^4}{(M^2 - 1)^2} - \frac{M^2}{M^2 - 1} \quad (9.56)$$

Thus,
$$\left(x + \frac{M^2}{M^2 - 1}\right)^2 + y^2 = \frac{M^2}{(M^2 - 1)^2} \quad (9.57)$$

Equation (9.57) is the equation of a circle as shown in Fig. 9.19 with center at

$$x = \frac{M^2}{1 - M^2} \qquad y = 0 \quad (9.58)$$

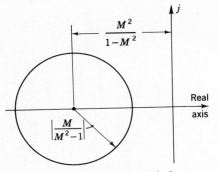

FIG. 9.19.   Typical M circle.

and radius

$$r = \left| \frac{M}{M^2 - 1} \right| \quad (9.59)$$

The closed-loop frequency response may be expressed in the form

$$\frac{C(j\omega)}{R(j\omega)} = Me^{j\alpha} \quad (9.60)$$

where $M = |C(j\omega)/R(j\omega)|$ and $\alpha = \measuredangle C(j\omega)/R(j\omega)$.

The loci of lines of constant phase angle α for the closed-loop response are also circles.   The circles of constant α are shown in Fig. 9.20.   From Eq. (9.53)

$$\alpha = \measuredangle \frac{x + jy}{1 + x + jy}$$

Multiplying numerator and denominator by the complex conjugate of the denominator gives

$$\alpha = \measuredangle \frac{x^2 + x + y^2 + jy}{(1 + x)^2 + y^2}$$

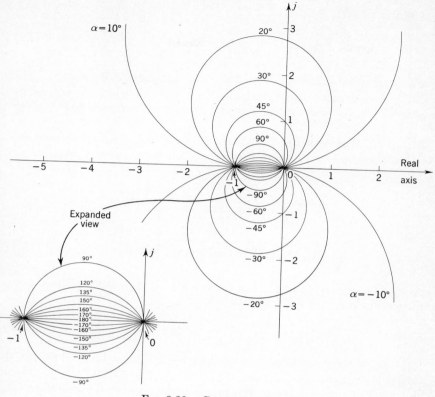

Fig. 9.20. Constant α circles.

By letting $N = \tan \alpha$, then

$$N = \tan \alpha = \frac{y}{x^2 + x + y^2}$$

This may be written in the form

$$x^2 + x + y^2 - \frac{y}{N} = 0$$

Completing the square gives

$$\left(x + \frac{1}{2}\right)^2 + \left(y - \frac{1}{2N}\right)^2 = \frac{N^2 + 1}{4N^2}$$

The centers of these circles are located at

$$x = -\tfrac{1}{2} \quad \text{and} \quad y = \tfrac{1}{2}N \tag{9.61}$$

The radius of each circle is

$$r = \frac{1}{2N} \sqrt{N^2 + 1} \qquad (9.62)$$

9.7 Correlation between Transient and Frequency Response. The transient response of a system can be ascertained from the frequency response. The correlation for a type 1 system is developed first.

Type 1 Systems. In Fig. 9.21 is shown the block diagram representation for a second-order type 1 system. As mentioned in Sec. 9.4, a

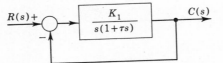

$R(s)+$ $\dfrac{K_1}{s(1+\tau s)}$ $C(s)$

Fig. 9.21.   Second-order type 1 system.

type 1 system has a lone s term in the denominator of $G(s)$. The closed-loop transfer function $C(s)/R(s)$ is

$$\frac{C(s)}{R(s)} = \frac{K_1/\tau}{s^2 + 1/\tau s + K_1/\tau} = \frac{\omega_n^2}{s^2 + 2\zeta\omega_n s + \omega_n^2} \qquad (9.63)$$

The closed-loop response is described by a second-order differential equation in which $\omega_n^2 = K_1/\tau$ and $2\zeta\omega_n = 1/\tau$ or $\zeta = 1/(2\sqrt{K_1\tau})$. Thus ζ and ω_n completely describe the transient behavior. To correlate the transient behavior with the frequency response, note that

$$M = \left| \frac{C(j\omega)}{R(j\omega)} \right| = \frac{\omega_n^2}{|(\omega_n^2 - \omega^2) + j(2\zeta\omega\omega_n)|}$$
$$= \frac{1}{\sqrt{[1 - (\omega/\omega_n)^2]^2 + (2\zeta\omega/\omega_n)^2}} \qquad (9.64)$$

The value of ω at which M is a maximum is obtained by differentiating Eq. (9.64) with respect to ω and then setting the resulting expression equal to zero. Thus,

$$\frac{\omega_m}{\omega_n} = \sqrt{1 - 2\zeta^2} \qquad 0 \le \zeta \le 0.707 \qquad (9.65)$$

where ω_m is the value of ω at which M is a maximum. Substituting ω_m/ω_n for ω/ω_n in Eq. (9.64) gives the maximum value of M which is designated M_m. That is,

$$M_m = \frac{1}{2\zeta\sqrt{1 - \zeta^2}} \qquad \begin{cases} 0 \le \zeta \le 0.707 \\ M_m \ge 1 \end{cases} \qquad (9.66)$$

The preceding result has significance only for $0 \leq \zeta \leq 0.707$, in which case $M_m \geq 1$. In Fig. 9.22 is shown a plot of corresponding values of M_m and ζ.

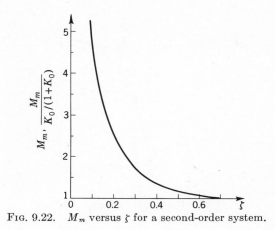

FIG. 9.22. M_m versus ζ for a second-order system.

As previously discussed, the zeros of the characteristic function which are located nearest the imaginary axis have a predominant effect upon the transient behavior of higher-order systems. Thus, the transient behavior of a higher-order, type 1 system for which $M_m \geq 1$ (the value of M_m may be obtained from a polar plot for the system) may be *approximated* by a second-order system whose damping ratio ζ as obtained from Fig. 9.22 corresponds to the value of M_m for the system.

ILLUSTRATIVE EXAMPLE 1. In Fig. 9.23 is shown the polar plot for a type 1 system for which $M_m = 1.6$ and $\omega_m = 3$. Determine the value of ζ and ω_n to be used for approximating the transient behavior.

SOLUTION. From Fig. 9.22, it follows that for $M_m = 1.6$, the corresponding value of ζ is 0.33. The value of ω_n may now be ascertained from Eq. (9.65). That is

$$\omega_n = \frac{\omega_m}{\sqrt{1 - 2\zeta^2}} = \frac{3}{\sqrt{1 - 2(0.33)^2}} = 3.4$$

It is to be noticed from Fig. 6.8 that for $\zeta > 0.707$ ($M_m < 1$) there is no overshoot of the response to a step change in the input. This is similar to the type of response that is obtained from a first-order system. Thus when M_m is less than 1 the transient response is approximated by an equivalent first-order system.

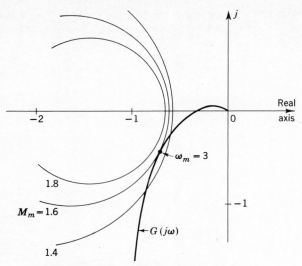

FIG. 9.23.　Polar plot for a type 1 system.

In Fig. 9.24 is shown a first-order, type 1 system.　The correlation between the frequency and transient response for this system is obtained by first writing the equation for the closed-loop response.

$$\frac{C(s)}{R(s)} = \frac{K_1}{K_1 + s} = \frac{1}{1 + (1/K_1)s} = \frac{1}{1 + \tau_c s}$$

where $\tau_c = 1/K_1$ is the closed-loop time constant.

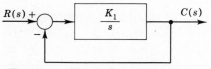

FIG. 9.24.　First-order type 1 system.

In Fig. 9.25 is shown a plot of the open-loop frequency response

$$G(j\omega) = \frac{K_1}{j\omega}$$

When the magnitude of $G(j\omega)$ is 1, then

$$|G(j\omega)| = \frac{K_1}{|j\omega_c|} = \frac{K_1}{\omega_c} = 1$$

where ω_c designates the value of ω at which $|G(j\omega)| = 1$.　That is, ω_c is the value of ω at which the $G(j\omega)$ plot crosses the unit circle as is illus-

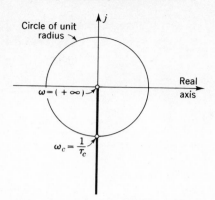

Fig. 9.25. Polar plot for $G(j\omega) = K_1/j\omega$.

trated in Fig. 9.25. Because $K_1 = \omega_c$ and $\tau_c = 1/K_1$, then

$$\tau_c = \frac{1}{K_1} = \frac{1}{\omega_c}$$

Thus, for type 1 systems in which $M_m < 1$, an indication of the equivalent time constant τ_c is obtained by taking the reciprocal of the angular frequency ω_c at which the $G(j\omega)$ plot crosses the unit circle.

The preceding results correlating transient and frequency response for type 1 systems are summarized in Table 9.2.

TABLE 9.2 CORRELATION CRITERIA FOR TYPE 1 SYSTEMS

$M_m < 1$	$M_m \geq 1$
$\tau_c = \dfrac{1}{\omega_c}$	$M_m = \dfrac{1}{2\zeta\sqrt{1 - \zeta^2}}$
	$\dfrac{\omega_m}{\omega_n} = \sqrt{1 - 2\zeta^2}$

For $M_m < 1$, the response is approximated by a first-order system in which τ_c describes the transient behavior. For $M_m \geq 1$, the response is approximated by a second-order system in which ζ and ω_n describe the transient behavior.

Although the preceding correlation criteria are developed for type 1 systems, these criteria yield good approximations for type 2 systems, type 3 systems, etc. In the next section, it is shown that the preceding correlation criteria should be modified somewhat for the case of type 0 systems.

Type 0 *Systems.* In Fig. 9.26 is shown the block-diagram representation for a second-order, type 0 system. The closed-loop, transfer func-

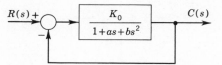

FIG. 9.26.   Second-order type 0 system.

tion $C(s)/R(s)$ is

$$\frac{C(s)}{R(s)} = \frac{K_0/b}{s^2 + (a/b)s + (1 + K_0)/b} = \frac{[K_0/(1 + K_0)]\omega_n^2}{s^2 + 2\zeta\omega_n s + \omega_n^2}$$

where $\omega_n^2 = (1 + K_0)/b$ and $2\zeta\omega_n = a/b$.

To correlate the frequency response with the transient response, note that

$$M = \left| \frac{C(j\omega)}{R(j\omega)} \right| = \frac{K_0/(1 + K_0)}{|1 - (\omega/\omega_n)^2 + 2j\zeta(\omega/\omega_n)|}$$

$$= \frac{K_0/(1 + K_0)}{\sqrt{[1 - (\omega/\omega_n)^2]^2 + (2\zeta\omega/\omega_n)^2}} \quad (9.67)$$

Differentiating to determine the value of ω at which M is a maximum gives the same result as for the corresponding type 1 system, that is

$$\omega_m = \omega_n \sqrt{1 - 2\zeta^2} \qquad 0 \leq \zeta \leq 0.707$$

Substituting ω_m for ω in Eq. (9.67) gives

$$M_m = \frac{K_0/(1 + K_0)}{2\zeta \sqrt{1 - \zeta^2}}$$

or

$$\frac{M_m}{K_0/(1 + K_0)} = \frac{1}{2\zeta \sqrt{1 - \zeta^2}} \begin{cases} 0 \leq \zeta \leq 0.707 \\ \dfrac{M_m}{K_0/(1 + K_0)} \geq 1 \end{cases} \quad (9.68)$$

Thus, for type 0 systems, the ordinate $M_m/[K_0/(1 + K_0)]$ of Fig. 9.22 is to be used. It is to be noted that for large values of K_0, the preceding criterion becomes the same as that for a type 1 system.

ILLUSTRATIVE EXAMPLE 2. In Fig. 9.27 is shown the polar plot for a type 0 system in which $M_m = 1.6$, $\omega_m = 3$, and $K_0 = 4$. Determine the value of ζ and ω_n to be used in approximating the transient behavior of this system.

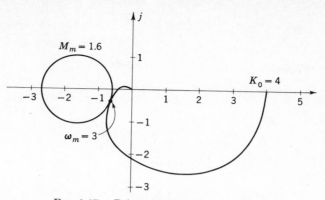

FIG. 9.27.   Polar plot for a type 0 system.

SOLUTION.   From Fig. 9.22, it follows that for $M_m/[K_0/(1 + K_0)] = 1.6/0.8 = 2$, the corresponding value of ζ is 0.26.   The value of ω_n is now ascertained from Eq. (9.65).   Thus,

$$\omega_n = \frac{\omega_m}{\sqrt{1 - 2\zeta^2}} = \frac{3}{\sqrt{1 - 2(0.26)^2}} = 3.22$$

For a type 0 system in which $M_m/[K_0/(1 + K_0)] < 1$, the transient behavior is best described by a first-order system.   In Fig. 9.28 is shown

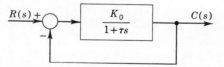

FIG. 9.28.   First-order type 0 system.

a first-order, type 0 system.   The closed-loop transfer function is

$$\frac{C(s)}{R(s)} = \frac{K_0}{1 + K_0 + \tau s} = \frac{K_0/(1 + K_0)}{1 + \tau_c s}$$

where $\tau_c = \tau/(1 + K_0)$ is the time constant for the closed-loop response. In Fig. 9.29 is shown a plot of the open-loop frequency response $G(j\omega)$. That is,

$$G(j\omega) = \frac{K_0}{1 + j\tau\omega}$$

This plot crosses a circle of radius r at $\omega = \omega_c$.   That is,

$$|G(j\omega)| = \frac{K_0}{\sqrt{1 + (\tau\omega_c)^2}} = r \tag{9.69}$$

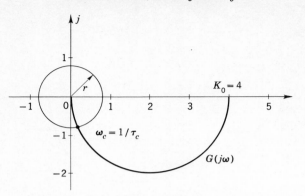

FIG. 9.29.   Polar plot for $G(j\omega) = K_0/(1 + j\tau\omega)$.

The value of r such that ω_c is the reciprocal of the closed-loop time constant is obtained by substituting $\omega_c = 1/\tau_c = (1 + K_0)/\tau$ into Eq. (9.69). This gives

$$K_0^2 = r^2[1 + (1 + K_0)^2]$$

or

$$r = \frac{K_0}{\sqrt{1 + (1 + K_0)^2}}$$

For large values of K_0, then the radius r approaches the unit circle such that the preceding criterion becomes the same as that for a type 1 system.

ILLUSTRATIVE EXAMPLE 3.   In Fig. 9.30 is shown the polar plot of a type 0 system.   Determine the value of τ_c to be used in approximating the transient behavior of this system.

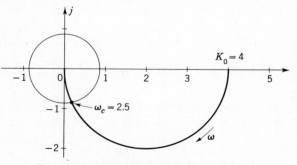

FIG. 9.30.   Polar plot for a type 0 system.

SOLUTION.   From the polar plot, it is seen that $K_0 = 4$.   The value of r is

$$r = \frac{4}{\sqrt{1 + (5)^2}} = \frac{4}{\sqrt{26}} = 0.785$$

The polar plot shows that $\omega_c = 2.5$.   Thus

$$\tau_c = \frac{1}{\omega_c} = 0.4$$

The preceding correlation criteria for type 0 systems are summarized in Table 9.3.   The preceding techniques for estimating the transient behavior are adequate for most design purposes.   In Appendix IV is shown an exact method for obtaining the transient response from the frequency response.

TABLE 9.3 CORRELATION CRITERIA FOR TYPE 0 SYSTEMS

$\dfrac{M_m}{K_0/(1 + K_0)} < 1$		$\dfrac{M_m}{K_0/(1 + K_0)} \geq 1$	
$\tau_c = \dfrac{1}{\omega_c}$		$\dfrac{M_m}{K_0/(1 + K_0)} = \dfrac{1}{2\zeta \sqrt{1 - \zeta^2}}$	
$r = \dfrac{K_0}{\sqrt{1 + (1 + K_0)^2}}$		$\dfrac{\omega_m}{\omega_n} = \sqrt{1 - 2\zeta^2}$	

9.8 Determining the Gain K to Yield a Desired M_m.   In Fig. 9.31 is shown a typical polar plot of $G(j\omega)$.   If the gain K of the original func-

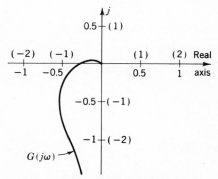

FIG. 9.31.   Typical polar plot.

tion is doubled, the value of $G(j\omega)$ is doubled at every point.   As shown in Fig. 9.31, it is not necessary to change the shape of the polar plot, but merely to change the scale by multiplying the old scale by the factor 2. Values of this new scale are shown in parentheses.   It is now shown how the gain K can be adjusted so that the polar plot $G(j\omega)$ will be tangent to any desired $M_m > 1$ circle.   This, in effect, is determining the gain K so that the system will have a desired M_m.

From Fig. 9.32, the line drawn from the origin, tangent to the desired M_m circle at the point P, has an included angle of ψ. The value of $\sin \psi$ is

$$\sin \psi = \frac{|M_m/(M_m^2 - 1)|}{|M_m^2/(1 - M_m^2)|} = \frac{1}{M_m} \tag{9.70}$$

A characteristic feature of the point of tangency P is that a line drawn from the point P perpendicular to the negative real axis intersects this axis at the -1 point. This characteristic may be proved from the geometry of Fig. 9.32.

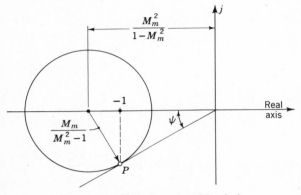

FIG. 9.32.   Tangent to an M_m circle.

The procedure for determining the gain K so that $G(j\omega)$ will have a desired value of M_m is as follows:

1.   Draw the polar plot for $G(j\omega)/K$.
2.   Draw the tangent line to the desired M_m circle [Eq. (9.70)].
3.   Draw the circle with center on the negative real axis that is tangent to both the $G(j\omega)/K$ plot and the tangent line, as is shown in Fig. 9.33.
4.   Erect the perpendicular to the negative real axis from point P, the point of tangency of this circle and the tangent line. This perpendicular intersects the negative real axis at a value $-A + j0 = -A$.
5.   In order that the circle drawn in step 3 correspond to the desired M_m circle, this point should be $-1 + j0 = -1$ rather than $-A$. The desired gain is that value of K which changes the scale so that this does become the -1 point; thus $K(-A) = -1$ or $K = 1/A$.

As is illustrated in Fig. 9.33, the perpendicular drawn from point P to the negative real axis intersects the negative real axis at a value of -0.05. However, this value should be -1. Multiplication of the scale by a factor of 20 (that is, $-0.05 \times 20 = -1$), as is shown in Fig. 9.33

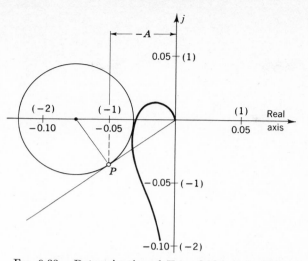

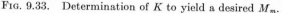

FIG. 9.33. Determination of K to yield a desired M_m.

by the numbers in parentheses, converts this point to the -1 point. Thus, the original function should have a gain of 20 in order that the circle drawn will be the desired M_m circle.

ILLUSTRATIVE EXAMPLE 1. Let it be desired to determine the gain K such that the unity feedback system for which $G(s) = K/[s(1 + 0.1s)]$ will have a maximum value $M_m = 1.4$. What values of ζ and ω_n should be used in approximating the transient behavior of this system?

SOLUTION. First construct the polar plot for

$$\frac{G(j\omega)}{K} = \frac{1}{j\omega(1 + 0.1j\omega)}$$

as is shown in Fig. 9.34. The value of ψ is obtained from Eq. (9.70).

$$\psi = \sin^{-1}\frac{1}{M_m} = \sin^{-1}\frac{1}{1.4} = 45.6° \qquad (9.71)$$

By trial and error, the circle which is tangent to both the $G(j\omega)/K$ plot and also to the line drawn at the angle $\psi = 45.6°$ is determined. The perpendicular drawn from point P intersects the negative real axis at the point $-A = -0.067$, or $A = 0.067$. Thus, the gain is $K = 1/0.067 = 16$.

From Fig. 9.22, for $M_m = 1.4$ the corresponding value of ζ is 0.422, and from Fig. 9.34, $\omega_m = 10.7$. Hence from Eq. (9.65) the value of ω_n is found to be

$$\omega_n = \frac{10.7}{\sqrt{1 - 2(0.422)^2}} = 13.35$$

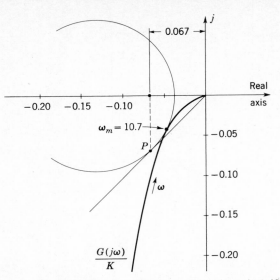

Fig. 9.34.   Polar plot for $G(j\omega)/K = 1/[j\omega(1 + j0.1\omega)]$.

ILLUSTRATIVE EXAMPLE 2. For the system shown in Fig. 9.35a, the transfer function $G(s)$ is

$$G(s) = \frac{100}{(1 + 0.1s)(s^2 + 8s + 25)} = \frac{4}{(1 + 0.1s)(s^2 + 8s + 25)/25}$$

The corresponding frequency response is

$$G(j\omega) = \frac{4}{(1 + 0.1j\omega)[1 - \omega^2/25 + j(8\omega/25)]}$$

1.   Determine the factor K_c by which the gain of the system should be changed such that the resulting system will have an M_m of 1.4.
2.   What values of ζ and ω_n should be used to approximate the transient behavior of this resulting system?

SOLUTION

1.   For an M_m of 1.4 the tangent line is constructed at an angle of $\psi = 45.6°$. As shown in Fig. 9.35b, the perpendicular from the point P to the real axis intersects the real axis at the point -1.85. In order that this be the minus one point, the original scale must be changed by a factor of $1/1.85 = 0.54$. This is the factor K_c by which the gain of the system should be changed. Thus,

New gain $= (K_c)(\text{original gain}) = (0.54)(4) = 2.16$

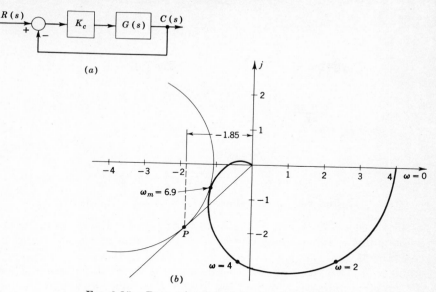

FIG. 9.35. Determination of change of gain K_c.

2. For this type 0 system,

$$\frac{M_m}{K_0/(1 + K_0)} = \frac{1.4}{2.16/3.16} = 2.05$$

From Fig. 9.22, the corresponding value of ζ is 0.25. The polar plot shows that $\omega_m = 6.9$. Hence from Eq. (9.65),

$$\omega_n = \frac{6.9}{\sqrt{1 - 2(0.25)^2}} = 7.37$$

This last example shows that if the $G(j\omega)$ plot is employed rather than the $G(j\omega)/K$ plot, then $-1/A$ is equal to the factor K_c by which the gain should be changed in order to obtain a desired M_m.

Log-Modulus Plots. In addition to log-magnitude and polar plots, another method of representing frequency-response information is log-modulus, or Nichols, plots.[1] The log-modulus curve is a plot of log $|G(j\omega)|$ versus $\angle G(j\omega)$ for various values of angular velocity ω. The log-modulus curve for $G(j\omega)/K = 1/[j\omega(1 + 0.1j\omega)]$ is constructed in Fig. 9.36. From the equation for $G(j\omega)/K$ it is seen that, for a given angular velocity ω, the corresponding phase angle and amplitude ratio can be obtained. These values determine one point on the log-modulus plot. By repeating this process for other values of ω, the log-modulus

[1] H. M. James, N. B. Nichols, and R. S. Phillips, "Theory of Servomechanisms," McGraw-Hill Book Company, New York, 1947.

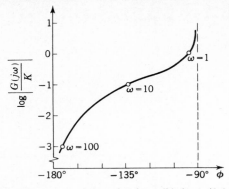

FIG. 9.36. Log-modulus plot for $1/[j\omega(1 + j0.1\omega)]$.

graph of $G(j\omega)/K$ shown in Fig. 9.36 is obtained. Every point on the log-modulus graph corresponds to a certain value of $G(j\omega)$. Lines of constant M and constant α which are circles on the polar plot (Figs. 9.18 and 9.20) become contours when drawn on the log-modulus plot. These M and α contours are shown in Fig. 9.37. It is now shown how the log-modulus techniques may be used to determine the gain K so that a system will have a desired value of M_m.

ILLUSTRATIVE EXAMPLE 3. Same as Illustrative Example 1, except use log-modulus techniques.

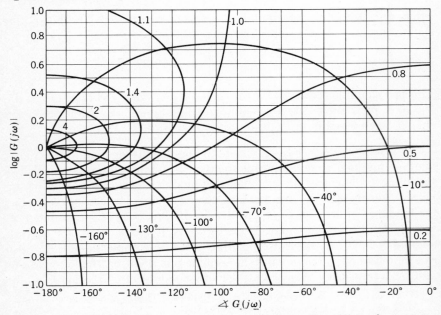

FIG. 9.37. Log-modulus representation for lines of constant M and lines of constant α.

SOLUTION. In Fig. 9.38 is shown the log-modulus plot of $G(j\omega)/K$ corresponding to the polar plot of Fig. 9.34. Changing the gain K does not affect the phase angle, but merely moves the log-modulus curve vertically up for K greater than 1 and down for K less than one. In Fig. 9.38 it is to be noticed that the original function represented by the solid line must be moved up 1.2 log units so that it will be tangent to the desired M_m

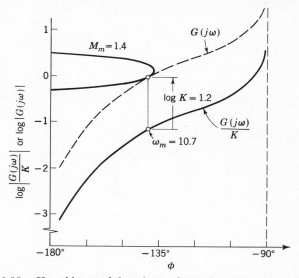

FIG. 9.38. Use of log-modulus plot to determine K for a desired M_m.

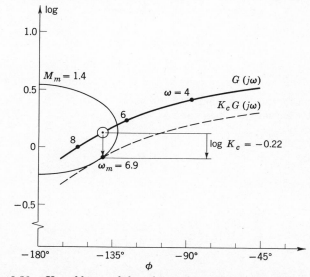

FIG. 9.39. Use of log-modulus plot to determine K_c for a desired M_m.

contour. Because log $K = 1.2$, it follows that the required gain is $K = 16$. The values of ζ and ω_n are found as before.

ILLUSTRATIVE EXAMPLE 4. Same as Illustrative Example 2, except use log-modulus techniques.

SOLUTION. In Fig. 9.39 is shown the log-modulus plot $G(j\omega)$ corresponding to the polar plot of Fig. 9.35b. Because log $K_c = -0.22$, then $K_c = 0.54$.

Problems

9.1 Each of the mechanical systems shown in Fig. P9.1 is excited sinusoidally by a force $f = f_0 \sin \omega t$. For each system, determine

(*a*) The equation for the amplitude ratio y_0/f_0
(*b*) The equation for the phase shift ϕ

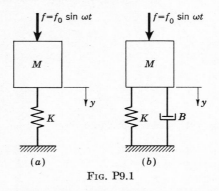

(*a*)   (*b*)

FIG. P9.1

9.2 Each of the mechanical systems shown in Fig. P9.2 is excited sinusoidally by a motion of the support $x = x_0 \sin \omega t$. For each system, determine

(*a*) The equation for the amplitude ratio y_0/x_0
(*b*) The equation for the phase shift ϕ

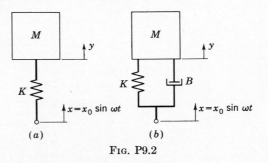

(*a*)   (*b*)

FIG. P9.2

9.3 In Fig. P9.3 is shown a Seismic Instrument. The motion of the pen relative to the base is $z = y - x$. Show that the differential equation relating z
to the motion of the base is

$$(MD^2 + BD + K)z = -MD^2x$$

(*a*) Determine the equation for the amplitude ratio z_0/x_0 for the case in which
the motion of the base is $x = x_0 \sin \omega t$.

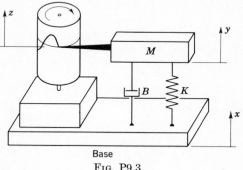

Base

FIG. P9.3

(*b*) Show that for very large values of ω/ω_n, $z_0/x_0 = -1$. Such an instrument
which may be used to measure displacements is called a vibrometer.

(*c*) Show that for small values of ω/ω_n

$$\frac{z_0}{a_0} = \frac{1}{\omega_n{}^2}$$

where

$$\ddot{x} = -x_0\omega^2 \sin \omega t = a_0 \sin \omega t$$

Such an instrument which measures acceleration is called an accelerometer.

9.4 For each of the following functions,

$$G(s) = \frac{10}{(1 + s)(1 + 0.1s)}$$

$$G(s) = \frac{10(1 + s)}{s(s^2 + 8s + 100)/100}$$

(*a*) Draw the asymptotes for the log-magnitude diagram.

(*b*) Sketch the polar plot.

9.5 For each of the functions given below, evaluate $|G(j\omega)|$ and $\phi = \angle G(j\omega)$
for $\omega = 4(1/0.25) = 16$, $\omega = 2(1/0.25) = 8$, $\omega = 1/0.25 = 4$, $\omega = \frac{1}{2}(1/0.25) = 2$,
and $\omega = (\frac{1}{4})(1/0.25) = 1$. [Note that values of ω in the vicinity of the break
frequency $(1/0.25)$ yield the most significant information.] Construct the exact
log-magnitude diagrams for each function, and sketch in the asymptotes.

(*a*) $G(j\omega) = \dfrac{10}{1 + 0.25j\omega}$

(*b*) $G(j\omega) = \dfrac{10}{j\omega(1 + 0.25j\omega)}$

(*c*) $G(j\omega) = \dfrac{10}{(1 + 0.25j\omega)^2}$

9.6 For the quadratic given below, evaluate $|G(j\omega)|$ and $\phi = \measuredangle G(j\omega)$ for values of $\omega/\omega_n = 4$, $\omega/\omega_n = 2$, $\omega/\omega_n = 1$, $\omega/\omega_n = \frac{1}{2}$, and $\omega/\omega_n = \frac{1}{4}$ and for $\zeta = 0.4$. Repeat for the case in which $\zeta = 0.1$. Construct the exact log-magnitude diagram, and sketch in the asymptotes.

$$G(j\omega) = \frac{10}{1 - (\omega/\omega_n)^2 + j2\zeta(\omega/\omega_n)}$$

9.7 Construct the polar plot for each of the $G(j\omega)$ functions given in Probs. 9.5 and 9.6.

9.8 The asymptotes of the log-magnitude diagram for two $G(j\omega)$ functions are shown in Fig. P9.8. For each case, the value of ϕ is $-270°$ at very high frequencies. Determine the equation for $G(j\omega)$, and evaluate the gain K for each case.

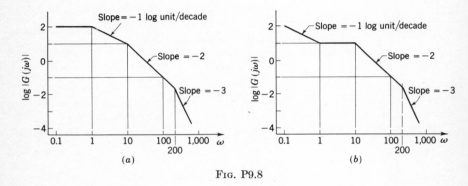

FIG. P9.8

9.9 For the system shown in Fig. P9.9, the frequency-response curves for $G_1(j\omega)$ and $G_2(j\omega)$ were determined experimentally. For both $G_1(j\omega)$ and $G_2(j\omega)$ the phase angle at very high frequencies is $\phi_1 = \phi_2 = -90°$. Construct the log-

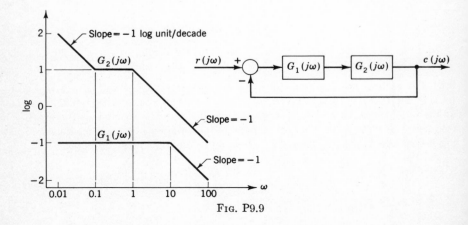

FIG. P9.9

magnitude plot for $G(j\omega) = G_1(j\omega)G_2(j\omega)$. Determine the equation for $G(j\omega)$, and evaluate the gain K.

9.10 Convert each of the systems shown in Fig. P9.10 to equivalent unity-feedback systems.

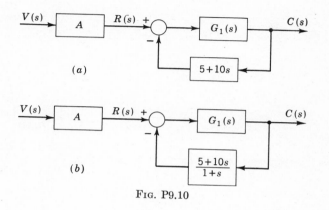

(a)

(b)

FIG. P9.10

9.11 (a) It is desired to have an M_m of 1.4 for a unity-feedback, type 0 control system in which $K_0 = 5$. From the polar plot of $G(j\omega)$, it is found that $-A = -\frac{1}{8}$ and $\omega_m = 4$. Determine the factor by which the gain should be changed to yield the desired value of M_m. What is the approximate damping ratio and natural frequency for the resulting system?

(b) Same as part (a) except for a type 1 system.

9.12 The polar plots of $G(j\omega)$ for two unity-feedback systems (system A and system B) are shown in Fig. P9.12. For each system, determine whether the response would be better approximated by a first- or a second-order system and also the corresponding value of τ or ζ and ω_n to be used.

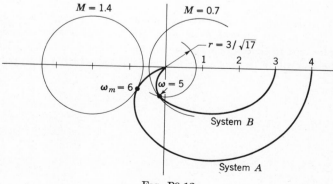

FIG. P9.12

9.13 The open-loop transfer function for the system shown in Fig. P9.13 is

$$G(s) = \frac{3}{(s^2 + 2\zeta\omega_n s + \omega_n{}^2)/\omega_n{}^2} = \frac{3}{(s^2 + 8s + 4)/4}$$

The polar plot is also shown.

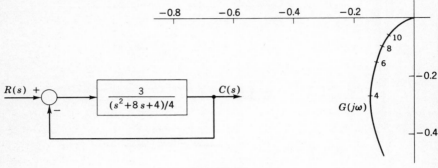

FIG. P9.13

(*a*) Determine the closed-loop transfer function $C(s)/R(s)$. What is the corresponding value of ζ and ω_n for this closed-loop transfer function?

(*b*) From the polar plot for $G(j\omega)$, determine the factor K_c by which the gain should be changed in order to yield an M_m of $2/\sqrt{3}$, ($\psi = \sin^{-1}\sqrt{3}/2 = 60°$). By using the correlation criterion between frequency response and transient response, determine the approximate value of ζ and ω_n for the resulting closed-loop system.

9.14 By use of polar plots, determine the value of K to yield an M_m of 1.4 for each of the following unity-feedback systems:

(*a*) $G(s) = \dfrac{K}{s(1 + 0.25s)}$ (*b*) $G(s) = \dfrac{K}{s(0.25s^2 + 0.40s + 1)}$

(*c*) $G(s) = \dfrac{K}{(1 + 0.25s)(0.25s^2 + 0.40s + 1)}$

9.15 Same as Prob. 9.14 except use log-modulus plots rather than polar plots.
9.16 For each system of Prob. 9.14 let $K = 4$, and then determine the factor K_c by which the gain should be changed in order to obtain an M_m of 1.4.
9.17 Same as Prob. 9.16 except use log-modulus plots rather than polar plots.

10

Improving system performance

Additional insight into the correlation between the shape of a polar plot and the dynamic behavior of a system is obtained by the Nyquist stability criterion.[1] For many design problems, it is not only necessary to change the gain K as discussed in the preceding chapter, but it is also necessary to reshape the polar plot. In this chapter, the significance of the Nyquist stability criterion is first presented, and then it is shown how system performance may be improved by reshaping the polar plot.

10.1 Nyquist Stability Criterion. The Nyquist criterion makes extensive use of conformal mapping. The process of conformal mapping is illustrated as follows: Consider the function

$$1 + G(s)H(s) = s^2 - 2s + 2 = (s - 1 - j)(s - 1 + j) \quad (10.1)$$

For each value of s, there is a corresponding value of the function $1 + G(s)H(s)$. It is necessary to specify the range of values of s so that the corresponding values of the function can be computed. For instance, suppose that it is desired to let s follow the path of the circumference of the circle shown in Fig. 10.1a. Because the center of the circle is the point $2 + j0$ and the radius is 2, then

$$s = 2 + 2e^{j\beta} \quad (10.2)$$

where β varies from $0°$ to $-90°$ to $-180°$, etc., as s traverses the circle in a clockwise direction. Substitution of s from Eq. (10.2) into Eq. (10.1) gives $1 + G(s)H(s)$ as a function of β, that is,

$$1 + G(s)H(s) = 2 + 4e^{j\beta} + 4e^{2j\beta} \quad (10.3)$$

A plot of the corresponding map of $1 + G(s)H(s)$ is shown in Fig. 10.1b. It is important to notice that there are two clockwise encirclements of the origin of the $1 + G(s)H(s)$ plot shown in Fig. 10.1b. Also, it should be noticed from Eq. (10.1) that the zeros ($s = 1 + j$ and $s = 1 - j$) of the function $1 + G(s)H(s)$ of Eq. 10.1 are located within the path of

[1] H. Nyquist, Regeneration Theory, *Bell System Tech. J.*, **11**: 126–147 (1932).

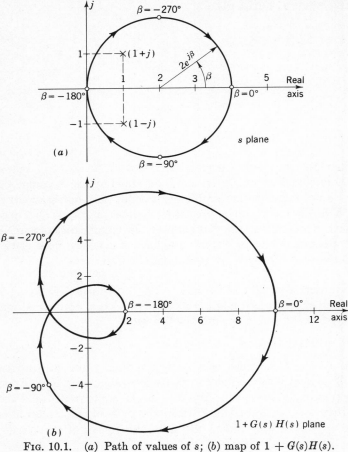

Fig. 10.1. (a) Path of values of s; (b) map of $1 + G(s)H(s)$.

values of s as shown in Fig. 10.1a. In general, it can be shown that there is one encirclement of the origin of the $1 + G(s)H(s)$ plot for each zero of $1 + G(s)H(s)$ which lies within the path of values for s. These encircle-ments are in the *same* sense as the motion around the path in the s plane, in this case, clockwise. For each pole of $1 + G(s)H(s)$ located within the path of values for s, there is one encirclement of the origin in the *opposite* sense. By a pole is meant a value of s which makes $1 + G(s)H(s)$ infinite. For example, consider the function.

$$1 + G(s)H(s) = \frac{1}{s^2 - 2s + 2} = \frac{1}{(s - 1 - j)(s - 1 + j)} \qquad (10.4)$$

The preceding function has two poles, $s = 1 + j$ and $s = 1 - j$.

The following general equation may be formulated,

$$N = Z - P \qquad (10.5)$$

where P = no. of poles of $1 + G(s)H(s)$ located inside path of values for s
Z = no. of zeros of $1 + G(s)H(s)$ located inside path of values for s
N = net no. of encirclements of origin of $1 + G(s)H(s)$ plane

When the net number of encirclements N is in the same sense as motion around the path of the s contour, an excess of zeros Z is indicated. The opposite sense signifies an excess of poles P. From Eq. (10.5), it follows that, when N is in the same sense, N is a positive number. Similarly, when N is in the opposite sense, N is a negative number.[1] Generally, the path of values for s is traversed in a clockwise direction. Thus, for a net number of clockwise encirclements N is positive, and there is an excess of zeros. For a net number of counterclockwise encirclements N is negative, and there is an excess of poles.

For control work, the path of values for s is usually taken as shown in Fig. 10.2. This contour is seen to proceed from the origin up the imagi-

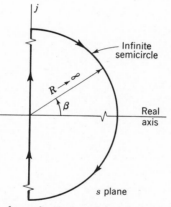

Fig. 10.2. Path of values of s that encloses the entire right half plane.

nary axis to infinity; then an infinite semicircle ($R \rightarrow \infty$) sweeps around to the bottom of the imaginary axis; whence it returns to the origin. This contour, in effect, encloses the entire right half plane.

As is discussed in Chap. 6, a system is basically unstable if any zeros of the characteristic function are located in the right half plane. By noting that

$$1 + G(s)H(s) = 1 + \frac{N_{G(s)}N_{H(s)}}{D_{G(s)}D_{H(s)}} = \frac{D_{G(s)}D_{H(s)} + N_{G(s)}N_{H(s)}}{D_{G(s)}D_{H(s)}} \qquad (10.6)$$

[1] Often Eq. (10.5) is written in the form $N = P - Z$. When this form is used, N is negative for a net number of encirclements in the same sense and is positive for the opposite sense.

it is apparent that the zeros of $1 + G(s)H(s)$ are also the zeros of the characteristic function. From Eq. (10.6), it is also to be noted that the poles of $1 + G(s)H(s)$ are the zeros of $D_{G(s)}D_{H(s)}$. Thus, by letting s assume the values indicated along the contour of Fig. 10.2, it follows that

$$Z = N + P \tag{10.7}$$

where Z = no. of zeros of characteristic function [i.e., zeros of $1 + G(s)H(s)$] in right half plane

P = no. of zeros of $D_{G(s)}D_{H(s)}$ [that is, poles of $1 + G(s)H(s)$] in right half plane

N = net no. of encirclements of origin of $1 + G(s)H(s)$ map

Because $G(s)H(s)$ is usually obtained in factored form, it is more convenient to construct the map for $G(s)H(s)$ rather than $1 + G(s)H(s)$. The effect of adding $+1$ to each point of the $G(s)H(s)$ map to obtain the $1 + G(s)H(s)$ map is accomplished simply by adding $+1$ to the scale of the real axis as is shown by the numbers in parentheses in Fig. 10.3b.

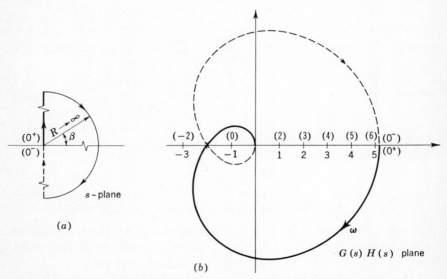

FIG. 10.3.   (a) Path of values of s; (b) map of $G(s)H(s)$ for a type 0 system.

It is seen that the -1 point of the $G(s)H(s)$ map corresponds to the origin of the $1 + G(s)H(s)$ map. Thus, N is equal to the net number of encirclements of the -1 point of the $G(s)H(s)$ plot. The application of the Nyquist stability criterion to type 0, type 1, and type 2 systems is now illustrated.

Type 0 System. Consider the following type 0 system

$$G(s)H(s) = \frac{52}{(s + 2)(s^2 + 2s + 5)} = \frac{52/10}{(0.5s + 1)(0.2s^2 + 0.4s + 1)} \quad (10.8)$$

In Fig. 10.3a is shown the path of values of s that encloses the entire right half plane. Along the positive imaginary axis (indicated by the heavy line), s equals $j\omega$. Thus, for this region Eq. (10.8) becomes

$$G(j\omega)H(j\omega) = \frac{5.2}{(1 + 0.5j\omega)(1 - 0.2\omega^2 + 0.4j\omega)}$$

This is the frequency response for the system. It is indicated by the heavy line in Fig. 10.3b. For values of s along the infinite semicircle of Fig. 10.3a, Eq. (10.8) becomes

$$G(s)H(s) = \lim_{R \to \infty} \frac{52}{(Re^{j\beta} + 2)(R^2 e^{2j\beta} + 2Re^{j\beta} + 5)} = \lim_{R \to \infty} \frac{52}{R^3 e^{3j\beta}} = 0$$

Thus, the $G(s)H(s)$ plot runs into the origin for values of s on the infinite semicircle.

For values of s on the negative imaginary axis (indicated by the dotted line) $s = -j\omega$. Because $G(-j\omega)H(-j\omega)$ is the complex conjugate of $G(j\omega)H(j\omega)$, the plot for $G(-j\omega)H(-j\omega)$ is obtained by reflecting the frequency response $G(j\omega)H(j\omega)$ about the real (horizontal) axis. The resulting $G(-j\omega)H(-j\omega)$ plot is shown dotted in Fig. 10.3b.

The poles of $1 + G(s)H(s)$ are the poles of $G(s)H(s)$. Because there are no poles of Eq. (10.8) in the right half plane (i.e. within the path of values of s) then $P = 0$. There are two clockwise encirclements of the minus-one point of Fig. 10.3b; hence $N = 2$. Note that the minus-one point of the $G(s)H(s)$ plot is the origin of the $1 + G(s)H(s)$ plot. Application of the Nyquist stability criterion to determine Z gives

$$Z = N + P = 2$$

Because there are two zeros of the characteristic function located in the right half plane, this system is basically unstable.

In general, for any type 0 system the frequency response $G(j\omega)H(j\omega)$ begins on the real axis for $\omega = 0$ and terminates at the origin for $\omega = \infty$. The $G(s)H(s)$ plot remains at the origin as the path of values of s traverses the infinite semicircle. For values of s along the negative imaginary axis (that is, $s = -j\omega$), then $G(-j\omega)H(-j\omega)$ is the complex conjugate of the frequency response $G(j\omega)H(j\omega)$.

Type 1 System. For a type 1 system, there is an s term in the denominator of $G(s)H(s)$. For example, consider the system

$$G(s)H(s) = \frac{40}{s(s + 1)(s + 4)} = \frac{10}{s(1 + s)(1 + 0.25s)} \quad (10.9)$$

In Fig. 10.4a it is to be noted that the assumed path of values of s excludes the origin. The reason for this will be made apparent in the following development.

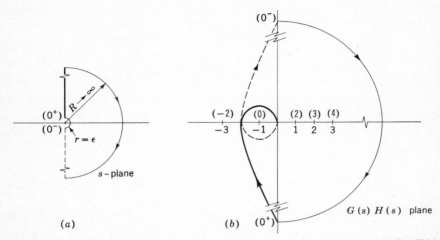

FIG. 10.4. (a) Path of values of s that excludes pole at origin; (b) map of $G(s)H(s)$ for a type 1 system.

The portion of the plot for $s = j\omega$ as ω takes on values from $(0+)$ to $(+\infty)$ is indicated by the heavy line. This is the frequency response for the system

$$G(j\omega)H(j\omega) = \frac{10}{j\omega(1 + j\omega)(1 + 0.25j\omega)}$$

For values of s on the infinite semicircle, the $G(s)H(s)$ plot runs into the origin, that is

$$G(s)H(s) = \lim_{R \to \infty} \frac{40}{(Re^{j\beta} + 1)(Re^{j\beta} + 4)} = \lim_{R \to \infty} \frac{40}{R^3 e^{3j\beta}} = 0$$

The dotted portion of the $G(s)H(s)$ plot corresponds to $s = -j\omega$, where $G(-j\omega)H(-j\omega)$ is the complex conjugate of $G(j\omega)H(j\omega)$. To complete the Nyquist plot it is necessary to connect the ends corresponding to $\omega = (0-)$ and $\omega = (0+)$. If the path of values of s were to run through the origin, then for $s = 0$, the function $G(s)H(s)$ in Eq. (10.9) would be infinite and there would be no indication of how to join the $\omega = (0-)$ and $\omega = (0+)$ ends of the $G(s)H(s)$ plot in Fig. 10.4b. Hence a small semicircle of radius ϵ is constructed about the origin as illustrated in Fig. 10.4a. The equation for $G(s)H(s)$ is obtained by the substitution of $s = \epsilon e^{j\beta}$ where β varies from $-90°$ to $0°$ to $+90°$ as s traverses the small semicircle.   Hence

$$G(s)H(s) = \lim_{\epsilon \to 0} \frac{40}{\epsilon e^{j\beta}(\epsilon e^{j\beta} + 1)(\epsilon e^{j\beta} + 4)} \approx \frac{40}{\epsilon e^{j\beta}(1)(4)}$$

$$\approx \frac{10}{\epsilon} e^{-j\beta} \approx \infty e^{-j\beta} \quad (10.10)$$

Thus $G(s)H(s)$ is an infinite semicircle.   As β goes from $-90°$ to $0°$ to $+90°$, then $G(s)H(s)$ traverses an infinite semicircle from $+90°$ to $0°$ to $-90°$.   The complete Nyquist plot is shown in Fig. 10.4b.

Because the origin has been excluded from the path of values of s, then from Eq. (10.9) it follows that there are no poles of $G(s)H(s)$ within the path of values of s, and thus $P = 0$.   As indicated in Fig. 10.4b, there are two clockwise encirclements of the -1 point so that $N = 2$.   Application of the Nyquist stability criterion gives

$$Z = N + P = 2$$

Thus, there are two roots of the characteristic equation in the right half plane.   Consequently the system is unstable.

The general procedure for constructing the complete Nyquist plot for a type 1 system is summarized as follows.   A type 1 system always has a pole at the origin, so that it is necessary to exclude the origin from the path of values of s as indicated in Fig. 10.4a.   The frequency response $G(j\omega)H(j\omega)$ corresponds to values of $s = j\omega$ as the path of values of s traverses the positive imaginary axis from $0+$ to $+\infty$.   For values of s on the infinite semicircle, the $G(s)H(s)$ plot runs into the origin.   As s traverses the negative imaginary axis, then $G(s)H(s) = G(-j\omega)H(-j\omega)$ is the complex conjugate of the frequency response.

This complex conjugate of the frequency response is obtained by "flipping" the frequency response plot about the horizontal axis.   To complete the Nyquist plot, the ends at $\omega = (0-)$ and $\omega = (0+)$ are joined by assuming values of s on the small semicircle of radius ϵ.   Eq. (10.10) holds for any type 1 system, that is

$$G(s)H(s) = \infty e^{-j\beta}$$

This is an infinite semicircle.

In the application of the Nyquist stability criterion it would make no difference if the origin were included in the path of values of s as shown in Fig. 10.5a or if it were excluded as shown in Fig. 10.4a.   For the case in which the origin is included, then β varies from $-90°$ to $-180°$ to $-270°$ as s traverses the small semicircle.   Thus from Eq. (10.10), the infinite semicircle goes from $90°$ to $180°$ to $270°$.   The resultant $G(s)H(s)$ plot is

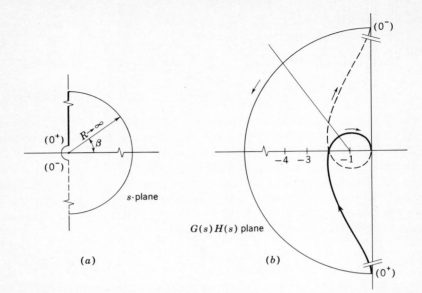

FIG. 10.5.   (a) Path of values of s that includes pole at origin; (b) map of $G(s)H(s)$
for a type 1 system.

shown in Fig. 10.5b.   For this case $N = +1$.   Because $s = 0$ is a pole
of $G(s)H(s)$ which is now included in the path of values of s, then $P = 1$.
Hence

$$Z = N + P = 1 + 1 = 2$$

Thus, the same result ($Z = 2$) is obtained whether the pole at the origin
is included or excluded from the path of values of s.   When a pole of
$G(s)H(s)$ occurs at the origin ($s = 0$), it is customary to exclude the origin
from the path of values of s as indicated in Fig. 10.4a.

A direct method for determining the net encirclements N of the minus-
one point is to draw a radial line from the -1 point out through the plot
as illustrated in Fig. 10.5b.   Note the direction of the arrow on the loci
at each point where the radial line crosses the loci.   In Fig. 10.5b, the
radial line crosses the loci three times.   At two crossings the direction of
the arrow is such as to rotate the radial line in a clockwise direction.   At
the third crossing the direction is such as to rotate the radial line in a
counterclockwise direction.   The value of N is the number of crossings
at which the arrow on the loci tends to rotate the radial line clockwise
minus the number of loci crossings at which the arrow tends to rotate
this vector counterclockwise.   Thus, for this case $N = 2 - 1 = 1$.   The
radial line may be drawn at any angle from the -1 point.

Type 2 System. A type 2 system is characterized by the fact that there is a double pole at the origin. For example, consider the system

$$G(s)H(s) = \frac{4(1 + s)}{s^2(1 + 0.1s)} \qquad (10.11)$$

As for a type 1 system, the path of values of s is taken to exclude the origin as shown in Fig. 10.6a. The frequency-response plot for this sys-

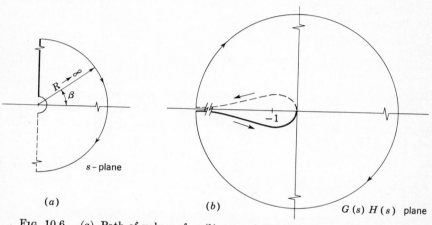

(a) (b) $G(s)H(s)$ plane

FIG. 10.6.   (a) Path of values of s; (b) map of $G(s)H(s)$ for a type 2 system.

tem is indicated by the heavy line in Fig. 10.6b. The $G(s)H(s)$ plot runs into the origin as s traverses the infinite semicircle. The $G(-j\omega)H(-j\omega)$ plot is merely the complex conjugate of the frequency response.

For values of s on the small semicircle which excludes the origin,

$$G(s)H(s) = \lim_{\epsilon \to 0} \frac{4(1 + \epsilon e^{j\beta})}{\epsilon^2 e^{2j\beta}(1 + 0.1\epsilon e^{j\beta})} \approx \frac{4}{\epsilon^2} e^{-j2\beta} \approx \infty e^{-j2\beta} \qquad (10.12)$$

Eq. (10.12) is valid for any type 2 system. As s traverses the small semicircle from $0-$ to $0+$ then β goes from $-90°$ to $0°$ to $+90°$. The corresponding infinite semicircle changes from $+180°$ to $0°$ to $-180°$ (i.e., the angle of the infinite semicircle is -2β).

For the $G(s)H(s)$ plot described by Eq. (10.11), there are no poles within the path of values of s so that P is zero. Because there are no encirclements of the minus-one point of Fig. 10.6b, then N is also zero. Thus, $Z = N + P = 0$ so that the system is basically stable.

When the polar plot for $G(s)H(s)$ goes through the -1 point, the system is on the borderline between being stable and unstable. For this case the characteristic equation has zeros on the imaginary axis. For example, from Fig. 10.3b, it is to be noticed that the polar plot crosses the negative real axis at a value of -2. If the gain were halved, the polar plot would go through the -1 point. For this case, the characteristic equation becomes

$$(s + 2)(s^2 + 2s + 5) + 26 = s^3 + 4s^2 + 9s + 36 \\ = (s + 4)(s^2 + 9) \tag{10.13}$$

Two zeros, $s = \pm j3$ are seen to lie on the imaginary axis.

Similarly, from Fig. 10.4b, it is to be noticed that the polar plot crosses the negative real axis at -2, also. Halving the gain yields for the characteristic equation

$$s(s + 1)(s + 4) + 20 = s^3 + 5s^2 + 4s + 20 \\ = (s + 5)(s^2 + 4) \tag{10.14}$$

Two zeros, $s = \pm j2$, are seen to lie on the imaginary axis.

For most systems, the open loop is stable. For this case, all the zeros of $D_G D_H$ lie in the left half plane ($P = 0$). Thus, the Nyquist stability criterion reduces to

$$Z = N$$

For a stable system ($Z = 0$), there are no net encirclements N of the -1 point.

In applying frequency-response methods, one always works with the open-loop response. It is well to note that the closed loop may be stable even though the open loop is unstable, and vice versa.

10.2 Gain Margin and Phase Margin. From the preceding discussion, the -1 point of the $G(s)H(s)$ map was seen to have great significance with regard to the stability of a system. In Fig. 10.7 is shown a typical $G(j\omega)H(j\omega)$ plot in the vicinity of the -1 point. If the gain were multiplied by an amount K_M, called the gain margin, the $G(j\omega)H(j\omega)$ plot would go through the -1 point. Thus, the gain margin is an indication of how much the gain can be increased before the curve goes through the critical point.

The angle γ in Fig. 10.7 is the angle measured from the negative real axis to where the polar plot crosses a circle of unit radius. If the angle γ is zero, the polar plot goes through the -1 point. The angle γ, called the phase margin, is thus seen to be another indication or measure of the closeness of the polar plot to the critical point.

Log-Modulus Plots. In Fig. 10.8 is shown the log-modulus plot corresponding to Fig. 10.7. Because $\log 1 = 0$, the $-1 + j0$ point on the log-modulus plot is defined by the ordinate $\log |G(j\omega)H(j\omega)| = 0$ and abscissa $\phi = -180°$. From Fig. 10.8, the vertical distance that the

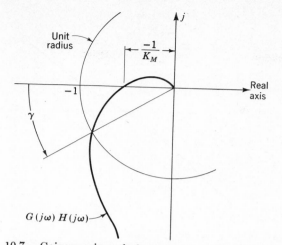

FIG. 10.7.   Gain margin and phase margin on the polar plot.

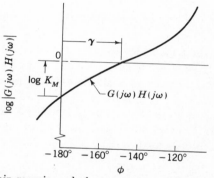

FIG. 10.8.   Gain margin and phase margin on the log-modulus plot.

$G(j\omega)H(j\omega)$ plot may be raised before it goes through the -1 point is $\log K_M$.

The value of the phase margin may be obtained from a log-modulus plot as follows: The horizontal line in Fig. 10.8 of $\log |G(j\omega)H(j\omega)| = \log 1 = 0$ corresponds to the unit circle of Fig. 10.7.   The angle γ between the point where this horizontal line intersects the $G(j\omega)H(j\omega)$ plot and the value $\phi = -180°$ is the phase margin γ.

ILLUSTRATIVE EXAMPLE 1.   The log-modulus plot of $G(j\omega)$ for a unity-feedback system is shown in Fig. 10.9.   What is the value of the gain margin and the phase margin for this system?   By what factor K_c should the gain of the system be changed so that M_m will be 1.4?   What is the new value for the gain margin and the phase margin?

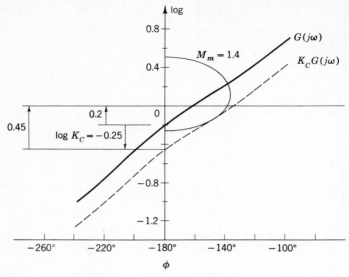

FIG. 10.9. Log-modulus plot for a system.

SOLUTION. From the $G(j\omega)$ plot for the original system, it follows that log $K_M = 0.2$, or $K_M = 1.59$, and $\gamma = 19°$. It is to be noted that a positive phase margin indicates a stable system, as does a gain margin greater than 1.

The factor K_c is obtained by moving the $G(j\omega)$ locus straight down until the new locus $K_cG(j\omega)$ is tangent to the desired $M_m = 1.4$ contour. From Fig. 10.9, it follows that

$$\log K_c = -0.25 \qquad \text{or} \qquad K_c = 0.563$$

The new gain margin is log $K_M = +0.45$ or $K_M = 2.81$, and the new phase margin is $\gamma = 45°$.

Bode Diagrams. In Fig. 10.10 is shown a Bode diagram. By entering the phase angle plot at $\phi = -180°$, it is noted that the corresponding value of log $|G(j\omega)H(j\omega)| = -0.3$. Hence, the gain of the system may be increased by $+0.3$ log units before the $G(j\omega)H(j\omega)$ curve goes through the -1 point. Thus, the value of log K_M may be represented graphically as illustrated in Fig. 10.10.

The unit circle of the polar plot corresponds to the horizontal line through the log magnitude plot at log $|G(j\omega)H(j\omega)| = 0$ in which case $|G(j\omega)H(j\omega)| = 1$. The phase margin γ is the difference between the corresponding angle and the angle $\phi = -180°$ as is illustrated in the angle diagram of Fig. 10.10.

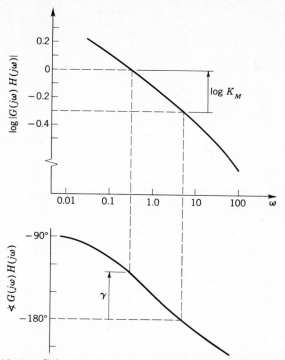

FIG. 10.10.   Gain margin and phase margin on the Bode diagram.

ILLUSTRATIVE EXAMPLE 2.   In Fig. 10.11 is shown the Bode diagram for a control system.   By what factor K_c should the gain of the system be changed such that the resulting phase margin is 45°?

SOLUTION.   By entering the angle plot at $\phi = -180° + \gamma = -135°$, the corresponding value of $\log |G(j\omega)H(j\omega)|$ is 0.3.   To have a phase margin of 45°, the magnitude diagram must be lowered by 0.3 log units.   Thus,

$$\log K_c = -0.3 = 9.7 - 10.0$$
or
$$K_c = 0.5$$

In Sec. 9.7 the transient response parameters ζ and ω_n were related to the frequency-response parameter M_m.   This correlation is limited to use with polar or log-modulus plots.   That is, M circles may be drawn on polar plots and M contours on log-modulus plots, but it is impossible to construct M lines on Bode diagrams because the magnitude and phase are on separate plots.   When designing with Bode diagrams, the transient and frequency response are correlated by relating ζ and ω_n to the phase margin.

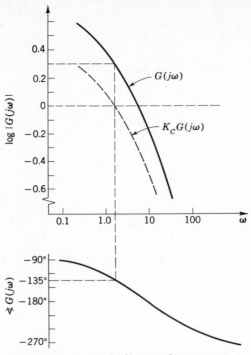

F$_{\text{IG}}$. 10.11.   Bode diagram for a system.

Correlation between ζ, ω_n, and Phase Margin.   It is now shown that the transient response parameters ζ and ω_n may also be related to the phase margin γ.   Although the following analysis is for a second-order, type 1 system, the results yield good approximations for higher-order systems and for systems of other type numbers such as a type 0 or a type 2 system.

The closed-loop transfer function for the system of Fig. 9.21 is

$$\frac{C(s)}{R(s)} = \frac{K/\tau}{s^2 + (1/\tau)s + K/\tau} = \frac{\omega_n^2}{s^2 + 2\zeta\omega_n s + \omega_n^2} \qquad (10.15)$$

where $\omega_n^2 = K/\tau$
$2\zeta\omega_n = 1/\tau$

and the subscript 1 has been omitted from K.

The open-loop frequency response is

$$G(j\omega) = \frac{K}{j\omega(1 + j\tau\omega)} \qquad (10.16)$$

By letting ω_c be the value of ω when $|G(j\omega)| = 1$, then

$$|G(j\omega)| = \frac{K}{\omega_c \sqrt{1 + \tau^2\omega_c^2}} = 1$$

Squaring gives

$$\tau^2\omega_c^4 + \omega_c^2 - K^2 = 0$$

or

$$\left(\frac{\tau}{K}\right)^2 \omega_c^4 + \frac{1}{K^2}\omega_c^2 - 1 = 0$$

Because $\tau/K = 1/\omega_n^2$ and $K = \omega_n^2\tau = \omega_n^2/2\zeta\omega_n = \omega_n/2\zeta$, then

$$\left(\frac{\omega_c}{\omega_n}\right)^4 + 4\zeta^2\left(\frac{\omega_c}{\omega_n}\right)^2 - 1 = 0$$

Application of the quadratic equation yields

$$\left(\frac{\omega_c}{\omega_n}\right)^2 = \sqrt{4\zeta^4 + 1} - 2\zeta^2 \tag{10.17}$$

The preceding expression relates ζ and the ratio ω_c/ω_n. A plot of this relationship is shown in Fig. 10.12.

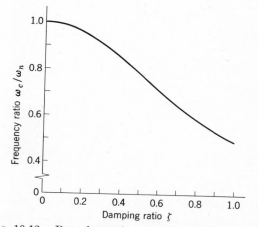

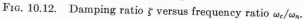

FIG. 10.12.   Damping ratio ζ versus frequency ratio ω_c/ω_n.

The phase angle γ is

$$\gamma = 180° + \angle G(j\omega_c)$$

where $\angle G(j\omega_c)$ is the angle of $G(j\omega)$ at which the polar plot crosses the unit circle. From Eq. (10.16), it follows that

$$\angle G(j\omega_c) = 0° - 90° - \tan^{-1}\tau\omega_c$$

Hence

$$\gamma = 90° - \tan^{-1}\tau\omega_c = \tan^{-1}\frac{1}{\tau\omega_c} = \tan^{-1}\frac{2\zeta}{\omega_c/\omega_n}$$

$$\gamma = \tan^{-1}\frac{2\zeta}{\sqrt{-2\zeta^2 + \sqrt{4\zeta^4 + 1}}} \tag{10.18}$$

In Fig. 10.13 is shown a plot of γ versus ζ. By knowing γ, then the value of ζ may be determined from this plot. The corresponding value of ω_c/ω_n may now be ascertained from Fig. 10.12.

ILLUSTRATIVE EXAMPLE 3. Determine the value of ζ and ω_n for the system shown by the dotted line in Fig. 10.11.

SOLUTION. For this system, the phase margin γ is 45°. From Fig. 10.13 the corresponding value of ζ is 0.425. Next from Fig. 10.12, the ratio

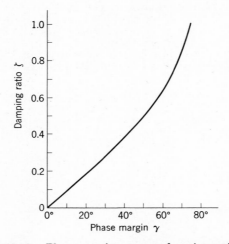

FIG. 10.13. Phase margin γ versus damping ratio ζ.

ω_c/ω_n is found to be 0.84. The frequency ω_c is the value of ω at which $\log |G(j\omega)H(j\omega)| = 0$. From Fig. 10.11, it is found that $\omega_c = 1.7$, and thus $\omega_n = 2.03$.

10.3 Lead Compensation. In Sec. 9.8, it is shown how the gain K is selected in order to obtain a desired value of M_m. A change in the gain K in effect changes the scale factor of the polar plot but does not change the basic shape of the plot. In the design of control systems, it is often necessary to change the shape of the polar plot in order to achieve the desired dynamic performance. A common means of doing this is to insert elements in series with the feedforward portion of the control. This method of compensating the performance of the control system is called series compensation.

In general, the frequency-response characteristics of a component which is used to provide series compensation are such that the output of the component either lags or leads the input. In some cases, it is advantageous to use a component in which the output lags the input for a certain range of frequencies and then the output leads the input for other frequencies. This is known as lag-lead series compensation. A component which is used to provide series compensation is sometimes referred to as a series equalizer.

In this section, the design of series lead compensators is discussed. The next two sections consider series lag compensators and series lag-lead compensators respectively.

In Fig. 10.14 is shown both an electrical and a mechanical component which have the general phase-lead characteristic given by

$$\frac{E_o(s)}{E_{in}(s)} = \frac{Y(s)}{X(s)} = \frac{\tau_2}{\tau_1}\frac{1 + \tau_1 s}{1 + \tau_2 s} \qquad \tau_1 > \tau_2$$

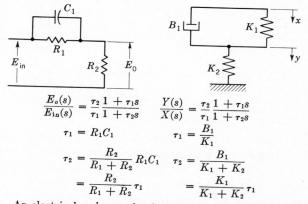

$$\frac{E_o(s)}{E_{in}(s)} = \frac{\tau_2}{\tau_1}\frac{1 + \tau_1 s}{1 + \tau_2 s} \qquad \frac{Y(s)}{X(s)} = \frac{\tau_2}{\tau_1}\frac{1 + \tau_1 s}{1 + \tau_2 s}$$

$$\tau_1 = R_1 C_1 \qquad \tau_1 = \frac{B_1}{K_1}$$

$$\tau_2 = \frac{R_2}{R_1 + R_2} R_1 C_1 \qquad \tau_2 = \frac{B_1}{K_1 + K_2}$$

$$= \frac{R_2}{R_1 + R_2} \tau_1 \qquad = \frac{K_1}{K_1 + K_2} \tau_1$$

FIG. 10.14. An electrical and a mechanical component used to obtain phase lead.

The frequency response for the preceding transfer function is

$$\frac{E_o(j\omega)}{E_{in}(j\omega)} = \frac{Y(j\omega)}{X(j\omega)} = \frac{\tau_2}{\tau_1}\frac{1 + j\tau_1\omega}{1 + j\tau_2\omega} \qquad \tau_1 > \tau_2 \qquad (10.19)$$

Because the steady-state gain ($\omega \approx 0$) is τ_2/τ_1, then additional amplification equal to τ_1/τ_2 must be provided to maintain the original system gain.

The construction of the log-magnitude diagram for Eq. (10.19) in which $\tau_2 = \tau_1/10$ is illustrated in Fig. 10.15. For the numerator, the break frequency occurs at $\omega = 1/\tau_1$, and for the denominator the break frequency occurs at $\omega = 1/\tau_2 = 10/\tau_1$. Adding the diagram for the

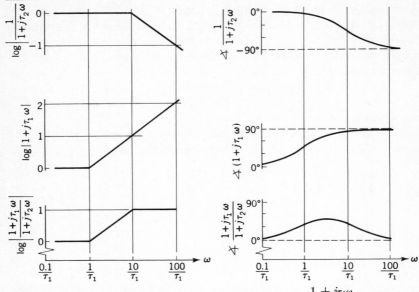

FIG. 10.15.   Construction of the log-magnitude diagram for $\dfrac{1 + j\tau_1\omega}{1 + j\tau_2\omega}$ in which $\tau_2 = \tau_1/10$.

numerator to that for the denominator yields the resultant diagram for phase lead.   Log-magnitude diagrams for $(1 + j\tau_1\omega)/(1 + j\tau_2\omega)$ when $\tau_2 = \tau_1/2$, $\tau_2 = \tau_1/10$, and $\tau_2 = \tau_1/\infty = 0$ are shown in Fig. 10.16.

The use of a phase-lead component placed in series with the feedforward portion of a control system to improve stability is now illustrated. In Fig. 10.17*a* and *b* the dashed curve is the frequency response of the uncompensated control system.   The corresponding $G(j\omega)$ function is indicated in Fig. 10.17*c*.   This control is one that would inherently be unstable.   The addition of the lead compensator $G_c(j\omega)$ to reshape the high-frequency portion of the polar plot is shown by the solid-line curves of Fig. 10.17*a* and *b*.   From the expanded scale of Fig. 10.17*b*, it is to be noted that lead compensation rotates a typical vector such as that for $\omega = 2$ in a counterclockwise direction away from the minus-one point. It is also to be noted that the length of this vector is increased.   Because of the counterclockwise rotation of a typical vector, the effect of lead compensation is to increase ω_m.   As was discussed in Sec. 9.7, this increases the speed of response of the system.

To select a lead compensator, it is necessary to be familiar with some of the general properties which are now derived.   The phase shift ϕ_c

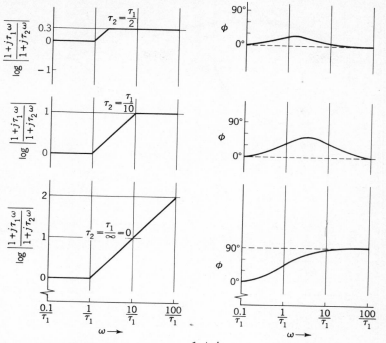

FIG. 10.16.   Log-magnitude diagrams for $\dfrac{1 + j\tau_1\omega}{1 + j\tau_2\omega}$ in which $\tau_2 = \tau_1/2$, $\tau_2 = \tau_1/10$, and $\tau_2 = \tau_1/\infty = 0$.

due to a lead compensator is

$$\phi_c = \measuredangle\, \frac{1 + j\tau_1\omega}{1 + j\tau_2\omega} = \tan^{-1}\tau_1\omega - \tan^{-1}\tau_2\omega \qquad (10.20)$$

Differentiating with respect to ω gives

$$\frac{d\phi_c}{d\omega} = \frac{\tau_1}{1 + (\tau_1\omega)^2} - \frac{\tau_2}{1 + (\tau_2\omega)^2}$$

Setting this derivative equal to zero and solving for ω yields the frequency $\omega = \omega_{cm}$ at which the phase shift is a maximum.   That is,

$$\tau_1[1 + (\tau_2\omega_{cm})^2] - \tau_2[1 + (\tau_1\omega_{cm})^2] = 0$$
$$(\tau_1 - \tau_2)(1 - \tau_1\tau_2\omega_{cm}{}^2) = 0$$
$$\omega_{cm}{}^2 = \frac{1}{\tau_1\tau_2}$$

In Fig. 10.18a is shown the log-magnitude diagram for a lead compensator.   It is to be noted that the maximum phase shift ϕ_{cm} occurs at the frequency $\omega_{cm} = 1/\sqrt{\tau_1\tau_2}$.   This frequency at which the maximum

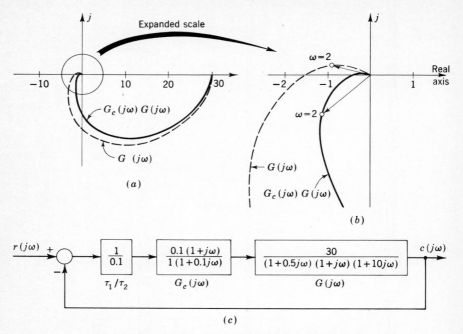

FIG. 10.17.   Use of phase lead to reshape a polar plot.

phase shift occurs is located at the midpoint between the break frequencies $\omega_1 = 1/\tau_1$ and $\omega_2 = 1/\tau_2$. Because frequency is plotted to a logarithmic scale the midpoint is

$$\log \omega_{cm} = \frac{1}{2}\left(\log \omega_1 + \log \omega_2\right) = \frac{1}{2}\log \omega_1 \omega_2 = \log \frac{1}{\sqrt{\tau_1 \tau_2}}$$

Hence $\omega_{cm} = 1/\sqrt{\tau_1 \tau_2}$.

The value of the maximum phase shift ϕ_{cm} is obtained by substitution of $\omega = \omega_{cm} = 1/\sqrt{\tau_1 \tau_2}$ into Eq. (10.20). That is,

$$
\begin{aligned}
\phi_{cm} &= \measuredangle \frac{1 + j\tau_1 \omega_{cm}}{1 + j\tau_2 \omega_{cm}} \frac{1 - j\tau_2 \omega_{cm}}{1 - j\tau_2 \omega_{cm}} \\
&= \measuredangle \frac{1 + \tau_1 \tau_2 \omega_{cm}^2 + j(\tau_1 - \tau_2)\omega_{cm}}{1 + \tau_1 \tau_2 \omega_{cm}^2} \\
&= \tan^{-1} \frac{(\tau_1 - \tau_2)\omega_{cm}}{1 + \tau_1 \tau_2 \omega_{cm}^2} = \tan^{-1} \frac{\sqrt{\tau_1/\tau_2} - \sqrt{\tau_2/\tau_1}}{2}
\end{aligned}
$$

This result shows that ϕ_{cm} is a function of the ratio τ_1/τ_2. In Fig. 10.18b is shown a plot of ϕ_{cm} versus $\log \tau_1/\tau_2$. The double scale for the horizontal axis displays both $\log \tau_1/\tau_2$ and τ_1/τ_2.

To select a lead compensator, it is necessary to specify the values of both τ_1 and τ_2. Because of the two unknowns τ_1 and τ_2, the selection of

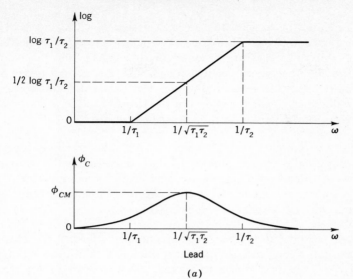

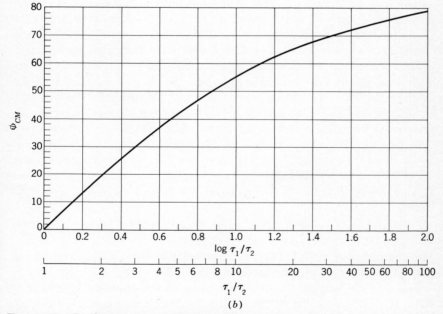

FIG. 10.18. Lead compensator characteristics: (a) log-magnitude diagram; (b) maximum phase shift ϕ_{cm} versus log τ_1/τ_2.

a lead compensator to achieve a desired design specification is basically a trial and error process. However, a systematic procedure which rapidly converges the trial and error process is described in the following examples. In the first example, the procedure for obtaining a desired phase margin is described. In the second example, the procedure for obtaining a desired value of M_m is described. In the third example, a procedure for obtaining a desired gain margin is described.

ILLUSTRATIVE EXAMPLE 1. The log-modulus plot of $G(j\omega)$ for a unity feedback system is shown in Fig. 10.19a. Determine the values of τ_1 and τ_2 for a series lead compensator such that the compensated system will have a phase margin of $45° \pm 3°$. What are the approximate values of ζ and ω_n for the resulting compensated system?

SOLUTION. From Fig. 10.18a, it is to be noted that when the phase shift is a maximum, the lead compensator increases the gain by a factor $\frac{1}{2} \log \tau_1/\tau_2$. The first step is to assume a value of τ_1/τ_2. For example, for $\tau_1/\tau_2 = 4$, then Fig. 10.18b shows that $\log \tau_1/\tau_2 = 0.6$ and $\phi_{cm} = 36°$. At the frequency $\omega_{cm} = 1/\sqrt{\tau_1\tau_2}$ the lead compensator increases the gain by a factor $\frac{1}{2} \log \tau_1/\tau_2 = 0.3$ and the phase angle is increased by $\phi_{cm} = 36°$. Thus, by measuring down -0.3 log units as shown in Fig. 10.19a, then when the lead compensator is added, the point indicated by the circle which corresponds to ω_{cm} will be raised vertically 0.3 log units to the zero horizontal axis and shifted to the right $36°$. The new location is indicated by the solid dot. To have a phase margin of $45°$, the solid dot should be located at the $\times$. Thus, it is necessary to assume a larger value of τ_1/τ_2. The result for $\tau_1/\tau_2 = 10$ is illustrated in Fig. 10.19b. It is to be noted that this yields a phase margin of $43°$ which is satisfactory. Because of the rapid convergence of this process, usually two or three trials suffice for obtaining the desired ratio τ_1/τ_2. The desired values of τ_1 and τ_2 are now computed from the relationships $\tau_1/\tau_2 = 10$ and $\omega_{cm} = 1/\sqrt{\tau_1\tau_2} = 2.6$. Hence,

$$\tau_1 = 1.2 \qquad \text{and} \qquad \tau_2 = 0.12$$

The complete log-modulus plot for the resulting $G_c(j\omega)G(j\omega)$ system may now be constructed as illustrated in Fig. 10.19c.

For a phase margin of $43°$, Fig. 10.13 shows that the approximate value of ζ is 0.425. From Fig. 10.12, it is found that $\omega_c/\omega_n = 0.84$, and from Fig. 10.19c, it is found that the crossover frequency ω_c is 2.6. Thus, the approximate value of the natural frequency ω_n is found to be 3.1.

ILLUSTRATIVE EXAMPLE 2. Same as preceding example except let it be desired to select a lead compensator such that $M_m = 1.4$.

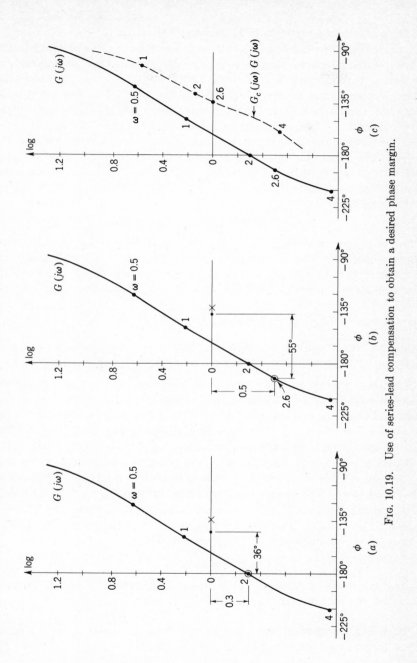

FIG. 10.19.   Use of series-lead compensation to obtain a desired phase margin.

SOLUTION. In Fig. 10.20a is shown the log-modulus plot $G(j\omega)$ for the uncompensated system and the $M = 1.4$ contour. The × is an initial guess at the point of tangency to this M contour. A horizontal line is drawn through this × as shown. As a first trial, it is assumed that $\tau_1/\tau_2 = 4$ and thus $\frac{1}{2} \log \tau_1/\tau_2 = 0.3$ and $\phi_{cm} = 36°$. The point indicated by the circle in Fig. 10.20a is thus raised 0.3 log units and shifted to the right 36°. The new location is indicated by the solid dot. Because the dot lies to the left of the ×, it is necessary to assume a larger value of τ_1/τ_2. The result for $\tau_1/\tau_2 = 8$ is shown in Fig. 10.20b. This result is seen to be satisfactory. The desired values of τ_1 and τ_2 are now computed from the relationships $\tau_1/\tau_2 = 8$ and $\omega_{cm} = 1/\sqrt{\tau_1\tau_2} = 2.8$. Thus it is found that

$$\tau_1 = 1.00 \qquad \text{and} \qquad \tau_2 = 0.125$$

The complete log-modulus diagram for the compensated system $G_c(j\omega)G(j\omega)$ may now be constructed as is illustrated in Fig. 10.20c.

From Fig. 9.22, for $M_m = 1.4$, the corresponding value of ζ is 0.422. Because $\omega_m = \omega_{cm} = 2.8$, then the approximate natural frequency is

$$\omega_n = \frac{\omega_m}{\sqrt{1 - 2\zeta^2}} = \frac{2.8}{\sqrt{1 - 2(0.422)^2}} = 4.3$$

ILLUSTRATIVE EXAMPLE 3. For the system of the preceding examples, determine the lead compensator such as to obtain a gain margin of 5.

SOLUTION. For a gain margin of 5, then $\log K_M = 0.7$. Thus, the resultant $G_c(j\omega)G(j\omega)$ plot must go through the × shown in Fig. 10.21a. As a first trial, it is assumed that $\tau_1/\tau_2 = 4$. By measuring back $\phi_{cm} = 36°$ from the vertical $\phi = -180°$ axis as is shown in Fig. 10.21a, then when the compensator is added, the point indicated by the circle will lie on the vertical $\phi = -180°$ axis. Because the compensator increases the gain by $\frac{1}{2} \log \tau_1/\tau_2 = 0.3$, then the circle is moved to the point indicated by the solid dot. The corresponding value of $\log K_M$ is 0.85 and thus $K_M = 6.3$. Because this is too great a value, it is necessary to use a smaller τ_1/τ_2 ratio. The result for $\tau_1/\tau_2 = 2.6$ is shown in Fig. 10.21b. For $\tau_1/\tau_2 = 2.6$ and $\omega_{cm} = 1/\sqrt{\tau_1\tau_2} = 3.6$, then

$$\tau_1 = 0.44 \text{ and } \tau_2 = 0.17$$

The log-modulus plot of the compensated system may now be constructed as illustrated in Fig. 10.21c.

10.4 Lag Compensation. The output lags the input for any component which has a transfer function of the form

$$\frac{E_o(s)}{E_{\text{in}}(s)} = \frac{Y(s)}{X(s)} = \frac{1 + \tau_2 s}{1 + \tau_1 s} \qquad \tau_1 > \tau_2 \qquad (10.21)$$

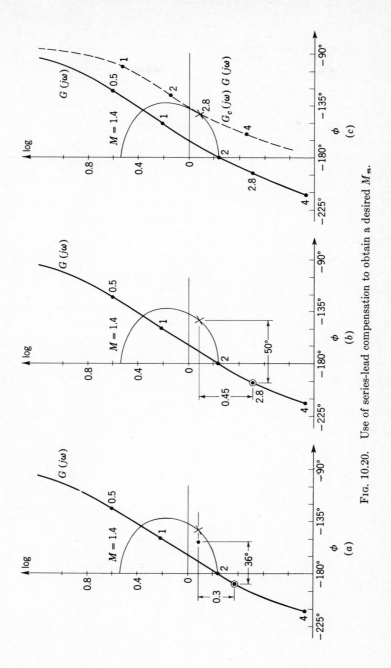

Fig. 10.20. Use of series-lead compensation to obtain a desired M_m.

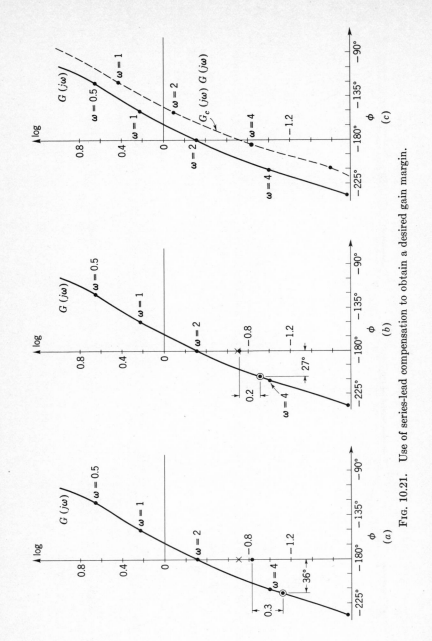

Fig. 10.21. Use of series-lead compensation to obtain a desired gain margin.

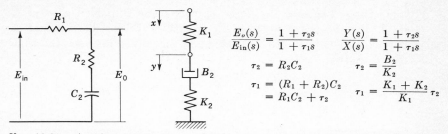

FIG. 10.22. An electrical and a mechanical component used to provide lag compensation.

The frequency response for the preceding transfer function is

$$\frac{E_o(j\omega)}{E_{in}(j\omega)} = \frac{Y(j\omega)}{X(j\omega)} = \frac{1 + j\tau_2\omega}{1 + j\tau_1\omega} \qquad \tau_1 > \tau_2 \qquad (10.22)$$

In Fig. 10.22 are shown both an electrical and a mechanical component in which the output lags the input, as is described by Eq. (10.22). The construction of the log-magnitude plot for Eq. (10.22) for the case in which $\tau_2 = \tau_1/10$ is illustrated in Fig. 10.23. For the term $1/(1 + j\tau_1\omega)$

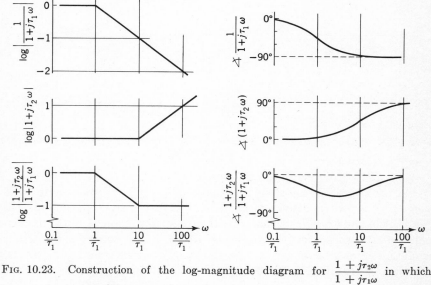

FIG. 10.23. Construction of the log-magnitude diagram for $\dfrac{1 + j\tau_2\omega}{1 + j\tau_1\omega}$ in which $\tau_2 = \tau_1/10$.

the break frequency occurs at $\omega = 1/\tau_1$, and for the numerator $1 + j\tau_2\omega$ the break frequency occurs at $\omega = 1/\tau_2 = 10/\tau_1$. The addition of the log-magnitude diagram for the numerator to that for the denominator yields the resulting diagram for $(1 + j\tau_2\omega)/(1 + j\tau_1\omega)$.

The resulting diagrams for three typical cases in which $\tau_2 = \tau_1/2$, $\tau_2 = \tau_1/10$, and $\tau_2 = \tau_1/\infty = 0$ are shown in Fig. 10.24.   The amount of phase lag which is introduced depends upon the spread between the time constants τ_1 and τ_2.

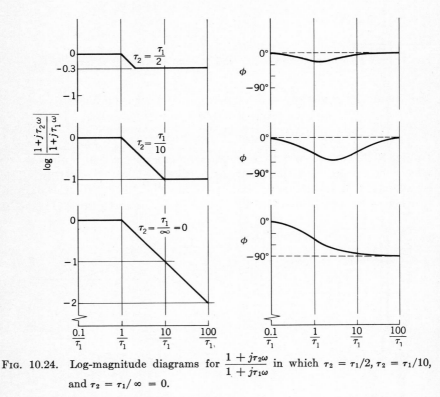

FIG. 10.24.   Log-magnitude diagrams for $\dfrac{1 + j\tau_2\omega}{1 + j\tau_1\omega}$ in which $\tau_2 = \tau_1/2, \tau_2 = \tau_1/10$, and $\tau_2 = \tau_1/\infty = 0$.

The use of a phase-lag component placed in series with the feedforward portion of a control system to improve stability is now illustrated.   In Fig. 10.25a and b the dashed curve is the frequency response of the uncompensated control system shown in Fig. 10.25c.   This control is one which would inherently be unstable.   The addition of series compensation $G_c(s)$ is shown in Fig. 10.25d.   This reshapes the high-frequency portion of the polar plot as is shown by the solid-line curves of Fig. 10.25a and b.   The resultant system has good dynamic response.   From the expanded view of the polar plot in Fig. 10.25b, it is to be noted that the effect of lag compensation is to shorten a typical vector such as that for $\omega = 0.5$ and also to rotate it in a clockwise direction.   The shortening is due to the attenuation.   By attenuation is meant multiplication by a factor less than

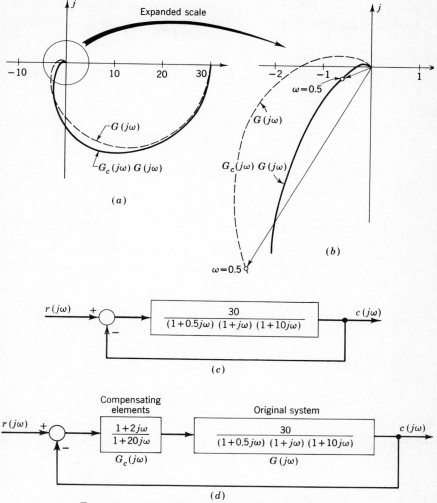

Fig. 10.25.   Use of phase lag to reshape a polar plot.

1.   The attenuation caused by use of lag compensation can be seen from Fig. 10.24.   The greater the spread in time constants τ_1 and τ_2, the more pronounced is the attenuation which occurs at higher frequencies.   Series lag compensation has little effect on the low-frequency portion of the curve.   By reshaping the polar plot, it has been possible to achieve good dynamic performance without changing the value of the gain K. Although it would have been possible to make this system stable by decreasing the gain K only, errors caused by friction, hysteresis, backlash,

etc., tend to predominate as the gain is decreased; thus, in general, the higher the value of K, the more accurate will be the control system.

In Fig. 10.26a is shown the log-magnitude diagram for a lag compensator. Comparison of Figs. 10.18a and 10.26a shows that the phase-shift

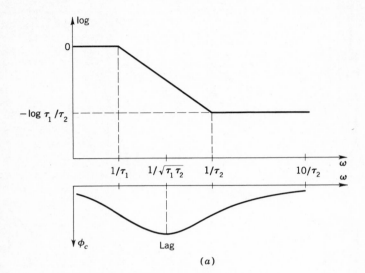

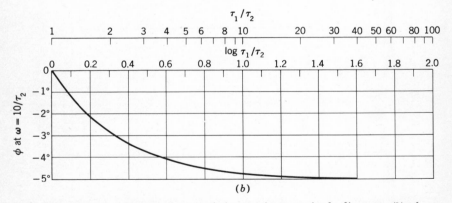

Fig. 10.26. Lag-compensator characteristics: (a) log-magnitude diagram; (b) phase shift ϕ at $\omega = 10/\tau_2$.

characteristics of a lag compensator are the same as for a lead compensator except that the sign of the phase angle is negative. Similarly, the sign of the log-magnitude characteristics for a lag and lead compensator is reversed.

The negative phase shift associated with lag compensation is usually undesirable.   The effectiveness of lag compensation is attributed to the attenuation which occurs at higher frequencies.   In Fig. 10.26a, it is to be noted that when $\omega = 10/\tau_2$, then the negative phase shift is very small. The solid line curve in Fig. 10.26b is a plot of the value of the negative phase shift at $\omega = 10/\tau_2$.   A significant difference between selecting a lag compensator and selecting a lead compensator is that for the lag compensator the region of small phase shift ($\omega = 10/\tau_2$) is located in the vicinity of the point of interest, i.e., the point indicated by the circle in the preceding examples, whereas for a lead compensator the region of maximum phase shift ($\omega = \omega_{cm}$) is located in the vicinity of the point of interest.

ILLUSTRATIVE EXAMPLE 1.   The log modulus diagram of $G(j\omega)$ for a unity-feedback system is shown in Fig. 10.27a.   Determine the lag compensator such that the compensated system will have a phase margin of 45°.

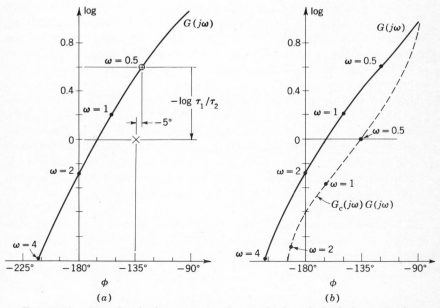

FIG. 10.27.   Use of series-lag compensation to obtain a desired phase margin.

SOLUTION.   For a phase margin of 45°, the resultant $G_c(j\omega)G(j\omega)$ plot must pass through the point indicated by the × in Fig. 10.27a.   From Fig. 10.26b, it is to be noted that for values of $\tau_1/\tau_2 > 4$, the phase shift introduced by a lag compensator at $\omega = 10/\tau_2$ is about $-5°$.   Thus, a vertical line is erected 5° to the right of the × as shown in Fig. 10.27a. The intersection of this vertical line with the $G(j\omega)$ plot is indicated by a circle. In order that the compensator move this point to the ×, then $-\log \tau_1/\tau_2 = -0.6$, and thus $\tau_1/\tau_2 = 4.0$. Figure 10.27a shows that the frequency $\omega = 10/\tau_2$ is 0.5. The particular values of τ_1 and τ_2 are now computed from the relationships $\tau_1/\tau_2 = 4$ and $10/\tau_2 = 0.5$. Thus,

$$\tau_1 = 80 \qquad \text{and} \qquad \tau_2 = 20$$

With these values of τ_1 and τ_2 the log-modulus diagram for the resultant compensated system $G_c(j\omega)G(j\omega)$ may now be constructed as shown in Fig. 10.27b.

For a phase margin of 45°, it follows from Fig. 10.21 that the approximate value of ζ is 0.425. Similarly, from Fig. 10.13 the ratio ω_c/ω_n is found to be 0.84. Because the cross-over frequency ω_c is 0.5, then the approximate natural frequency ω_n is found to be 0.6.

It is to be noted that the values of τ_1 and τ_2 for this lag compensator are larger than the values of τ_1 and τ_2 for the corresponding lead compensator (see Illustrative Example 1). Thus, the system with lag compensation is slower than the corresponding system with lead compensation. This fact is also substantiated by noting that the approximate natural frequency for the system with lag compensation is considerably smaller ($\omega_n = 0.6$) than the approximate natural frequency for the system with lead compensation ($\omega_n = 3.1$).

By proceeding in a manner similar to that described for lead compensators, it is possible to select lag compensators to yield a desired M_m or a desired gain margin. When selecting a compensator to yield a desired phase margin or a desired gain margin, one may use either Bode diagrams or log-modulus diagrams. Because it is not possible to construct M contours on Bode diagrams, it is necessary to use log-modulus diagrams for obtaining a compensator to yield a desired value of M_m.

10.5 Lag-Lead Compensation. A lag-lead compensator is a series combination of a lag and a lead network. The general transfer function for a lag-lead compensator is

$$\frac{E_o(s)}{E_{in}(s)} = \frac{Y(s)}{X(s)} = \frac{1 + c\tau_2 s}{1 + c\tau_1 s}\frac{1 + \tau_1 s}{1 + \tau_2 s} \qquad \tau_1 > \tau_2 \qquad (10.23)$$

where $c > 1$ is a constant. The substitution of $j\omega$ for s gives

$$\frac{E_o(j\omega)}{E_{in}(j\omega)} = \frac{Y(j\omega)}{X(j\omega)} = \frac{1 + jc\tau_2\omega}{1 + jc\tau_1\omega}\frac{1 + j\tau_1\omega}{1 + j\tau_2\omega} \qquad (10.24)$$

Rather than using a lag and a lead compensator in series, it is possible to use a single compensator as is shown in Fig. 10.28.

The log-magnitude diagram for a typical lag-lead compensator is shown in Fig. 10.29. Because $c\tau_1 > c\tau_2 > \tau_1 > \tau_2$, the first break frequency

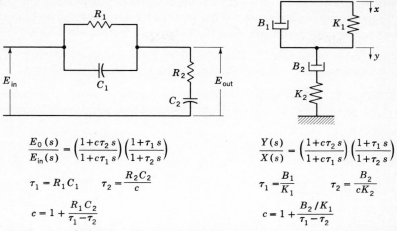

$$\frac{E_0(s)}{E_{in}(s)} = \left(\frac{1+c\tau_2 s}{1+c\tau_1 s}\right)\left(\frac{1+\tau_1 s}{1+\tau_2 s}\right)$$

$$\tau_1 = R_1 C_1 \qquad \tau_2 = \frac{R_2 C_2}{c}$$

$$c = 1 + \frac{R_1 C_2}{\tau_1 - \tau_2}$$

$$\frac{Y(s)}{X(s)} = \left(\frac{1+c\tau_2 s}{1+c\tau_1 s}\right)\left(\frac{1+\tau_1 s}{1+\tau_2 s}\right)$$

$$\tau_1 = \frac{B_1}{K_1} \qquad \tau_2 = \frac{B_2}{cK_2}$$

$$c = 1 + \frac{B_2/K_1}{\tau_1 - \tau_2}$$

FIG. 10.28.   An electrical and a mechanical component used to provide lag-lead compensation.

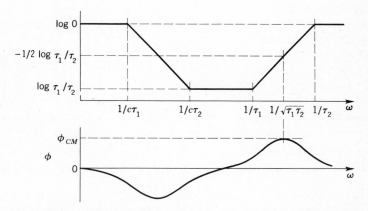

FIG. 10.29.   Log-magnitude diagram for a lag-lead compensator.

occurs at $1/c\tau_1$. This break frequency belongs to a denominator term, so that the magnitude plot has a slope of -1 log units/decade between $1/c\tau_1$ and $1/c\tau_2$. The second break frequency, $1/c\tau_2$, is associated with a numerator term, and thus the magnitude plot again becomes horizontal. The third break frequency, $1/\tau_1$, also occurs in the numerator. This results in a slope of $+1$ log unit/decade in the region from $1/\tau_1$ to $1/\tau_2$. Finally the break frequency, $1/\tau_2$, which occurs in the denominator causes the magnitude curve to become horizontal again. It is to be noted that the maximum phase shift ϕ_{cm} occurs at $\omega = 1/\sqrt{\tau_1\tau_2}$ and the corresponding attenuation is $-\frac{1}{2} \log \tau_1/\tau_2$. This is the same as for a lead compensator only (see Fig. 10.18a) except that the sign of the log of the magnitude is negative. This feature makes the lag-lead compensator considerably more effective than the lead compensator only.

ILLUSTRATIVE EXAMPLE 1. Same as Illustrative Example 1, Sec. 10.3, except use a lag-lead compensator rather than a lead compensator.

SOLUTION. In Fig. 10.30a is shown the log-modulus plot for the uncompensated system $G(j\omega)$. As a first trial, it is assumed that $\tau_1/\tau_2 = 2$,

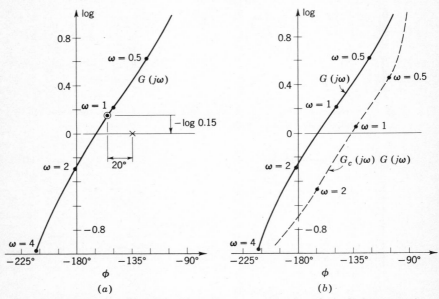

FIG. 10.30. Use of series lag-lead compensator to obtain a desired phase margin.

thus $\phi_{cm} = 20°$ and $-\tfrac{1}{2} \log \tau_1/\tau_2 = -0.15$ log units. The circle in Fig. 10.30a will be shifted downward -0.15 log units and it will be moved to the right 20°. The resulting location is indicated by the $\times$. The corresponding phase margin is $\gamma = 45°$.

The particular values of τ_1 and τ_2 for this lag-lead compensator are determined from the relationships $\tau_1/\tau_2 = 2$ and $\omega_{cm} = 1/\sqrt{\tau_1\tau_2} = 1.1$. Thus, it is found that $\tau_1 = 1.30$ and $\tau_2 = 0.65$.

A factor of 5 provides a reasonable separation between the second and third break frequencies (see Fig. 10.29), that is, $1/\tau_1 = 5(1/c\tau_2)$. Solving this relationship for c gives

$$c = 5\frac{\tau_1}{\tau_2} = 10$$

Having specified the compensator, the log-modulus diagram for the resulting compensated system may now be constructed as shown in Fig. 10.30b. As is indicated by Fig. 10.29, lag-lead compensation does not affect the low- or high-frequency regions but rather the mid-frequency region.

10.6 Internal Feedback. Another method commonly used to alter frequency-response characteristics is that of providing a separate internal-feedback path about certain components. In employing log-magnitude diagrams to investigate the effect of internal feedback, the use of a few approximations affords much simplification. This approximate analysis in effects puts the designer in the right "ball park." In the latter design stages, it may be desirable to make an exact analysis. The approximations which are used to evaluate the effect of placing a feedback element $H_1(s)$ around a component $G_1(s)$ as shown in Fig. 10.31 are that, when

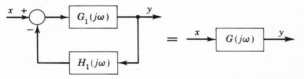

FIG. 10.31. Internal feedback $H_1(s)$ placed about an element $G_1(s)$.

$|G_1(j\omega)H_1(j\omega)| \ll 1$,

$$G(j\omega) = \frac{G_1(j\omega)}{1 + G_1(j\omega)H_1(j\omega)} \approx G_1(j\omega) \qquad (10.25)$$

For the case when $|G_1(j\omega)H_1(j\omega)| \gg 1$,

$$G(j\omega) = \frac{G_1(j\omega)}{1 + G_1(j\omega)H_1(j\omega)} \approx \frac{G_1(j\omega)}{G_1(j\omega)H_1(j\omega)} = \frac{1}{H_1(j\omega)} \qquad (10.26)$$

When $|G_1(j\omega)H_1(j\omega)| = 1$, then $|G_1(j\omega)| = |1/H_1(j\omega)|$; thus the intersection of the log-magnitude diagram for $|G_1(j\omega)|$ and that for $|1/H_1(j\omega)|$ determines the point at which $|G_1(j\omega)H_1(j\omega)| = 1$. It follows from Eqs. (10.25) and (10.26) that the frequency response is altered only when $|G_1(j\omega)H_1(j\omega)| \gg 1$. The application of the use of internal feedback is now demonstrated.

In Fig. 10.32a is shown a component which has a unity-feedback path $[H_1(j\omega) = 1]$ around it. The log-magnitude diagram for $G_1(j\omega)$ is the dashed line in Fig. 10.32b. The plot for $1/H_1(j\omega) = 1$ is indicated by the long- and short-dashed line. As shown in Fig. 10.32b, the curve of $\log |G_1(j\omega)|$ intersects that for $\log |1/H_1(j\omega)|$ at $\omega = 3.16$. Thus, for $\omega < 3.16$, the response is approximated by $1/H_1(j\omega)$, and for $\omega > 3.16$,

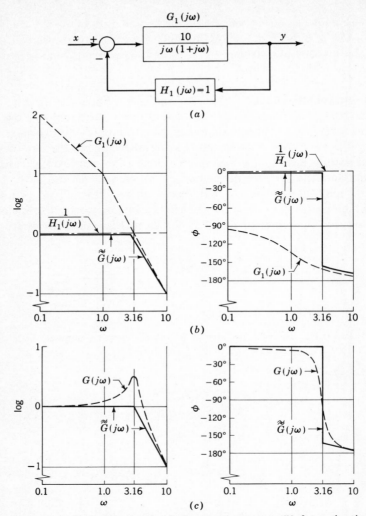

FIG. 10.32.   (a) Unity feedback placed about a component; (b) determination of the approximate frequency response; (c) comparison of the approximate and exact frequency response.

the response is approximated by $G_1(j\omega)$.   The exact value for $G(j\omega)$ is obtained by solving the equation $G(j\omega) = G_1(j\omega)/[1 + G_1(j\omega)H_1(j\omega)]$. In Fig. 10.32c are shown both the exact value of $G(j\omega)$ and also the approximation $\tilde{\tilde{G}}(j\omega)$.

In applying this procedure, it makes no difference whether $H_1(j\omega)$ is a constant or some function of the frequency ω.   The intersection of the log-magnitude plot for $\log |G_1(j\omega)|$ and that for $\log |1/H_1(j\omega)|$ determines the frequency ω at which $|G_1(j\omega)H_1(j\omega)| = 1$, whence the approximations are made.

Usually at high frequencies $|G_1(j\omega)H_1(j\omega)| \ll 1$, and thus it follows that internal feedback does not affect the high-frequency response. However, the low-frequency response $1/H_1(j\omega)$ is determined entirely by the feedback component.

In summary, this approximation converts an internal-feedback path to an approximate open-loop element for which a standard analysis can be made. With the use of inverse polar plots, as is next described, no approximations are employed.

10.7 Inverse Polar Plots. A plot of the function $G^{-1}(j\omega) = 1/G(j\omega)$ is called an inverse polar plot. In Fig. 10.33 is shown a typical inverse

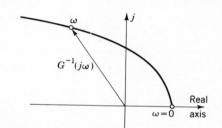

Fig. 10.33. Typical inverse polar plot $G^{-1}(j\omega)$.

polar plot of the function $G^{-1}(j\omega)$. At any frequency ω, the vector from the origin to the graph defines the vector $G^{-1}(j\omega)$ for that frequency. The length of the vector is $|G^{-1}(j\omega)| = |1/G(j\omega)|$, and the angle is

$$\measuredangle G^{-1}(j\omega) = \measuredangle \frac{1}{G(j\omega)} = -\measuredangle G(j\omega)$$

A plot of M circles and α lines for inverse polar plots is accomplished by first taking the reciprocal of Eq. (9.52), i.e.,

$$\frac{R(j\omega)}{C(j\omega)} = \frac{1 + G(j\omega)}{G(j\omega)} = G^{-1}(j\omega) + 1 \tag{10.27}$$

A typical vector $G^{-1}(j\omega)$ as shown in Fig. 10.33 may be written in the general form $G^{-1}(j\omega) = x + jy$. Substitution of this general representation for $G^{-1}(j\omega)$ into Eq. (10.27) gives

$$\frac{R(j\omega)}{C(j\omega)} = x + 1 + jy \tag{10.28}$$

Because $M = |C(j\omega)/R(j\omega)|$, from the magnitude of Eq. (10.28) it follows that

$$\left| \frac{R(j\omega)}{C(j\omega)} \right| = \frac{1}{M} = \sqrt{(x + 1)^2 + y^2}$$

Squaring this result gives

$$(x + 1)^2 + y^2 = \frac{1}{M^2} \tag{10.29}$$

Thus, on the inverse plane, lines of constant M are circles of radius $1/M$. The center of these concentric M circles is at the point $x = -1$ and $y = 0$, that is, the -1 point. A plot of these M circles on the inverse plane is shown in Fig. 10.34. Because the reciprocal of -1 is still -1, this point

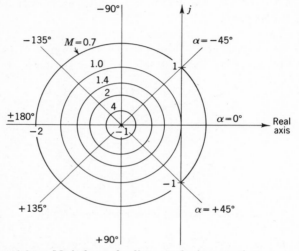

FIG. 10.34. M circles and α lines on the inverse plane.

has the same significance for an inverse polar plot as for a direct polar plot. Polar plots are referred to as direct polar plots when it is necessary to distinguish them from inverse polar plots.

The lines of constant $\alpha = \angle[C(j\omega)/R(j\omega)] = -\angle[R(j\omega)/C(j\omega)]$ are determined from Eq. (10.28) as follows:

$$\alpha = -\angle\frac{R(j\omega)}{C(j\omega)} = -\tan^{-1}\frac{y}{x+1} \tag{10.30}$$

When plotted on the inverse plane, as is shown in Fig. 10.34, constant α contours are radial straight lines which pass through the $-1 + j0$ point.

As is illustrated in Fig. 10.35, the angle ψ of a radial line drawn from the origin tangent to any M circle is

$$\sin\psi = \frac{|1/M|}{|-1|} = \frac{1}{M} \tag{10.31}$$

The use of the inverse polar plot for determining the gain K to yield a desired value of M_m is similar to that for the direct polar plot. Consider

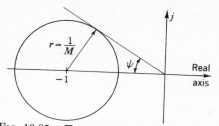

Fig. 10.35. Tangent line to an M circle.

the same function $G(j\omega) = K/[j\omega(1 + 0.1j\omega)]$ discussed in Chap. 9. The plot of the inverse function

$$\frac{K}{G(j\omega)} = KG^{-1}(j\omega) = j\omega(1 + 0.1j\omega) \qquad (10.32)$$

is shown in Fig. 10.36. For a desired $M_m = 1.4$, the angle ψ of the tangent line is

$$\psi = \sin^{-1}\frac{1}{M_m} = \sin^{-1}\frac{1}{1.4} = 45.6° \qquad (10.33)$$

Next construct by trial and error the circle which is tangent to both the $KG^{-1}(j\omega)$ plot and the tangent line. In order that this circle be the desired M_m circle, its center must be at the -1 point. From Fig. 10.36, it

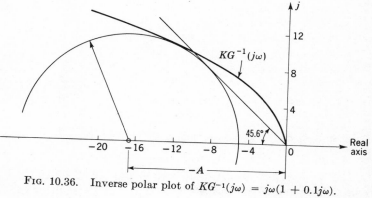

Fig. 10.36. Inverse polar plot of $KG^{-1}(j\omega) = j\omega(1 + 0.1j\omega)$.

is to be seen that the center is at $-A = -16.7$. To convert this to the -1 point, the scale factor must be multiplied by $1/A = 1/16.7 = 0.06$. The resulting function $G^{-1}(j\omega)$, which is tangent to the desired M circle, is

$$G^{-1}(j\omega) = \frac{1}{A}[KG^{-1}(j\omega)] = 0.06j\omega(1 + 0.1j\omega)$$

or
$$G(j\omega) = \frac{16.7}{j\omega(1 + 0.1j\omega)}$$

Thus, the value of A yields directly the required gain K.

The general procedure in obtaining K by use of the inverse polar plot is:

1. Plot the inverse function $KG^{-1}(j\omega)$.
2. Construct the tangent line in accordance with Eq. (10.31).
3. By trial and error, determine the circle which is tangent to both the $KG^{-1}(j\omega)$ plot and the tangent line.
4. The desired gain is $K = A$.

When the function $G^{-1}(j\omega)$ is plotted rather than $KG^{-1}(j\omega)$, then A is equal to the factor K_c by which the gain should be changed to yield the desired M_m.

ILLUSTRATIVE EXAMPLE 1. Consider the function

$$G(j\omega) = \frac{5}{j\omega(1 + 0.1j\omega)}$$

The inverse polar plot $G^{-1}(j\omega)$ is shown in Fig. 10.37. Determine the factor K_c by which the gain should be changed such that the resulting plot is tangent to the $M_m = 1.4$ circle.

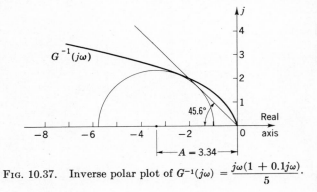

FIG. 10.37. Inverse polar plot of $G^{-1}(j\omega) = \dfrac{j\omega(1 + 0.1j\omega)}{5}$.

SOLUTION. In order that the point $-A$ in Fig. 10.37 be the -1 point, it is necessary to divide the scale by $A = 3.34$. The resulting function is

$$\frac{1}{A}G^{-1}(j\omega) = \frac{1}{AG(j\omega)} = \frac{1}{K_c G(j\omega)}$$

or
$$K_c G(j\omega) = \frac{(3.34)(5)}{j\omega(1 + 0.1j\omega)} = \frac{16.7}{j\omega(1 + 0.1j\omega)}$$

The preceding analysis shows that $K_c = A$.

The major advantage of using the inverse plane is realized for systems with internal feedback. The reciprocal of Eq. (10.25) is

$$G^{-1}(j\omega) = \frac{1 + G_1(j\omega)H_1(j\omega)}{G_1(j\omega)} = G_1^{-1}(j\omega) + H_1(j\omega) \qquad (10.34)$$

The vectors $G_1^{-1}(j\omega)$ and $H_1(j\omega)$ may be added as vector quantities to yield $G^{-1}(j\omega)$, as is illustrated in Fig. 10.38.

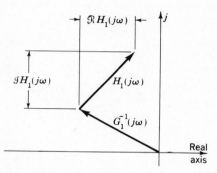

FIG. 10.38.   Vector addition of $G_1^{-1}(j\omega)$ and $H_1(j\omega)$ to yield $G^{-1}(j\omega)$.

ILLUSTRATIVE EXAMPLE 2.   For the system shown in Fig. 10.39a, let it be desired to determine K_1 so that $M_m = 1.4$.

SOLUTION.   For this system

$$G(j\omega) = K_2 \frac{G_1(j\omega)}{1 + G_1(j\omega)H_1(j\omega)} \qquad (10.35)$$

or $$G^{-1}(j\omega) = \frac{1}{K_2}[G_1^{-1}(j\omega) + H_1(j\omega)] = \frac{1}{K_1}\frac{K_1 G_1^{-1}(j\omega)}{K_2} + \frac{H_1(j\omega)}{K_2} \qquad (10.36)$$

First construct the plot for

$$\frac{H_1(j\omega)}{K_2} = 5\frac{1 + 0.4j\omega}{10} = 0.5 + 0.2j\omega \qquad (10.37)$$

As is shown in Fig. 10.39b, the real part of $H_1(j\omega)/K_2$ is always 0.5 and the imaginary part is $0.2j$ for $\omega = 1$, $0.4j$ for $\omega = 2$, etc.   The function $K_1 G_1^{-1}(j\omega)/K_2$ is

$$\frac{1}{K_2}[K_1 G_1^{-1}(j\omega)] = \frac{j\omega(1 + 2j\omega)}{10} = -0.2\omega^2 + 0.1j\omega \qquad (10.38)$$

The value of $K_1 G_1^{-1}(j\omega)/K_2$ for $\omega = 1$ and 2 is added to the $H_1(j\omega)/K_2$ plot, as is shown by the solid arrows in Fig. 10.39b.   Multiplication of each $K_1 G_1^{-1}(j\omega)/K_2$ vector by $1/K_1$ to obtain $G_1^{-1}(j\omega)/K_2$ is effected by

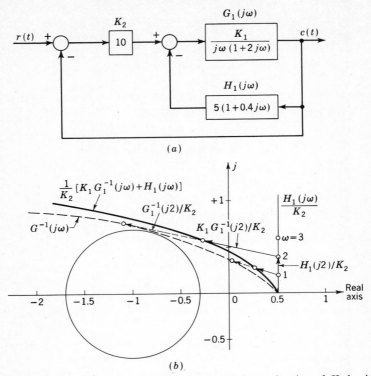

FIG. 10.39. (a) System with internal feedback; (b) determination of K_1 by inverse polar plots.

changing the length of each of these vectors by the factor $1/K_1$, as indicated by the dashed extension of each vector.   The required value of $1/K_1$ is the factor which makes the resulting inverse polar plot $G^{-1}(j\omega)$ tangent to the desired M_m circle.   In this case, $1/K_1 = 2$, or $K_1 = 0.5$.

ILLUSTRATIVE EXAMPLE 3.   For the system shown in Fig. 10.40a, the value of K_1 is 10 and K_2 is 2.5.   From the inverse polar plot $1/K_2G_1(j\omega)$ of Fig. 10.40b, the value of M_m is found to be 5.   If it be desired to obtain an M_m of 1.4 by the use of an internal-feedback loop as shown in Fig. 10.41a, what feedback element $H_1(j\omega)$ should be used?

SOLUTION.   The equation for the inverse polar plot with internal feedback is

$$\frac{1}{G(j\omega)} = \frac{1}{K_2}\frac{1 + G_1(j\omega)H_1(j\omega)}{G_1(j\omega)} = \frac{1}{K_2G_1(j\omega)} + \frac{H_1(j\omega)}{K_2} \qquad (10.39)$$

The quantity $H_1(j\omega)/K_2$ must be such that when it is added to $1/K_2G_1(j\omega)$ the resulting plot will be tangent to the $M = 1.4$ circle.   To do this, it is

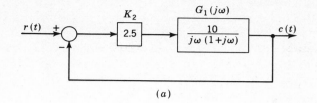

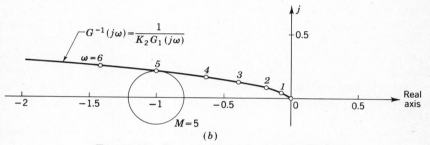

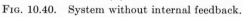

FIG. 10.40. System without internal feedback.

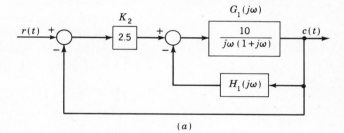

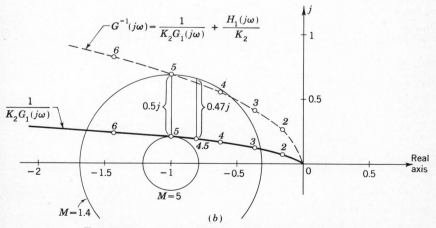

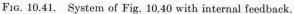

FIG. 10.41. System of Fig. 10.40 with internal feedback.

necessary only to raise the original plot vertically. It is to be seen from Fig. 10.38 that the horizontal component of $H_1(j\omega)$ is its real part $\Re\, H_1(j\omega)$ and the vertical component is its imaginary part $\Im\, H_1(j\omega)$. It is thus necessary only that $H_1(j\omega)$ be purely imaginary, i.e., of the form $H_1(s) = \beta s$ or $H_1(j\omega) = j\beta\omega$. In Fig. 10.41$b$, it is to be noted that, at $\omega = 5$, the addition of $H_1(j5)/K_2 = 0.5j$ to the $1/K_2G_1(j5)$ plot causes the resulting curve to pass through the top of the $M = 1.4$ circle. For this case, the value of β is $j\beta5/2.5 = 0.5j$, or $\beta = 0.25$. The resulting curve may now be constructed as indicated by the dashed line in Fig. 10.41b. Because this curve is not tangent to the $M = 1.4$ circle, another trial value must be taken. From the dashed loci of Fig. 10.41b, it now appears that the point of tangency is more likely to occur in the neighborhood of $\omega = 4.5$. The addition of $H_1(j4.5)/K_2 = 0.47j$ to $1/K_2G_1(j4.5)$ causes the new resulting curve to be tangent to the desired M circle. In this case $j\beta4.5/2.5 = 0.47j$, or $\beta = 0.26$. Thus, the desired result is $H_1(j\omega) = 0.26j\omega$.

When $H_1(j\omega)$ is a constant, $H_1(j\omega)$ is entirely real. As may be seen from Fig. 10.41b, the effect of a constant $H_1(j\omega)$ is to shift the inverse plot horizontally to the right. Suppose in the preceding problem that it is desired to increase the speed of response by having ω_m equal to 6 rather than 4.5. After assuming a few trial values for $H_1(j6)/K_2$, it is found that $H_1(j6)/K_2 = 0.6 + 0.4j$ makes the resultant plot tangent to the $M = 1.4$ circle at $\omega = 6$, as is illustrated in Fig. 10.42. Because

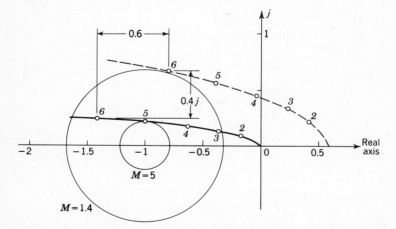

FIG. 10.42.   Use of inverse polar plots to increase speed of response.

$H_1(j6)/K_2 = 0.6 + 0.4j = 0.6 + j\beta6$, then $\beta = 0.4/6 = 0.067$, whence the required $H_1(j\omega)$ is

$$H_1(j\omega) = K_2(0.6 + j\beta\omega) = 1.5 + j0.167\omega \qquad (10.40)$$

The general procedure followed in this illustrative example was to assume a value of $H_1(j\omega)$ which makes a point lie on the desired M circle. From this assumed value, the general equation for the resulting plot was obtained. When the assumed point is not the point of tangency, then another trial point must be selected.

10.8 Stability Criteria in the Inverse Plane. The inverse function $1/[G(s)H(s)]$ may be expressed in terms of numerator and denominator terms as follows:

$$\frac{1}{G(s)H(s)} = \frac{D_G D_H}{N_G N_H}$$

In Fig. 10.43 is shown the complete inverse polar plot for the function

$$G(s)H(s) = \frac{10(s + 2)}{s(s + 1)(s + 4)}$$

or

$$\frac{1}{G(s)H(s)} = \frac{s(s + 1)(s + 4)}{10(s + 2)}$$

As s proceeds up the vertical (imaginary) axis of Fig. 10.43a, then the corresponding inverse plot in Fig. 10.43b is indicated by the heavy line.

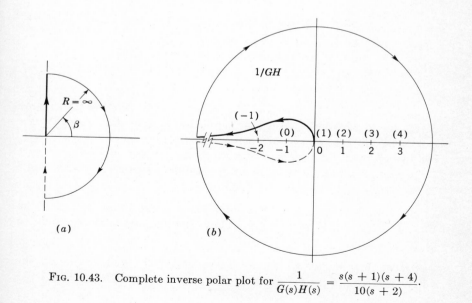

Fig. 10.43.   Complete inverse polar plot for $\dfrac{1}{G(s)H(s)} = \dfrac{s(s + 1)(s + 4)}{10(s + 2)}$.

For values of s on the infinite semicircle $s = Re^{j\beta}$, then

$$\frac{1}{G(s)H(s)} \approx \frac{R^3 e^{3j\beta}}{Re^{j\beta}} = R^2 e^{2j\beta}$$

In general, if n is the highest order of s in the denominator of $G(s)H(s)$ and m is the highest order of s in the numerator of $G(s)H(s)$, then for values of s on the infinite semicircle

$$\frac{1}{G(s)H(s)} = R^{n-m} e^{j(n-m)\beta}$$

Because β changes by an angle of $-\pi$, then the corresponding inverse plot transcribes an infinite semicircle which goes through the angle $-(n-m)\pi$. The negative imaginary axis $s = -j\omega$ is the complex conjugate of the positive imaginary axis $s = j\omega$; thus the portion shown dotted is the mirror image of the heavy-line portion.

The effect of adding $(+1)$ to the $1/GH$ plot is obtained by the new scale shown in parentheses above the real axis of Fig. 10.43*b*. Thus, the -1 point of the $1/GH$ plot is seen to be the origin of the $(1/GH) + 1$ plot. With respect to numerator and denominator terms this new plot is

$$\frac{1}{GH} + 1 = \frac{D_G D_H}{N_G N_H} + 1 = \frac{N_G N_H + D_G D_H}{N_G N_H}$$

Application of the Nyquist stability criterion to the inverse plot shows that

$$Z = N + P$$

where Z = number of zeros of the characteristic equation $(N_G N_H + D_G D_H)$ in the right half plane
  P = number of zeros of $N_G N_H$ in the right half plane
  N = net number of encirclements of the origin of the $1 + 1/GH$ plot (that is, -1 point of the $1/GH$ plot)

It is to be noted that N and Z have the same meaning for inverse plots as for direct plots. However, P is the number of zeros of $N_G N_H$ when using inverse polar plots whereas P is the number of zeros of $D_G D_H$ when using direct polar plots. For the system of Fig. 10.43, $N = 0$ and $P = 0$. Application of the Nyquist stability criterion shows that $Z = N + P = 0$. Hence, the system is stable.

ILLUSTRATIVE EXAMPLE 1. Determine the inverse polar plot and the value of Z for the type 0 system whose direct polar plot is shown in Fig. 10.3.

SOLUTION. For a type 0 system the inverse polar plot begins on the positive real axis at the value $1/K$. The heavy-line portion of Fig. 10.44

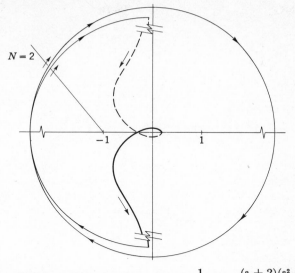

FIG. 10.44. Complete inverse polar plot for $\dfrac{1}{G(s)H(s)} = \dfrac{(s+2)(s^2+2s+5)}{52}$.

is the portion of the inverse plot for $s = j\omega$. The dotted line is the portion for $s = -j\omega$. From Eq. 10.8, it is to be noted that $n - m = 3$. Thus, the inverse plot transcribes an infinite semicircle which goes through the angle $-(n-m)\pi = -3\pi$. For the system of Fig. 10.44, $N = 2$ and $P = 0$. Application of the Nyquist stability criterion gives $Z = N + P = 2$. Thus, the system is basically unstable as was previously determined using the direct polar plot.

On direct polar plots instability is indicated when the frequency response crosses the negative real axis outside the -1 point (e.g., see Fig. 10.3). On inverse polar plots instability is indicated when the frequency response crosses the negative real axis inside the -1 point (e.g., see Fig. 10.44).

Problems

10.1 For each of the $G(s)H(s)$ plots shown in Fig. P10.1, the path of values for s is the same as that shown in Fig. 10.2. For each plot, determine the number of roots of the characteristic equation which are located in the right half plane ($P = 0$ in all cases).

For each stable system, determine the factor by which the gain should be changed so that the system will just become unstable.

For each unstable system, determine the factor by which the gain should be changed so that the system will just become stable.

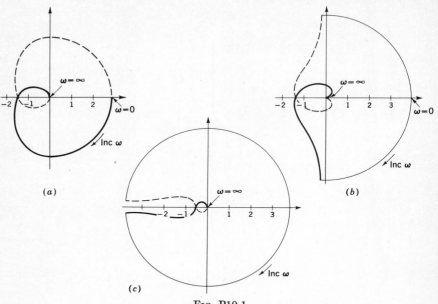

Fig. P10.1

10.2 For each of the following unity-feedback systems, sketch the complete $G(s)$ plot, and determine the number of roots of the characteristic equation that lie in the right half plane:

(a) $G(s) = \dfrac{10}{(1 + 0.25s)(0.25s^2 + 0.40s + 1)}$

(b) $G(s) = \dfrac{10}{s(1 + 0.25s)}$

(c) $G(s) = \dfrac{10}{s^2(1 + 0.25s)}$

(d) $G(s) = \dfrac{10(1 + s)}{s^2(1 + 0.25s)}$

10.3 Plot the log-magnitude diagram for the system given in Prob. 10.2(a). For this system, determine

(a) The gain margin and the phase margin

(b) The factor by which the gain should be changed to yield a gain margin of 5

(c) The factor by which the gain should be changed to yield a phase margin of 40°

10.4 The open-loop transfer function for a unity-feedback system is

$$G(s) = \frac{2}{s(1 + s)(1 + 2s)}$$

The Bode diagram for this system is shown in Fig. P10.4

(a) Determine the factor K_c by which the gain should be changed such that the resulting system will have a phase margin of 45°.

(b) Determine the factor K_c by which the gain should be changed such that the resulting system has a gain margin of 5.

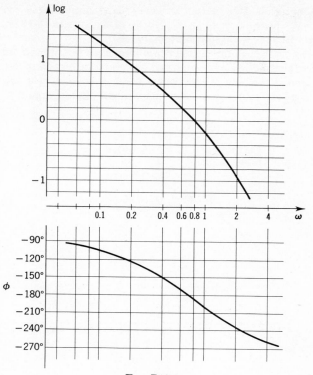

FIG. P10.4

10.5 The Nichols plot of $G(j\omega)$ for a unity-feedback system is shown in Fig. P10.5.

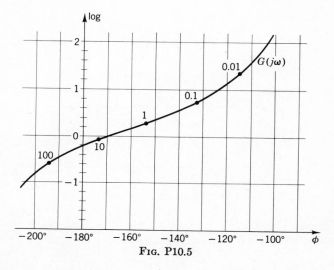

FIG. P10.5

(*a*) Determine the gain margin and the phase margin for this system.

(*b*) By what factor K_c should the gain K of the system be changed such that the system will have a phase margin of 45°?

10.6 A plot of $G(j\omega)$ for a unity-feedback system is shown in Fig. P10.6. What is the value of the gain margin and phase margin for this system? By what factor K_c should the gain of the system be changed such that M_m will be 1.4? What are the new values of the gain margin and phase margin?

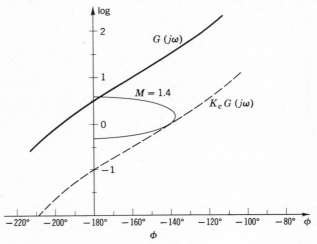

FIG. P10.6

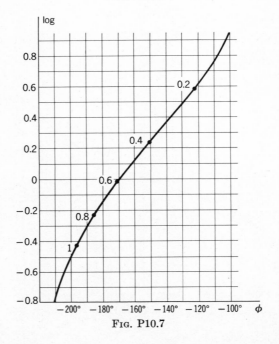

FIG. P10.7

10.7 The log-modulus diagram for a control system is shown in Fig. P10.7. Determine the values of τ_1 and τ_2 for a series lead compensator such that the resulting system will have a phase margin of $35° \pm 3°$.

10.8 Same as Prob. 10.7 except use a lag compensator.

10.9 Same as Prob. 10.7 except use a lag-lead compensator.

10.10 The log-magnitude diagram shown in Fig. P10.10 is for the unity-feedback system:

$$G(s) = \frac{4}{(s + 1)[(s^2 + 8s + 25)/25]}$$

(*a*) Find the values of τ_1 and τ_2 for a series lag-lead compensator such that the resulting system will have a phase margin of $45° \pm 3°$.

(*b*) Use Fig. P10.10 to construct the log-modulus plot for this system. Using this plot, verify the results of part (*a*).

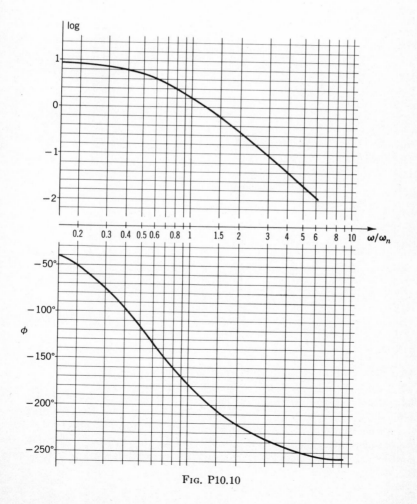

Fig. P10.10

10.11 In Fig. P10.11 is shown the log-magnitude diagram for the unity feedback system:

$$G(s) = \frac{2.5}{s(1 + 0.25s)(1 + s)}$$

Determine the values of τ_1 and τ_2 for a series lead compensator $(1 + \tau_1 s)/(1 + \tau_2 s)$ such that the resulting system will have a phase margin of $45° \pm 5°$.

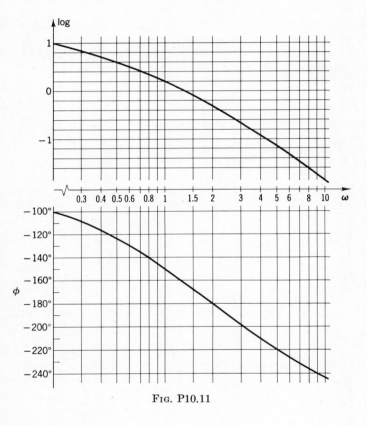

Fig. P10.11

10.12 Same as Prob. 10.11 except use a lag compensator.
10.13 Same as Prob. 10.11 except use a lag-lead compensator.
10.14 Construct the approximate log-magnitude plots for each of the two systems shown in Fig. P10.14. For each system, write the equation for the open-loop transfer function corresponding to the asymptotes. To obtain the exact transfer function for each system, use block-diagram algebra to eliminate the minor feedback loops. Compare the exact and approximate transfer functions.

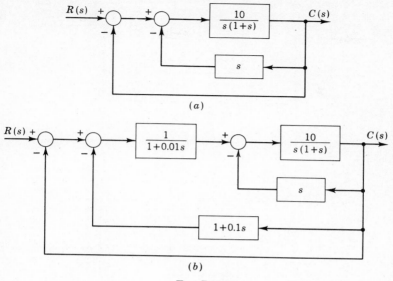

(a)

(b)

FIG. P10.14

10.15 Same as Prob. 9.14, but use inverse polar plots to determine the value of the gain K to yield an M_m of 1.4.

10.16 The inverse polar plot for the unity-feedback system

$$G_1(s) = \frac{2.5}{s(1 + 0.25s)(1 + s)} = \frac{10}{s(s + 1)(s + 4)}$$

is shown in Fig. P10.16. For internal feedback compensation of the form $H_1(s) = \alpha + \beta s$, determine the values of α and β such that the resulting system will have an M_m of 1.4 and ω_m occurs about $\omega = 2$.

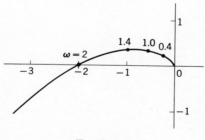

FIG. P10.16

10.17 Use inverse polar plots to determine the value of β such that the system of Fig. P10.17 will have an M_m of 1.4.

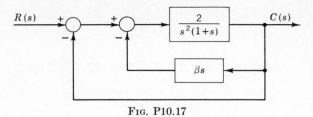

Fig. P10.17

10.18   For the system shown in Fig. P10.18, determine the value of K_1 to yield an M_m of 1.4.

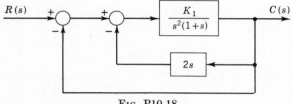

Fig. P10.18

10.19   Same as Prob. 10.2 except use the inverse plane.
10.20   Same as Prob. 10.3 except use the inverse plane, rather than the log-magnitude diagram.

11

Describing functions

In Fig. 11.1 is shown a nonlinear element N in which x is the input and y is the output. The describing function method is applicable for any

FIG. 11.1. Nonlinear element N.

nonlinearity N which has the characteristic that if the input is a sinusoid $(x = x_0 \sin \omega t)$, the output y is a periodic function.[1,2] Because of its simplicity and wide range of applicability, the describing function method is probably the most versatile technique for investigating nonlinear effects.

11.1 The Describing Function. The operating characteristics of an on-off control element are shown in Fig. 11.2. When the input x is greater than zero, the value of the output is Y_0. When x is less than zero, the output is $-Y_0$. The equation for this element is

$$y = \begin{cases} Y_0 & x > 0 \\ -Y_0 & x < 0 \end{cases} \tag{11.1}$$

A plot of the sinusoidal input $x = x_0 \sin \omega t$ is drawn vertically down from the on-off contactor characteristic of Fig. 11.2. The corresponding output is shown horizontally to the right.

Another nonlinearity which is frequently encountered is that of dead zone, or dead band, which is illustrated in Fig. 11.3. For $x > D$, the output is $k(x - D) = k(x_0 \sin \omega t - D)$. The overall equation of operation is

$$y = \begin{cases} k(x_0 \sin \omega t - D) & x > D \\ 0 & 0 \le x \le D \end{cases} \tag{11.2}$$

[1] R. J. Kochenburger, A Frequency Response Method for Analyzing and Synthesizing Contactor Servomechanisms, *Trans. AIEE*, **69**: 270–284 (1950).

[2] J. G. Truxal, "Automatic Feedback Control System Synthesis," McGraw-Hill Book Company, New York, 1955.

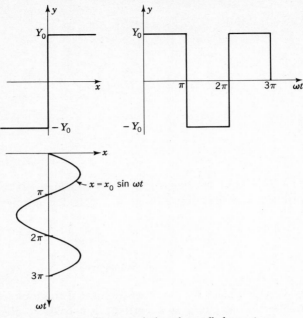

Fɪɢ. 11.2.   Characteristics of on-off element.

With the aid of Fig. 11.3, it follows that $D = x_0 \sin \beta$, or

$$\beta = \sin^{-1} \frac{D}{x_0} \tag{11.3}$$

Nonlinearities are usually such that for a sinusoidal input ($x = x_0 \sin \omega t$), the output y is an odd function of period 2π. As is illustrated in Fig. 11.4, an odd function has symmetry such that if the portion for the first half of the period (0 to π) is reflected about a vertical axis through π, and then reflected about the horizontal axis, it falls upon (coincides with) the function for the second half of the period (π to 2π). The Fourier series representation for an odd function of period 2π is

$$f(\theta) = B_1 \sin \theta + B_2 \sin 2\theta + B_3 \sin 3\theta + \cdots \tag{11.4}$$

where $B_n = \dfrac{1}{\pi} \displaystyle\int_0^{2\pi} f(\theta) \sin n\theta \, d\theta$

$$= \frac{2}{\pi} \int_0^{\pi} f(\theta) \sin n\theta \, d\theta \qquad n = 1, 2, 3, \ldots \tag{11.5}$$

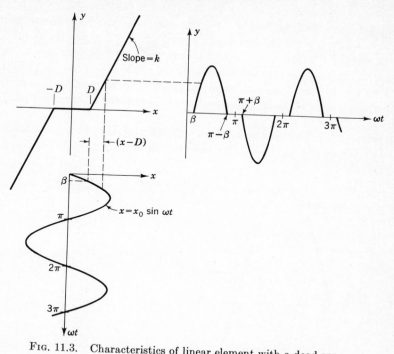

FIG. 11.3.   Characteristics of linear element with a dead zone.

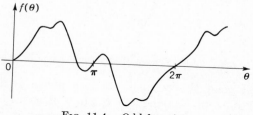

FIG. 11.4.   Odd function.

The value of B_n for the on-off element of Fig. 11.2 is

$$B_n = \frac{2}{\pi} \int_0^\pi Y_0 \sin n\theta \, d\theta = -\frac{2Y_0}{n\pi} [\cos n\theta]_0^\pi$$

$$= \begin{cases} \dfrac{4Y_0}{n\pi} & n = 1, 3, 5, \ldots \\ 0 & n = 2, 4, 6, \ldots \end{cases}$$

The resulting Fourier series representation for y is

$$y = \frac{4Y_0}{\pi} (\sin \omega t + \tfrac{1}{3} \sin 3\omega t + \tfrac{1}{5} \sin 5\omega t + \cdots) \qquad (11.6)$$

where $\theta = \omega t$. The coefficients B_2, B_4, B_6, . . . are zero whenever the function has the additional symmetry such that if the portion from 0 to $\pi/2$ is reflected about a vertical axis through $\pi/2$, it falls upon (coincides with) the portion for the interval from $\pi/2$ to π. Thus, in the interval 0 to π the function is an even function with respect to the vertical axis through $\pi/2$. This is the case for the functions shown in Figs. 11.2 and 11.3.

In Fig. 11.5 is shown the original output y of Fig. 11.2, and also the first two terms of the series expansion for this function. The sum of all

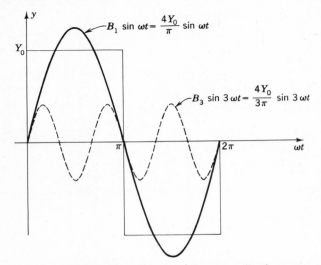

FIG. 11.5.   Graphical interpretation of series expansion for a square wave.

the terms would yield the original function which is a square wave. However, the fundamental component $B_1 \sin \omega t$ is seen to yield the most significant contribution. Good results are obtained in the analysis of such nonlinear control elements by approximating the output by its fundamental component.

$$y \approx B_1 \sin \omega t \qquad (11.7)$$

The two major reasons why the fundamental component yields good results in approximating the characteristics of a nonlinear element are:

1.   The fundamental component yields the most significant contribution to the output.
2.   The higher-frequency terms such as $B_3 \sin 3\omega t$, $B_5 \sin 5\omega t$, . . . are progressively attenuated more by the other linear components in the system. Consequently, they have less of an effect upon the operating characteristics of the system.

The operation of the on-off element of Fig. 11.2 is thus approximated by the ratio

$$N = \frac{y}{x} \approx \frac{B_1 \sin \omega t}{x_0 \sin \omega t} = \frac{B_1}{x_0} = \frac{4Y_0}{\pi x_0} \tag{11.8}$$

where $N = y/x$ is called the describing function because it describes the relationship between the output and input.

For the element with dead zone shown in Fig. 11.3, it follows that when $x_0 > D$

$$
\begin{aligned}
B_1 &= \frac{2}{\pi} \int_0^\pi f(\theta) \sin\theta \, d\theta = \frac{2}{\pi} \int_\beta^{\pi-\beta} k(x_0 \sin\theta - x_0 \sin\beta) \sin\theta \, d\theta \\
&= \frac{2kx_0}{\pi} \left[\left(\frac{\theta}{2} - \frac{\sin 2\theta}{4} \right) + \cos\theta \sin\beta \right]_\beta^{\pi-\beta} \\
&= \frac{2kx_0}{\pi} \left(\frac{\pi - 2\beta}{2} - \frac{\sin 2\beta}{2} \right)
\end{aligned}
$$

Thus, the describing function N is

$$N = \frac{y}{x} \approx \frac{B_1}{x_0} = \begin{cases} \dfrac{k}{\pi}(\pi - 2\beta - \sin 2\beta) & x_0 > D \\ 0 & 0 \le x_0 \le D \end{cases} \tag{11.9}$$

When $0 \le x_0 \le D$ the output is zero.

Because $\beta = \sin^{-1}(D/x_0)$, a plot of N/k versus x_0/D may be constructed as shown in Fig. 11.6.

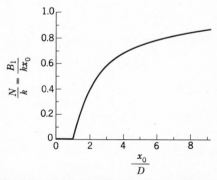

FIG. 11.6. Plot of describing function for linear element with dead zone.

Adding (or subtracting) the describing functions for known nonlinearities yields the describing function for the sum (or difference) of the nonlinearities. For example, Fig. 11.7 shows that subtracting N_2 from N_1 yields the nonlinearity N whose characteristic is

$$N = N_1 - N_2 \tag{11.10}$$

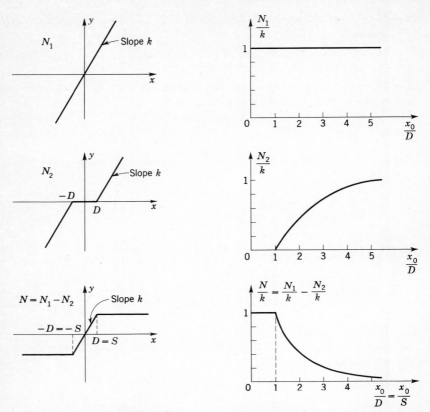

FIG. 11.7.   Graphical subtraction of the describing function for N_2 from that for N_1 to obtain $N = N_1 - N_2$.

The equation for N_1 is

$$N_1 = \frac{y}{x} = k \qquad \text{or} \qquad \frac{N_1}{k} = 1 \qquad (11.11)$$

For convenience in graphically subtracting the describing function for N_2 from N_1, the horizontal scale is made the same for both describing functions (that is, x_0/D).   The function $N_1/k = 1$ is independent of x_0 and thus is also independent of x_0/D.

The equation for N is obtained by subtracting Eq. (11.9) from (11.11). Thus,

$$N = \begin{cases} \dfrac{k}{\pi}\,(2\beta + \sin 2\beta) & x_0 > D \quad \text{or} \quad \dfrac{x_0}{D} > 1 \\[4mm] k & 0 \le x_0 \le D \quad \text{or} \quad 0 \le \dfrac{x_0}{D} \le 1 \end{cases} \qquad (11.12)$$

The resultant nonlinearity $N = N_1 - N_2$ is the characteristic of an element which saturates. For an element which saturates the output varies in proportion to the input ($y = kx$) until saturation occurs. The value of x at which saturation occurs is $D = S$, and the corresponding value of y which is the maximum value that y attains is $kD = kS$.

11.2 Stability Analysis. In Fig. 11.8a is shown a control system which has a nonlinear component represented by N. The component N may

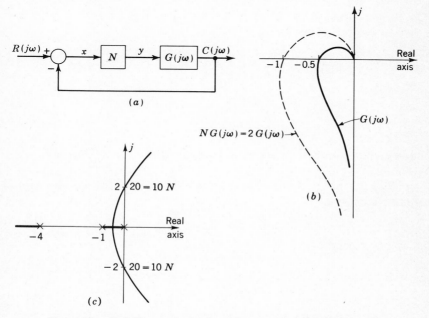

FIG. 11.8. Stability analysis of a system with a nonlinear element.

be considered as a variable gain. The value of N, the variable gain, depends upon the amplitude of the input signal x_0. The frequency response for linear elements such as $G(j\omega)$ depends on frequency only.

In Fig. 11.8b is shown the polar plot for the system whose transfer function is

$$G(s) = \frac{2.5}{s(1 + 0.25s)(1 + s)} \qquad (11.13)$$

If the gain is doubled, the polar plot would go through the -1 point. Thus, the system is unstable for $N \geq 2$.

Suppose that the nonlinearity is the dead zone N of Fig. 11.6. For $k = 4$, it follows that N is greater than or equal to 2 when $N/k \geq \frac{2}{4} = 0.5$. Thus, from Fig. 11.6 instability results when $x_0/D \geq 2.5$ or

$x_0 \geq 2.5D$. If the value of k is 1, instability results when $N/k \geq 2$. Instability cannot occur for this case because the maximum attainable value of N/k is 1.

In addition to the polar plot of Fig. 11.8b, the same information could also have been obtained by use of the log-magnitude diagram, log-modulus plot, or the inverse polar plot. The root-locus method is also well suited to this type of problem. The characteristic equation for this system is

$$s(s + 1)(s + 4) + 10N = 0 \qquad (11.14)$$

The corresponding root-locus plot is shown in Fig. 11.8c. Application of Routh's criterion shows that

$$s^3 + 5s^2 + 4s + 20N = 0$$

$$
\begin{array}{ccc}
1 & 4 & 0 \\
5 & 10N & 0 \\
\dfrac{(20 - 10N)}{5} & 0 & \\
10N & &
\end{array}
$$

The system becomes unstable when the gain $10N$ is 20. Thus instability results for $N \geq 2$.

Another method for investigating stability is to note that the overall system response is

$$\frac{C(j\omega)}{R(j\omega)} = \frac{NG(j\omega)}{1 + NG(j\omega)} \qquad (11.15)$$

Instability results if

$$NG(j\omega) = -1$$

or

$$G(j\omega) = -\frac{1}{N} \qquad (11.16)$$

By plotting $G(j\omega)$ and $-1/N$ as shown in Fig. 11.9, an unstable system is indicated if the two curves intersect. The function $-1/N$ is plotted

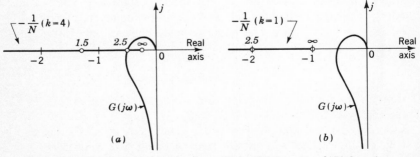

Fig. 11.9. Plots of $G(j\omega)$ and $-1/N$ for (a) $k = 4$ and (b) $k = 1$.

by obtaining N/k for various values of x_0/D from Fig. 11.6, and then computing $-1/N$ from the equation

$$-\frac{1}{N} = -\frac{1}{k(N/k)}$$

For example, when $x_0/D = \infty$, then $N/k = 1$. Thus, $-1/N = -1/k$. For $k = 4$, then $-1/N = -\frac{1}{4}$. For $k = 1$, then $-1/N = -1$. Figure 11.9a is for $k = 4$, and Fig. 11.9b is for $k = 1$. The values of x_0/D are italicized along the $-1/N$ curves. An unstable system results for $k = 4$. The critical value is $x_0/D \geq 2.5$. For the case in which $k = 1$, the system is always stable.

11.3 Describing Functions with a Phase Shift. The preceding discussion was limited to describing functions in which there was no phase shift between the input $x = x_0 \sin \omega t$ and the fundamental component $y = B_1 \sin \omega t$. In Fig. 11.10 is shown the input-output relationship for an on-off (contactor) element which has a hysteresis loop of width Δ in addition

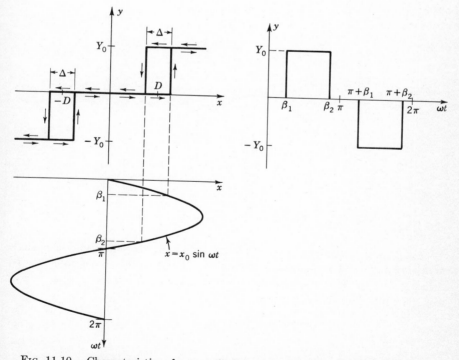

FIG. 11.10.   Characteristics of an on-off element with hysteresis and dead zone.

to the dead zone.[1] Starting from $x = 0$, as the amplitude x of the input is increased, the contactor does not close until x exceeds the value $D + \Delta/2$. The contactor then remains closed until the value of the input becomes less than $D - \Delta/2$. As indicated by the arrows in Fig. 11.10, in the region $(D - \Delta/2) \leq x \leq (D + \Delta/2)$ the value of the output depends upon the past history (i.e., whether x is increasing or decreasing). A similar phenomenon occurs for negative values of x. The angle β_1 at which the contactor closes and the angle β_2 at which it opens again are obtained from Fig. 11.10 as follows:

$$\sin \beta_1 = \frac{D + \Delta/2}{x_0}$$
$$\sin \beta_2 = \frac{D - \Delta/2}{x_0} \tag{11.17}$$

In Fig. 11.11 is shown an enlarged view of the contactor output and the first harmonic component. The square-wave output begins at the

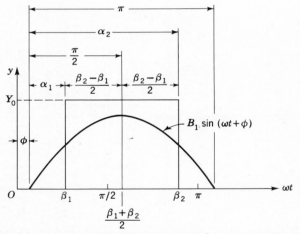

FIG. 11.11.   Fundamental component of contactor output.

angle β_1 and terminates at β_2. Thus, it is symmetrical about the angle $(\beta_1 + \beta_2)/2$. The equation for the fundamental harmonic is $B_1 \sin (\omega t + \phi)$. When $\omega t = (\beta_1 + \beta_2)/2$, then $\sin (\omega t + \phi) = 1$ or $\omega t + \phi = \pi/2$. Thus, the phase angle ϕ is

$$\phi = \frac{\pi}{2} - \frac{\beta_1 + \beta_2}{2} \tag{11.18}$$

[1] Kochenburger, *op. cit.*

The amplitude of the fundamental harmonic component is

$$B_1 = \frac{2Y_0}{\pi} \int_{\alpha_1}^{\alpha_2} \sin\theta \, d\theta = -\frac{2Y_0}{\pi} \left[\cos\theta\right]_{\pi/2-(\beta_2-\beta_1)/2}^{\pi/2+(\beta_2-\beta_1)/2}$$

$$= \frac{4Y_0}{\pi} \sin\frac{\beta_2-\beta_1}{2} \tag{11.19}$$

The describing function N is the ratio of the output (as approximated by the fundamental harmonic) to the input. That is

$$N = \frac{y}{x} = \frac{B_1 \sin(\omega t + \phi)}{x_0 \sin\omega t} = |N| \underline{/\phi} \tag{11.20}$$

The magnitude of the describing function is

$$|N| = \frac{B_1}{x_0} = \frac{4Y_0}{\pi x_0} \sin\frac{\beta_2-\beta_1}{2}$$

Convenient graphs as shown in Fig. 11.12 for determining the magnitude $|N|$ and phase shift ϕ of the describing function are obtained by rewriting

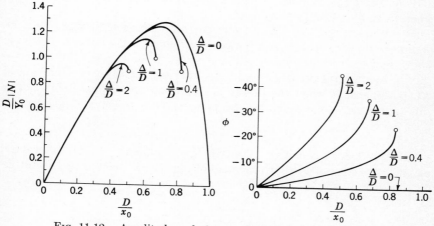

Fig. 11.12. Amplitude and phase angle of describing function.

Eqs. (11.18) and (11.20) in the following form

$$\frac{D}{Y_0} |N| = \frac{4}{\pi} \frac{D}{x_0} \sin\frac{\beta_2-\beta_1}{2} \tag{11.21}$$

$$\phi = \frac{\pi}{2} - \frac{1}{2}\left[\sin^{-1}\frac{D+\Delta/2}{x_0} + \sin^{-1}\frac{D-\Delta/2}{x_0}\right] \tag{11.22}$$

In Fig. 11.13 is shown the curve of $G(j\omega)$ for the system shown in Fig. 11.8. Because $N = |N|e^{j\phi}$ and $-N = |N|e^{j(\phi-180°)}$, then

$$-\frac{1}{N} = \left|\frac{1}{N}\right| e^{-j(\phi-180°)}$$

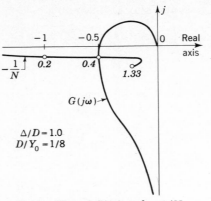

Fig. 11.13. Plot of $G(j\omega)$ and $-1/N$.

The curve of $-1/N$ of Fig. 11.13 is drawn for the case in which $\Delta/D = 1.0$ and $D/Y_0 = \frac{1}{8}$. Values of D/x_0 are italicized. Instability results when $D/x_0 \geq 0.4$ or $x_0 \leq 2.5D$.

In summary, the describing function has a phase shift whenever the nonlinear element is such that for a given value of x the output may have more than one value. The particular value depends upon the past history or manner in which the input x is varying. The root-locus method is not applicable when the describing function has a phase shift. For this case, direct polar plots, inverse polar plots, or log-modulus diagrams must be used.

11.4 Frequency-sensitive Describing Functions. The differential equation for the portion of the system of Fig. 11.14 enclosed by the dotted

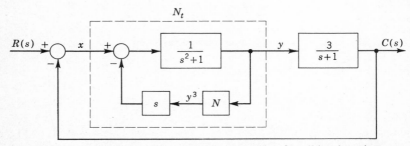

Fig. 11.14. System with a frequency-sensitive describing function.

box is

$$(x - Dy^3) = (D^2 + 1)y$$

or

$$\ddot{y} + 3y^2\dot{y} + y = x \qquad (11.23)$$

In the preceding sections it was assumed that if the input is $x = x_0 \sin \omega t$, then the fundamental component of the output has the form $y = y_0 \sin (\omega t + \phi)$. For nonlinear differential equations, it is more convenient to employ the equivalent form.[1,2,3]

$$
\begin{aligned}
y &= y_0 \sin \omega t \\
x &= x_0 \sin (\omega t - \phi)
\end{aligned}
\tag{11.24}
$$

Substitution of these forms for x and y into Eq. (11.23) gives

$$-y_0\omega^2 \sin \omega t + 3y_0^3\omega \sin^2 \omega t \cos \omega t + y_0 \sin \omega t = x_0 \sin (\omega t - \phi)$$

or

$$y_0(1 - \omega^2) \sin \omega t + 3y_0^3\omega(\cos \omega t - \cos^3 \omega t) = x_0 \sin (\omega t - \phi)$$

Replacing $\cos^3 \omega t$ by $(3 \cos \omega t + \cos 3\omega t)/4$ and neglecting higher-order harmonics (that is, $\cos 3\omega t$) gives

$$y_0(1 - \omega^2) \sin \omega t + \tfrac{3}{4}y_0^3\omega \cos \omega t = x_0 (\cos \phi \sin \omega t - \sin \phi \cos \omega t)$$

Equating $\sin \omega t$ terms and $\cos \omega t$ terms shows that

$$
\begin{aligned}
y_0(1 - \omega^2) &= x_0 \cos \phi \tag{11.25} \\
\tfrac{3}{4}y_0^3\omega &= -x_0 \sin \phi \tag{11.26}
\end{aligned}
$$

The total describing function N_t for the portion of the system of Fig. 11.14 enclosed by the dotted box is

$$N_t = \frac{y_0}{x_0} e^{j\phi} = \rho(\cos \phi + j \sin \phi)$$

where $\rho = y_0/x_0$.

Dividing Eq. (11.26) by (11.25) gives

$$\phi = \tan^{-1} \frac{3\omega(\rho x_0/2)^2}{1 - \omega^2} \tag{11.27}$$

Similarly, squaring Eqs. (11.25) and (11.26) and adding gives

$$x_0^2 = \frac{4}{3\omega\rho^3} [1 - \rho^2(1 - \omega^2)^2]^{\frac{1}{2}} \tag{11.28}$$

From Eq. (11.28), a family of curves of ρ versus x_0 for constant values of ω can be constructed. Similarly, from Eq. (11.27) a family of curves of ρ versus ϕ for constant values of ω may be constructed.

[1] J. J. Stoker, "Nonlinear Vibrations in Mechanical and Electrical Systems," Interscience Publishers, Inc., New York, 1950.

[2] E. Mishkin and L. Braun, Jr., "Adaptive Control Systems," McGraw-Hill Book Co., New York, 1961.

[3] G. J. Thaler and M. P. Pastel, "Analysis and Design of Feedback Control Systems," McGraw-Hill Book Co., New York, 1962.

The function $-1/N_t$ is

$$- \frac{1}{N_t} = - \frac{e^{-j\phi}}{\rho} = \frac{x_0}{y_0} (- \cos \phi + j \sin \phi) \tag{11.29}$$

The real part of $-1/N_t$ may be expressed in the form

$$\Re - \frac{1}{N_t} = - \frac{x_0}{y_0} \cos \phi = -(1 - \omega^2) \tag{11.30}$$

The frequency response for $G(s) = 3/(1 + s)$ is

$$G(j\omega) = \frac{3}{1 + j\omega} \cdot \frac{1 - j\omega}{1 - j\omega} = \frac{3}{1 + \omega^2} - j \frac{3\omega}{1 + \omega^2} \tag{11.31}$$

Equating the real part of $G(j\omega)$ and the real part of $(-1/N_t)$ shows that these are equal when $\omega = \sqrt{2}$. In Fig. 11.15a is shown the polar

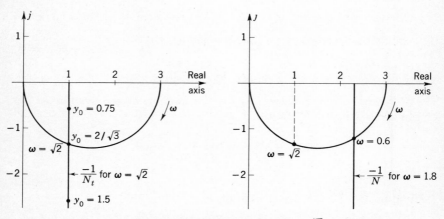

Fig. 11.15. Plot of $G(j\omega)$ and $-1/N_t$ for (a) $\omega = \sqrt{2}$ and (b) $\omega = 1.8$.

plot $G(j\omega)$ and the $-1/N_t$ plot for $\omega = \sqrt{2}$. The real part of $-1/N_t$ given by Eq. (11.30) is $-(1 - 2) = 1.0$. The imaginary part of $-1/N_t$ is

$$\mathfrak{g} - \frac{1}{N_t} = \frac{x_0}{y_0} \sin \phi = - \frac{3}{4} y_0{}^2 \omega = \frac{-3\sqrt{2}}{4} y_0{}^2$$

Equating the imaginary parts of $-1/N_t$ and $G(j\omega)$ shows that at the intersection $\omega = \sqrt{2}$ the value of y_0 is $2/\sqrt{3}$. At this intersection $|G(j\omega)| = \sqrt{3}$ and $|1/N_t| = \sqrt{3}$, hence sustained oscillations result in that the loop gain $|N_t| |G(j\omega)| = 1$. For $y_0 < 2/\sqrt{3}$ then $|N_t| > 1/\sqrt{3}$. The amplitude of y_0 increases because the loop gain

$$|N_t| |G(j\omega)| > 1$$

For $y_0 > 2/\sqrt{3}$, then $|N_t| < 1/\sqrt{3}$. The amplitude of y_0 now decreases because the loop gain is less than 1. Thus, the intersection $\omega = \sqrt{2}$ and $y_0 = 2/\sqrt{3}$ represents a point of sustained oscillation.

In Fig. 11.15b is shown the $-1/N_t$ plot for $\omega = 1.8$. The real part of $-1/N_t$ is $-(1 - 3.24) = 2.24$. The value of ω on the $G(j\omega)$ plot at which the real part of $G(j\omega)$ is 2.24 is $\Re \, G(j\omega) = 3/(1 + \omega^2)$. Solving for ω gives $\omega = 0.6$. Such a mismatch does not represent a sustained oscillation. In summary, although many $-1/N_t$ plots for various constant values of ω may intersect the $G(j\omega)$ plot, instability results only when the $-1/N_t$ curve drawn for a certain value of ω intersects the $G(j\omega)$ plot at the same frequency.

An alternate method of solving this problem is to obtain the describing function for the nonlinearity only, and then to proceed to construct the root-locus plot for the system. The output from the nonlinear element is

$$y_0{}^3 \sin^3 \omega t = y_0{}^3 \frac{3 \sin \omega t - \sin 3\omega t}{4}$$

Neglecting the higher-order harmonic yields for the describing function

$$N = \frac{3y_0{}^3 \sin \omega t/4}{y_0 \sin \omega t} = \frac{3}{4} y_0{}^2 \tag{11.32}$$

The transfer function for the portion of the system enclosed by the dotted box of Fig. 11.14 is

$$\frac{G}{1 + GH} = \frac{1/(s^2 + 1)}{1 + Ns/(s^2 + 1)} = \frac{1}{s^2 + Ns + 1}$$

Thus, the characteristic equation for the entire system is

$$s^3 + (N + 1)s^2 + (N + 1)s + 4 = 0 \tag{11.33}$$

Application of Routh's criterion to determine the value of N at which the system becomes unstable gives

$$
\begin{array}{ccc}
1 & N + 1 & 0 \\
N + 1 & 4 & 0 \\
\dfrac{[(N + 1)^2 - 4]}{N + 1} & 0 & 0 \\
4 & 0 & 0
\end{array}
$$

Thus, instability results when $(N + 1) \leq 2$ or $N \leq 1.0$. From Eq. (11.32), it follows that $y_0 \leq 2/\sqrt{3}$.

To construct the root-locus plot, the characteristic equation is written in the form

$$(s^3 + 4) + Ks(s + 1) = 0$$

where $K = N + 1$. The three cube roots of (-4) are $1.59\underline{/60°}$, $1.59\underline{/180°}$, and $1.59\underline{/-60°}$. The root-locus plot is shown in Fig. 11.16. When the

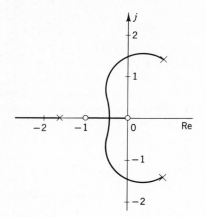

FIG. 11.16.   Root-locus plot for $(s^3 + 4) + Ks(s + 1)$ where $K = N + 1$.

locus crosses the imaginary axis the value of $K = N + 1$ is 2. Thus, the characteristic equation is

$$s^3 + 2s^2 + 2s + 4 = (s^2 + 2)(s + 2)$$

The corresponding three roots are $s = \pm j\omega = \pm j\sqrt{2}$ and $s = -2$. Thus, $\omega = \sqrt{2}$ is the frequency of oscillation.

For the case in which $y_0 < \sqrt{3}/2$, and thus $K = (N + 1) < 2$, the system has a pair of roots in the right half plane. The oscillation grows until $y_0 = \sqrt{3}/2$. If the oscillations are such that $y_0 > \sqrt{3}/2$, and thus $K = (N + 1) > 2$, all of the roots of the characteristic equation are in the left half plane. The oscillations now decrease until $y_0 = \sqrt{3}/2$. In summary, $y_0 = \sqrt{3}/2$ and $\omega = \sqrt{2}$ represent an oscillatory state toward which the system tends. Such a state is referred to as a stable limit cycle.

11.5 Optimum Switched Systems. The describing function method of the preceding sections enables one to determine whether or not an on-off system is stable. This section discusses methods for determining the switching schedule of an on-off controller so as to obtain optimum performance.

In Fig. 11.17 is shown an on-off controller which drives a pure inertial load. Depending upon whether the error is positive or negative, the controller actuates the motor to supply full positive torque for accelerating the load or full negative torque for decelerating the load. The equa-

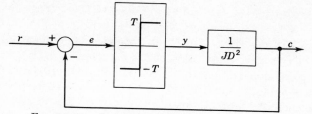

Fɪɢ. 11.17. On-off controller with inertial load.

tion of operation for this system is

$$r - \frac{1}{JD^2} y = e$$

or

$$c = r - e = \frac{1}{JD^2} y \tag{11.34}$$

The value of y is

$$y = \begin{cases} T & e > 0 \\ -T & e < 0 \end{cases} \tag{11.35}$$

For investigating the effect of initial conditions only, $r = 0$ and $c = -e$.
In terms of e, the differential equation of operation is

$$\ddot{e} = -\frac{y}{J} = \begin{cases} \dfrac{T}{J} & e < 0 \\ -\dfrac{T}{J} & e > 0 \end{cases}$$

In terms of c, the differential equation of operation for this system is

$$\ddot{c} = \begin{cases} \dfrac{T}{J} & c < 0 \\ -\dfrac{T}{J} & c > 0 \end{cases} \tag{11.36}$$

Because these differential equations are the same, it suffices to work in
terms of c. By noting that $\ddot{c} = \dot{c}\, d\dot{c}/dc$, then

$$\dot{c}\, d\dot{c} = \pm \frac{T}{J} dc$$

Integration yields

$$\dot{c}^2 = \pm 2 \frac{T}{J} c + K \tag{11.37}$$

where $K = \dot{c}(0)^2 \mp 2(T/J)c(0)$. This is recognized as the equation for
a family of parabolas in which c is the x coordinate and $\dot{c}$ is the y coordinate. When the plus sign holds in Eq. (11.37), the parabolas are as

shown to the left of the vertical axis in Fig. 11.18a. The plus sign holds for $c < 0$. When the negative sign holds in Eq. (11.37), the parabolas are as shown to the right of the vertical axis. The negative sign holds for $c > 0$. The particular parabola is determined by the value of K which, in turn, depends on the initial conditions, $c(0)$ and $\dot{c}(0)$. This system never achieves equilibrium operation in that corresponding values of c and $\dot{c}$ merely follow a closed cyclic path. The double coordinate scale of Fig. 11.18a shows that this graph serves equally well as the e, $\dot{e}$ plot or the c, $\dot{c}$ plot.

The optimum switching schedule becomes apparent if the parabolas of Fig. 11.18a are extended and if the parabolas which go into the origin

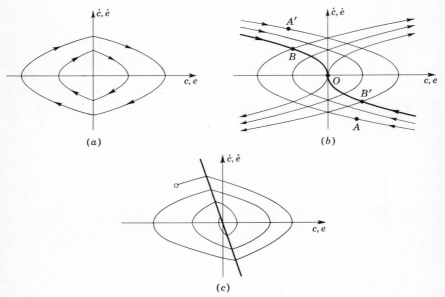

Fig. 11.18.   Response trajectories.

are also drawn as shown in Fig. 11.18b. The only parabolas which come into the origin are the BO and $B'O$ parabolas. For optimum response the system remains on its initial parabola until it reaches the BO or $B'O$ parabolas. The system then switches to the BO or $B'O$ parabola and thus proceeds to the origin. For example, if the starting point is A the system remains on this parabola to the point B and then proceeds into the origin. Similarly, if the starting point is A' the system proceeds to B' and then into the origin. Any other switching routes intersect the BO or $B'O$ parabola farther away from the origin. Hence, the sequence of remaining on the initial parabola until the system arrives at the

BO or *B'O* parabola is the fastest route to the origin (i.e., optimum response).

It should also be noted that there is but one switching involved (i.e., at the *BO* or *B'O* parabola). In Fig. 11.18*c* is shown the trajectory when switching occurs along a straight line. Although the response is not optimum, it is quite adequate. In practice, it is considerably easier to have switching occur along a straight line rather than a parabola.

Problems

11.1 Determine the describing function N for each of the nonlinear elements shown in Fig. P11.1.

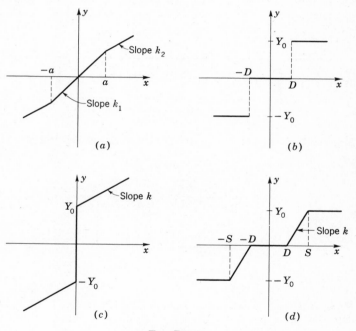

Fig. P11.1

11.2 The equation for B_n for a function of period 2π may be written in the form

$$B_n = \frac{1}{\pi} \int_0^\pi f(\theta) \sin n\theta \, d\theta + \frac{1}{\pi} \int_\pi^{2\pi} f(\theta) \sin n\theta \, d\theta$$

For an odd function, $f(\theta) = -f(2\pi - \theta)$ in the interval π to 2π. By making the change of variable from θ to $(2\pi - \theta)$ in the second integral for B_n show that

$$B_n = \frac{2}{\pi} \int_0^\pi f(\theta) \sin n\theta \, d\theta$$

11.3 When the function $f(\theta)$ of Prob. 11.2 has the additional symmetry such that in the interval 0 to π it is an even function about the vertical $\theta = \pi/2$ axis, then $f(\theta) = f(\pi - \theta)$. The result of Prob. 11.2 may be written in the form

$$B_n = \frac{2}{\pi} \int_0^{\pi/2} f(\theta) \sin n\theta \, d\theta + \frac{2}{\pi} \int_{\pi/2}^{\pi} f(\theta) \sin n\theta \, d\theta$$

By making the change of variable from θ to $(\pi - \theta)$ in the last integral, show that

$$B_n = \begin{cases} \dfrac{4}{\pi} \int_0^{\pi/2} f(\theta) \sin n\theta \, d\theta & n = 1, 3, 5, \ldots \\ 0 & n = 2, 4, 6, \ldots \end{cases}$$

11.4 For the system shown in Fig. P11.4, the gain is $K = 3$. Determine the range of values of x_0 for which the system is stable if
   (a) The nonlinear element is dead zone for which $k = 4$.
   (b) The nonlinear element is saturation for which $k = 5$.
   (c) The nonlinear element is an on-off device for which $Y_0 = 10$.

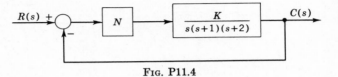

Fɪɢ. P11.4

11.5 Same as Prob. 11.4 except for the system shown in Fig. P11.5. The value of K is 3.

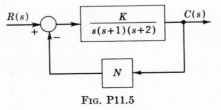

Fɪɢ. P11.5

11.6 Same as Prob. 11.4 except for the system shown in Fig. P11.6. The value of K is 12.

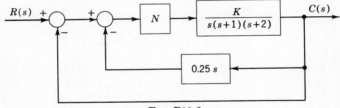

Fɪɢ. P11.6

11.7 Same as Prob. 11.4 except for the system shown in Fig. P11.7. The value of K is 24/5.

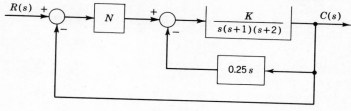

Fig. P11.7

11.8 Same as Prob. 11.4 except for the system shown in Fig. P11.8. The value of K is 24. For the dead zone and saturation use $k = 2$ rather than $k = 4$ of Prob. 11.4.

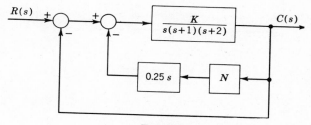

Fig. P11.8

11.9 Same as Prob. 11.4 except for the system shown in Fig. P11.7. The value of K is 24. For the dead zone and saturation use $k = 2$ rather than $k = 4$ of Prob. 11.4.

11.10 Determine the describing function N for each of the nonlinear elements shown in Fig. P11.10.

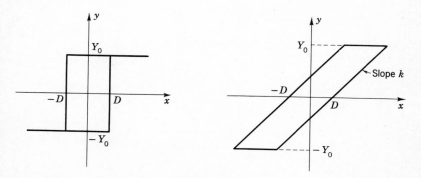

Fig. P11.10

11.11 Determine the equation for the magnitude and the equation for the phase of the describing function N for the following nonlinear equation

$$\ddot{y} + y^3 = x$$

11.12 The dotted box of Fig. 11.14 is replaced by the nonlinearity

$$y^2\dot{y} - y = x$$

Determine the frequency and amplitude of oscillation of the resulting system.

11.13 For the system of Fig. P11.13, determine the equation for the $e, \dot{e}$ plot and the equation for the $c, \dot{c}$ plot when $r = 0$.

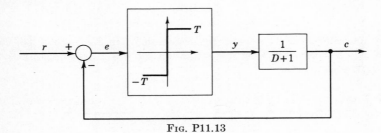

Fig. P11.13

12

The phase-plane and Liapunov methods

The phase-plane method is basically a graphical procedure for determining the transient response of first- or second-order nonlinear systems. The Liapunov method is an extension of these stability concepts to higher order nonlinear systems.

12.1 The Phase-plane Method. Consider the second-order nonlinear differential equation

$$\ddot{y} + f_1(y,\dot{y})\dot{y} + f_2(y,\dot{y})y = f(y,\dot{y}) \tag{12.1}$$

where $f_1(y,\dot{y})$, $f_2(y,\dot{y})$, and $f(y,\dot{y})$ are various functions of y and $\dot{y}$.

For the case in which $f_1(y,\dot{y})$ and $f_2(y,\dot{y})$ are both constant, Eq. (12.1) reduces to a linear differential equation with constant coefficients.

By letting

$$\dot{y} = v \tag{12.2}$$

then

$$\ddot{y} = \frac{dv}{dt} = \frac{dy}{dt}\frac{dv}{dy} = v\frac{dv}{dy} \tag{12.3}$$

The substitution of these values of $\dot{y}$ and $\ddot{y}$ into Eq. (12.1) gives

$$v\frac{dv}{dy} + f_1(y,v)v + f_2(y,v)y = f(y,v)$$

or

$$\frac{dv}{dy} = -f_1(y,v) - \frac{f_2(y,v)}{v}y + \frac{f(y,v)}{v} \tag{12.4}$$

The second-order differential equation, Eq. (12.1), may thus be represented by the two first-order equations, Eqs. (12.2) and (12.4).

To illustrate the basic principles involved in the phase-plane method, consider the mass-spring system shown in Fig. 12.1. The equation of

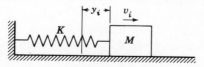

Fig. 12.1. Mass-spring system.

motion is

$$M\ddot{y} + Ky = 0 \tag{12.5}$$

For $\dot{y} = v$, then $\ddot{y} = v(dv/dy)$. Thus,

$$Mv\,\frac{dv}{dy} = -Ky$$

The solution of this first-order differential equation is obtained directly by integration.

$$\int v\,dv = -\frac{K}{M}\int y\,dy$$

Thus

$$v^2 + \frac{K}{M}\,y^2 = C \tag{12.6}$$

The constant of integration is obtained by evaluating this result at $t = 0$.

$$C = v_i{}^2 + \frac{K}{M}\,y_i{}^2$$

where y_i = initial displacement
$\quad\ \ v_i$ = initial velocity

A phase-plane trajectory is a plot of all corresponding values of y and v that satisfy the system equation for a given set of initial conditions. A particular phase-plane trajectory for Eq. (12.6) is shown in Fig. 12.2a.

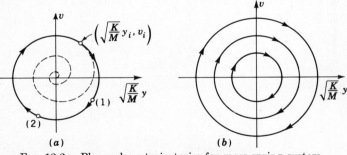

FIG. 12.2. Phase-plane trajectories for mass-spring system.

The starting point has the coordinates $(\sqrt{K/M}y_i,v_i)$. Different trajectories corresponding to different values of the constant, $v_i{}^2 + (K/M)y_i{}^2$, are shown in Fig. 12.2b. The initial conditions determine the value of the constant which in turn determines the particular trajectory. The family of trajectories for a given system is called a phase portrait. Note that Eq. (12.6) is the equation for an ellipse.

From Eq. (12.3), the slope of the phase trajectory dv/dy is

$$\frac{dv}{dy} = \frac{1}{v}\,\ddot{y}$$

On the y axis the value of v is zero. Thus, each trajectory crosses the y axis at right angles $(dv/dy = \infty)$.

Because $y = \int v\, dt$, then for positive values of v the position y increases. That is, for values of v above the horizontal axis $v > 0$, the arrows on the trajectories indicate y moving to the right. For negative values of v (i.e., below the horizontal axis), the arrows on the trajectories show y decreasing by going to the left. Thus, as time increases, corresponding values of y and v proceed in a clockwise direction along the phase trajectory.

The time required for the operating point to move from any point (1) on a trajectory to a second point (2), as indicated in Fig. 12.2a may be computed by integrating the equation

$$dt = \frac{dy}{v}$$

Thus,

$$t_2 - t_1 = \int_{y_1}^{y_2} \frac{dy}{v} = \int_{y_1}^{y_2} \frac{dy}{\sqrt{C - (K/M)y^2}}$$

When v is a more complicated function, this integration can become very difficult to evaluate. A graphical technique for approximating $\Delta t = t_2 - t_1$ is illustrated in Fig. 12.3. If the change is sufficiently small so

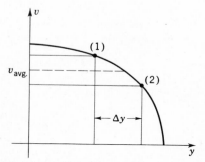

Fig. 12.3. Graphical interpretation of $t = t_2 - t_1 = \Delta y / v_{\text{av}}$.

that v does not vary much from its average value, then

$$\Delta t \approx \frac{\Delta y}{v_{\text{av}}}$$

The trajectory for any conservative system in which there is no damping to dissipate energy must be a closed path. If there were damping in the system, the path of operation would be a spiral in toward the origin as is indicated by the dashed line in Fig. 12.2a.

Coulomb Friction. When there is coulomb friction existing between the mass M of Fig. 12.1 and the surface over which it is sliding, the equation of motion is

$$M\ddot{y} + Ky = -\mu Mg \qquad v > 0 \qquad (12.7)$$
$$M\ddot{y} + Ky = \mu Mg \qquad v < 0 \qquad (12.8)$$

where μ is the coefficient of friction.

By making the substitution $y_r = y + \mu Mg/K$ where y_r indicates motion to the right ($v > 0$), Eq. (12.7) becomes

$$M\ddot{y}_r + Ky_r = 0 \qquad (12.9)$$

It is seen that $\dot{y}_r = \dot{y} = v$ and $\ddot{y}_r = \ddot{y}$. The preceding equation is similar to Eq. (12.5), and thus its solution is

$$v^2 + \frac{K}{M} y_r{}^2 = v^2 + \frac{K}{M} \left(y + \frac{\mu Mg}{K}\right)^2 = C_r \qquad (12.10)$$

This is the equation for a family of ellipses in the (y,v) coordinate system. Any ellipse may be plotted as a circle by changing the scale factor. Thus, on $(\sqrt{K/M}\, y,v)$ coordinates the phase portrait for Eq. (12.10) is a family of circles of radius $\sqrt{C_r}$ whose center is at the point $y = -\mu Mg/K$. Because Eq. (12.10) is valid for $v > 0$, only semicircles above the y axis may be obtained from this expression, as shown in Fig. 12.4. For the case in which $v < 0$, the substitution $y_L = y - \mu Mg/K$ is made in Eq.

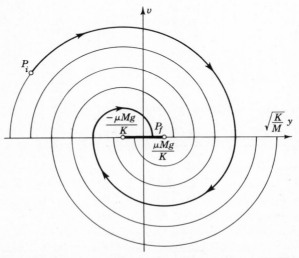

FIG. 12.4.   Phase-plane portrait for mass-spring system with friction.

(12.8). This yields

$$M\ddot{y}_L + Ky_L = 0$$

The solution of the preceding expression is

$$v^2 + \frac{K}{M} y_L{}^2 = v^2 + \frac{K}{M} \left(y_L - \frac{\mu Mg}{K} \right)^2 = C_L \qquad (12.11)$$

Equation (12.11) yields the family of semicircles drawn below the y axis of Fig. 12.4.

If P_i is the starting point as indicated in Fig. 12.4, the path of motion is that of the heavy line. The final position at which the mass comes to rest is indicated by P_f. Because of coulomb friction, the at-rest position is not at the origin of the phase portrait.

Isoclines. For the general case of a nonlinear system, it may not be possible to obtain a mathematical expression for the trajectories. When this is so, the trajectories may be constructed by a mathematical interpretation of Eq. (12.4). That is

$$m = \frac{dv}{dy} = -f_1(y,v) - f_2(y,v) \frac{y}{v} + \frac{f(y,v)}{v}$$

Solving for v gives

$$v = \frac{-f_2(y,v)y + f(y,v)}{m + f_1(y,v)} \qquad (12.12)$$

where $m = dv/dy$ is the tangent to the trajectory at the point (y,v). For a given slope m, Eq. (12.12) describes a line such that every trajectory has the same slope m as it crosses this line. Such a line is called an *isocline*.

To illustrate this method, consider the equation

$$\ddot{y} + 2\dot{y} + 5y = 3 \qquad (12.13)$$

where $f_1(y,v) = 2$, $f_2(y,v) = 5$, and $f(y,v) = 3$. The equation for the isoclines is

$$v = \frac{-5y + 3}{m + 2} \qquad (12.14)$$

The isoclines for $m = -8, -4, -2, 0, 4$, and ∞ are shown in Fig. 12.5. The short crosslines on the isoclines are drawn at the slope indicated by the value of m for the isocline. These crosslines are horizontal on the $m = 0$ isocline and vertical on the $m = \infty$ isocline. As indicated in Fig. 12.5, the phase trajectory is drawn so that it is always tangent to these crosslines. From Eq. (12.12) it follows that the isoclines are straight lines when $f_1(y,v)$, $f_2(y,v)$, and $f(y,v)$ are constant.

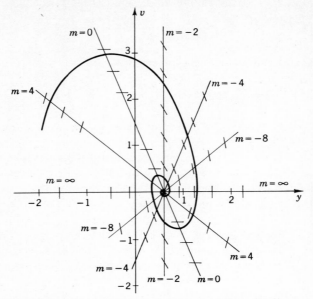

Fig. 12.5.   Construction of phase portrait from isoclines.

Pell's Method.   This method for constructing phase trajectories is applicable for equations of the form

$$\ddot{y} + g(\dot{y}) + f(y) = 0 \qquad (12.15)$$

or
$$v\frac{dv}{dy} + g(v) + f(y) = 0$$

The slope dv/dy is

$$\frac{dv}{dy} = \frac{-g(v) - f(y)}{v} \qquad (12.16)$$

To apply Pell's method, first construct the $g(v)$ vs. v plot and the $f(y)$ vs. y plot as per the coordinate directions shown in Figs. 12.6a and 12.6b.   The two plots are then superimposed upon each other as shown in Fig. 12.6c. To obtain the tangent to the trajectory at the point (y_i, v_i), transfer with a divider the value $f(y_i)$ to BC on the y axis, and then transfer $g(v_i)$ to AB on the y axis.   The slope of the line from A to the starting point is $v/(AB + BC) = v/[g(v_i) + f(y_i)]$.   The perpendicular to this line (through the starting point) has the slope

$$\frac{dv}{dy} = \frac{-g(v_i) - f(y_i)}{v_i}$$

Thus, the slope to the trajectory at the starting point has been determined graphically.   By proceeding to construct other segments which are tangent to the trajectory, the entire phase trajectory can be constructed.

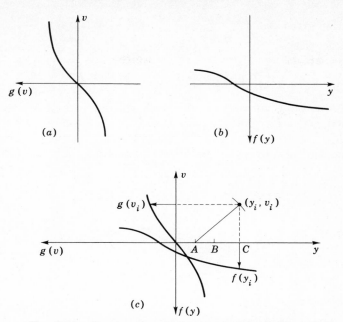

Fɪɢ. 12.6.   Construction of phase portrait by Pell's method.

Equation (12.13) is converted to the form of Eq. (12.15) by making the change of variable $5y - 3 = 5x$, in which case $\dot{y} = \dot{x}$ and $\ddot{y} = \ddot{x}$. Thus,

$$\ddot{x} + 2\dot{x} + 5x = 0$$

The function $g(\dot{x})$ is $2\dot{x}$ and $f(x)$ is $5x$.

The Delta Method.   In this method for constructing trajectories, small segments of the trajectory are approximated by circular arcs.   The delta method is applicable to nonlinear equations of the form

$$\ddot{y} + f(y,v) + \omega_n{}^2 y = 0 \tag{12.17}$$

Letting $v = \dot{y}$ and solving for dv/dy gives

$$\frac{dv}{dy} = -\frac{[\omega_n{}^2 y + f(y,v)]}{v}$$

In the vicinity of a point in the (y,v) plane, the function $f(y,v)$ may be regarded as remaining constant.   By letting $f(y,v) = \omega_n{}^2 \delta$, then the preceding equation becomes

$$\frac{v\,dv}{\omega_n{}^2} + (y + \delta)\,dy = 0$$

Integration gives

$$\frac{v^2}{\omega_n{}^2} + (y^2 + 2\delta y) = C$$

or

$$\left(\frac{v}{\omega_n}\right)^2 + (y + \delta)^2 = C + \delta^2 = R^2 \tag{12.18}$$

With v/ω_n as the vertical axis and y the horizontal axis, this is recognized as the equation for a circle with center at $y = -\delta$, $(v/\omega_n) = 0$, and radius R.

In Fig. 12.7 is shown the application of the delta method to the non-

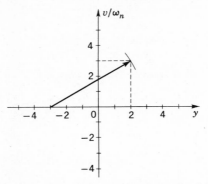

FIG. 12.7. Construction of phase portrait by the delta method.

linear differential equation

$$\ddot{y} + \frac{y\dot{y}}{2} + y = 0$$

For $y = 2$ and $\dot{y} = 3$, the center of the circle is $y = -\delta = -y\dot{y}/2 = -3$, $v = 0$, and the radius is $R = \sqrt{3^2 + (2 + 3)^2} = \sqrt{34}$. To put a nonlinear equation in the proper form for the application of the delta method, it is sometimes necessary to add and subtract a term proportional to y.

12.2 Feedback Systems. A feedback control system which has a nonlinear element N following the actuating signal e is shown in Fig. 12.8a. The differential equation for the input $x = e$ to the nonlinear element in terms of y and the system input r is

$$e = r - \frac{y}{D^2 + D + 1} \tag{12.19}$$

An on-off nonlinear element N is shown in Fig. 12.8b. For this element

$$\begin{aligned} y &= 1 & e &> 0 \\ y &= -1 & e &< 0 \end{aligned} \tag{12.20}$$

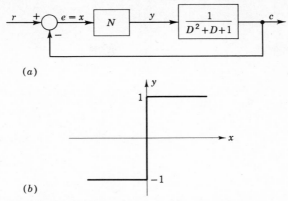

(a)

(b)

FIG. 12.8. Nonlinear system with an on-off element.

To construct the phase plane (e vs. $\dot{e}$) for investigating the effect of initial conditions only, substitute $r = 0$ and the appropriate value of y into Eq. (12.19). Thus,

$$\ddot{e} + \dot{e} + e = -y = -1 \qquad e > 0$$
$$\ddot{e} + \dot{e} + e = -y = 1 \qquad e < 0 \tag{12.21}$$

For the $e > 0$ interval, $f_1 = 1$, $f_2 = 1$, and $f = -1$. Thus, from Eq. (12.12), the equation for the isoclines is

$$v = \dot{e} = \frac{-e - 1}{m + 1} \qquad e > 0$$

For the $e < 0$ interval, $f_1 = 1$, $f_2 = 1$, and $f = 1$. Thus,

$$v = \dot{e} = \frac{-e + 1}{m + 1} \qquad e < 0$$

The corresponding isoclines for $e > 0$ and $e < 0$ are shown in Fig. 12.9. The phase trajectory is for the initial conditions $e(0) = -2$ and $\dot{e}(0) = 0$.

Ordinarily, it is of more interest to construct the $(c,\dot{c})$ phase plane for the output. Using the relationship $e = r - c$ to eliminate e from Eq. (12.19) gives

$$c = \frac{y}{D^2 + D + 1}$$

or

$$\ddot{c} + \dot{c} + c = y \tag{12.22}$$

Next, Eq. (12.20) is converted from ranges of e to ranges of c. For investigating the effect of initial conditions only, $r = 0$ and $e = r - c = -c$. For $e > 0$, then $c < 0$. Similarly, for $e < 0$, then $c > 0$. Thus, Eq.

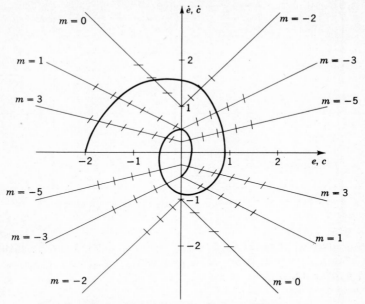

Fig. 12.9.   Phase-plane for system of Fig. 12.8.

(12.20) becomes

$$y = -1 \qquad c > 0$$
$$y = 1 \qquad c < 0$$

Substituting the appropriate values of y into Eq. (12.22) gives

$$\ddot{c} + \dot{c} + c = y = -1 \qquad c > 0$$
$$\ddot{c} + \dot{c} + c = y = 1 \qquad c < 0 \tag{12.23}$$

These differential equations are the same as Eq. (12.21). Thus, the isoclines for the $(c,\dot{c})$ phase plane are exactly the same as those for the $(e,\dot{e})$ phase plane. That is,

$$v = \dot{c} = \frac{-c - 1}{m + 1} \qquad c > 0$$
$$v = \dot{c} = \frac{-c + 1}{m + 1} \qquad c < 0 \tag{12.24}$$

When Fig. 12.9 is regarded as the $(c,\dot{c})$ phase plane, then the trajectory shown represents the response for $c(0) = -2$ and $\dot{c}(0) = 0$.

Step-function Response. For a step function of height h, then $e = (r - c) = (h - c)$ or $c = h - e$. For $e > 0$, then $c < h$. Similarly, for

$e < 0$, then $c > h$. Thus, in terms of c Eq. (12.20) becomes

$$y = -1 \qquad c > h$$
$$y = 1 \qquad c < h$$

With these boundary conditions, Eq. (12.22) becomes

$$\ddot{c} + \dot{c} + c = -1 \qquad c > h$$
$$\ddot{c} + \dot{c} + c = 1 \qquad c < h \tag{12.25}$$

The isoclines are

$$v = \dot{c} = \frac{-c - 1}{m + 1} \qquad c > h$$
$$v = \dot{c} = \frac{-c + 1}{m + 1} \qquad c < h \tag{12.26}$$

These isoclines are the same as those given by Eq. (12.24) except that the transition now occurs at $c = h$ rather than at $c = 0$. Thus, adding h to the values of c on the horizontal axis of Fig. 12.9 yields the phase plane for obtaining the step-function response.

This same technique is also used to construct the phase plane for investigating other nonlinearities such as dead zone, saturation, etc. (see Probs. 12.9 and 12.10).

12.3 Singular Points. In general the differential equation for a nonlinear system may be written in the form

$$\frac{dv}{dy} = \frac{P(y,v)}{Q(y,v)} \tag{12.27}$$

A singular point is a point at which

$$P(y,v) = 0 \qquad \text{and} \qquad Q(y,v) = 0 \tag{12.28}$$

Thus, $dv/dy = 0/0$ is indeterminant at a singular point.

The Taylor series expansion for $P(y,v)$ in the vicinity of the singular point (y_s,v_s) is

$$P(y,v) = y_s + v_s + (y - y_s) \frac{\partial P}{\partial y}\Big|_{\substack{y=y_s \\ v=v_s}} + (v - v_s) \frac{\partial P}{\partial v}\Big|_{\substack{y=y_s \\ v=v_s}} + \cdots$$

Similarly, the expansion for $Q(y,v)$ is

$$Q(y,v) = y_s + v_s + (y - y_s) \frac{\partial Q}{\partial y}\Big|_{\substack{y=y_s \\ v=v_s}} + (v - v_s) \frac{\partial Q}{\partial v}\Big|_{\substack{y=y_s \\ v=v_s}} + \cdots$$

The preceding expansions are simplified when the singular point occurs at the origin, $y_s = 0$ and $v_s = 0$. A singular point is transferred to the origin by making the change of variable $y = y_1 + y_s$ and $v = y_2 + v_s$. For $y_1 = y - y_s$ and $y_2 = v - v_s$, then at the singular point, $y_{1_s} = y_s -$

$y_s = 0$ and $y_{2_s} = v_s - v_s = 0$. The following analysis loses none of its generality by transferring the singular point to the origin. The transformed equation corresponding to Eq. (12.27) is

$$\frac{dy_2}{dy_1} = \frac{F(y_1, y_2)}{G(y_1, y_2)} \tag{12.29}$$

The Taylor series expansions about the origin for $F(y_1, y_2)$ and $G(y_1, y_2)$ are

$$F(y_1, y_2) = y_1 \frac{\partial F}{\partial y_1}\Big|_{\substack{y_1=0\\y_2=0}} + y_2 \frac{\partial F}{\partial y_2}\Big|_{\substack{y_1=0\\y_2=0}} + \cdots$$
$$= cy_1 + dy_2 + \cdots$$
$$G(y_1, y_2) = y_1 \frac{\partial G}{\partial y_1}\Big|_{\substack{y_1=0\\y_2=0}} + y_2 \frac{\partial G}{\partial y_2}\Big|_{\substack{y_1=0\\y_2=0}} + \cdots$$
$$= ay_1 + by_2 + \cdots$$

The preceding partial derivatives are constants (a, b, c, and d) after being evaluated at $y_1 = 0$ and $y_2 = 0$. In the vicinity of the origin, the higher order terms in the preceding expansion may be neglected. Hence, Eq. (12.29) becomes

$$\frac{dy_2}{dy_1} = \frac{cy_1 + dy_2}{ay_1 + by_2} \tag{12.30}$$

The solution of this differential equation is simplified by further transforming it to the canonical form

$$\frac{dx_2}{dx_1} = \frac{K_2 \, x_2}{K_1 \, x_1} \tag{12.31}$$

To determine the equations for K_1 and K_2 in terms of the known constants (a, b, c, d), write the denominator and numerator of Eqs. (12.30) and (12.31) in the form

$$\dot{y}_1 = ay_1 + by_2$$
$$\dot{y}_2 = cy_1 + dy_2 \tag{12.32}$$

and

$$\dot{x}_1 = K_1 x_1 + 0$$
$$\dot{x}_2 = 0 + K_2 x_2 \tag{12.33}$$

The corresponding matrix representations are

$$\begin{bmatrix} \dot{y}_1 \\ \dot{y}_2 \end{bmatrix} = \begin{bmatrix} a & b \\ c & d \end{bmatrix} \begin{bmatrix} y_1 \\ y_2 \end{bmatrix} \qquad \text{or} \qquad \dot{\mathbf{y}} = A\mathbf{y} \tag{12.34}$$

and

$$\begin{bmatrix} \dot{x}_1 \\ \dot{x}_2 \end{bmatrix} = \begin{bmatrix} K_1 & 0 \\ 0 & K_2 \end{bmatrix} \begin{bmatrix} x_1 \\ x_2 \end{bmatrix} \qquad \text{or} \qquad \dot{\mathbf{x}} = K\mathbf{x} \tag{12.35}$$

Boldface notation is used to designate a column matrix and capital letters designate coefficient matrices. The matrix B which transforms the y_1,y_2 coordinate system to the x_1,x_2 system is

$$\begin{bmatrix} x_1 \\ x_2 \end{bmatrix} = \begin{bmatrix} \alpha & \beta \\ \gamma & \delta \end{bmatrix} \begin{bmatrix} y_1 \\ y_2 \end{bmatrix} \qquad \text{or} \qquad \mathbf{x} = B\mathbf{y}$$

Differentiation shows that

$$\dot{\mathbf{x}} = B\dot{\mathbf{y}} = BA\mathbf{y}$$

Another representation for $\dot{\mathbf{x}}$ is

$$\dot{\mathbf{x}} = K\mathbf{x} = KB\mathbf{y}$$

Subtracting the first representation for $\dot{\mathbf{x}}$ from the second gives

$$[BA - KB]\mathbf{y} = 0$$

Multiplying out this matrix shows that

$$[(a - K_1)\alpha + c\beta]y_1 + [b\alpha + (d - K_1)\beta]y_2 = 0$$
$$[(a - K_2)\gamma + c\delta]y_1 + [b\gamma + (d - K_2)\delta]y_2 = 0$$

Because y_1 and y_2 cannot be zero, then all of the coefficients must be zero.

$$(a - K_1)\alpha + c\beta = 0 \qquad (a - K_2)\gamma + c\delta = 0$$
$$b\alpha + (d - K_1)\beta = 0 \qquad b\gamma + (d - K_2)\delta = 0$$

In order that the solution of each of these sets of equations not be trivial (that is, $\alpha = \beta = \gamma = \delta = 0$), then each determinant must vanish.

$$\begin{vmatrix} a - K_1 & c \\ b & d - K_1 \end{vmatrix} = 0 \qquad \begin{vmatrix} a - K_2 & c \\ b & d - K_2 \end{vmatrix} = 0$$

Solving for K_1 and K_2 gives

$$K_{1,2} = \frac{(a + d) \pm \sqrt{(a - d)^2 + 4bc}}{2} \qquad (12.36)$$

The behavior of the phase-plane trajectories in the vicinity of the singular point is now analyzed for various combinations of K_1 and K_2.

CASE I. K_1 and K_2 are real and $K_2/K_1 > 0$. From Eq. (12.36), it follows that K_1 and K_2 are real if

$$(a - d)^2 + 4bc > 0 \qquad (12.37)$$

In order that K_1 and K_2 have the same sign ($K_1/K_2 > 0$), it is necessary that $[(a - d)^2 + 4bc] < (a + d)^2$, or

$$bc - ad < 0 \qquad (12.38)$$

For Case I, Eq. (12.31) becomes

$$\frac{dx_2}{x_2} = \frac{K_2}{K_1}\frac{dx_1}{x_1}$$

The solution is

$$x_2 = Cx_1{}^{K_2/K_1} \tag{12.39}$$

A plot of the corresponding trajectories is shown in Fig. 12.10. Such singular points are called *nodes*. To determine the direction of the

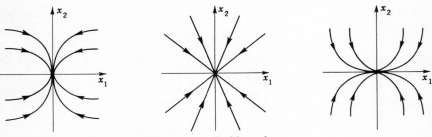

FIG. 12.10.   Stable nodes.

arrows on these trajectories, replace $\dot{y}_1$ by Dy_1 and $\dot{y}_2$ by Dy_2 in Eq. (12.32) and then solve simultaneously for y_1. Thus,

$$[D^2 - (a + d)D - (bc - ad)]y_1 = (D - K_1)(D - K_2)y_1 = 0 \tag{12.40}$$

The roots or eigenvalues K_1 and K_2 are the same as those given by Eq. (12.36). This equation has a stable response when the roots K_1 and K_2 are both negative. This is so when

$$a + d < 0 \tag{12.41}$$

If the trajectory is stable in the y_1,y_2 plane, it will also be stable in the x_1,x_2 plane. Thus, the arrows in Fig. 12.10 are for a stable system in that the trajectories go into the origin, and thus come to rest.

When K_1 and K_2 are positive, the response is unstable. This is so when

$$a + d > 0 \tag{12.42}$$

The arrows in Fig. 12.10 should be reversed to indicate unstable nodes when $a + d > 0$.

CASE II. K_1 and K_2 are real and $K_2/K_1 < 0$.   As given by Eq. (12.37), the roots are real when

$$(a - d)^2 + 4bc > 0$$

In order that K_1 and K_2 have different signs ($K_2/K_1 < 0$), it is necessary that

$$bc - ad > 0 \tag{12.43}$$

The equation for the trajectories for Case II is the same as Eq. (12.39) except that K_2/K_1 is now negative.   A plot of the corresponding trajectories is shown in Fig. 12.11.   This type of singularity is called a *saddle point*.   Because one root is negative and the other positive, then Case II always represents an unstable response.

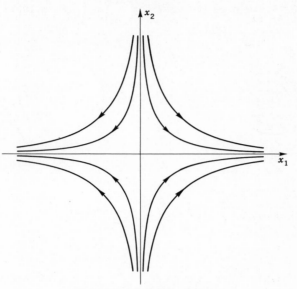

FIG. 12.11.   Saddle point.

CASE III. K_1 and K_2 are complex conjugates.   From Eq. (12.36), K_1 and K_2 are complex conjugate when

$$(a - d)^2 + 4bc < 0 \tag{12.44}$$

When $d = a$ and $c = -b$, then from Eq. (12.36) the complex conjugate roots are $K_{1,2} = a \pm jb$.   Thus, Eq. (12.30) becomes

$$\frac{dy_2}{dy_1} = \frac{-by_1 + ay_2}{ay_1 + by_2} \tag{12.45}$$

The polar representation for y_1 and y_2 is

$$y_1 = r \cos \phi$$
$$y_2 = r \sin \phi$$

Thus, Eq. (12.45) becomes

$$\frac{r \cos \phi \, d\phi + \sin \phi \, dr}{-r \sin \phi \, d\phi + \cos \phi \, dr} = \frac{-br \cos \phi + ar \sin \phi}{ar \cos \phi + br \sin \phi}$$

After cross multiplying this reduces to

$$\frac{dr}{r} = -\frac{a}{b} d\phi$$

The solution is

$$r = Ce^{-a(\phi/b)} \qquad (12.46)$$

For positive values of a, the singular point is an unstable focus, as shown in Fig. 12.12a. For negative values of a, the singular point is a stable

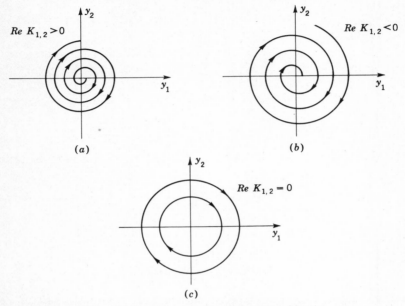

FIG. 12.12. Focal point. (a) Unstable; (b) stable; (c) center.

focus as shown in Fig. 12.12b. When a is zero, the singular point is a vortex, or center, as shown in Fig. 12.12c.

For the more general case, the real part of $K_{1,2}$ is $(a + d)/2$. By designating $K_{1,2}$ as $A \pm jB$, then Eq. (12.31) becomes

$$\frac{\dot{x}_2}{\dot{x}_1} = \frac{Ax_2 + jBx_2}{Ax_1 + jBx_1}$$

Letting $x_1 = u_1 + ju_2$ and $x_2 = u_1 - ju_2$ shows that

$$\frac{\dot{u}_2}{\dot{u}_1} = \frac{-Bu_1 + Au_2}{Au_1 + Bu_2}$$

This has the same form as Eq. (12.45). Thus, when the real part $A = (a + d)/2$ is positive, the singular point is an *unstable focus*. When the real part is negative, the singular point is a *stable focus*. When the real part is zero, the singular point is a *vortex*, or *center*.

12.4 Liapunov's Direct Method. For second-order systems, the coordinates for the phase plane are position and velocity. Third-order systems require a phase space with coordinates of position, velocity, and acceleration.[1] Because of the difficulties of working graphically in three-dimensional space, the phase-plane method becomes exceedingly cumbersome. Thus, for third and higher order nonlinear systems it has become necessary to develop other methods of analysis. One of the most promising methods for investigating the behavior of higher order systems is the method known as Liapunov's second method or more simply Liapunov's direct method.[2,3]

The state-space notation is a convenient symbolism for representing higher order systems. To illustrate this notation, consider the third-order feedback control system with the nonlinear element N shown in Fig. 12.13a. The differential equation relating the output c and input r is

$$\dddot{c} + \frac{\tau_1 + \tau_2}{\tau_1\tau_2}\ddot{c} + \frac{1}{\tau_1\tau_2}\dot{c} + \frac{N}{\tau_1\tau_2}c = \frac{N}{\tau_1\tau_2}r \tag{12.47}$$

By letting $x_1 = c$, $x_2 = \dot{c}$, and $x_3 = \ddot{c}$, the preceding third-order equation

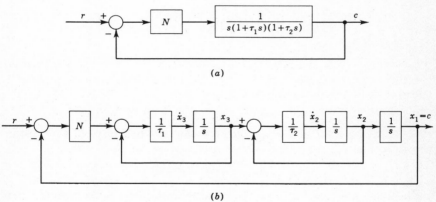

(a)

(b)

FIG. 12.13. Nonlinear system.

is converted to the following three first-order equations.

$$\begin{aligned}
\dot{x}_1 &= x_2 \\
\dot{x}_2 &= x_3 \\
\dot{x}_3 &= -\frac{\tau_1 + \tau_2}{\tau_1\tau_2}x_3 - \frac{1}{\tau_1\tau_2}x_2 - \frac{N}{\tau_1\tau_2}x_1 + \frac{N}{\tau_1\tau_2}r
\end{aligned} \tag{12.48}$$

[1] Y. H. Ku, "Analysis and Control of Nonlinear Systems," The Ronald Press Company, New York, 1958.

[2] A. M. Liapunov, "On the General Problem of Stability of Motion," Ph.D. Thesis, Kharkov, 1892. Princeton University Press, Princeton, N.J., 1949.

[3] J. LaSalle and S. Lefschetz, "Stability by Liapunov's Direct Method," Academic Press Inc., New York, 1961.

The terms x_1, x_2, and x_3 are called the state variables.   For investigating stability, one is not interested in the particular excitation r.   Thus, by letting $f_1 = x_2$, $f_2 = x_3$, and $f_3 = -[Nx_1 + x_2 + (\tau_1 + \tau_2)x_3]/\tau_1\tau_2$, the preceding equations have the form

$$\begin{aligned}\dot{x}_1 &= f_1(\mathbf{x}) \\ \dot{x}_2 &= f_2(\mathbf{x}) \\ \dot{x}_3 &= f_3(\mathbf{x})\end{aligned} \qquad (12.49)$$

The matrix representation for these equations is

$$\dot{\mathbf{x}} = \mathbf{f}(\mathbf{x}) \qquad (12.50)$$

There is usually more than one state-space representation for a system. For example, the block diagram of Fig. 12.13a may be drawn in the form shown in Fig. 12.13b.   From this block diagram, an alternate state space representation is

$$\begin{aligned}\dot{x}_1 &= x_2 \\ \dot{x}_2 &= \frac{1}{\tau_2}x_3 - \frac{1}{\tau_2}x_2 \\ \dot{x}_3 &= -\frac{N}{\tau_1}x_1 - \frac{1}{\tau_1}x_3 + \frac{N}{\tau_1}r\end{aligned} \qquad (12.51)$$

By letting $f_1 = x_2$, $f_2 = (x_3 - x_2)/\tau_2$, and $f_3 = -(Nx_1 + x_3)/\tau_1$, then for $r = 0$ the preceding set of equations has the same form as Eq. (12.50). Regardless of the particular state space representation, Eq. (12.50) is a general representation for an nth-order nonlinear system.

ILLUSTRATIVE EXAMPLE 1.   Consider the mass-spring-damper system shown in Fig. 12.14a.   The equation of motion for this system is

$$M\ddot{y} + B\dot{y} + Ky = 0$$

By letting $x_1 = y$ and $x_2 = \dot{x}_1 = \dot{y}$, then the state-space representation is

$$\begin{aligned}\dot{x}_1 &= x_2 = f_1 \\ \dot{x}_2 &= -\frac{Kx_1 + Bx_2}{M} = f_2\end{aligned} \qquad (12.52)$$

The potential energy stored in the spring is the area under the force-deflection curve shown in Fig. 12.14b.   The static deflection δ_{st} is due to the load W.   The potential energy stored in the spring at this reference position is

$$(PE)_i = \tfrac{1}{2}W\delta_{st}$$

The additional potential energy in the spring due to a deflection y from the reference position is

$$PE = \int_0^y (W + Ky)\,dy = Wy + \int_0^y Ky\,dy = Wy + \frac{Ky^2}{2}$$

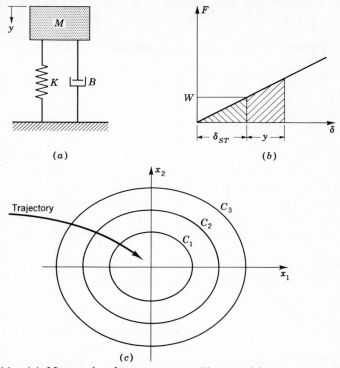

FIG. 12.14. (a) Mass-spring-damper system; (b) potential energy stored in spring; (c) plot of energy function for the system.

The potential energy of the mass is

$$PE = -W(\delta_{st} + y)$$

The kinetic energy of the mass is

$$KE = \tfrac{1}{2}M\dot{y}^2$$

After replacing y by x_1 and $\dot{y}$ by x_2, the sum of the potential and kinetic energy for the system is $Kx_1{}^2/2 + Mx_2{}^2 - (PE)_i$. Consider now the function

$$V(\mathbf{x}) = \frac{Kx_1{}^2}{2} + \frac{Mx_2{}^2}{2} = C \qquad (12.53)$$

A plot of this scalar function for constant values $C_3 > C_2 > C_1$ is shown in Fig. 12.14c. As a point $\mathbf{x}$ in the phase plane proceeds across C_3 to C_2 to C_1 toward the origin, the value of $V(\mathbf{x})$ is decreasing. Thus, if $\dot{V}(\mathbf{x}) < 0$, then $V(\mathbf{x})$ decreases with time and the trajectory approaches the origin as shown in Fig. 12.14c. For $\dot{V}(\mathbf{x}) = 0$, the trajectory remains on a path of constant C. For $\dot{V}(\mathbf{x}) > 0$, the trajectory goes away from the origin. For the system of Fig. 12.14, the derivative $\dot{V}(\mathbf{x})$ is

$$\dot{V}(\mathbf{x}) = \frac{dV(\mathbf{x})}{dt} = \frac{\partial V}{\partial x_1}\dot{x}_1 + \frac{\partial V}{\partial x_2}\dot{x}_2 = Kx_1\dot{x}_1 + Mx_2\dot{x}_2$$

Using Eq. (12.52) to evaluate the derivative along the trajectories of the system gives

$$\dot{V}(\mathbf{x}) = Kx_1x_2 - \frac{Mx_2(Kx_1 + Bx_2)}{M} = -Bx_2{}^2 \qquad (12.54)$$

For $B > 0$ (positive damping), $\dot{V}(\mathbf{x}) < 0$ and the trajectory approaches the origin. For $B = 0$ (no damping), the trajectory remains on a path of constant C. For $B < 0$ (negative damping), the trajectory goes away from the origin. As is illustrated in this example, the phase plane is the state space and its coordinates are the state variables.

The preceding concepts may be extended to formulate a general stability criterion, but first it is necessary to define some terms.

Definiteness of Sign. A scalar function $V(\mathbf{x}) = V(x_1, x_2, \ldots, x_n)$ is positive definite in some neighborhood of the origin if in this neighborhood

1. $V(\mathbf{x})$ is continuous
2. $V(\mathbf{x}) > 0$ $(\mathbf{x} \neq 0)$
3. $V(0) = 0$

When the neighborhood includes all values of $x_1, x_2, \ldots, x_n$, then the function is said to be globally positive definite. Equation (12.53) is globally positive definite. Unless otherwise stated, it is assumed that the function is global.

A scalar function is positive semidefinite in some neighborhood of the origin, if

1. $V(\mathbf{x})$ is continuous
2. $V(\mathbf{x}) \geq 0$ $(\mathbf{x} \neq 0)$
3. $V(0) = 0$

Positive semidefinite and positive definite functions are distinguished by condition (2). For a positive semidefinite function, $V(\mathbf{x})$ goes to zero even though all the x's are not zero. An example of a positive semidefinite function for the two-dimensional case (x_1, x_2) is

$$V(\mathbf{x}) = x_1{}^2$$

For $x_2 \neq 0$, this function is zero along the entire $x_1 = 0$ axis.

Changing the sign of a positive definite function yields a negative definite function. Likewise, changing the sign of a positive semidefinite function yields a negative semidefinite function.

A scalar function $V(\mathbf{x})$ is indefinite if it takes on both positive and negative values in some neighborhood of the origin. An example of an indefinite function is

$$V(\mathbf{x}) = x_1 x_2$$

A Liapunov function $V(\mathbf{x})$ is a scalar function which is positive definite, such that $V(\mathbf{x}) = C$ represents a family of closed surfaces in n-dimensional space. The linearly independent variables $x_1, x_2, \ldots, x_n$ are the coordinates of the n-dimensional state space. As shown in Fig. 12.14c, these closed surfaces should be such that the closed surface formed for $V(\mathbf{x}) = C$ contains within itself all of the surfaces for smaller values of C. Thus, the surfaces progressively become larger as C increases and do not intersect. This requires that $V(\mathbf{x})$ increases as any one of the state variables increases. In order that a Liapunov function be global, it must have the additional requirement that $V(\mathbf{x})$ becomes infinite if anyone of the state variables becomes infinite.

Stability Criteria. If a system possesses a Liapunov function such that $\dot{V}(\mathbf{x})$ is negative semidefinite $[\dot{V}(\mathbf{x}) \leq 0]$ along the trajectories of the system, then the origin is said to be stable in the sense of Liapunov. For this case, the trajectory approaches the origin when $\dot{V}(\mathbf{x}) < 0$. The trajectory remains on a path of constant $V(\mathbf{x})$ when $\dot{V}(\mathbf{x}) = 0$. Such a trajectory is called a limit cycle.

If a system possesses a Liapunov function such that $\dot{V}(\mathbf{x}) < 0$ is negative definite along the trajectories of the system, then the origin is said to be asymptotically stable. For this case, equilibrium is obtained at the origin.

If a system possesses a Liapunov function such that $\dot{V}(\mathbf{x}) > 0$ is positive definite along the trajectories of the system, then the origin is said to be unstable. For this case, the trajectories move away from the origin.

If $\dot{V}(\mathbf{x})$ is indefinite, the test fails as neither stability nor instability has been proved. Thus, one must try a different $V(\mathbf{x})$ function. A system may have many Liapunov functions. However, when one has been found to prove that the origin is stable, then it is stable. Similarly, if a function is found which shows that the origin is unstable, then it is unstable. The major obstacle in applying Liapunov's method is that of obtaining a satisfactory Liapunov function to prove stability, or instability, as the case may be.

12.5 Generating Liapunov Functions. Because a Liapunov function must be positive definite, one is initially tempted to assume that $V(\mathbf{x})$ has a general form such as the square of the Euclidean norm. That is,

$$V(\mathbf{x}) = \|\mathbf{x}\|^2 = x_1^2 + x_2^2 + \cdots + x_n^2 \tag{12.55}$$

It is immediately apparent that the quadratic form is even more general. That is,

$$V(\mathbf{x}) = \sum_{i=1}^{n} \sum_{j=1}^{n} a_{ij}x_i x_j \tag{12.56}$$

where $a_{ij} = a_{ji}$. Malkin[1] has shown that such a Liapunov function will prove stability or instability for linear systems. Unfortunately, for non-linear systems such functions usually fail to prove stability or instability.

ILLUSTRATIVE EXAMPLE 1. The mass-spring-damper system shown in Fig. 12.15 has a nonlinear spring $K = g(y)$ and a nonlinear damper

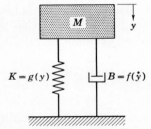

FIG. 12.15. Nonlinear mass-spring-damper system.

$B = f(\dot{y})$. The equation of motion is

$$M\ddot{y} + f(\dot{y})\dot{y} + g(y)y = 0$$

By letting $x_1 = y$ and $x_2 = \dot{x}_1 = \dot{y}$, the state-space representation is

$$\dot{x}_1 = x_2 = f_1$$
$$\dot{x}_2 = -\frac{g(x_1)}{M}x_1 - \frac{f(x_2)}{M}x_2 = f_2 \tag{12.57}$$

Consider the function

$$V(\mathbf{x}) = \tfrac{1}{2}Mx_2{}^2 + \int_0^{x_1} g(x_1)x_1\,dx_1 \tag{12.58}$$

If $g(x_1)x_1 > 0$ for $x_1 > 0$ and $g(x_1)x_1 < 0$ for $x_1 < 0$ [that is, $g(x_1) > 0$ for $x_1 \neq 0$], then $V(\mathbf{x})$ satisfies the requirements for a Liapunov function. The value of $\dot{V}(\mathbf{x})$ for this system is

$$\dot{V}(\mathbf{x}) = \frac{\partial V}{\partial x_1}\dot{x}_1 + \frac{\partial V}{\partial x_2}\dot{x}_2 = g(x_1)x_1\dot{x}_1 + Mx_2\dot{x}_2$$

[1] I. G. Malkin, "Theory of Stability of Motion," Gostekhizdat, Moscow, 1952. English translation, Commerce Department, AEC translation 3352, Washington.

Using Eq. (12.57) to evaluate the derivative along the trajectories of the system gives

$$\dot{V}(\mathbf{x}) = g(x_1)x_1x_2 + x_2[-g(x_1)x_1 - f(x_2)x_2] = -f(x_2)x_2{}^2 \quad (12.59)$$

The system thus approaches equilibrium at the origin $[\dot{V}(\mathbf{x}) < 0]$ for any damping function such that $f(x_2) > 0$.

General techniques for generating Liapunov functions for nonlinear systems are described in the following.

12.6 The Variable-gradient Method.[1,2] To develop this method, first note that the derivative $\dot{V}(\mathbf{x})$ is

$$\dot{V}(\mathbf{x}) = \frac{dV}{dt} = \frac{\partial V}{\partial x_1}\dot{x}_1 + \frac{\partial V}{\partial x_2}\dot{x}_2 + \cdots + \frac{\partial V}{\partial x_n}\dot{x}_n$$

$$= \frac{\partial V}{\partial x_1}f_1 + \frac{\partial V}{\partial x_2}f_2 + \cdots + \frac{\partial V}{\partial x_n}f_n$$

$$= \nabla V \cdot \mathbf{f} \quad (12.60)$$

In the variable-gradient method, the gradient vector ∇V is assumed to have the general form

$$\nabla V = \begin{bmatrix} a_{11}x_1 + a_{12}x_2 + \cdots + a_{1n}x_n \\ a_{21}x_1 + a_{22}x_2 + \cdots + a_{2n}x_n \\ \cdots\cdots\cdots\cdots\cdots\cdots\cdots \\ a_{n1}x_1 + a_{n2}x_2 + \cdots + a_{nn}x_n \end{bmatrix} = \begin{bmatrix} v_1 \\ v_2 \\ \cdots \\ v_n \end{bmatrix} \quad (12.61)$$

The necessary and sufficient condition for a vector ∇V to be a gradient is that

$$\nabla \times \nabla V = 0$$

This relationship holds when the curl equations are satisfied. The curl equations are

$$\frac{\partial v_i}{\partial x_j} = \frac{\partial v_j}{\partial x_i} \begin{cases} i \neq j \\ i, j = 1, 2, \ldots, n \end{cases} \quad (12.62)$$

For a third-order system $(n = 3)$, the curl equations are

$$\frac{\partial v_1}{\partial x_2} = \frac{\partial v_2}{\partial x_1} \qquad \frac{\partial v_1}{\partial x_3} = \frac{\partial v_3}{\partial x_1} \qquad \frac{\partial v_2}{\partial x_3} = \frac{\partial v_3}{\partial x_2}$$

There are $n(n-1)/2$ curl equations.

To meet future requirements on $V(\mathbf{x})$, namely closure, the generality

[1] D. G. Schultz and J. E. Gibson, The Variable Gradient Method for Generating Liapunov Functions, *Trans. AIEE*, **81**: (2), 203–210 (1962).

[2] D. G. Schultz, "The Variable Gradient Method of Generating Liapunov Functions with Applications to Automatic Control Systems," Ph.D. Thesis, Purdue University, 1962.

of the gradient is reduced.   In this connection, the following assumptions are made to ensure that one of the variables (x_n) appears as a quadratic in $V(\mathbf{x})$.

1. $$a_{ij} = k_{ij} + f_{ij}(x_1, x_2, \ldots, x_{n-1})$$
2. $$a_{ii} = k_{ii} + f_{ii}(x_i) \tag{12.63}$$
3. $$a_{nn} = 2$$

Thus, each coefficient a_{ij} is assumed to be composed of a constant part k_{ij} and a variable part f_{ij}.   For the diagonal coefficient a_{ii} the variable part is a function of x_i only.   In order that the curl equations be satisfied, it is necessary that $k_{ij} = k_{ji}$.

ILLUSTRATIVE EXAMPLE 1.   In Fig. 12.16a is shown a feedback control system in which the nonlinear element N cubes the actuating signal e.

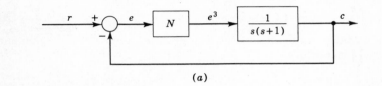

(a)

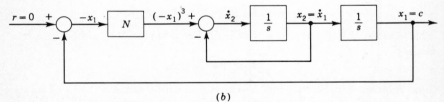

(b)

FIG. 12.16.   System with a nonlinear element.

From the equivalent representation for this system, Fig. 12.16b, the state-space equations are found to be

$$\dot{x}_1 = x_2 = f_1$$
$$\dot{x}_2 = -x_1^3 - x_2 = f_2 \tag{12.64}$$

SOLUTION.   Assume ∇V is of the form

$$\nabla V = \begin{bmatrix} a_{11}x_1 & +a_{12}x_2 \\ a_{12}x_1 & +2x_2 \end{bmatrix} \tag{12.65}$$

Thus,

$$\dot{V}(\mathbf{x}) = \nabla V \cdot \mathbf{f} = [(a_{11}x_1 + a_{12}x_2)(a_{21}x_1 + 2x_2)] \begin{bmatrix} x_2 \\ -x_2 - x_1^3 \end{bmatrix}$$
$$= (a_{11} - a_{21} - 2x_1^2)x_1x_2 - (2 - a_{12})x_2^2 - a_{21}x_1^4 \tag{12.66}$$

By choosing $a_{11} = a_{21} + 2x_1^2$, then the first term vanishes. Furthermore, if $0 < a_{12} < 2$, then each of the last two terms is negative. With these constraints it is seen that $\dot{V}(\mathbf{x})$ is negative definite. For a constant a_{21}, then $a_{12} = a_{21}$. The gradient ∇V that has been constructed is

$$\nabla V = \begin{bmatrix} (a_{21}x_1 + 2x_1^3) & +a_{21}x_2 \\ a_{21}x_1 & +2x_2 \end{bmatrix} \tag{12.67}$$

For a second-order system, there is but one curl equation. For this system, it is

$$\frac{\partial v_1}{\partial x_2} = a_{21} = \frac{\partial v_2}{\partial x_1}$$

With the curl equation satisfied, we now proceed to construct $V(\mathbf{x})$ from ∇V. Thus

$$V(\mathbf{x}) = \int_0^{\mathbf{x}} \nabla V \cdot d\mathbf{x} = \int_0^{x_1} (a_{21}x_1 + 2x_1^3 + a_{21}x_2) \, dx_1$$
$$+ \int_0^{x_2} (a_{21}x_1 + 2x_2) \, dx_2$$
$$= \left(\frac{a_{21}}{2} + \frac{x_1^2}{2}\right) x_1^2 + a_{21}x_1x_2 + x_2^2 \tag{12.68}$$

To check that $V(\mathbf{x})$ is positive definite, first note that Eq. (12.68) is the quadratic form. Thus, $V(\mathbf{x})$ may be expressed as the matrix

$$V(\mathbf{x}) = \mathbf{x}^T A \mathbf{x}$$

where

$$A = \begin{bmatrix} \dfrac{a_{21} + x_1^2}{2} & \dfrac{a_{21}}{2} \\ \dfrac{a_{21}}{2} & 1 \end{bmatrix}$$

If the matrix A is positive definite, then $V(\mathbf{x})$ is positive definite. By Sylvester's theorem, a matrix A is positive definite if all its minors are positive definite. The minors of A are

$$\frac{a_{21} + x_1^2}{2} > 0$$
$$\frac{a_{21} + x_1^2}{2} - \frac{a_{21}^2}{4} = \frac{a_{21}(2 - a_{21})}{4} + \frac{x_1^2}{2} > 0$$

The first minor requires that $a_{21} > 0$ and the second requires that $(2 - a_{21}) > 0$. Thus, $V(x)$ is positive definite if

$$0 < a_{21} < 2 \tag{12.69}$$

This is the same constraint that was placed on a_{21} in the construction of ∇V.

In effect, Eq. (12.68) describes an infinite set of Liapunov functions for this system in that $0 < a_{12} < 2$. Because

$$\dot{V}(\mathbf{x}) = -(2 - a_{21})x_2{}^2 - a_{21}x_1{}^4$$

is globally negative definite, then this system is globally asymptotically stable.

12.7 The Format Method. This method developed by J. L. Peczkowski[1,2] is based upon the following theorem.

Theorem. If $[D(\mathbf{x})]$ is a diagonal $n \times n$ matrix such that

$$D\mathbf{f} \cdot \mathbf{f} = \dot{V}(\mathbf{x}) \tag{12.70}$$

and if $[P(\mathbf{x})]$ is a real, skew-symmetric matrix such that

$$\nabla V = [D + P]\mathbf{f} \tag{12.71}$$

and if the curl equations are satisfied, then

$$\dot{V}(\mathbf{x}) = \nabla V \cdot \mathbf{f} \tag{12.72}$$

A diagonal matrix has elements on the principal diagonal only. For example,

$$D(\mathbf{x}) = \begin{bmatrix} d_{11} & 0 & 0 \\ 0 & d_{22} & 0 \\ 0 & 0 & d_{33} \end{bmatrix} \tag{12.73}$$

When $D(\mathbf{x})$ has but one element, $d_{ii} = L(\mathbf{x})$, then

$$\dot{V}(\mathbf{x}) = D\mathbf{f} \cdot \mathbf{f} = d_{ii}f_i{}^2 = L(\mathbf{x})f_i{}^2$$

Because $f_i{}^2$ is positive, then $\dot{V}(\mathbf{x})$ will be semidefinite or definite if $L(\mathbf{x})$ is sign definite. A skew-symmetric matrix has no elements on the diagonal and in addition, $p_{ji} = -p_{ij}$. Thus,

$$P(\mathbf{x}) = \begin{bmatrix} 0 & -p_{12} & -p_{13} \\ p_{12} & 0 & -p_{23} \\ p_{13} & p_{23} & 0 \end{bmatrix} \tag{12.74}$$

For a skew-symmetric matrix, $P + P^T = 0$ and $P\mathbf{f} \cdot \mathbf{f} = 0$.

To generate Liapunov functions by the Format method

1. Write the vector format

$$\nabla V = [D + P]\mathbf{f}$$

[1] J. L. Peczkowski, "A Format Method for Generating Liapunov Functions," Ph.D. Thesis, University of Notre Dame, 1966.

[2] J. L. Peczkowski and R. W. Liu, "A Format Method for Generating Liapunov Functions," *Trans. ASME*, **89**:(2), Series D (June, 1967).

2.   Choose the arbitrary functions p_{ij} and d_{ii}, to satisfy the curl equations, and thus obtain P and D.

3.   The functions $V(\mathbf{x})$ and $\dot{V}(\mathbf{x}) = D\mathbf{f} \cdot \mathbf{f}$ may now be constructed.

Because $D(\mathbf{x})$ may have different forms, it is customary to assume first that $D(\mathbf{x})$ contains but the d_{11} element [that is, $\dot{V}(\mathbf{x}) = d_{11}f_1{}^2$]. If this does not yield a satisfactory Liapunov function, then assume that $D(x)$ contains but the d_{22} element. After exhausting all the single-element possibilities, then different forms are tried.

ILLUSTRATIVE EXAMPLE 1.   Use the format method to generate a satisfactory Liapunov function for the system of Fig. 12.16.

SOLUTION.   Write the vector format.

$$\boldsymbol{\nabla} V = [D + P]\mathbf{f} = \begin{bmatrix} L & -p \\ p & 0 \end{bmatrix} \begin{bmatrix} x_2 \\ -x_2 - x_1{}^3 \end{bmatrix}$$

where

$$[D + P] = \begin{bmatrix} L & 0 \\ 0 & 0 \end{bmatrix} + \begin{bmatrix} 0 & -p \\ p & 0 \end{bmatrix} = \begin{bmatrix} L & -p \\ p & 0 \end{bmatrix}$$

and $\mathbf{f}$ is obtained from Eq. (12.64).

Performing the preceding matrix multiplication gives

$$\boldsymbol{\nabla} V = \begin{bmatrix} Lx_2 + px_2 + px_1{}^3 \\ px_2 \end{bmatrix}$$

The curl equation $\partial v_1/\partial x_2 = \partial v_2/\partial x_1$ shows that

$$\frac{\partial[(L + p)x_2]}{\partial x_2} + x_1{}^3 \frac{\partial p}{\partial x_2} = x_2 \frac{\partial p}{\partial x_1}$$

For the first trial, assume that p is constant. Thus,

$$\frac{\partial[(L + p)x_2]}{\partial x_2} = 0$$

The curl equation is satisfied if $L = -p$ is constant. Thus, $\boldsymbol{\nabla} V$ becomes

$$\boldsymbol{\nabla} V = \begin{bmatrix} px_1{}^3 \\ px_2 \end{bmatrix}$$

Integration to obtain the Liapunov function gives

$$V(\mathbf{x}) = \int_0^{\mathbf{x}} \boldsymbol{\nabla} V \cdot d\mathbf{x} = \int_0^{x_1} px_1{}^3 \, dx_1 + \int_0^{x_2} px_2 \, dx_2 = \frac{px_1{}^4}{4} + \frac{px_2{}^2}{2} \quad (12.75)$$

The derivative along the trajectories is

$$\dot{V}(\mathbf{x}) = -px_2{}^2 \quad (12.76)$$

For $p > 0$, then $V(\mathbf{x})$ is positive definite and $\dot{V}(\mathbf{x})$ is negative definite. For $p < 0$, then $V(\mathbf{x})$ is negative definite and $\dot{V}(\mathbf{x})$ is positive definite. The stability theorems are unaffected if all of the signs are reversed.

Thus, this system is globally asymptotically stable for all values of p. There is no need to assume other forms of D or other forms of the p functions to obtain other Liapunov functions. It is to be noted that although the Liapunov functions of Eqs. (12.68) and (12.75) are different, they both yield the same result.

ILLUSTRATIVE EXAMPLE 2. Use the format method to generate a satisfactory Liapunov function for Lienard's equation.

$$\ddot{y} + f(y)\dot{y} + g(y) = 0 \qquad (12.77)$$

SOLUTION. In phase coordinates this equation becomes

$$\dot{x}_1 = x_2$$
$$\dot{x}_2 = -g(x_1) - f(x_1)x_2$$

The vector format is

$$\nabla V = \begin{bmatrix} Lf_1 & -pf_2 \\ pf_1 & 0 \end{bmatrix} = \begin{bmatrix} Lx_2 + pg(x_1) + pf(x_1)x_2 \\ px_2 \end{bmatrix}$$

For the first trial it is assumed that p is constant. Thus, the curl equation is

$$\frac{\partial}{\partial x_2}[L + pf(x_1)]x_2 = 0$$

The curl equation is satisfied if $L = -pf(x_1)$. Thus, ∇V becomes

$$\nabla V = \begin{bmatrix} pg(x_1) \\ px_2 \end{bmatrix}$$

Line integration gives

$$V(\mathbf{x}) = p \int_0^{x_1} g(x_1)\, dx_1 + \frac{px_2{}^2}{2} \qquad (12.78)$$

If $g(x_1) > 0$ for $x_1 > 0$ and $g(x_1) < 0$ for $x_1 < 0$ [that is, $g(x_1)x_1 > 0$ for $x_1 \neq 0$], then $V(\mathbf{x})$ satisfies the requirements for a Liapunov function. The derivative $\dot{V}(\mathbf{x})$ is

$$\dot{V}(\mathbf{x}) = -pf(x_1)x_2{}^2 \qquad (12.79)$$

For $f(x_1) > 0$, the origin is asymptotically stable. If $\int_0^{x_1} g(x_1)\, dx_1 \to \infty$ as x_1 becomes infinite, then the origin is globally asymptotically stable.

In addition to its use for determining whether a singular point is stable, or unstable, Liapunov's method is also used to determine:

1. Stability domains of initial points
2. Stability domains of parameters
3. Stability of optimal control systems
4. Conditions for nonlinearities to guarantee stability
5. Estimates of solutions

Problems

12.1 Determine the general equation for the phase trajectory for each of the following:

(a) $\ddot{y} + y = 0$
(b) $\ddot{y} + \dot{y} = 0$
(c) $\ddot{y} + y^3 = 0$
(d) $\ddot{y} + \sin y = 0$

Sketch the trajectories for each of the preceding cases.

12.2 Determine the equation for the isoclines for each of the following systems:

(a) $\ddot{y} + y = 0$
(b) $\ddot{y} + 2\dot{y} + 4y = 0$
(c) $\ddot{y} + |\dot{y}|\dot{y} + y = 0$

Sketch the trajectories for each of these systems.

12.3 Use Pell's method to sketch the trajectories in the vicinity of the point $y = 2$ and $\dot{y} = 3$ for each of the systems of Prob. 12.2.

12.4 Use the delta method to sketch the trajectories in the vicinity of the point $y = 2$ and $\dot{y} = 3$ for each of the systems of Prob. 12.2.

12.5 Determine the equation of the isoclines for each of the following:

(a) $\ddot{y} + B\dot{y} + Ky = 0$
(b) $\ddot{y} + B\dot{y} + Ky^3 = 0$

Sketch the trajectories for the case in which $B = K = 1$ and for the case in which $B = -1$ and $K = 1$.

12.6 For the nonlinear system of Fig. P12.6a, the nonlinearity N is the on-off element whose characteristics are shown in Fig. P12.6b. For $r = 0$, sketch the isoclines for the $c, \dot{c}$ plot and also the $e, \dot{e}$ plot.

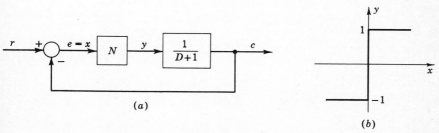

(a)

(b)

Fig. P12.6

12.7 Same as Prob. 12.6 except that the nonlinear element is saturation whose characteristics are shown in Fig. P12.7.

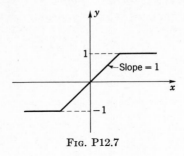

FIG. P12.7

12.8 Same as Prob. 12.6 except that the nonlinear element is dead zone whose characteristics are shown in Fig. P12.8.

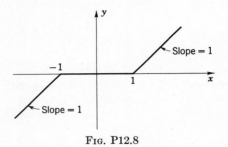

FIG. P12.8

12.9 For the system shown in Fig. P12.9a, the nonlinear element N is saturation whose characteristics are shown in Fig. P12.9b.   For $r = 0$, sketch the c, $\dot{c}$ plot and also the e, $\dot{e}$ plot.

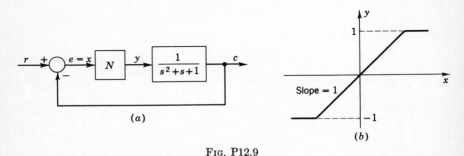

FIG. P12.9

12.10 Same as Prob. 12.9 except that the nonlinear element N is dead zone whose characteristics are shown in Fig. P12.8.

12.11 For the system shown in Fig. P12.11, the nonlinearity N is the on-off element whose characteristics are shown in Fig. P12.6b. For $r = 0$, sketch the isoclines for the c, $\dot{c}$ plot and also the e, $\dot{e}$ plot.

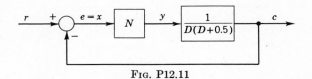

FIG. P12.11

12.12 For the system shown in Fig. P12.12a, the nonlinearity N is the on-off element whose characteristics are shown in Fig. P12.12b. For $r = 0$, sketch the isoclines for the c, $\dot{c}$ plot and also the e, $\dot{e}$ plot.

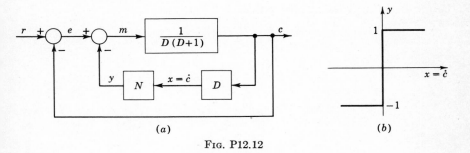

(a)   (b)

FIG. P12.12

12.13 For the differential equation

$$\ddot{y} + 2\zeta\omega_n\dot{y} + \omega_n^2 y = 0$$

specify the type singular point for

(a) $\zeta \geq 1$
(b) $0 < \zeta < 1$
(c) $\zeta = 0$
(d) $-1 < \zeta < 0$
(e) $-1 \leq \zeta$

12.14 For the system shown in Fig. P12.14, specify the singular points as a function of the gain K.

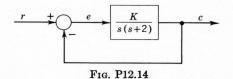

FIG. P12.14

12.15 For the system shown in Fig. P12.15, specify the singular points as a function of the gain K.

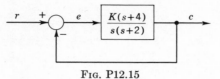

$$\text{Fig. P12.15}$$

12.16 Show that the equation for the undamped simple pendulum shown in Fig. P12.16 is $ML^2\ddot{\phi} + MgL \sin \phi = 0$, or

$$\ddot{\phi} + \frac{g}{L} \sin \phi = 0$$

Locate and identify the singular points.

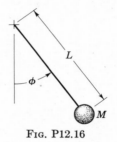

$$\text{Fig. P12.16}$$

12.17 Show that the equation for the damped simple pendulum shown in Fig. P12.17 is $ML^2\ddot{\phi} + BL\dot{\phi} + MgL \sin \phi = 0$, or

$$\ddot{\phi} + \frac{B}{ML} \dot{\phi} + \frac{g}{L} \sin \phi = 0$$

Locate and identify the singular points.

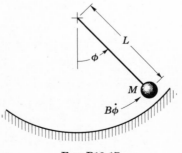

$$\text{Fig. P12.17}$$

12.18 The Van der Pol equation is

$$\ddot{y} - \mu(1 - y^2)\dot{y} + y = 0$$

where μ is a constant. Locate and identify the singular points.

12.19 Figure P12.19 shows a feedback control system with an unknown non-linearity $g(x)$. Use the format method to show that a suitable $V(\mathbf{x})$ function is

$$V(\mathbf{x}) = p \left[B \int_0^{x_1} g(x_1)x_1 \, dx_1 + \tfrac{1}{2}x_2^2 \right]$$

where $x = x_1$ and $\dot{x} = \dot{x}_1 = x_2$. Show that the corresponding $\dot{V}(\mathbf{x})$ function is

$$\dot{V}(\mathbf{x}) = -p \left(1 + \frac{dy}{dx_1} \right) x_2^2$$

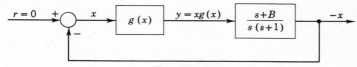

FIG. P12.19

12.20 Same as Prob. 12.19 except use the variable-gradient method.

12.21 Use the format method to obtain a Liapunov function for Van der Pol's equation which is given in Prob. 12.18.

12.22 The transfer function of the feedforward elements for a feedback control system is

$$G(s) = \frac{1}{s(s+1)}$$

The feedback path contains a nonlinear element $f(x_1)$. Use the format method to show that the system will be stable if the feedback element is such that $\int_0^{x_1} f(x_1) \, dx_1 \geq 0$.

13

Sampled-data systems

Recently, numerous systems have been devised which utilize digital computers as control elements. Such systems are generally sampled-data systems. That is, the information fed into a digital computer is the value (sample) of the corresponding signal at some instant of time. The computed output remains unchanged until new information (another sample) is fed into the digital computer.

Another well-known application of the sampled-data process is the time sharing of telemetered information from spacecraft. Instead of temperature at five different places in the vehicle and pressure at three different places being telemetered back on eight different channels, each signal uses the same channel for one second out of eight. A similar application occurs in the control of industrial processes in which system variables such as temperature, pressure, and flow are sampled periodically in order to make more effective use of the expensive control equipment, especially the digital computer. Another example is a guidance system that utilizes radar scanning in which a given sector, or region, is scanned once every revolution. Thus, in any given direction the signal is sampled at a rate equal to the scan rate of the radar. Sampling is inherent in some applications (e.g., radar scanning), it is necessary in other applications (e.g., to enter data into digital computers), and finally, sampling is desirable for other applications (e.g., time sharing).

13.1 The Sampler. A schematic representation of a sampler switch is shown in Fig. 13.1a. The switch closes every T seconds to admit the input signal. A typical input signal is represented by the continuous function $f(t)$ shown in Fig. 13.1b. The shaded pulses represent the signal at the output of the sampler. When the pulse duration is much shorter than the system time constants, the output of the sampler may be approximated by the train of impulses $f^*(t)$, as is illustrated in Fig. 13.1c. The term $f^*(t)$ is read f star of t.

The area of each impulse is equal to the value of the input signal at the time $t = nT$ of the particular impulse. Thus, the area of the nth

410

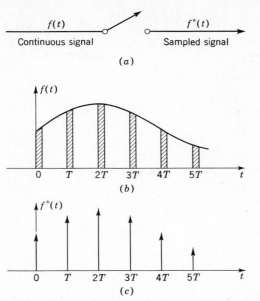

FIG. 13.1.   (a) Sampler switch;   (b) continuous input $f(t)$ and output at switch (shaded pulses); (c) impulse approximation of switch output, $f^*(t)$.

impulse which occurs at time $t = nT$ is $f(nT)$.   The equation for the entire train of impulses is

$$f^*(t) = f(0)u_1(t) + f(T)u_1(t - T) + f(2T)u_1(t - 2T) + \cdots$$
$$= \sum_{n=0}^{\infty} f(nT)u_1(t - nT) \qquad (13.1)$$

where $u_1(t)$ is a unit impulse at $t = 0$ and $u_1(t - nT)$ is a unit impulse at $t = nT$.

The Laplace transform of the sampled signal is

$$F^*(s) = \mathcal{L}[f^*(t)] = f(0) + f(T)e^{-Ts} + f(2T)e^{-2Ts} + \cdots$$
$$= \sum_{n=0}^{\infty} f(nT)e^{-nTs} \qquad (13.2)$$

To illustrate the preceding concepts, consider the continuous input

$$f(t) = e^{-at}$$

The corresponding sampled signal $f^*(t)$ is

$$f^*(t) = u_1(t) + e^{-aT}u_1(t - T) + e^{-2aT}u_1(t - 2T) + \cdots$$
$$= \sum_{n=0}^{\infty} e^{-anT}u_1(t - nT)$$

The Laplace transform of the input $f(t)$ is

$$F(s) = \mathcal{L}[f(t)] = \frac{1}{s + a}$$

The Laplace transform of the sampled signal $f^*(t)$ is

$$F^*(s) = \mathcal{L}[f^*(t)] = 1 + e^{-aT}e^{-sT} + e^{-2aT}e^{-2sT} + \cdots$$
$$= 1 + e^{-(s+a)T} + e^{-2(s+a)T} + \cdots$$
$$= \sum_{n=0}^{\infty} e^{-n(s+a)T}$$

The Laplace transform of a sampled signal is an infinite series. In the following, it is seen that the z transform greatly simplifies the analysis of such systems.[1-5]

13.2 The z Transform.   The simple substitution

$$z = e^{Ts}$$

converts the Laplace transform to the z transform.   Making this substitution in Eq. (13.2) gives

$$Z[f^*(t)] = F(z) = f(0) + \frac{f(T)}{z} + \frac{f(2T)}{z^2} + \cdots$$
$$= \sum_{n=0}^{\infty} f(nT)z^{-n} \tag{13.3}$$

where $F(z)$ designates the z transform of $f^*(t)$.

ILLUSTRATIVE EXAMPLE 1.   Determine the z transform for a unit step function.   For this function $f(nT) = 1$ for $n = 0, 1, 2, \ldots$; thus application of Eq. (13.3) gives

$$Z[u^*(t)] = 1 + \frac{1}{z} + \frac{1}{z^2} + \cdots = \frac{z}{z - 1} \tag{13.4}$$

This series is convergent for $|z| > 1$.   In solving problems by z transforms, the term z acts as a dummy operator.   There is no need to specify

[1] W. Hurewicz, chap. 5 in H. M. James, N. B. Nichols, and R. S. Phillips (eds.), "Theory of Servomechanisms," Vol. 25, MIT Radiation Laboratory Series, McGraw-Hill Book Company, New York, 1947.

[2] J. R. Ragazzini and L. A. Zadeh, The Analysis of Sampled-data Servo-systems, *Trans. AIEE*, **71**: (2), 225–234 (1952).

[3] W. K. Linvill, Sampled-data Control Systems Studied through Comparison of Sampling with Amplitude Modulation, *Trans. AIEE*, **70**: 1779–1788 (1951).

[4] J. R. Ragazzini and G. F. Franklin, "Sampled-data Control Systems," McGraw-Hill Book Company, New York, 1958.

[5] E. Jury, "Sampled-data Control Systems," John Wiley & Sons, Inc., New York, 1958.

the values of z over which $F(z)$ is convergent.   It suffices to know that such values exist.

ILLUSTRATIVE EXAMPLE 2.   Determine the z transform of the exponential e^{-at}.   For this function $f(nT) = e^{-anT}$, thus

$$Z(e^{-anT}) = 1 + \frac{e^{-aT}}{z} + \left(\frac{e^{-aT}}{z}\right)^2 + \cdots = \frac{z}{z - e^{-aT}} \qquad (13.5)$$

In Table 13.1 is given a partial listing of Laplace transforms and corresponding z transforms for commonly encountered functions.

TABLE 13.1. z TRANSFORMS

Description	Time function	Laplace transform	z transform
Unit impulse	$u_1(t)$	1	1
Unit step	$u(t)$	$\dfrac{1}{s}$	$\dfrac{z}{z - 1}$
Ramp	t	$\dfrac{1}{s^2}$	$\dfrac{Tz}{(z - 1)^2}$
Quadratic	$\dfrac{t^2}{2}$	$\dfrac{1}{s^3}$	$\dfrac{T^2z(z + 1)}{2(z - 1)^3}$
Exponential	e^{-a}	$\dfrac{1}{s + a}$	$\dfrac{z}{z - e^{-aT}}$
Exponential times $\cos \dfrac{\pi}{T} t$	$e^{-at} \cos \dfrac{\pi}{T} t$		$\dfrac{z}{z + e^{-aT}}$
Constant raised to power t	$a^{t/T}$	$\dfrac{1}{s - (1/T) \ln a}$	$\dfrac{z}{z - a} \quad (a > 0)$
Constant raised to power t times $\cos \dfrac{\pi}{T} t$	$a^{t/T} \cos \dfrac{\pi}{T} t$		$\dfrac{z}{z + a} \quad (a > 0)$
Sinusoidal	$\sin \omega t$	$\dfrac{\omega}{s^2 + \omega^2}$	$\dfrac{z \sin \omega T}{z^2 - 2z \cos \omega T + 1}$
Cosine	$\cos \omega t$	$\dfrac{s}{s^2 + \omega^2}$	$\dfrac{z^2 - z \cos \omega T}{z^2 - 2z \cos \omega T + 1}$
Multiplication by e^{-at}	$e^{-at}f(t)$	$F(s + a)$	$F(ze^{aT})$
Delay by time nT	$f(t - nT)$	$e^{-nTs}F(s)$	$\dfrac{1}{z^n} F(z)$

When the Laplace transform of a function is known, the corresponding z transform may be obtained by the partial-fraction method.

ILLUSTRATIVE EXAMPLE 3.   Determine the z transform for the function whose Laplace transform is

$$F(s) = \frac{1}{s(s + 1)} = \frac{1}{s} - \frac{1}{s + 1}$$

From Table 13.1, the z transform corresponding to $1/s$ is $z/(z-1)$ and that corresponding to $1/(s+1)$ is $z/(z-e^{-T})$. Thus,

$$F(z) = \frac{z}{z-1} - \frac{z}{z-e^{-T}} = \frac{z(1-e^{-T})}{(z-1)(z-e^{-T})} \tag{13.6}$$

ILLUSTRATIVE EXAMPLE 4.   Determine the z transform of $\cos \omega t$. It is known that the Laplace transform is $s/(s^2+\omega^2)$. Thus, performing a partial fraction expansion gives

$$\mathcal{L}(\cos \omega t) = \frac{s}{s^2+\omega^2} = \frac{\frac{1}{2}}{s+j\omega} + \frac{\frac{1}{2}}{s-j\omega}$$

The corresponding z transform is

$$Z(\cos n\omega T) = \frac{1}{2}\left[\frac{z}{z-e^{-j\omega T}} + \frac{z}{z-e^{j\omega T}}\right] = \frac{z^2 - z(e^{j\omega T}+e^{-j\omega T})/2}{z^2 - z(e^{j\omega T}+e^{-j\omega T})+1}$$

$$= \frac{z^2 - z\cos \omega T}{z^2 - 2z\cos \omega T + 1} \tag{13.7}$$

The Residue Method.   This is a powerful technique for obtaining z transforms.   In Appendix V, Eq. (V.12), it is shown that the z transform of $f^*(t)$ may be expressed in the form

$$F(z) = Z[f^*(t)] = \sum \text{residues of } F(s) \frac{z}{z-e^{sT}} \text{ at poles of } F(s) \tag{13.8}$$

When the denominator of $F(s)$ contains a linear factor of the form $s-r$ such that $F(s)$ has a first-order pole at $s = r$, the corresponding residue R is

$$R = \lim_{s \to r} (s-r)\left[F(s) \frac{z}{z-e^{sT}}\right] \tag{13.9}$$

When $F(s)$ contains a repeated pole of order q, the residue is

$$R = \frac{1}{(q-1)!} \lim_{s \to r} \frac{d^{q-1}}{ds^{q-1}}\left[(s-r)^q F(s) \frac{z}{z-e^{sT}}\right] \tag{13.10}$$

As is illustrated by the following examples, the determination of residues is similar to evaluating the constants in a partial-fraction expansion.

ILLUSTRATIVE EXAMPLE 5.   Determine the z transform of a unit step function.   For $F(s) = 1/s$, there is but one pole at $s = 0$. The corresponding residue is

$$R = \lim_{s \to 0} s\left(\frac{1}{s} \frac{z}{z-e^{sT}}\right) = \frac{z}{z-1}$$

This verifies the result of Eq. (13.4).

ILLUSTRATIVE EXAMPLE 6. Determine the z transform of e^{-at}. For this function $F(s) = 1/(s + a)$ which has but one pole at $s = -a$. Thus,

$$R = \lim_{s \to -a} (s + a) \left[\frac{1}{(s + a)} \frac{z}{z - e^{sT}} \right] = \frac{z}{z - e^{-aT}}$$

This verifies the result of Eq. (13.5).

ILLUSTRATIVE EXAMPLE 7. Determine the z transform for the function whose Laplace transform is

$$F(s) = \frac{1}{s(s + 1)}$$

The poles of $F(s)$ occur at $s = 0$ and $s = -1$. The residue due to the pole at $s = 0$ is

$$R_1 = \lim_{s \to 0} s \left[\frac{1}{s(s + 1)} \frac{z}{z - e^{sT}} \right] = \frac{z}{z - 1}$$

The residue due to the pole at $s = -1$ is

$$R_2 = \lim_{s \to -1} (s + 1) \left[\frac{1}{s(s + 1)} \frac{z}{z - e^{sT}} \right] = - \frac{z}{z - e^{-T}}$$

Adding these two residues verifies the result given by Eq. (13.6).

ILLUSTRATIVE EXAMPLE 8. Determine the z transform of $\cos \omega t$. The Laplace transform is

$$F(s) = \frac{s}{s^2 + \omega^2} = \frac{s}{(s - j\omega)(s + j\omega)}$$

The poles are at $s = j\omega$ and at $s = -j\omega$. Thus,

$$R_1 = \left(\frac{s}{s + j\omega} \frac{z}{z - e^{sT}} \right)_{s=j\omega} = \frac{1}{2} \frac{z}{z - e^{j\omega T}}$$

$$R_2 = \left(\frac{s}{s - j\omega} \frac{z}{z - e^{sT}} \right)_{s=-j\omega} = \frac{1}{2} \frac{z}{z - e^{-j\omega T}}$$

Adding these two residues verifies the result given by Eq. (13.7).

ILLUSTRATIVE EXAMPLE 9. Determine the z transform corresponding to the function $f(t) = t$. The Laplace transform is

$$F(s) = \frac{1}{s^2}$$

This has a second-order pole at $s = 0$. Application of Eq. (13.10) gives

$$R = \frac{d}{ds} \left(\frac{z}{z - e^{sT}} \right)_{s=0} = \left(\frac{zTe^{sT}}{(z - e^{sT})^2} \right)_{s=0} = \frac{Tz}{(z - 1)^2}$$

Theorems. The following basic theorems extend the usefulness of the z-transform method. In addition these theorems help one to obtain a better understanding of z transformations.

Delay by Time nT. The z transform of a function $f(t)$ which is delayed a time nT is

$$Z[f(t - nT)] = \frac{1}{z^n}\, F(z) \tag{13.11}$$

Thus, multiplication of a z transform by $1/z^n$ has the effect of delaying the function a time nT. For Laplace transforms, multiplication by e^{-as} has the effect of delaying the function a time a.

Proof: The equation for the delayed function $f^*(t - nT)$ is

$$f^*(t - nT) = f(0)u(t - nT) + f(T)u[t - (n + 1)T]$$
$$+ f(2T)u[t - (n + 2)T] + \cdots$$

The Laplace transform is

$$\mathcal{L}[f^*(t - nt)] = f(0)e^{-nTs} + f(T)e^{-(n+1)Ts} + f(2T)e^{-(n+2)Ts} + \cdots$$
$$= e^{-nTs}[f(0) + f(T)e^{-Ts} + f(2T)e^{-2Ts} + \cdots]$$

The z transform for a delayed function is now obtained by letting $z = e^{sT}$. Thus

$$Z[f(t - nT)] = z^{-n} \sum_{n=0}^{\infty} f(nT)z^{-n} = z^{-n}F(z)$$

Multiplication by e^{-at}. The z transform of $e^{-at}f^*(t)$ is

$$Z[e^{-at}f^*(t)] = F(ze^{aT}) \tag{13.12}$$

Thus, replacing z in $F(z)$ by ze^{aT} yields the transform for $e^{-at}f(t)$. It is recalled that the Laplace transform of $e^{-at}f(t)$ is equal to $F(s + a)$. That is, replacing s by $s + a$ gives the effect of multiplying by e^{-at}.

Proof: From Eq. (13.9)

$$Z[e^{-at}f^*(t)] = \sum_{n=0}^{\infty} f(nT)e^{-anT}z^{-n} = \sum_{n=0}^{\infty} f(nT)(ze^{aT})^{-n}$$

Partial Differentiation. This theorem states that

$$Z\left[\frac{\partial}{\partial a}\, [f(t,a)] \right] = \frac{\partial}{\partial a}\, [F(z,a)] \tag{13.13}$$

This theorem is useful for ascertaining additional z transforms. For example, it is known that the z transform of e^{at} is $z/(z - e^{aT})$. Thus

$$Z\left[\frac{\partial}{\partial a}\, e^{at} \right] = Z[te^{at}] = \frac{\partial}{\partial a}\, \frac{z}{z - e^{aT}} = \frac{Tze^{aT}}{(z - e^{aT})^2}$$

For the case in which $a = 0$,

$$Z[t] = \frac{Tz}{(z-1)^2}$$

By proceeding in a similar manner, the z transforms for t^2, t^3, etc., are also obtained.

Initial-value Theorem. The area of the first impulse $f(0)$ of the sampled function $f^*(t)$ is

$$f(0) = \lim_{z \to \infty} F(z) \tag{13.14}$$

This theorem is verified directly by taking the limit as z approaches infinity in Eq. (13.3).

Final-value Theorem. The area of the impulse $f(nT)$ as n becomes infinite is

$$f(\infty) = \lim_{z \to 1} \frac{z-1}{z} F(z) \tag{13.15}$$

Proof: Consider the following sums S_n and S_{n-1}.

$$S_n = f(0) + \frac{f(T)}{z} + \cdots + \frac{f[(n-1)T]}{z^{n-1}} + \frac{f(nT)}{z^n}$$

$$S_{n-1} = f(0) + \frac{f(T)}{z} + \cdots + \frac{f[(n-1)T]}{z^{n-1}}$$

Dividing the second series by z, and then subtracting the second from the first gives

$$\left(S_n - \frac{1}{z} S_{n-1}\right) = \left(1 - \frac{1}{z}\right)f(0) + \cdots + \left(1 - \frac{1}{z}\right)\frac{f[(n-1)T]}{z^{n-1}} + \frac{f(nT)}{z^n}$$

Taking the limit as z approaches 1 gives

$$\lim_{z \to 1}\left(S_n - \frac{1}{z} S_{n-1}\right) = f(nT)$$

When n is very large, $S_{n-1} \approx S_n \approx F(z)$. Thus, the final-value theorem given by Eq. (13.15) is verified.

13.3 Inverse z Transforms. Inspection of Table 13.1 shows that z transforms tend to be more complicated than corresponding Laplace transforms. Fortunately, there are some relatively simple techniques for obtaining inverse z transforms.

Partial-fraction Method. To illustrate this method, let it be desired to obtain the inverse z transform for the function

$$F(z) = \frac{(1 - e^{-T})z}{(z-1)(z - e^{-T})} \tag{13.16}$$

Performing a partial-fraction expansion gives

$$F(z) = \left[\frac{1 - e^{-T}}{(z - 1)(z - e^{-T})} \right] z = \left[\frac{K_1}{z - 1} + \frac{K_2}{z - e^{-T}} \right] z$$

$$= \frac{z}{z - 1} - \frac{z}{z - e^{-T}}$$

From Table 13.1 the corresponding time function is

$$f(t) = 1 - e^{-t}$$

Thus, the inverse $f^*(t)$ is

$$f^*(t) = \sum_{n=0}^{\infty} (1 - e^{nT})u_1(t - nT) \qquad (13.17)$$

Division Method.   Dividing the numerator of $F(z)$ by the denominator yields a power series of the form

$$F(z) = C_0 + C_1 z^{-1} + C_2 z^{-2} + \cdots \qquad (13.18)$$

The corresponding inverse is

$$f^*(t) = \sum_{n=0}^{\infty} C_n u_1(t - nT)$$

To obtain the inverse of Eq. (13.16) by the division method, divide the numerator of Eq. (13.16) by the denominator.   That is

$$F(z) = 0 + (1 - e^{-T})z^{-1} + (1 - e^{-2T})z^{-2} + (1 - e^{-3T})z^{-3} + \cdots$$

Inverting verifies the result given by Eq. (13.17).

Residue Method.   To develop this method, first write the basic relationship for $F(z)$ in the form

$$F(z) = f(0) + \frac{f(T)}{z} + \cdots + \frac{f[(n-1)T]}{z^{n-1}} + \frac{f(nT)}{z^n}$$

$$+ \frac{f[(n+1)T]}{z^{n+1}} + \cdots$$

Multiplication by z^{n-1} gives

$$F(z)z^{n-1} = f(0)z^{n-1} + \cdots + f[(n-1)T] + \frac{f(nT)}{z}$$

$$+ \frac{f[(n+1)T]}{z^2} + \cdots \qquad (13.19)$$

From complex variable theory it is known that the coefficient $f(nT)$ of the $1/z$ term of the preceding Laurent expansion is

$$f(nT) = \frac{1}{2\pi j} \int_C F(z)z^{n-1}\,dz$$
$$= \Sigma \text{ residues of } F(z)z^{n-1} \text{ at poles of } F(z) \qquad (13.20)$$

Because z^{n-1} has no poles, all of the poles are due to the function $F(z)$. The contour C is any closed path which encloses all the poles of $F(z)z^{n-1}$.

Replacing the function $F(s)z/(z - e^{-sT})$ in Eqs. (13.9) and (13.10) by $F(z)z^{n-1}$ yields the following equations for determining the residues in Eq. (13.20). In particular, the residue due to a first-order pole at $z = r$ is

$$R = \lim_{z \to r} (z - r)[F(z)z^{n-1}] \qquad (13.21)$$

Similarly, the residue due to a repeated pole of order q is

$$R = \frac{1}{(q-1)!} \lim_{z \to r} \frac{d^{q-1}}{dz^{q-1}} [(z - r)^q F(z)z^{n-1}] \qquad (13.22)$$

Application of the residue method to determine the inverse of Eq. (13.16) gives

$$R_1 = \left[\frac{(1 - e^{-T})z^n}{z - e^{-T}} \right]_{z=1} = 1$$

$$R_2 = \left[\frac{(1 - e^{-T})z^n}{z - 1} \right]_{z=e^{-T}} = -e^{-nT}$$

Adding these residues yields the result given by Eq. (13.17).

As another example, determine the inverse z transform for the function

$$F(z) = \frac{Tz}{(z - 1)^2}$$

This function has a second-order pole at $z = 1$, thus

$$R = \lim_{z \to 1} \frac{d}{dz} Tz^n = (nTz^{n-1})_{z=1} = nT$$

For the sampled signal $f^*(t) = nT$, the corresponding time function is $f(t) = t$.

13.4 Block-diagram Algebra. In writing the transfer function for feedback control systems with sampling switches, one encounters some terms which are starred and some which are not. Thus, it is necessary to develop some mathematical techniques for handling such mixed terms. In Fig. 13.2a is shown a sampling switch followed by a linear element whose transfer function is $G(s)$. If all of the initial conditions are zero,

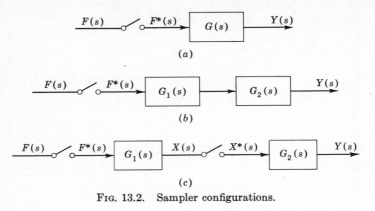

Fig. 13.2.   Sampler configurations.

then the transformed equation for the output $Y(s)$ is

$$Y(s) = F^*(s)G(s) \tag{13.23}$$

For $0 < t < T$, the response $y(t)$ is that due to the first impulse at $t = 0$ of area $f(0)$. Thus, for this interval

$$y(t) = \mathcal{L}^{-1}[f(0)G(s)] = f(0)\mathcal{L}^{-1}[G(s)] = f(0)g(t) \tag{13.24}$$

where $g(t) = \mathcal{L}^{-1}[G(s)]$ is the response of the linear element to a unit impulse which occurs at $t = 0$.

For $T < t < 2T$, the response $y(t)$ is that due to the impulse at $t = 0$ plus that at $t = T$. For this interval, $F^*(s) = f(0) + f(T)e^{-Ts}$. Thus,

$$Y(s) = [f(0) + f(T)e^{-Ts}]G(s)$$

Inverting gives

$$y(t) = f(0)g(t) + f(T)g(t - T) \tag{13.25}$$

where $g(t - T) = \mathcal{L}^{-1}[G(s)e^{-Ts}]$ is the response of the linear element to a unit impulse which occurs at time $t = T$. The response $y(t)$ for the interval $2T < t < 3T$ is

$$y(t) = f(0)g(t) + f(T)g(t - T) + f(2T)g(t - 2T)$$

In general, the response $y(t)$ is

$$y(t) = \sum_{n=0}^{\infty} f(nT)g(t - nT) \tag{13.26}$$

When n is such that $nT > t$, then $g(t - nT)$ is zero. That is, the impulse response is zero for negative time.

Taking the limit as t approaches 0 in Eq. (13.24), and the limit as t approaches T in Eq. (13.25), etc., yields the value of $y(nT)$ at the sampling instants.

$$y(0) = f(0)g(0)$$
$$y(T) = f(0)g(T) + f(T)g(0)$$
$$y(2T) = f(0)g(2T) + f(T)g(T) + f(2T)g(0) \qquad (13.27)$$
$$\cdots \cdots \cdots \cdots \cdots \cdots \cdots \cdots \cdots \cdots$$
$$y(nT) = f(0)g(nT) + f(T)g[(n-1)T] + \cdots$$

In Fig. 13.3 is shown a response function $y(t)$ which is discontinuous at the sampling instants. This occurs when the order of the denominator

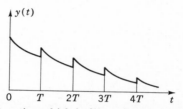

Fig. 13.3. Response function which is discontinuous at the sampling instants.

of $G(s)$ exceeds the order of the numerator by only one. When the order of the denominator exceeds the numerator by two or more, $y(t)$ is continuous. When $y(t)$ is continuous, Eq. (13.27) yields the values at the sampling instants. When $y(t)$ is discontinuous, Eq. (13.27) yields the values immediately after the sampling instants [that is, $y(0+)$, $y(T+)$, $y(2T+) \cdots$]. Figure 13.1 shows that the values in Eq. (13.2) would also be the values immediately following the sampling instants if the function were discontinuous. Replacing f by y in Eq. (13.2) gives

$$Y^*(s) = y(0) + y(T)e^{-Ts} + y(2T)e^{-2Ts} + \cdots$$

Substitution of the values from Eq. (13.27) into the preceding expression gives

$$\begin{aligned} Y^*(s) &= f(0)[g(0) + g(T)e^{-Ts} + g(2T)e^{-2Ts} + \cdots] \\ &\quad + f(T)e^{-Ts}[g(0) + g(T)e^{-Ts} + g(2T)e^{-2Ts} + \cdots] \\ &\quad + f(2T)e^{-2Ts}[g(0) + g(T)e^{-Ts} + g(2T)e^{-2Ts} + \cdots] \\ &\quad + \cdots \\ &= [f(0) + f(T)e^{-Ts} + \cdots][g(0) + g(T)e^{-Ts} + \cdots] \end{aligned}$$

Thus,

$$Y^*(s) = F^*(s)G^*(s) \qquad (13.28)$$

The term $G^*(s)$ is called the *pulse-transfer function* of the system.

Comparison of Eqs. (13.23) and (13.28) reveals a basic mathematical relationship for starring quantities. That is, starring both sides of

Eq. (13.23) gives

$$[Y(s)]^* = Y^*(s)$$
$$[F^*(s)G(s)]^* = F^*(s)[G(s)]^* = F^*(s)G^*(s)$$

Letting $z = e^{sT}$ in Eq. (13.28) yields the z-transform relationship

$$Y(z) = F(z)G(z) \tag{13.29}$$

For the sampler configuration of Fig. 13.2b, the Laplace transform relationship is

$$Y(s) = F^*(s)G_1(s)G_2(s)$$

Starring gives

$$Y^*(s) = F^*(s)[G_1(s)G_2(s)]^* = F^*(s)G_1G_2{}^*(s)$$

where

$$G_1G_2{}^*(s) = [G_1(s)G_2(s)]^*$$

The corresponding z transform is

$$Y(z) = F(z)G_1G_2(z) \tag{13.30}$$

ILLUSTRATIVE EXAMPLE 1.   Determine the z transform for Fig. 13.2b, when $G_1(s) = 1/s$ and $G_2(s) = 1/(s + 1)$.   The product $G_1(s)G_2(s)$ is

$$G_1(s)G_2(s) = \frac{1}{s(s + 1)}$$

The z transform for this function is given by Eq. (13.6).   That is,

$$G_1G_2(z) = \frac{z(1 - e^{-T})}{(z - 1)(z - e^{-T})} \tag{13.31}$$

For the sampler configuration shown in Fig. 13.2c, the Laplace relationships are

$$X(s) = F^*(s)G_1(s)$$
$$Y(s) = X^*(s)G_2(s)$$

Starring the first equation and then substituting this result for $X^*(s)$ into the second equation gives

$$Y(s) = F^*(s)G_1{}^*(s)G_2(s)$$

Starring gives

$$Y^*(s) = F^*(s)G_1{}^*(s)G_2{}^*(s)$$

The corresponding z transform is

$$Y(z) = F(z)G_1(z)G_2(z) \tag{13.32}$$

ILLUSTRATIVE EXAMPLE 2.   Determine the z transform for Fig. 13.2c, when $G_1(s) = 1/s$ and $G_2(s) = 1/(s + 1)$.   From Eqs. (13.4) and (13.5), it follows that

$$G_1(z) = \frac{z}{z-1}$$

and

$$G_2(z) = \frac{z}{z - e^{-T}}$$

Thus

$$G_1(z)G_2(z) = \frac{z^2}{(z-1)(z - e^{-T})} \qquad (13.33)$$

From the two preceding examples it is to be noted that

$$G_1G_2(z) \neq G_1(z)G_2(z) \qquad (13.34)$$

The function $G_1G_2(z)$ is the z transform corresponding to the product $G_1(s)G_2(s)$ whereas the function $G_1(z)G_2(z)$ is the product of the z transform for $G_1(s)$ and the z transform for $G_2(s)$.

Two sampled-data feedback control systems are shown in Fig. 13.4. The general procedure for determining the transformed equation for a

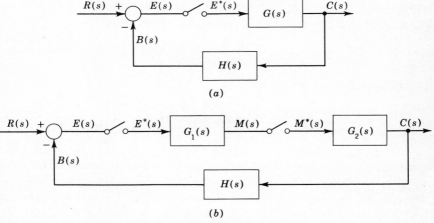

(a)

(b)

Fig. 13.4.   Sampled-data systems.

sampled-data system is

1. In addition to the actual system input R, regard all switch outputs (starred quantities) as inputs.
2. In addition to the system output C, regard all switch inputs as outputs.
3. Write equations for each output in terms of its inputs.
4. Star quantities as necessary in order to determine $C(z)$.

Application of this method to the system shown in Fig. 13.4a gives

$$C(s) = E^*(s)G(s)$$
$$E(s) = R(s) - E^*(s)G(s)H(s)$$

Starring gives

$$C^*(s) = E^*(s)G^*(s)$$
$$E^*(s) = R^*(s) - E^*(s)GH^*(s)$$

Solving the last equation for $E^*(s)$ and substituting into the first gives

$$C^*(s) = \frac{G^*(s)}{1 + GH^*(s)} R^*(s)$$

The corresponding z transform is

$$C(z) = \frac{G(z)}{1 + GH(z)} R(z) \tag{13.35}$$

The equations relating the inputs and outputs of Fig. 13.4b are

$$C(s) = M^*(s)G_2(s)$$
$$M(s) = E^*(s)G_1(s)$$
$$E(s) = R(s) - M^*(s)G_2(s)H(s)$$

Starring all equations, and then solving for $C^*(s)$ gives

$$C^*(s) = \frac{G_1^*(s)G_2^*(s)}{1 + G_1^*(s)G_2H^*(s)} R^*(s)$$

The corresponding z transform is

$$C(z) = \frac{G_1(z)G_2(z)}{1 + G_1(z)G_2H(z)} R(z) \tag{13.36}$$

13.5 Transient Response.   Routh's criterion, the root-locus method, and the frequency response methods used to investigate the transient response and stability of continuous systems may also be extended to sampled-data systems.   For continuous systems, it was found that a system is unstable if any root of the characteristic equation is in the right half of the s plane.   This right half plane may be designated by $\sigma + j\omega$ in which $\sigma > 0$.   The corresponding portion of the z plane is

$$z = e^{sT} = e^{\sigma T}e^{j\omega T}$$

The magnitude is

$$|z| = e^{\sigma T}$$

For $\sigma > 0$, then $|z| > 1$.   As is illustrated in Fig. 13.5, the right half of the s plane corresponds to the outside of the unit circle of the z plane. Thus, for stability, all the roots of the z-transformed characteristic equation must lie within the unit circle.

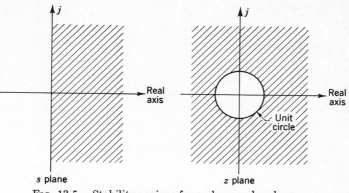

FIG. 13.5. Stability regions for s plane and z plane.

Consider now the sampled-data system shown in Fig. 13.6. The z transform for the output $C(z)$ is

$$C(z) = \frac{G(z)}{1 + G(z)} R(z) = \frac{N_{G(z)}}{D_{G(z)} + N_{G(z)}} R(z) \qquad (13.37)$$

where $G(z) = N_{G(z)}/D_{G(z)}$ in which $N_{G(z)}$ is the numerator of $G(z)$ and $D_{G(z)}$ is the denominator of $G(z)$. The z-transformed characteristic

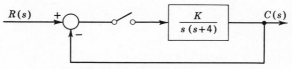

FIG. 13.6. Sampled-data system.

equation is

$$N_{G(z)} + D_{G(z)} = 0 \qquad (13.38)$$

The partial fraction expansion for $G(s)$ is

$$G(s) = \frac{K}{4} \left(\frac{1}{s} - \frac{1}{s + 4} \right)$$

The corresponding z transform is

$$G(z) = \frac{K}{4} \left(\frac{z}{z - 1} - \frac{z}{z - e^{-4T}} \right) = \frac{z(1 - e^{-4T})K/4}{(z - 1)(z - e^{-4T})} \qquad (13.39)$$

Thus, the characteristic equation for this system is

$$(z - 1)(z - e^{-4T}) + z(1 - e^{-4T})K/4 = 0 \qquad (13.40)$$

Routh's Criterion. To apply this criterion, it is necessary to transform the unit circle of the z plane to the vertical imaginary axis of the λ plane.

This is accomplished by the transformation

$$\lambda = \frac{z + 1}{z - 1}$$

Solving for z gives

$$z = \frac{\lambda + 1}{\lambda - 1} \tag{13.41}$$

When the characteristic equation is expressed in terms of λ, then Routh's criterion may be applied in the same manner as for continuous systems.

ILLUSTRATIVE EXAMPLE 1.   For a sampling period $T = \frac{1}{4}$ second, determine the value of K such that the system shown in Fig. 13.6 becomes unstable.   That is, roots of the characteristic equation lie on the unit circle of the z plane (i.e., the imaginary axis of the λ plane).

SOLUTION.   For $T = \frac{1}{4}$, Eq. (13.40) becomes

$$(z - 1)(z - 0.368) + 0.158Kz = 0$$

Using Eq. (13.41) to transform from the z plane to the λ plane gives

$$\frac{0.158K\lambda^2 + 1.264\lambda + (2.736 - 0.158K)}{(\lambda - 1)^2} = 0 \tag{13.42}$$

The Routh array for the numerator is

$0.158K$	$(2.736 - 0.158K)$	0
1.264	0	
$(2.736 - 0.158K)$	0	

Thus, this system is unstable for

$$K \geq \frac{2.736}{0.158} = 17.3$$

In Fig. 7.2 is shown the root-locus plot for the continuous system corresponding to Fig. 13.6.   The continuous system is stable for all values of K.

If, in the preceding example, the sampling rate is increased from 4 samples per second ($T = \frac{1}{4}$) to 10 samples per second ($T = \frac{1}{10}$), then the system would be unstable for $K \geq 42$.   In general, making the sampling time shorter tends to make the system behave more like the corresponding continuous system.   Usually, stability is improved as the sampling rate is increased.

Root Locus.   All of the techniques for constructing root-locus plots for continuous systems (in the s plane) apply equally well to sampled-data systems (in the z plane).   For example, for $T = \frac{1}{4}$ the characteristic equation given by Eq. (13.40) becomes

$$(z - 1)(z - 0.368) + 0.158Kz = 0 \tag{13.43}$$

This characteristic equation has an × at $z = 1$ and at $z = 0.368$. There is a ⊙ at $z = 0$. The complete root-locus plot may now be constructed as is shown in Fig. 13.7. This root-locus plot crosses the unit

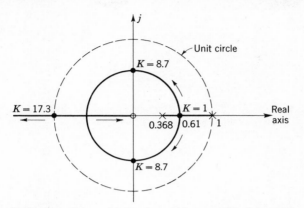

Fig. 13.7. Root-locus plot for $(z - 1)(z - 0.368) + 0.158Kz = 0$.

circle at $z = -1$. The value of the gain $(0.158K)$ at any point on a root-locus plot is the product of the distance from this point to each × divided by the distance from this point to each ⊙. Thus, the value of $(0.158K)$ at which the system becomes unstable is $0.158K = (1.368)(2)/(1)$, or

$$K = \frac{2.736}{0.158} = 17.3$$

This verifies the result ascertained by Routh's criterion.

Two horizontal lines of constant b are shown in the s plane of Fig. 13.8a. The corresponding paths in the z plane are radial straight lines.

$$z = e^{sT} = e^{(a \pm jb)T} = e^{aT}e^{\pm jbT}$$

The angle of inclination of these radial lines is $\theta = \pm bT$.

Two vertical lines of constant a are shown in the s plane of Fig. 13.8b. The corresponding paths in the z plane are circles of radius e^{aT}. For negative values of a the circles are inside the unit circle of the z plane. For positive values of a the circles lie outside the unit circle of the z plane.

Radial lines of constant damping ratio $\zeta = \cos \beta$ are shown in Fig. 13.8c. In polar coordinates $s = a \pm jb = -\zeta\omega_n \pm j\omega_n \sqrt{1 - \zeta^2}$. Thus

$$z = e^{-\zeta\omega_n T}e^{\pm j\omega_n \sqrt{1-\zeta^2}T}$$

The corresponding paths in the z plane are logarithmic spirals. For $\beta < 90°$ the spirals decay within the unit circle, and for $\beta > 90°$ the spirals grow outside the unit circle.

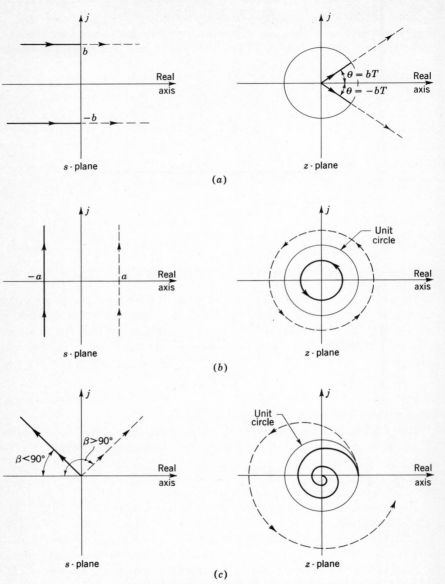

Fig. 13.8. Corresponding paths in the s plane and z plane.

Consider now how a given point, $z = re^{j\theta}$, in the z plane maps back into the s plane. For

$$z = re^{j\theta} = e^{sT} = e^{(a \pm jb)T}$$
$$\ln r + j\theta = aT \pm jbT \qquad -\pi < \theta < \pi$$

Equating real and imaginary parts shows that

$$\ln r = aT$$
$$\theta = \pm bT \qquad -\pi < \theta < \pi$$

This verifies the fact that a circle of constant r in the z plane is a vertical line of constant a in the s plane. Similarly, a ray at angle θ in the z plane is a horizontal line of constant b in the s plane.

ILLUSTRATIVE EXAMPLE 2. Determine the response of the system of Fig. 13.6 to a unit step-function excitation for the case in which $T = \frac{1}{4}$ and $K = 1$.

SOLUTION. Substitution of these values into Eq. (13.39) gives

$$G(z) = \frac{0.158z}{(z-1)(z-0.368)} \tag{13.44}$$

Substitution of $G(z)$ and $R(z) = z/(z-1)$ into Eq. (13.37) gives

$$C(z) = \frac{G(z)}{1+G(z)} R(z) = \frac{0.158z}{[(z-1)(z-0.368) + 0.158z]} \frac{z}{z-1} \tag{13.45}$$

For $K = 1$, the root-locus plot of Fig. 13.7 shows that the characteristic equation has a repeated root at $z = 0.61$. Thus

$$C(z) = \frac{0.158z^2}{(z-0.61)^2(z-1)}$$

Using the long division method to determine the inverse gives

$$\frac{0.158z^{-1} + 0.350z^{-2} + 0.524z^{-3} + \cdots}{z^3 - 2.21z^2 + 1.58z - 0.368 \overline{)0.158z^2}}$$

Because

$$C(z) = c(0) + c(T)z^{-1} + c(2T)z^{-2} + c(3T)z^{-3} + \cdots$$

then

$$\begin{aligned}
c(0) &= 0 \\
c(T) &= 0.158 \\
c(2T) &= 0.350 \\
c(3T) &= 0.524 \\
&\cdots\cdots\cdots
\end{aligned} \tag{13.46}$$

A plot of the response $c(nT)$ at the sampling instants is shown in Fig. 13.9. An alternate method for determining the response at the sampling instants is provided by the difference equation method.

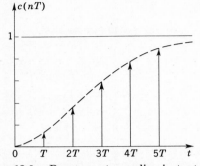

FIG. 13.9.   Response at sampling instants.

Difference Equations.   To determine the inverse z transform by this method, first write the equation for $C(z)$, Eq. (13.45), in the form

$$C(z) = \frac{0.158z}{[(z - 1)(z - 0.368) + 0.158z]}\, R(z)$$

Thus $$z^2 C(z) - 1.21zC(z) + 0.368C(z) = 0.158zR(z) \qquad (13.47)$$

Application of Eq. (13.11) gives

$$Z[c(t + 2T)] - 1.21Z[c(t + T)] + 0.368Z[c(t)] = 0.158Z[r(t + T)]$$

The inverse z transform is

$$c[(n + 2)T] - 1.21c[(n + 1)T] + 0.368c(nT) = 0.158r[(n + 1)T]$$

Comparison of this difference equation with Eq. (13.47) shows that multiplication of the z transform of a function by z corresponds to a forward time shift of one period.   The difference equation is converted to a more convenient form for computational purposes by letting $k = (n + 2)T$. Thus,

$$c(k) = 1.21c(k - 1) - 0.368c(k - 2) + 0.158r(k - 1) \quad (13.48)$$

This difference equation gives the value $c(k)$ at the kth sampling instant in terms of values at preceding sampling instants.   Application of this result to obtain the values at the sampling instants gives

$$\begin{aligned}
c(0) &= 0 \\
c(1) &= 0.158r(0) = 0.158 \\
c(2) &= 1.21c(1) + 0.158r(1) = 0.350 \\
c(3) &= 1.21c(2) - 0.368c(1) + 0.158r(2) = 0.524
\end{aligned}$$

. . . .

The difference-equation method may also be used to solve differential equations when the value of the excitation at equally spaced intervals is known. This is a powerful numerical method for solving differential equations.

13.6 Frequency Response. In the preceding, it has been shown how Laplace transformations, Routh's criterion, and the root-locus method are extended to sampled data systems. In a similar manner, the Nyquist criterion and frequency-response techniques may also be extended for the analysis of sampled-data systems.

Nyquist Criterion. As one traverses the path of Fig. 10.2 in the direction of the arrows, the right half plane is seen to the right. Similarly, as the Nyquist path shown in Fig. 13.10 is traversed, the exterior of the unit

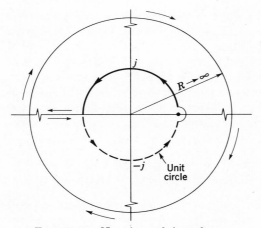

FIG. 13.10. Nyquist path in z plane.

circle is seen to the right. As z proceeds out the negative axis of Fig. 13.10, the map $GH(z)$ approaches the origin $GH(z) = 0$ as z approaches minus infinity. For values of z on the infinite semicircle $R = \infty$, the map $GH(z)$ remains at the origin $GH(z) = 0$. As indicated in Fig. 13.10, for values of z on the negative axis, the path is traversed in opposite directions so that the map in this region cancels. Thus, it is only necessary to construct the map for values of z on the unit circle.

By noting that

$$1 + GH(z) = 1 + \frac{N_{GH(z)}}{D_{GH(z)}} = \frac{D_{GH(z)} + N_{GH(z)}}{D_{GH(z)}} \qquad (13.49)$$

it is apparent that the zeros of $1 + GH(z)$ are the roots of the characteristic equation. Similarly, the poles of $1 + GH(z)$ are the roots of $D_{GH(z)}$. The Nyquist stability criterion is applied to sampled data systems in the same manner as for continuous systems (see Sec. 10.1). Thus,

$$Z = N + P \tag{13.50}$$

where Z = number of zeros of $1 + GH(z)$ within the assumed path of values of z. This is equal to the number of roots of the characteristic equation that are located outside the unit circle.

P = number of poles of $1 + GH(z)$ within the assumed path of values of z. This is equal to the number of roots of $D_{GH(z)}$ outside the unit circle.

N = net number of encirclements of the origin of the $1 + GH(z)$ plot. This is equal to the net number of encirclements of the -1 point of the $GH(z)$ plot.

The region exterior of the unit circle in Fig. 13.10 is traversed in a clockwise sense. Thus, N is positive for clockwise encirclements of the -1 point, and N is negative for counterclockwise encirclements.

For continuous systems in which $G(s)H(s)$ contains an s factor in the denominator (i.e., type 1 or higher type number systems), the origin of the s plane was excluded from the path of values of s as is illustrated in Fig. 10.3. The corresponding sampled-data system contains a $z - 1$ factor in the denominator of $GH(z)$. Thus, it is necessary to exclude the $+1$ point of the z plane as is shown in Fig. 13.10.

ILLUSTRATIVE EXAMPLE 1. Apply the Nyquist stability criterion to the system of Fig. 13.6 for which $GH(z) = G(z)$ is given by Eq. (13.44).

SOLUTION. The value of $G(z)$ for some typical values of z on the unit circle of Fig. 13.10 are

$$G(j) = \frac{0.158j}{(j - 1)(j - 0.368)} = 0.106\underline{/-155.2°}$$

$$G(-1) = \frac{-0.158}{(-2)(-1.368)} = 0.058\underline{/-180°}$$

$$G(-j) = 0.106\underline{/155.2°}$$

The equation for the values of z on the small semicircle that excludes the $+1$ point is $z = 1 + \epsilon e^{j\theta}$ where θ goes from $-90°$ to $0°$ to $90°$. Thus

$$G(1 + \epsilon e^{j\theta}) = \frac{0.158(1 + \epsilon e^{j\theta})}{\epsilon e^{j\theta}(0.632 + \epsilon e^{j\theta})}$$

$$\approx \frac{0.158}{\epsilon(0.632)} e^{-j\theta} \approx \infty e^{-j\theta}$$

The corresponding polar plot is shown in Fig. 13.11.   For this plot $N = 0$. Because the roots of $D_{G(z)}(z = 0.368$ and $z = 1)$ are located within the contour of Fig. 13.10, then $P = 0$.   Application of the Nyquist stability criterion, Eq. (13.50), shows that $Z = 0$, and thus the system is stable.

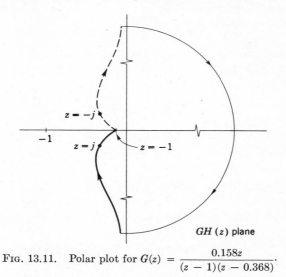

$$z = -j$$
$$-1$$
$$z = j$$
$$z = -1$$

$GH(z)$ plane

FIG. 13.11.   Polar plot for $G(z) = \dfrac{0.158z}{(z-1)(z-0.368)}$.

As is shown in Fig. 13.11, the polar plot crosses the negative real axis at the value (-0.058).   If the gain is increased by the factor $(1/0.058) = 17.3$, then the plot will pass through the -1 point.   This factor, the gain margin, has the same significance for sampled-data systems as for continuous systems.   Similarly, phase margin and M circles are employed to give an indication of the closeness of the polar plot to the minus one point.   Constructing the polar plot for different sampling periods T shows the effect of varying the sampling period upon the system behavior.

For the case of continuous systems, it is necessary to vary ω from 0 to ∞ in order to ascertain the frequency response.   For sampled-data systems, the path of the frequency response, $s = j\omega$, is

$$z = e^{sT} = e^{j\omega T} = e^{j2\pi\omega/\omega_s}$$

where $\omega_s = 2\pi/T$ is the sampling rate.   As z traverses the unit circle of Fig. 13.10, the real frequency ω varies from 0 to ω_s.   Thus, for sampled data systems the entire frequency response is contained in the frequencies $0 \leq \omega \leq \omega_s$.   For other frequencies $[n\omega_s \leq \omega \leq (n+1)\omega_s]$ the polar plot repeats itself.

The solid line portion of the polar plot of Fig. 13.11 is that due to values of z on the upper half of the unit circle of Fig. 13.10.   The dotted portion is that due to values of z on the lower half of the unit circle. Because of the symmetry of these two portions about the horizontal (real) axis, it is only necessary to construct the polar plot for values on the upper half of the unit circle (that is, $z = e^{j\theta}$ where $0 \le \theta \le \pi$). This is also the case when designing with Bode or Nichols plots. The corresponding range of real frequencies is $0 \le \omega \le \omega_s/2$.

13.7 Filters. Sampled-data systems usually incorporate a filter as is illustrated in Fig. 13.12. A perfect filter would convert the sampled

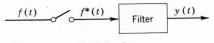

Hold circuit

Fig. 13.12.   Schematic representation of sampler and filter.

signal $f^*(t)$ back to the continuous input $f(t)$. That is, the output $y(t)$ of the filter would equal $f(t)$. If such a perfect filter were possible, then the sampled-data system would behave the same as the continuous system.

Zero-order Hold. The most commonly used filter is that in which the value of the last sample is retained until the next sample is taken. This type filter is called a zero-order hold, or boxcar generator. The dashed curve in Fig. 13.13 represents the continuous function $f(t)$. The vertical

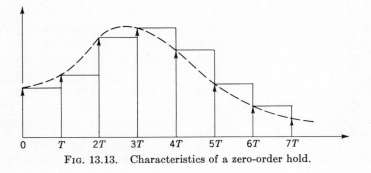

Fig. 13.13.   Characteristics of a zero-order hold.

arrows at the sampling instants are the impulses which represent the sampled signal $f^*(t)$. Because the zero-order hold retains the value of $f(t)$ at each sampling instant, then $y(t)$ is the series of steps shown in Fig. 13.13. The equation for this series of steps (i.e., pulse functions) is

$$y(t) = f(0)[u(t) - u(t - T)] + f(T)[u(t - T) - u(t - 2T)]$$
$$+ f(2T)[u(t - 2T) - u(t - 3T)] + \cdots$$

The Laplace transform is

$$Y(s) = f(0) \left(\frac{1 - e^{-Ts}}{s} \right) + f(T) \left(\frac{e^{-Ts} - e^{-2Ts}}{s} \right)$$

$$+ f(2T) \left(\frac{e^{-2Ts} - e^{-3Ts}}{s} \right) + \cdots$$

$$= \left(\frac{1 - e^{-Ts}}{s} \right) [f(0) + f(T)e^{-Ts} + f(2T)e^{-2Ts} + \cdots]$$

$$= \frac{1 - e^{-Ts}}{s} F^*(s)$$

This result shows that the Laplace transform for a zero-order hold is

$$\frac{1 - e^{-Ts}}{s} \tag{13.51}$$

Suppose that a zero-order hold is added to the system of Fig. 13.6. The new block diagram for this system is shown in Fig. 13.14. The

FIG. 13.14. Sampled-data system with a zero-order hold.

transfer function for the hold is included in the overall transfer function $G(s)$. Thus,

$$G(s) = (1 - e^{-Ts}) \frac{K}{s^2(s + 4)} \tag{13.52}$$

To determine $G(z)$ when $G(s)$ contains a $(1 - e^{-Ts})$ factor, first write Eq. (13.52) in the form

$$G(s) = G_1(s)G_2(s) \tag{13.53}$$

where $G_1(s) = 1 - e^{-Ts}$ and $G_2(s)$ is the remaining portion of $G(s)$. The function $G_1(s)$ is the Laplace transform of a unit impulse at the origin and a negative unit impulse at $t = T$. The corresponding time function $g_1(t)$ is shown in Fig. 13.15. Because this time function $g_1(t)$ exists only

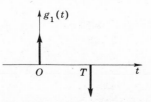

FIG. 13.15. Time function $g_1(t) = \mathcal{L}^{-1}[G_1(s)] = \mathcal{L}^{-1}(1 - e^{-Ts})$.´

at the sampling instants, the sampled function $g_1^*(t)$ will be the same as $g_1(t)$. Thus,

$$G_1(s) = G_1^*(s)$$

Substitution of this result into Eq. (13.53) shows that

$$G(s) = G_1^*(s)G_2(s)$$

Starring gives

$$G^*(s) = G_1^*(s)G_2^*(s)$$

The corresponding z transform is

$$G(z) = G_1(z)G_2(z) = (1 - z^{-1})G_2(z)$$
$$= \frac{z - 1}{z} G_2(z) \tag{13.54}$$

For the case of Eq. (13.52)

$$G_2(s) = \frac{K}{s^2(s + 4)} = \frac{K}{16}\left(\frac{4}{s^2} - \frac{1}{s} + \frac{1}{s + 4}\right)$$

Thus,

$$G_2(z) = \frac{K}{16}\left(\frac{4Tz}{(z - 1)^2} - \frac{z}{z - 1} + \frac{z}{z - e^{-4T}}\right)$$

Substitution of this result into Eq. (13.54) gives

$$G(z) = \frac{K}{16}\left(\frac{4T}{z - 1} - 1 + \frac{z - 1}{z - e^{-4T}}\right) = \frac{K}{16}\left(\frac{4T}{z - 1} + \frac{e^{-4T} - 1}{z - e^{-4T}}\right)$$

For $T = \frac{1}{4}$, then $G(z)$ becomes

$$G(z) = \frac{0.368K(z - 0.718)}{16(z - 1)(z - 0.368)} \tag{13.55}$$

The corresponding characteristic equation for this sampled-data system is

$$D_{G(z)} + N_{G(z)} = (z - 1)(z - 0.368) + 0.023K(z - 0.718) = 0 \tag{13.56}$$

Replacing z by $(\lambda + 1)/(\lambda - 1)$ so that Routh's criterion may be applied gives

$$0.0067K\lambda^2 + (1.264 + 0.0328K)\lambda + (2.736 - 0.0395K) = 0$$

The Routh array is

$$\begin{array}{cc} 0.0067K & (2.736 - 0.0395K) \\ (1.264 + 0.0328K) & 0 \\ (2.736 - 0.0395K) & 0 \end{array}$$

Thus, the system becomes unstable for

$$K \geq \frac{1.264}{0.0328} = 38.5$$

Without the zero-order hold, this system becomes unstable for $K \geq 17.3$.

From the characteristic equation, Eq. (13.56), the root-locus plot may be constructed as shown in Fig. 13.16. The root-locus plot crosses the unit circle at $K = 38.5$. Repeated roots, $z = 0.65$, occur at $K = 3.1$.

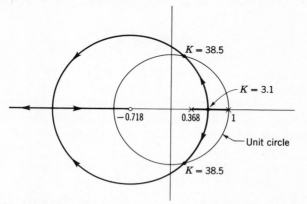

FIG. 13.16. Root-locus plot for $(z - 1)(z - 0.368) + 0.023K(z - 0.718)$.

First-order Hold. The characteristics of a first-order hold are illustrated in Fig. 13.17a. For the region $nT < t < (n + 1)T$ the output

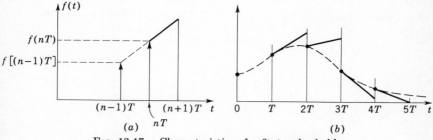

FIG. 13.17. Characteristics of a first-order hold.

is the straight line that is the extrapolation of the two preceding sampled values. That is

$$f(t) = f(nT) + f'(nT)(t - nT) \qquad nT < t < (n + 1)T$$

where the slope $f'(nT)$ is

$$f'(nT) = \frac{f(nT) - f[(n - 1)T]}{T}$$

The behavior of a first-order hold is illustrated in Fig. 13.17b. The dashed curve is the continuous function $f(t)$. The output of the first-order hold is the series of straight-line segments. For a first-order hold the Laplace transform is

$$\left(\frac{1}{s} + \frac{1}{Ts^2}\right)(1 - e^{-Ts})$$

The entire class of higher-order hold circuits is revealed by writing the power-series approximation for $f(t)$ between the sampling instants $nT < t < (n+1)T$. Thus

$$f(t) = f(nT) + f'(nT)(t - nT) + \frac{f''(nT)}{2!}(t - nT) + \cdots \quad (13.57)$$

A zero-order hold approximates $f(t)$ by the first term, a first-order hold approximates $f(t)$ by the first two terms, a second-order hold approximates $f(t)$ by the first three terms, etc. Because of practical considerations, first-order and higher-order holds are seldom used. By far, the zero-order hold is the most commonly used circuit.

Exponential Hold. One of the simplest filters is the exponential hold. The transfer function for an exponential hold is

$$G(s) = \frac{T}{1 + Ts} \quad (13.58)$$

Many components have this transfer function, and thus may be used as exponential hold filters. The output from an exponential hold is an exponential decay between the sampling periods as is illustrated in Fig. 13.18. At each sampling instant, there is a step change or discontinuity

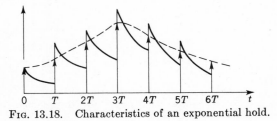

Fig. 13.18.   Characteristics of an exponential hold.

between successive exponential decays. The amount of the step change at each sampling instant is equal to the value (area) of the impulse at the particular sampling instant.

13.8 Frequency Spectrum. The continuous signal $f(t)$ and the impulse approximation $f^*(t)$ shown in Fig. 13.1 appear to be similar. However, the frequency characteristics of these signals are quite different. An investigation of the frequency spectrum will thus be seen to yield some interesting, basic features of sampled-data systems.

The exponential form of the Fourier series for a periodic function is

$$f(t) = \frac{1}{T} \sum_{n=-\infty}^{\infty} C_n e^{jn\omega_0 t}$$

where

$$C_n = \int_{-T/2}^{T/2} f(t) e^{-jn\omega_0 t}\, dt$$

and

$$\omega_0 = \frac{2\pi}{T}$$

For the case in which $f(t) = u_1(t)$ is a unit impulse, then $C_n = 1$. Thus, the Fourier series representation for the train of impulses which occur every T seconds as shown in Fig. 13.19 is

$$i(t) = \frac{1}{T} \sum_{n=-\infty}^{\infty} e^{jn\omega_0 t}$$

where $i(t)$ is a train of unit impulses. The sampled signal $f^*(t)$ may be

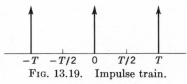

$$-T \quad -T/2 \quad 0 \quad T/2 \quad T$$
FIG. 13.19. Impulse train.

expressed in the form

$$f^*(t) = f(t)i(t) = f(t)\frac{1}{T} \sum_{n=-\infty}^{\infty} e^{jn\omega_s t} \tag{13.59}$$

where $\omega_s = \omega_0 = 2\pi/T$ is the sampling rate. Taking the Laplace transform gives

$$F^*(s) = \int_0^\infty f^*(t) e^{-st}\, dt = \frac{1}{T} \sum_{n=-\infty}^{\infty} \int_0^\infty f(t) e^{-(s-jn\omega_s)t}\, dt$$

$$= \frac{1}{T} \sum_{n=-\infty}^{\infty} F(s - jn\omega_s) = \frac{1}{T} \sum_{n=-\infty}^{\infty} F(s + jn\omega_s) \tag{13.60}$$

Because of the infinite summation, the sign in the preceding result may be plus or minus. Equation (13.60) is a very important result. It shows that $F^*(s)$ is a periodic reproduction of $F(s)$. In Fig. 13.20a is shown an amplitude spectrum $|F(j\omega)|$ which is bandwidth limited (that is, $-\omega_1 < \omega < \omega_2$). The amplitude spectrum $|F^*(j\omega)|$ shown in Fig.

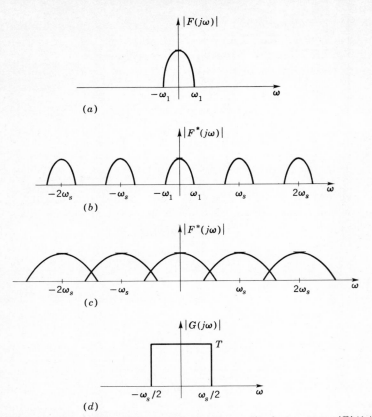

Fig. 13.20. (a) Amplitude spectrum $|F(j\omega)|$; (b) amplitude spectrum $|F^*(j\omega)|$; (c) amplitude spectrum when $\omega_1 > \omega_s/2$; (d) frequency characteristics of an ideal filter.

13.20b is seen to be a periodic representation of $(1/T)|F(j\omega)|$. If $\omega_1 > \omega_s/2$, then overlapping occurs as indicated in Fig. 13.20c. For this case, the original signal cannot be recovered exactly from the sampled signal. The sampling theorem states that if $f(t)$ is bandwidth limited, then $f(t)$ can be reconstructed exactly from $f^*(t)$ when the sampling frequency is $\omega_s \geq 2\omega_1$.

If the signal in Fig. 13.20b is multiplied by the function shown in Fig. 13.20d, then the original function is recovered. Thus, Fig. 13.20d represents the frequency characteristics for an ideal filter.

In Fig. 13.21a is shown a schematic diagram $G(s)$ of the ideal filter. The response of this ideal filter to a unit impulse is

$$g(t) = \mathcal{L}^{-1}[G(s)] = \frac{1}{2\pi j} \int_{\sigma-j\infty}^{\sigma+j\infty} G(s)e^{st} \, ds$$

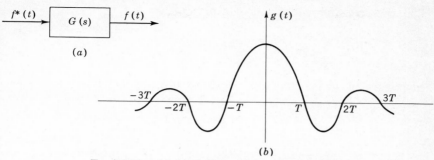

FIG. 13.21. (a) Ideal filter; (b) impulse response.

Making the change of variable $s = j\omega$ gives

$$g(t) = \frac{1}{2\pi} \int_{-\infty}^{\infty} G(j\omega)e^{j\omega t}\, d\omega = \frac{1}{2\pi} \int_{-\omega_s/2}^{\omega_s/2} Te^{j\omega t}\, dt$$

$$= \frac{T}{\pi t}\left(\frac{e^{j\omega_s t/2} - e^{-j\omega_s t/2}}{2j}\right)$$

$$= \frac{\sin (\omega_s t/2)}{\omega_s t/2} = \frac{\sin (\pi t/T)}{\pi t/T}$$

A plot of this impulse response is shown in Fig. 13.21b. It is to be noted that there is an output for $t < 0$, but the unit impulse does not occur until $t = 0$. Such a filter which responds before it is excited is not physically realizable. However, the preceding analysis can be used as a basis for an analytical procedure for recovering $f(t)$ from the sampled signal $f^*(t)$. From Fig. 13.21a, it follows that $F(s) = F^*(s)G(s)$, thus

$$f(t) = \mathcal{L}^{-1}[F(s)] = \mathcal{L}^{-1}[F^*(s)G(s)]$$

Application of the convolution integral gives

$$f(t) = \int_{-\infty}^{\infty} f^*(\tau)g(t - \tau)\, d\tau$$

$$= \int_{-\infty}^{\infty} \sum_{n=-\infty}^{\infty} f(nT)u_1(\tau - nT)g(t - \tau)\, d\tau$$

$$= \sum_{n=-\infty}^{\infty} f(nT) \int_{-\infty}^{\infty} g(t - \tau)u_1(\tau - nT)\, d\tau$$

The unit impulse $u_1(\tau - nT)$ is zero everywhere except at time $\tau = nT$ when the impulse occurs. Thus, the preceding limits of integration may be changed to $nT - \epsilon$ and $nT + \epsilon$. During this brief interval, the function $g(t - \tau) = g(t - nT)$ may be regarded as remaining constant.

Thus, the preceding equation becomes

$$f(t) = \sum_{n=-\infty}^{\infty} f(nT)g(t - nT) \int_{nT-\epsilon}^{nT+\epsilon} u_1(t - nT)\, dt$$

The integral of the unit impulse is equal to its area which is unity. Hence

$$f(t) = \sum_{n=-\infty}^{\infty} f(nT)g(t - nT) = f(0)g(t) + f(T)g(t - T) + \cdots \quad (13.61)$$

The geometric interpretation of Eq. (13.61) is illustrated in Fig. 13.22. The first term, $f(0)g(t)$, is shown in Fig. 13.22a, the second term $f(T)g(t - T)$ is shown in Fig. 13.22b, etc. Adding all these curves yields the original signal $f(t)$.

It is interesting to compare the frequency characteristics of the commonly used zero-order hold and the exponential hold to that of the ideal

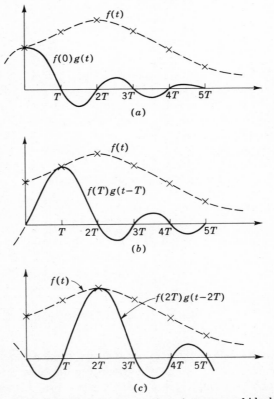

FIG. 13.22. Geometric interpretation of response of ideal filter.

filter shown in Fig. 13.20*d*. Replacing *s* by *jω* in the transfer function for a zero-order hold, Eq. (13.51) gives

$$G(j\omega) = \frac{1 - e^{-j\omega T}}{j\omega} = \frac{e^{-j\omega T/2}(e^{j\omega T/2} - e^{-j\omega T/2})}{j\omega}$$

$$= Te^{-j\omega T/2} \frac{\sin(\omega T/2)}{\omega T/2} \tag{13.62}$$

A plot of $|G(j\omega)|$ is shown in Fig. 13.23*a*. Similarly, for an exponential hold, it follows from Eq. (13.58) that

$$G(j\omega) = \frac{T}{1 + jT\omega} \tag{13.63}$$

A typical plot of $|G(j\omega)|$ is shown in Fig. 13.23*b*. This is referred to as a low-pass filter in that it passes low frequencies with little change whereas

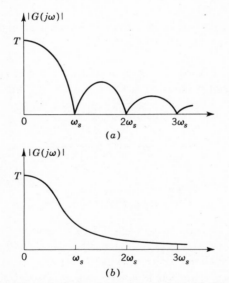

FIG. 13.23. Frequency characteristics of (*a*) a zero-order hold; (*b*) an exponential hold.

high frequencies are greatly attenuated. Many components in control systems are low-pass elements. When such elements follow the sampler, it is not necessary to use a filter. However, adding a filter usually improves the performance.

In summary, the ideal filter described in this section can recover $f(t)$ exactly only if $f(t)$ is bandwidth limited and if $\omega_s \geq 2\omega_1$. In the next section, techniques for reconstructing $f(t)$ in a pointwise manner are described. These methods do not require that $f(t)$ be bandwidth limited.

13.9 Response between Sampling Instants. Two different time functions which have the same sampled values are illustrated in Fig. 13.24.

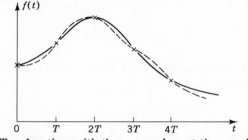

Fig. 13.24. Two functions with the same values at the sampling instants.

The inverse z transform $Z^{-1}[F(z)] = f^*(t)$ yields the value of the function at the sampling instants. Two methods for determining the behavior between sampling instants are Linvill's[1-2] synthetic-sampler method and Barker's[3] modified z-transform method.

Synthetic-sampler Method. The dotted box in Fig. 13.25 represents a fictitious, or synthetic, sampler which is inserted in series with the actual

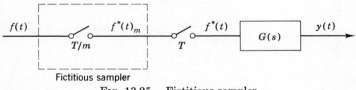

Fictitious sampler

Fig. 13.25. Fictitious sampler.

sampler. The sampling rate of the fictitious sampler is m times that of the actual sampler ($m = 2, 3, \ldots$). The corresponding period is T/m. At submultiples of the sampling period T/m, when the fictitious sampler is closed, the actual sampler is open. Thus, the fictitious sampler does not affect the operation of the system. The fictitious sampler does not actually exist, but is merely employed as an aid for understanding the following analysis.

From Eq. (13.26) the continuous output $y(t)$ is

$$y(t) = \sum_{n=0}^{\infty} f(nT)g(t - nT)$$

---

[1] Linvill, *op. cit.*

[2] W. K. Linvill and R. W. Sittler, *IRE Convention Record*, (1), 99–104 (1953).

[3] R. H. Barker, The Pulse Transfer Function and Its Application to Sampling Servo Systems, *Proc. IEEE*, **99**: (4), 302–317 (December, 1952).

Submultiples of the sampling period are represented by the term kT/m where $k = 0, 1, 2, \ldots$. For example, if $m = 3$, the successive intervals kT/m are 0, $T/3$, $2T/3$, T, $4T/3$, $\ldots$. The value of the output at the submultiple intervals is obtained by letting $t = kT/m$ in the preceding equation.

$$y\left(\frac{kT}{m}\right) = \sum_{n=0}^{\infty} f(nT)g\left(\frac{kT}{m} - nT\right) \tag{13.64}$$

The output at the submultiple sampling instants $y(kT/m) = y^*(t)_m$ may also be expressed as an impulse train. That is,

$$y^*(t)_m = \sum_{k=0}^{\infty} y\left(\frac{kT}{m}\right) u_1\left(t - \frac{kT}{m}\right)$$

The Laplace transform is

$$Y^*(s)_m = \sum_{k=0}^{\infty} y\left(\frac{kT}{m}\right) e^{-kTs/m}$$

The corresponding z transform is

$$Y(z)_m = \sum_{k=0}^{\infty} y\left(\frac{kT}{m}\right) z^{-k/m} \tag{13.65}$$

Substituting $y(kT/m)$ from Eq. (13.64) into the preceding expression gives

$$Y(z)_m = \sum_{k=0}^{\infty} \sum_{n=0}^{\infty} f(nT)g\left[\left(\frac{k}{m} - n\right)T\right] z^{-k/m}$$

$$= \sum_{k=0}^{\infty} \sum_{n=0}^{\infty} f(nT)z^{-n}g\left[\left(\frac{k}{m} - n\right)T\right] z^{-(k/m-n)} \tag{13.66}$$

Consider the expansion of a typical term in which $m = 2$ and $n = 3$,

$$\sum_{k=0}^{\infty} f(3T)z^{-3}g\left[\left(\frac{k}{2} - 3\right)T\right] z^{-(k/2-3)}$$

$$= f(3T)z^{-3}\left[g(0)z^0 + g\left(\frac{T}{2}\right)z^{-\frac{1}{2}} + g(T)z^{-1} + g\left(\frac{3T}{2}\right)z^{-\frac{3}{2}} + \cdots\right]$$

$$= f(3T)z^{-3}\sum_{l=0}^{\infty} g\left(\frac{lT}{m}\right)z^{-l/m}$$

For a physically realizable system the impulse response $g(t)$ is zero for negative time. Thus, the first term to appear in brackets is for $k = 6$ in which case $g[(k/2 - 3)T] = g(0)$. From the preceding result, the general form of Eq. (13.66) is

$$Y(z)_m = \sum_{n=0}^{\infty} f(nT)z^{-n} \sum_{l=0}^{\infty} g\left(\frac{lT}{m}\right)z^{-l/m}$$
$$= F(z)G(z)_m \tag{13.67}$$

where
$$G(z)_m = [G(z)]_{\substack{z=z^{1/m} \\ T=T/m}}$$

Thus, $G(z)_m$ is obtained by substituting $z^{1/m}$ for z and T/m for T in $G(z)$. The result given by Eq. (13.67) may also be obtained by letting $k/m -$ $n = l/m$ where $l = 0, 1, 2, \ldots$, in Eq. (13.66).

The equation for $C(z)_m$ for the system of Fig. 13.26 is obtained as

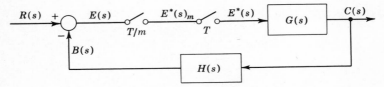

FIG. 13.26. Sampled-data system with a fictitious sampler.

follows

$$C(z)_m = E(z)G(z)_m \tag{13.68}$$
$$E(s) = R(s) - E^*(s)G(s)H(s)$$

Starring gives

$$E^*(s) = R^*(s) - E^*(s)GH^*(s)$$

Thus,

$$E(z) = R(z) - E(z)GH(z)$$

Solving this last equation for $E(z)$ and then substituting $E(z)$ into the first equation gives the desired result.

$$C(z)_m = \frac{G(z)_m}{1 + HG(z)} R(z) \tag{13.69}$$

To illustrate the preceding concepts, let it be desired to determine the response midway between the sampling instants for the system of Fig. 13.6 to a unit step-function excitation. For $K = 1$ and $T = \frac{1}{4}$, the response at the sampling instants is shown in Fig. 13.9.

For this system $HG(z) = G(z)$ is given by Eq. (13.39). Replacing T

by $T/m = T/2$ and z by $z^{1/m} = z^{1/2}$ gives

$$G(z)_m = \frac{z^{1/2}(1 - e^{-2T})K/4}{(z^{1/2} - 1)(z^{1/2} - e^{-2T})}$$

For $K = 1$ and $T = \frac{1}{4}$, this becomes

$$G(z)_m = \frac{0.098z^{1/2}}{(z^{1/2} - 1)(z^{1/2} - 0.607)}$$

For $K = 1$ and $T = \frac{1}{4}$, the function $G(z)$ is given by Eq. (13.44). Substitution of these results into Eq. (13.69) gives

$$C(z)_m = \frac{0.098z^{1/2}}{(z^{1/2} - 1)(z^{1/2} - 0.607)} \frac{(z - 1)(z - 0.368)}{[(z - 1)(z - 0.368) + 0.158z]} R(z)$$

To eliminate fractional powers of z, let $w = z^{1/2}$. Thus,

$$C(w)_m = \frac{0.098w(w^4 - 1.368w^2 + 0.368)}{(w - 1)(w - 0.607)(w^4 - 1.21w^2 + 0.368)} R(w)$$

Cross-multiplying yields

$$(w^6 - 1.61w^5 - 0.60w^4 + 1.91w^3 - 0.37w^2 - 0.59w + 0.22)C(w)_m$$
$$= (0.098w^5 - 1.34w^3 + 0.036w)R(w) \quad (13.70)$$

The significance of replacing $z^{1/2}$ by w is seen by noting that because

$$C(z_m) = c(0) + c\left(\frac{T}{2}\right)z^{-1/2} + c(T)z^{-1} + c\left(\frac{3T}{2}\right)z^{-3/2} + c(2T)z^{-2} + \cdots$$

then

$$C(w)_m = c(0) + c\left(\frac{T}{2}\right)w^{-1} + c(T)w^{-2} + c\left(\frac{3T}{2}\right)w^{-3} + c(2T)w^{-4} + \cdots$$

Thus, the w sampling instants are the desired submultiple sampling instants.

The difference equation associated with Eq. (13.70) is

$$C(k) = 1.61c(k - 1) + 0.60c(k - 2) - 1.91c(k - 3) + 0.37c(k - 4)$$
$$+ 0.59c(k - 5) - 0.22c(k - 6) = 0.098r(k - 1)$$
$$- 0.134r(k - 3) + 0.036r(k - 5) \quad (13.71)$$

Because

$$R(z) = r(0) + r(T)z^{-1} + r(2T)z^{-2} + \cdots$$

then replacing z^{-1} by w^{-2} gives

$$R(w) = r(0) + 0w^{-1} + r(T)w^{-2} + 0w^{-3} + r(2T)w^{-4} + \cdots$$

Thus, $r = 0$ at the 1, 3, 5, . . . sampling instants of w.

Application of Eq. (13.70) to obtain the values at the submultiple sampling instants gives

$$c(0) = 0$$
$$c(1) = 0.098r(1) = 0.098$$
$$c(2) = 1.61c(1) = 0.158$$
$$c(3) = 1.61c(2) + 0.60c(1) + 0.098r(2) - 1.34r(0) = 0.277$$
$$c(4) = 1.61c(3) + 0.60c(2) - 1.91c(1) = 0.350$$
$$\cdot \ \cdot$$

This inverse could also have been obtained by the long-division method. For $R(z) = z/(z-1)$, then $R(w) = w^2/(w^2-1)$. Thus, substituting this value of $R(w)$ into Eq. (13.70), and then dividing the numerator of $C(w)_m$ by the denominator yields the desired values as the coefficients of the answer.

Modified z Transform.   Multiplication of the Laplace transform of a function by $e^{-\Delta Ts}$ has the effect of delaying the signal by a time ΔT. Inserting a time delay $0 < \Delta < 1$ enables one to obtain the value of the function between sampling periods.   As is illustrated in Fig. 13.27, the

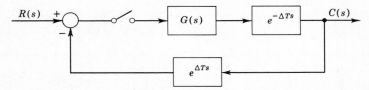

FIG. 13.27.   Sampled-data system with time delay $e^{-\Delta Ts}$ in feedforward path and time advance $e^{\Delta Ts}$ in feedback path.

time delay $e^{-\Delta Ts}$ in the forward loop delays the output by a time ΔT.   It is necessary to put a time advance $e^{\Delta Ts}$ in the feedback loop so that the feedback signal will be unaffected by the time delay.

The Laplace transform for a delayed unit step function $u(t - \Delta T)$ which is sampled is

$$F^*(s) = 0 + e^{-Ts} + e^{-2Ts} + \cdots \qquad (13.72)$$

The corresponding z transform, which is called the modified z transform, is

$$F(z) = 0 + z^{-1} + z^{-2} + \cdots = \frac{1}{z-1} \qquad (13.73)$$

Similarly, the Laplace transform for a sampled delayed exponential, $e^{-a(t-\Delta T)}$, is

$$F^*(\Delta,s) = \sum_{n=0}^{\infty} e^{-a(nT-\Delta T)}e^{-nTs} = 0 + e^{-a(1-\Delta)T}e^{-Ts} + e^{-a(2-\Delta)T}e^{-2Ts} + \cdots$$

By letting $m = 1 - \Delta$, then

$$F^*(m,s) = 0 + e^{-amT}e^{-Ts} + e^{-a(m+1)T}e^{-2Ts} + \cdots$$

The corresponding modified z transform is

$$F(m,z) = e^{-amT}(z^{-1} + e^{-aT}z^{-2} + e^{-2aT}z^{-3} + \cdots)$$
$$= \frac{e^{-amT}}{z - e^{-aT}} \tag{13.74}$$

The modified z transforms for some common functions are given in Table 13.2. An extensive list of modified z transforms is given in Barker's original paper.

TABLE 13.2

Time function $f(t)$	Laplace transform $F(s)$	Modified z transform $F(m,z)$
$u(t)$	$\dfrac{1}{s}$	$\dfrac{1}{z - 1}$
e^{-at}	$\dfrac{1}{s + a}$	$\dfrac{e^{-amT}}{z - e^{-aT}}$
t	$\dfrac{1}{s^2}$	$\dfrac{mT}{z - 1} + \dfrac{T}{(z - 1)^2}$
te^{-at}	$\dfrac{1}{(s + a)^2}$	$Te^{-amT}\left[\dfrac{m}{z - e^{-aT}} + \dfrac{e^{-aT}}{(z - e^{-aT})^2}\right]$

For the system of Fig. 13.27, it follows that

$$C(m,s) = E^*(s)G(m,s)$$
$$E(s) = R(s) - E^*(s)G(s)$$

Starring each of these relationships and then obtaining the corresponding z transforms gives

$$C(m,z) = E(z)G(m,z)$$
$$E(z) = R(z) - E(z)G(z)$$

Eliminating $E(z)$ yields the output relationship

$$C(m,z) = \frac{G(m,z)}{1 + G(z)} R(z) \tag{13.75}$$

Inverting $C(m,z)$ gives $c(m,nT)$ whence the value of the output at various points between the sampling instants is obtained.

With both the synthetic sampler and modified z-transform method, the computational effort can become quite extensive for the analysis of more complex systems. Thus, it is usually necessary to use a digital computer to obtain the inverse z transforms.

Problems

13.1 Determine the z transform of each of the following functions:

(a) $f(t) = 1 - e^{-at}$ (b) $f(t) = a^{t/T}$

(c) $f(t) = t^2$

13.2 Determine the z transform corresponding to each of the following Laplace transforms:

(a) $F(s) = \dfrac{a}{s(s + a)}$ (b) $F(s) = \dfrac{\omega}{s^2 + \omega^2}$

(c) $F(s) = \dfrac{1}{(s + a)^2}$

13.3 Determine the z transform of each of the following functions:

(a) $f(t) = te^{at}$ (b) $f(t) = \sin \omega t$

(c) $f(t) = e^{at} \sin \omega t$

Verify the resulting answers by inverting to obtain the original time functions.

13.4 Determine the z transform of each of the following functions:

(a) $\sinh \omega t$ (b) $\cosh \omega t$

Verify the resulting answers by inverting to obtain the original time functions.

13.5 Use block-diagram algebra to determine $C(z)$ for each of the systems shown in Fig. P13.5.

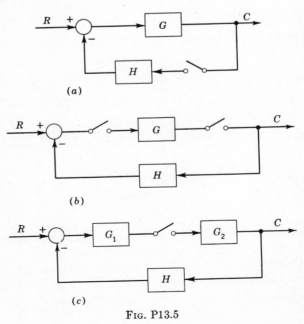

(a)

(b)

(c)

Fig. P13.5

13.6 In Fig. P13.6 is shown a sampled-data system whose sampling rate is $T = 1$.

(a) Apply Routh's criterion to determine whether or not the system becomes unstable.

(b) Construct the root-locus plot for the system.

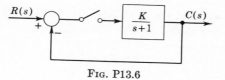

FIG. P13.6

13.7 Determine the unit step-function response for the system of Prob. 13.6 for the case in which $K = 1$.

13.8 For the system shown in Fig. 13.6 in the text, it is desired to use a sampling rate $T = 1$ rather than $T = \frac{1}{4}$. Determine the value of K at which the system becomes unstable.

13.9 In Fig. 13.7 is shown the root-locus plot for the system of Fig. 13.6 when $T = \frac{1}{4}$. Determine the unit step-function response when $K = 8.7$.

13.10 Construct the Nyquist plot for the system of Prob. 13.6 for the case in which $K = 1$. What is the resulting gain margin?

13.11 In Fig. P13.11 is shown a sampled-data system whose sampling rate is $T = 1$.

(a) Apply Routh's criterion to determine whether or not the system becomes unstable.

(b) Construct the root-locus plot for the system.

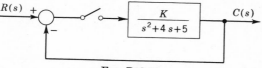

FIG. P13.11

13.12 Construct the Nyquist plot and then determine the gain margin for the system of Prob. 13.11 for the case in which $K = 5$.

13.13 For the system shown in Fig. P13.11, it is desired to use a sampling rate $T = 2$. Determine the value of K at which the system becomes unstable.

13.14 The system shown in Fig. P13.14 is the same as that shown in Fig. P13.6 except that a zero-order hold has been added. Determine the value of the gain K at which the system with the zero-order hold becomes unstable.

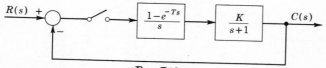

FIG. P13.14

13.15 Same as Prob. 13.14 except use an exponential hold rather than a zero-order hold.

13.16 Show that starring the equation $Y(s) = G(s)F^*(s)$ gives

$$Y^*(s) = [G(s)F^*(s)]^* = \sum_{n=-\infty}^{\infty} [G(s + jn\omega_s) \sum_{k=-\infty}^{\infty} F(s + jk\omega_s + jn\omega_s)]$$

Replace $n + k$ by l and thus proceed to show that $Y^*(s) = G^*(s)F^*(s)$.

13.17 For the system shown in Fig. P13.17 the sampling period is $T = 1$. Determine the exact response to a unit step function during each of the first three sampling intervals. Sketch this response and compare it to the response of the continuous system (i.e., without the sampler).

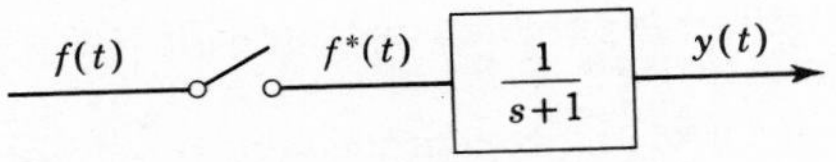

$$f(t) \quad \diagup \quad f^*(t) \quad \boxed{\dfrac{1}{s+1}} \quad y(t)$$

FIG. P13.17

13.18 Use the synthetic-sampler method to determine the response midway between the sampling instants for the system of Prob. 13.17.

13.19 Use the modified z-transform method to determine the response midway between the sampling instants for the system of Prob. 13.17.

14

Statistical methods and adaptive control systems

An adaptive control system is one in which the controller adapts itself, or changes, in accordance with changes in the process to be controlled.

For example, the lift and drag coefficients of high-speed aircraft and missiles at high altitudes are considerably different from the corresponding coefficients at low altitudes. The flight dynamics vary so greatly that a flight controller which yields good behavior at low altitudes could result in unstable flight control at high altitudes. The characteristics of most processes to be controlled vary so little or so slowly that a fixed controller suffices to yield good behavior over the entire range of operation. However, although the number of applications requiring adaptive controllers is relatively few, their importance is immense. In order to appreciate and understand the techniques used in the design of adaptive control systems, it is necessary to be familiar with the basic principles of statistics.

14.1 Discrete Random Variables. When the outcome of an event can take on only a finite number of specific values, then the random variable x is called a discrete random variable. Examples of discrete random variables include events, or experiments, associated with dice, cards, or number wheels in which there are a finite number of specific outcomes.

Suppose that a particular event, or experiment, has n possible outcomes $x_1, x_2, \ldots, x_n$. After N experiments have been conducted, it is found that n_1 represents the number of times that x_1 has been the outcome, n_2 the number of times that x_2 has resulted, etc. The probability $P(x_i)$ of the occurrence of the event x_i is

$$P(x_i) = \lim_{N \to \infty} \frac{n_i}{N} \tag{14.1}$$

where N the total number of samples is

$$N = n_1 + n_2 + \cdots + n_i + \cdots + n_n = \sum_{i=1}^{n} n_i$$

In Fig. 14.1 is shown a number wheel.   After a spin of the arrow, the three possible outcomes are $x_1 = 1$, $x_2 = 2$, and $x_3 = 3$.   In Fig. 14.2a

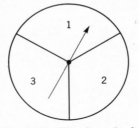

Fig. 14.1.   Number wheel.

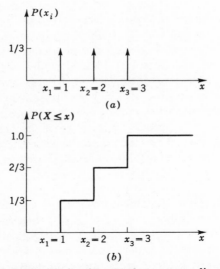

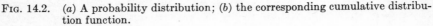

Fig. 14.2.   (a) A probability distribution; (b) the corresponding cumulative distribution function.

is shown the probability distribution plot for this experiment.   The horizontal axis shows each event and the vertical axis shows the probability of occurrence of each event.

The probability that the outcome X of an event will be less than or equal to a particular value x is the summation of the probabilities of all the events for which the outcome X is less than or equal to x.   For example, for $x = 2.5$, the probability that $X \leq x$ is

$$P(X \leq x) = P(x_1) + P(x_2) = \frac{1}{3} + \frac{1}{3} = \frac{2}{3}$$

The term $P(X \leq x)$ is called the cumulative distribution function. In Fig. 14.2b is shown the cumulative distribution function corresponding to Fig. 14.2a. In this development, the anticipated (unknown) outcome of an event is indicated by X whereas a particular value or specific outcome is indicated by x.

In Fig. 14.3a is shown a more general probability distribution plot. The probabilities of the events are $P(x_1) = 0.3$, $P(x_2) = 0.2$, $P(x_3) = 0.4$, and $P(x_4) = 0.1$.

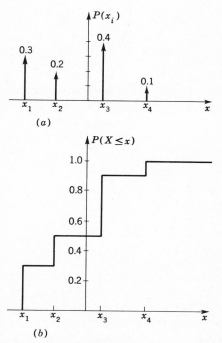

FIG. 14.3. (a) A general probability distribution; (b) the corresponding cumulative distribution function.

In Fig. 14.3b is shown the cumulative distribution function corresponding to Fig. 14.3a. For $x_3 \leq x < x_4$, the probability that $X \leq x$ is

$$P(X \leq x) = P(x_1) + P(x_2) + P(x_3)$$

In general, it follows that

$$P(X \leq x) = P(x_1) + P(x_2) + \cdots + P(x_i) = \sum_{i=1}^{x_i \leq x} P(x_i) \quad (14.2)$$

where the summation is taken over all events for which $x_i \leq x$.

The average value x_{av} is also referred to as the expected value $E(x)$.

The average, or expected, value is

$$x_{av} = E(x) = \frac{n_1 x_1 + n_2 x_2 + \cdots + n_n x_n}{N}$$

$$= x_1 P(x_1) + x_2 P(x_2) + \cdots + x_n P(x_n) = \sum_{i=1}^{n} x_i P(x_i) \quad (14.3)$$

The average value of the sum of the squares of x is the expected value $E(x^2)$ of the average of the summation of the squares of x. That is

$$x_{av}^2 = E(x^2) = \frac{n_1 x_1^2 + n_2 x_2^2 + \cdots + n_n x_n^2}{N}$$

$$= \sum_{i=1}^{n} x_i^2 \frac{n_i}{N} = \sum_{i=1}^{n} x_i^2 P(x_i) \quad (14.4)$$

Joint Probability. In Fig. 14.4 is shown a second number wheel in which there are two equally likely outcomes $y_1 = 1$ and $y_2 = 2$. By

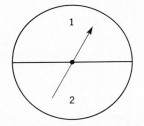

FIG. 14.4.   Number wheel.

joint probability is meant the probability of two events occurring. The probability of getting a particular x_i by spinning the wheel in Fig. 14.1 is $\frac{1}{3}$, and the probability of a particular y_j by spinning the wheel in Fig. 14.4 is $\frac{1}{2}$. Thus, for any $i = 1, 2,$ or 3 and for any $j = 1$ or 2, the joint probability is

$$P(x_i, y_j) = P(x_i)P(y_j) = \frac{1}{6}$$

The joint probability distribution plot for these two events is shown in Fig. 14.5a. The intersection of a particular x_i and y_j coordinate specifies the particular event. The vertical axis denotes the probability of these events occurring jointly.

In Fig. 14.5b is shown the joint cumulative distribution function corresponding to Fig. 14.5a. The vertical axis $P(X \leq x, Y \leq y)$ indicates the probability that the outcome X is less than or equal to a particular value x, and also that the outcome Y is less than or equal to a specific value y. To illustrate the meaning of the joint cumulative distribution function, consider the region in which $2 \leq x < 3$ and $1 \leq y < 2$. There are two events ($x_1 = 1$ and $x_2 = 2$) such that $X \leq x$. There is but one

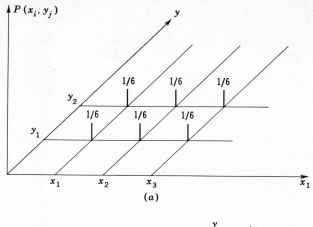

(a)

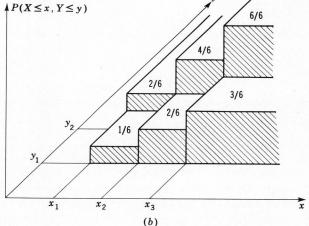

(b)

FIG. 14.5.   (a) A joint probability distribution; (b) the corresponding joint cumulative distribution function.

event ($y_1 = 1$) such that $Y \leq y$. There are two joint events (x_1y_1 and x_2y_1) such that $X \leq x$ and $Y \leq y$; thus

$$P(X \leq x, \, Y \leq y) = P(x_1,y_1) + P(x_2,y_1) = \tfrac{1}{6} + \tfrac{1}{6} = \tfrac{1}{3}$$

Next consider the region for which $2 \leq x < 3$ and $2 \leq y < \infty$. As before, events x_1 and x_2 satisfy the $X \leq x$ condition. The events $y_1 = 1$ and $y_2 = 2$ satisfy the $Y \leq y$ condition. There are four joint events which satisfy both conditions: x_1y_1, x_2y_1, x_1y_2, and x_2y_2. Thus

$$P(X \leq x, \, Y \leq y) = P(x_1,y_1) + P(x_2,y_1) + P(x_1,y_2) + P(x_2,y_2) = \tfrac{4}{6}$$

In general, the joint cumulative distribution function is seen to be the summation of the probabilities of all possible events in which $x_i \leq x$ and

$y_j \leq y$. That is,

$$P(X \leq x, Y \leq y) = [P(x_1,y_1) + P(x_2,y_1) + \cdots + P(x_i,y_1)]$$
$$+ [P(x_1,y_2) + P(x_2,y_2) + \cdots + P(x_i,y_2)]$$
$$+ \cdots + [P(x_1,y_j) + P(x_2,y_j) + \cdots$$
$$+ P(x_i,y_j)]$$

$$= \sum_{j=1}^{y_i \leq y} \sum_{i=1}^{x_i \leq x} P(x_i,y_j) \tag{14.5}$$

The average, or expected, value of the product xy is the summation of all the xy products divided by the total number of samples. Thus

$$xy_{\text{av}} = E(xy)$$
$$= \frac{n_{11}x_1y_1 + n_{12}x_1y_2 + n_{21}x_2y_1 + n_{22}x_2y_2 + n_{31}x_3y_1 + n_{32}x_3y_2}{N}$$
$$= \sum_{j=1}^{2} \sum_{i=1}^{3} x_iy_j \frac{n_{ij}}{N}$$

where n_{ij} is the number of occurrences of the x_iy_j event and N is the total number of events. The probability of the x_iy_j event occurring is

$$P(x_i,y_j) = \lim_{N \to \infty} \frac{n_{ij}}{N}$$

In general, if y has m possible states and x has n possible states, then

$$xy_{\text{av}} = E(xy) = \sum_{j=1}^{m} \sum_{i=1}^{n} x_iy_jP(x_i,y_j) \tag{14.6}$$

14.2 Continuous Random Variables. When the outcome of an event, or experiment, can take on any value over a continuum, then x is referred to as a continuous random variable. For example, the output of a component may be a position, or voltage, x, which at any instant of time may assume any value within its range of operation. In Fig. 14.6a is shown the first recording of a continuous random signal $x(t)$. In Fig. 14.6b is shown a second recording of the same signal which was taken at some other time. A third recording which was taken at still some other time is shown in Fig. 14.6c. Each recording of the random signal x is called a sample function. A collection of such sample functions is referred to as an ensemble.

In Fig. 14.7 at $N = 1$ is plotted the value of the first recording at time t_1, at $N = 2$ is plotted the value of the second recording at time t_1, etc. Thus, Fig. 14.7 is a plot of the value of each sample function at time t_1. The horizontal line designates a specific value x. The probability that at some time t_1 the outcome X will be less than or equal to x is

$$P(X \leq x) = \lim_{N \to \infty} \frac{n_1}{N} \tag{14.7}$$

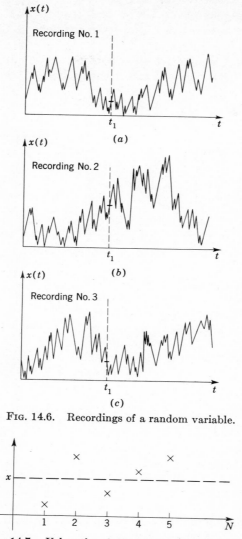

FIG. 14.6.   Recordings of a random variable.

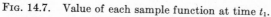

FIG. 14.7.   Value of each sample function at time t_1.

where n_1 is the number of samples for which $X \leq x$ and N is the total number of samples.

The process is said to be stationary if the value of $P(X \leq x)$ does not depend upon the time t_1. That is, Eq. (14.7) yields the same result regardless of the particular value of t_1 used in the measurement. Such a signal, which has the statistical property that $P(X \leq x)$ is independent of time, is called a stationary random signal. The statistical properties of a particular component do not change day by day. Thus, in the testing of control systems one usually encounters stationary random signals.

In Fig. 14.8 is a cumulative distribution function for a continuous random function. The vertical axis is the probability that the outcome

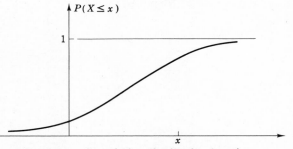

FIG. 14.8. Cumulative distribution function.

X will be less than or equal to a particular value x [that is, $P(X \leq x)$]. The outcome cannot be less than or equal to $-\infty$; hence $P(X \leq -\infty) = 0$. Similarly, the outcome must be less than or equal to $+\infty$, so that $P(X \leq +\infty) = 1$. As is illustrated in Fig. 14.8, all cumulative distribution functions go from 0 at $-\infty$ to 1 at $+\infty$.

In Fig. 14.9 is shown the same cumulative distribution function of Fig. 14.8. The probability that the outcome X is less than or equal to a

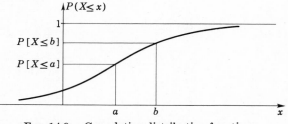

FIG. 14.9. Cumulative distribution function.

particular value a is $P(X \leq a)$. Similarly, the probability that X is less than or equal to b is $P(X \leq b)$. The difference between these two values is the probability that the outcome is greater than a but less than or equal to b. That is,

$$P(a < X \leq b) = P(X \leq b) - P(X \leq a)$$

The right-hand side of the preceding expression is the difference between the ordinates corresponding to a and b in Fig. 14.9.

If $x + \Delta x$ is slightly greater than x, then the probability that the outcome is greater than x but less than or equal to $x + \Delta x$ is

$$P(x < X \le x + \Delta x) = P(X \le x + \Delta x) - P(X \le x)$$

Dividing and multiplying the right-hand side by Δx gives

$$P(x < X \le x + \Delta x) = \left[\frac{P(X \le x + \Delta x) - P(X \le x)}{\Delta x} \right] \Delta x$$

As is illustrated in Fig. 14.10a, the term in brackets is the slope of the

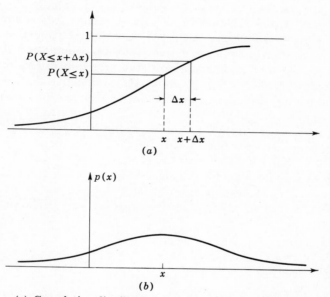

Fig. 14.10. (a) Cumulative distribution function; (b) probability density function.

cumulative distribution function.   That is,

$$\lim_{\Delta x \to 0} \left[\frac{P(X \le x + \Delta x) - P(X \le x)}{\Delta x} \right] = \frac{d}{dx} P(X \le x) = p(x) \quad (14.8)$$

The term $p(x)$ is called the probability density function.   In Fig. 14.10b is shown the probability density function which is the derivative (slope) of the cumulative distribution function shown in Fig. 14.10a.

Integration of $p(x)$ between the limits of a and b shows that

$$\int_a^b p(x)\,dx = \int_a^b \frac{d}{dx} P(X \le x)\,dx = P(X \le b) - P(X \le a)$$
$$= P(a < X \le b) \quad (14.9)$$

Hence, the area under the probability density function from a to b is the difference in ordinates of the cumulative distribution function from a to b. Other interesting properties of the probability density function are

$$\int_{-\infty}^{x} p(x)\, dx = P(X \le x) - P(X \le -\infty) = P(X \le x) \qquad (14.10)$$

$$\int_{-\infty}^{\infty} p(x)\, dx = P(X \le \infty) - P(X \le -\infty) = 1 \qquad (14.11)$$

The second result shows that the total area under the probability density function is always equal to one.

As is illustrated in Fig. 14.3b, the cumulative distribution function for a discrete random variable is a series of step functions. Because the derivative of a step function is an impulse whose area is equal to the change in the step function, it follows that the probability distribution plot shown in Fig. 14.3a is the derivative of the cumulative distribution function shown in Fig. 14.3b. Thus, the probability distribution plot for a discrete variable corresponds to the probability density function for a continuous variable. The cumulative distribution function for a discrete random variable has the same significance as the cumulative distribution function for a continuous random variable.

The probability distribution plot for a discrete variable is shown in Fig. 14.11a. The probability of the x_i event is $P(x_i)$. At the midpoint between each spike (impulse) in Fig. 14.11a a vertical line is dropped to the x axis of Fig. 14.11b. The probability that the discrete variable lies within the Δx interval about x_i is also equal to $P(x_i)$. The shaded pulse

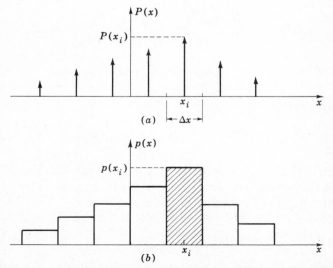

Fig. 14.11. Approximation of probability distribution spikes by pulses.

shown in Fig. 14.11*b* is drawn such that its area $p(x_i)\,\Delta x$ is equal to the probability $P(x_i)$. When the discrete probabilities are close together such that Δx is very small, then the series of pulse functions shown in Fig. 14.11*b* approaches the smooth curve of the probability density function for a continuous variable.

Replacing $P(x_i)$ in Eqs. (14.2), (14.3), and (14.4) by $p(x_i)\,\Delta x$ converts these equations for discrete random variables into the corresponding equations for continuous random variables. That is,

$$P(X \le x) = \sum_{i=1}^{x_i \le x} P(x_i) = \sum_{i=1}^{x_i \le x} p(x_i)\,\Delta x = \int_{-\infty}^{x} p(x)\,dx \qquad (14.12)$$

$$x_{\mathrm{av}} = E(x) = \sum_{i=1}^{n} x_i P(x_i) = \sum_{i=1}^{n} x_i p(x_i)\,\Delta x = \int_{-\infty}^{\infty} x p(x)\,dx \qquad (14.13)$$

$$x_{\mathrm{av}}^{2} = E(x^2) = \sum_{i=1}^{n} x_i^{2} P(x_i) = \sum_{i=1}^{n} x_i^{2} p(x_i)\,\Delta x$$
$$= \int_{-\infty}^{\infty} x^2 p(x)\,dx \qquad (14.14)$$

Joint Probability. In Fig. 14.12*a* is shown a typical spike (impulse) of a joint probability distribution for discrete random variables. The

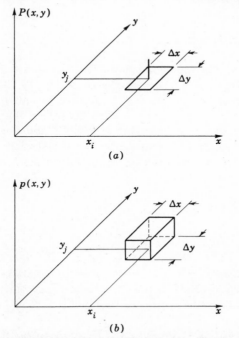

(a)

(b)

Fig. 14.12. Approximation of joint probability distribution spikes by boxes.

probability of the joint event (x_i, y_j) is $P(x_i, y_j)$. The probability that the discrete variables lie within the incremental region $\Delta x \, \Delta y$ is also $P(x_i, y_j)$. The height of the box $p(x_i, y_j)$ shown in Fig. 14.12b is such that its volume $p(x_i, y_j) \, \Delta x \, \Delta y$ is equal to the discrete probability $P(x_i, y_j)$. By proceeding in this manner, the discrete joint probability distribution is converted to box form. The surface formed by the top of the boxes approaches the joint probability density function for continuous variables. Replacing spikes by boxes for the case of two variables is analogous to replacing spikes by pulses in the case of one variable.

The partial derivative with respect to x of the joint cumulative distribution function is the tangent to this surface with y constant. That is

$$\frac{\partial}{\partial x} P(X \le x, \, Y \le y) = \lim_{\Delta x \to 0} \frac{1}{\Delta x} [P(X \le x + \Delta x, \, Y \le y)$$
$$- P(X \le x, \, Y \le y)]$$

The partial of the preceding function with respect to y is

$$\frac{\partial^2 P}{\partial x \, \partial y} = \frac{\partial^2 P}{\partial y \, \partial x}$$
$$= \lim_{\substack{\Delta x \to 0 \\ \Delta y \to 0}} \frac{1}{\Delta x \, \Delta y} \{[P(X \le x + \Delta x, \, Y \le y + \Delta y)$$
$$- P(X \le x + \Delta x, \, Y \le y)]$$
$$- [P(X \le x, \, Y \le y + \Delta y) - P(X \le x, \, Y \le y)]\} \quad (14.15)$$

The first bracket on the right-hand side is the probability that $X \le x + \Delta x$ and that $y < Y \le y + \Delta y$ (see shaded strip of Fig. 14.13a). The second bracket is the probability that $X \le x$ and again that $y < Y \le y + \Delta y$ (see shaded strip of Fig. 14.13b). The difference between these two quantities is the probability that the outcome X and the outcome Y will lie within the incremental area $\Delta x \, \Delta y$ shown shaded in Fig. 14.13c. From Eq. (14.15) it follows that the probability that X and Y lie within the incremental area $\Delta x \, \Delta y$, is

$$P[x < X \le x + \Delta x, \, y < Y \le y + \Delta y] = \frac{\partial^2 P}{\partial x \, \partial y} \Delta x \, \Delta y = p(x,y) \, \Delta x \, \Delta y$$
$$(14.16)$$

The term $\partial^2 P / \partial x \, \partial y$ is called the joint probability density function. It is usually designated as $p(x,y)$. Because $p(x,y) \, \Delta x \, \Delta y$ is the probability that X and Y lie within the incremental region $\Delta x \, \Delta y$, then the probability that the joint outcome (X,Y) lies within a region R is

$$P[(X,Y) \in R] = \int_R \int p(x,y) \, dx \, dy \quad (14.17)$$

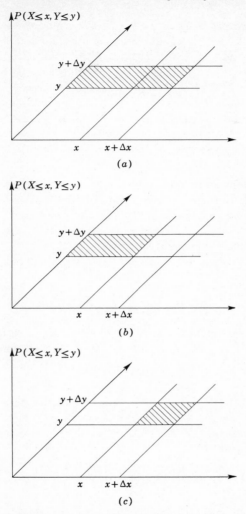

Fig. 14.13.   Geometric interpretation of joint probability density function.

Because the probability of an event that is certain is unity,

$$P[X \leq \infty, \, Y \leq \infty] = \int_{-\infty}^{\infty} \int_{-\infty}^{\infty} p(x,y) \, dx \, dy = 1 \qquad (14.18)$$

Hence, the total volume under the density function is unity.

The similarities between the equations for two discrete random variables and two continuous random variables are seen by replacing $P(x_i, y_j)$

in Eqs. (14.5) and (14.6) by $p(x_i,y_j)\,\Delta x\,\Delta y$.   Thus

$$P[X \le x,\, Y \le y] = \sum_{j=1}^{y_j \le y} \sum_{i=1}^{x_i \le x} P(x_iy_j) = \sum_{j=1}^{y_j \le y} \sum_{i=1}^{x_i \le x} p(x_iy_j)\,\Delta x\,\Delta y$$

$$= \int_{-\infty}^{y} \int_{-\infty}^{x} p(x,y)\,dx\,dy \tag{14.19}$$

$$xy_{\text{av}} = E(x,y) = \sum_{j=1}^{m} \sum_{i=1}^{n} x_iy_jP(x_i,y_j) = \sum_{j=1}^{m} \sum_{i=1}^{n} x_iy_jp(x_i,y_j)\,\Delta x\,\Delta y$$

$$= \int_{-\infty}^{\infty} \int_{-\infty}^{\infty} xyp(x,y)\,dx\,dy \tag{14.20}$$

14.3 Correlation Functions.   The ergodic hypothesis for stationary random signals is that the averages obtained by statistical methods (i.e., ensemble averages) are the same as the time averages.   The ensemble averages, x_{av} and xy_{av}, are given by Eqs. (14.13) and (14.20).   The corresponding time averages are

$$x_{\text{av}} = \lim_{T \to \infty} \frac{1}{2T} \int_{-T}^{T} x(t)\,dt \tag{14.21}$$

$$xy_{\text{av}} = \lim_{T \to \infty} \frac{1}{2T} \int_{-T}^{T} x(t)y(t)\,dt \tag{14.22}$$

In Fig. 14.14 is shown a recording of the sample signal.   The probability that the outcome X_1 at time t_1 is between x_1 and $x_1 + \Delta x_1$ and

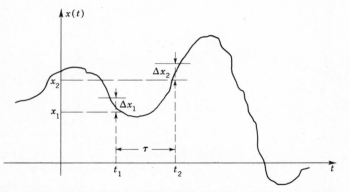

Fig. 14.14.   A sampled signal in which $x(t)$ lies within Δx_1 and Δx_2.

that the outcome X_2 at time t_2 is between x_2 and $x_2 + \Delta x_2$ is obtained directly from Eq. (14.16).   That is,

$$P(x_1 < X_1 \le x_1 + \Delta x_1,\, x_2 < X_2 \le x_2 + \Delta x_2) = p(x_1,x_2)\,\Delta x_1\,\Delta x_2$$

For a stationary process, this result is independent of the starting time t_1. Hence, the probability density $p(x_1,x_2)$ is seen to be a function of the time difference $t_2 - t_1 = \tau$. From Eq. (14.20), it follows that the average value of the product is

$$x_1x_{2\mathrm{av}} = E(x_1,x_2) = \int_{-\infty}^{\infty} \int_{-\infty}^{\infty} x_1x_2p(x_1,x_2)\,dx_1\,dx_2 = \phi_{xx}(\tau) \quad (14.23)$$

This ensemble average is called the autocorrelation function for the random signal $x(t)$. The autocorrelation function is usually represented by the symbol $\phi_{xx}(\tau)$. From the ergodic hypothesis, it follows that the preceding ensemble average for $x_1 = x(t)$ and $x_2 = x(t + \tau)$ is equal to the time average. That is,

$$\phi_{xx}(\tau) = \lim_{T \to \infty} \frac{1}{2T} \int_{-T}^{T} x(t)x(t + \tau)\,dt \quad (14.24)$$

Consider now two different random signals $x(t)$ and $y(t)$. The probability that at time t the outcome X lies between x and $x + \Delta x$ and that at time $t + \tau$ the outcome Y lies between y and $y + \Delta y$ is

$$p(x,y)\,\Delta x\,\Delta y$$

From Eq. (14.20), it follows that the average value of the product xy is

$$xy_{\mathrm{av}} = E(xy) = \int_{-\infty}^{\infty} \int_{-\infty}^{\infty} xyp(x,y)\,dx\,dy = \phi_{xy}(\tau) \quad (14.25)$$

The average value of the product xy is called the cross-correlation function. It is usually denoted by the symbol $\phi_{xy}(\tau)$. By the ergodic hypothesis, it follows that the cross-correlation function may be expressed in the form

$$\phi_{xy}(\tau) = \lim_{T \to \infty} \frac{1}{2T} \int_{-T}^{T} x(t)y(t + \tau)\,dt \quad (14.26)$$

The preceding has been concerned with the time-varying characteristics of stationary random signals. To make effective use of statistical methods, it is also necessary to consider the frequency characteristics of such signals.

Frequency Characteristics. The equation for the Laplace transform of a function $f(t)$ is

$$F(s) = \int_{0}^{\infty} f(t)e^{-st}\,dt$$

The lower limit of integration is taken as zero because the behavior prior to time $t = 0$ is accounted for by the initial conditions. If the lower limit is taken as $-\infty$, the initial conditions may be ignored. This particular Laplace transform, called the two-sided Laplace transform, is

$$F(s) = \int_{-\infty}^{\infty} f(t)e^{-st}\,dt$$

The equation for the inverse is

$$f(t) = \frac{1}{2\pi j} \int_{\sigma-j\infty}^{\sigma+j\infty} F(s)e^{st} \, ds$$

where $s = \sigma + j\omega$. Replacing s by $j\omega$ in the preceding expressions yields the corresponding equation for the Fourier transform and the equation for its inverse. That is,

$$F(j\omega) = \int_{-\infty}^{\infty} f(t)e^{-j\omega t} \, dt = F(\omega) \tag{14.27}$$

$$f(t) = \frac{1}{2\pi} \int_{-\infty}^{\infty} F(\omega)e^{j\omega t} \, d\omega \tag{14.28}$$

Because j is a constant, it is more appropriate to designate $F(j\omega)$ as $F(\omega)$. It is to be noted that the direct Fourier transform, Eq. (14.27), enables one to obtain the frequency characteristics $F(\omega)$ of a time function $f(t)$. Similarly, the inverse Fourier transform, Eq. (14.28), enables one to obtain the time function $f(t)$ when the frequency behavior $F(\omega)$ is known.

The exponential form of the Fourier series representation for a periodic function $f(t)$ is

$$f(t) = \sum_{n=-\infty}^{\infty} C_n e^{jn\omega_0 t} \tag{14.29}$$

where

$$C_n = \frac{1}{T} \int_{-T/2}^{T/2} f(t)e^{-jn\omega_0 t} \, dt$$

The term $C_n e^{jn\omega_0 t}$ is a rotating vector of length $|C_n|$ and angular position $\angle(C_n + n\omega_0 t)$. A harmonic analysis thus shows that $f(t)$ may be regarded as a sum of sinusoidal terms. Figure 14.15 shows a typical plot of the amplitude spectrum $|C_n|$ versus n.

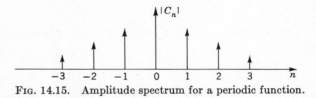

Fig. 14.15. Amplitude spectrum for a periodic function.

Squaring Eq. (14.29) and integrating both sides over the period gives

$$\int_{-T/2}^{T/2} f^2(t) \, dt = \int_{-T/2}^{T/2} \left(\sum_{n=-\infty}^{\infty} C_n e^{jn\omega_0 t} \right)\left(\sum_{m=-\infty}^{\infty} C_m e^{jm\omega_0 t} \right)$$

Because

$$\int_{-T/2}^{T/2} C_n C_m e^{j(n+m)\omega_0 t}\, dt = \begin{cases} 0 & m \neq -n \\ \dfrac{C_n C_{-n}}{T} = \dfrac{|C_n|^2}{T} & m = -n \end{cases}$$

then

$$\int_{-T/2}^{T/2} f^2(t)\, dt = \frac{1}{T} \sum_{n=-\infty}^{\infty} |C_n|^2 \qquad (14.30)$$

This is Parseval's formula for a periodic function. If $f(t)$ is the voltage across a 1-ohm resistor, then the left-hand side is seen to be the power dissipated. Hence, Parseval's formula shows that the total energy in a periodic signal is proportional to the sum of the squares of $|C_n|$. It is thus seen that the energy in a periodic signal is concentrated at discrete frequencies.

Consider now the case of a nonperiodic function such as

$$f(t) = \begin{cases} e^{-at} & t \geq 0 \\ 0 & t < 0 \end{cases}$$

The Fourier transform for this function is

$$F(\omega) = \frac{1}{a + j\omega}$$

The magnitude is

$$|F(\omega)| = 1/\sqrt{a^2 + \omega^2}$$

A plot of the amplitude density spectrum, $|F(\omega)|$ versus ω, is shown in Fig. 14.16.

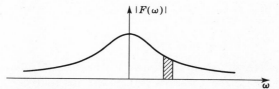

Fig. 14.16. Amplitude density spectrum for a nonperiodic function.

To develop Parseval's formula for a nonperiodic function first take the Fourier transform of the function

$$g(\tau) = \int_{-\infty}^{\infty} f(t)f(t + \tau)\, dt$$

Thus,

$$G(\omega) = \int_{-\infty}^{\infty} \left[\int_{-\infty}^{\infty} f(t)f(t + \tau)\, dt \right] e^{-j\omega\tau}\, dt$$

Replacing τ by $\lambda - t$ and rearranging gives

$$G(\omega) = \int_{-\infty}^{\infty} f(t)e^{j\omega t}\,dt \int_{-\infty}^{\infty} f(\lambda)e^{j\omega\lambda}\,d\lambda = F(-\omega)F(\omega) = |F(\omega)|^2$$

Inverting gives

$$g(\tau) = \int_{-\infty}^{\infty} f(t)f(t+\tau)\,d\tau = \frac{1}{2\pi}\int_{-\infty}^{\infty} |F(\omega)|^2\,d\omega$$

Letting $\tau = 0$ gives Parseval's integral formula

$$\int_{-\infty}^{\infty} f^2(t)\,dt = \frac{1}{2\pi}\int_{-\infty}^{\infty} |F(\omega)|^2\,d\omega \tag{14.31}$$

By regarding $f(t)$ as the voltage across a 1-ohm resistor, then the left-hand side is seen to be the power dissipated. Hence, the total energy in a nonperiodic signal is proportional to the integral of the $|F(\omega)|^2$. The square of the ordinate of the shaded pulse shown in Fig. 14.16 is thus seen to be a measure of the energy in the signal in the vicinity of the frequency at which the pulse is located.

The autocorrelation function $\phi_{xx}(\tau)$ contains information regarding the time behavior of a random signal. From Eqs. (14.27) and (14.28) it follows that

$$\Phi_{xx}(\omega) = \int_{-\infty}^{\infty} \phi_{xx}(\tau)e^{-j\omega\tau}\,d\tau \tag{14.32}$$

$$\phi_{xx}(\tau) = \frac{1}{2\pi}\int_{-\infty}^{\infty} \Phi_{xx}(\omega)e^{j\omega\tau}\,d\tau \tag{14.33}$$

where $\Phi_{xx}(\omega)$ which is the Fourier transform of the autocorrelation function is called the *power density spectrum*. The term $\Phi_{xx}(\omega)$ contains the frequency characteristics of a random signal.

The significance of the power-density spectrum $\Phi_{xx}(\omega)$ is ascertained as follows. For $\tau = 0$, then Eqs. (14.24) and (14.33) show that

$$\phi_{xx}(0) = \lim_{T \to \infty} \frac{1}{2T}\int_{-T}^{T} x^2(t)\,dt = \frac{1}{2\pi}\int_{-\infty}^{\infty} \Phi_{xx}(\omega)\,d\omega \tag{14.34}$$

When the random signal $x(t)$ is the voltage across a 1-ohm resistor, then $\phi_{xx}(0)$ is seen to be the total average power dissipated by the resistor. From Eq. (14.34), it follows that the total average power is proportional to the total area under the power-density spectrum curve, $\Phi_{xx}(\omega)$. Consider the following power-density spectrum

$$\Phi_{xx}(\omega) = \begin{cases} 0 & \omega < \omega_1 \\ \Phi_{xx} & \omega_1 \le \omega \le \omega_2 \\ 0 & \omega > \omega_2 \end{cases}$$

For this case the total average power is equal to the integral of $\Phi_{xx}(\omega)$ from ω_1 to ω_2. In general, it follows that the area under the power-density spectrum curve from ω_1 to ω_2 is proportional to the average power between the frequencies ω_1 and ω_2. If the sample function $x(t)$ contains only frequencies in the narrow range $\omega_0 - \Delta\omega/2$ to $\omega_0 + \Delta\omega/2$, where ω_0 is the center frequency and $\Delta\omega$ is the range, then from Eq. (14.34) it follows that

$$\lim_{T \to \infty} \frac{1}{2T} \int_{-T}^{T} x^2(t)\, dt = \frac{1}{2\pi} \int_{\omega_0 - \Delta\omega/2}^{\omega_0 + \Delta\omega/2} \Phi_{xx}(\omega)\, d\omega = \frac{\Delta\omega}{2\pi} \Phi_{xx}(\omega_0)$$

where $\Phi_{xx}(\omega_0)$ is the value of the power density spectrum at the frequency ω_0. In the experimental procedure commonly used to measure $\Phi_{xx}(\omega_0)$, the sample function $x(t)$ is passed through a narrow bandpass filter of center frequency ω_0 and bandwidth $\Delta\omega$. The left-hand side of the preceding expression is then evaluated by squaring, integrating, and averaging the filter output, whence $\Phi_{xx}(\omega_0)$ may be determined.

A test signal which is commonly used for identifying the dynamics of a process is white noise. This signal is characterized by a flat power-density spectrum. In practice, white noise can be generated over a finite range of frequencies only. It would require infinite power to generate white noise for an infinite range of frequencies.

ILLUSTRATIVE EXAMPLE 1.   Determine the autocorrelation function for white noise, $\Phi_{xx}(\omega) = K$.

SOLUTION.   From Eq. (14.27), it follows that

$$\Phi_{xx}(\omega) = \int_{-\infty}^{\infty} \phi_{xx}(\tau)e^{-j\omega\tau}\, d\tau$$

If $\phi_{xx}(\tau)$ is an impulse of area K, then

$$\Phi_{xx}(\omega) = \int_{0-}^{0+} K u_1(\tau)\, d\tau = K \int_{0-}^{0+} u_1(\tau)\, d\tau = K \tag{14.35}$$

Hence, the autocorrelation function for white noise is an impulse of area K.

14.4 Adaptive Control Systems.   A major problem in the design of adaptive control systems is that of identifying the dynamics of the process to be controlled. In Fig. 14.17 is shown a schematic diagram of a process.

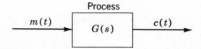

FIG. 14.17.   Schematic diagram of a process.

The convolution integral representation (see Appendix II) for the response $c(t)$ is

$$c(t) = \int_{-\infty}^{t} m(\tau)g(t - \tau)\, d\tau \tag{14.36}$$

where $g(t)$ is the response of the process to a unit impulse which occurs at time $t = 0$, and thus $g(t - \tau)$ is the response to a unit impulse at time $t = \tau$. Making the change of variable $x = t - \tau$ gives

$$c(t) = \int_0^\infty g(x)m(t - x)\, dx$$

Because the impulse response $g(x)$ is zero for $x < 0$, the lower limit of integration may be extended to $-\infty$. Thus,

$$c(t) = \int_{-\infty}^\infty g(x)m(t - x)\, dx \tag{14.37}$$

The cross correlation between the input $m(t)$ and output $c(t)$ is

$$\phi_{mc}(\tau) = \lim_{T \to \infty} \frac{1}{2T} \int_{-T}^T m(t - \tau)c(t)\, dt \tag{14.38}$$

The substitution of $c(t)$ from Eq. (14.37) into Eq. (14.38) yields

$$\phi_{mc}(\tau) = \lim_{T \to \infty} \frac{1}{2T} \int_{-T}^T m(t - \tau) \int_{-\infty}^\infty g(x)m(t - x)\, dx\, dt \tag{14.39}$$

Interchanging the order of integration gives

$$\phi_{mc}(\tau) = \int_{-\infty}^\infty g(x) \left[\lim_{T \to \infty} \frac{1}{2T} \int_{-T}^T m(t - \tau)m(t - x)\, dt \right] dx$$

The autocorrelation function $\phi_{mm}(\tau)$ is

$$\phi_{mm}(\tau) = \lim_{T \to \infty} \frac{1}{2T} \int_{-T}^T m(t)m(t + \tau)\, dt$$

Replacing τ by $\tau - x$ and t by $t - \tau$ shows that the term in brackets in Eq. (14.39) is the autocorrelation function of $m(t)$ with argument $\tau - x$. That is,

$$\phi_{mm}(\tau - x) = \lim_{T \to \infty} \frac{1}{2T} \int_{-T}^T m(t - \tau)m(t - x)\, dx$$

Thus, Eq. (14.39) may be expressed in the form

$$\phi_{mc}(\tau) = \int_{-\infty}^\infty g(x)\phi_{mm}(\tau - x)\, dx \tag{14.40}$$

Because Eqs. (14.37) and (14.40) have identical forms, it follows that when the input to the process is the autocorrelation function $\phi_{mm}(\tau)$, then the output is the cross-correlation function $\phi_{mc}(\tau)$.

In itself, Eq. (14.40) is very useful in that it relates the cross-correlation function to the impulse response and the autocorrelation function. For example, if the input $m(t)$ is white noise whose autocorrelation function is the impulse $\phi_{mm}(\tau) = Ku_1(\tau)$, then Eq. (14.40) shows that

$$\phi_{mc}(\tau) = K \int_{-\infty}^{\infty} g(x)u_1(\tau - x) \, dx = K \int_{\tau-}^{\tau+} g(x)u_1(\tau - x) \, dx$$

$$= Kg(\tau) \int_{\tau-}^{\tau+} u_1(\tau - x) \, dx = Kg(\tau) \tag{14.41}$$

Because the impulse exists only at $x = \tau$, then the integration is from a time slightly less than τ to a time slightly greater than τ. For this interval, $g(x) = g(\tau)$. The last integral is recognized as the area of a unit impulse. Equation (14.41) shows that when the input is white noise, then the cross correlation between the input and output is K times the value of the impulse response $g(t)$ at time $t = \tau$. In Fig. 14.18 is

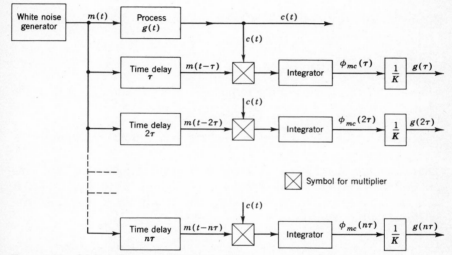

FIG. 14.18. Method for obtaining the impulse response at time $t = \tau, 2\tau, \ldots, n\tau$.

shown a schematic diagram for obtaining

$$\phi_{mc}(\tau) = \lim_{T \to \infty} \frac{1}{2T} \int_{-\infty}^{\infty} c(t)m(t - \tau) \, dt \tag{14.42}$$

Dividing by K yields the value of the impulse response at time $t = \tau$, $2\tau, \ldots, n\tau$. Equation (14.42) shows that the integration time should be infinite. In practice, the integration time is sufficiently long so as to obtain good results, but not so long that the dynamics of the process change appreciably during the measurement (i.e., the system remains time invariant).

Usually, it is desired to determine the dynamics of the process during normal operation. As illustrated in Fig. 14.19, it is necessary to super-impose the test signal upon the normal input $r(t)$. It is now shown that

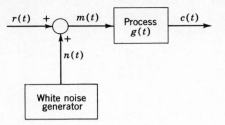

FIG. 14.19. System with test signal $n(t)$.

the preceding identification technique is unaffected by the normal input $r(t)$. From the convolution integral, the response $c(t)$ is

$$
\begin{aligned}
c(t) &= \int_{-\infty}^{t} [r(x) + n(x)]g(t - x)\, dx \\
&= \int_{-\infty}^{t} r(x)g(t - x)\, dx + \int_{-\infty}^{t} n(x)g(t - x)\, dx \\
&= c_r(t) + c_n(t)
\end{aligned}
$$

where $c_r(t)$ is the portion of the response due to $r(t)$ and $c_n(t)$ is that due to $n(t)$. The cross correlation between $n(t)$ and $c(t)$ is

$$
\phi_{nc}(\tau) = \lim_{T \to \infty} \frac{1}{2T} \left[\int_{-T}^{T} n(t - \tau)c_r(t)\, dt + \int_{-T}^{T} n(t - \tau)c_n(t)\, dt \right]
$$

This expression has the same form as Eq. (14.38). By following the same procedure as that employed in going from Eq. (14.38) to Eq. (14.40), it is found that the preceding expression may be written in the same form as Eq. (14.40). That is,

$$
\phi_{nc}(\tau) = \int_{-\infty}^{\infty} g(x)\phi_{nr}(\tau - x)\, dx + \int_{-\infty}^{\infty} g(x)\phi_{nn}(\tau - x)\, dx
$$

Because $r(t)$ and $n(t)$ are uncorrelated, then $\phi_{nr}(\tau) = 0$. Hence

$$
\phi_{nc}(\tau) = \int_{-\infty}^{\infty} g(x)\phi_{nn}(\tau - x)\, dx \tag{14.43}
$$

For white noise, $\phi_{nn}(\tau - x)$ is an impulse of area K which occurs at $\tau = x$. Thus, Eq. (14.43) becomes

$$
\phi_{nc}(\tau) = Kg(\tau)
$$

In Fig. 14.20 is shown a schematic diagram for obtaining

$$
\phi_{nc}(\tau) = \lim_{T \to \infty} \frac{1}{2T} \int_{-\infty}^{\infty} c(t)n(t - \tau)\, dt = Kg(\tau)
$$

Comparison of Figs. 14.19 and 14.20 shows that this method of process identification is independent of the normal input $r(t)$.

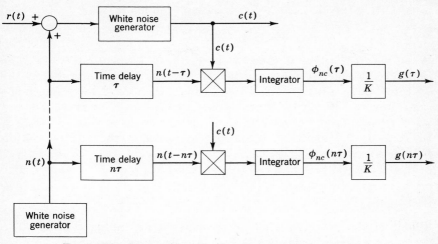

Fig. 14.20. Process identification during normal operation.

Discrete-interval Binary Noise. A major disadvantage of using white noise as the test signal for process identification is the long integration time required to obtain good accuracy. A test signal which has characteristics similar to that of white noise, but needs less integration time is periodic discrete-interval binary noise.

In Fig. 14.21a is shown a signal $x(t)$ which has a value of x_0 or $-x_0$. This signal is called discrete-interval binary noise (DIBN). Such a

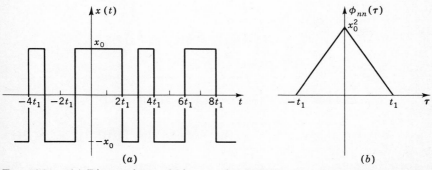

Fig. 14.21. (a) Discrete interval binary noise (DIBN); (b) autocorrelation function for DIBN.

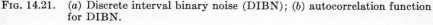

signal may be generated by sampling a wide-band noise source every t_1 seconds, and then setting $x(t)$ equal to x_0 if the noise source is positive or setting $x(t)$ equal to $-x_0$ if the noise source is negative. Because of this switching method, the sign of $x(t)$ varies in a random manner from interval to interval.   The autocorrelation function is

$$\phi_{xx}(\tau) = E[x(t)x(t+\tau)]$$

When τ is greater than t_1, then t and $t + \tau$ lie in different intervals.   The signs of $x(t)$ and $x(t + \tau)$ may be the same or opposite, and thus the expected value is zero.   When τ is $\frac{1}{3}$ of t_1, then t and $t + \tau$ are in the same interval $\frac{2}{3}$ of the time.   While in the same interval, $x(t)$ and $x(t + \tau)$ must have the same sign.   Thus, the expected value is $(2x_0^2)/3$. In general, the expected value of the product (the autocorrelation function) is

$$\phi_{nn}(\tau) = \begin{cases} \left(1 - \dfrac{\tau}{t_1}\right) x_0^2 & \tau < t_1 \\ 0 & \tau \ge t_1 \end{cases}$$

A plot of the autocorrelation function is shown in Fig. 14.21b.   The preceding analysis holds equally well for negative values of τ as for positive, hence $\phi_{nn}(\tau)$ is symmetrical about the vertical $\tau = 0$ axis (i.e., an even function).

When a representative sample of nonperiodic discrete-interval binary noise of period $T = nt_1$ is selected to form a periodic noise, the resulting signal is periodic discrete interval binary noise.   The autocorrelation function for periodic DIBN is shown in Fig. 14.22.   This is the same

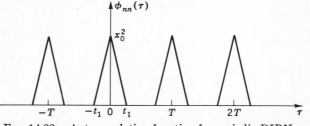

Fig. 14.22.   Autocorrelation function for periodic DIBN.

autocorrelation function as for the nonperiodic DIBN (Fig. 14.21b) except that it reoccurs periodically.

For a periodic signal, the average over one period is the same as the average over all periods.   Thus, from Eq. (14.24), the autocorrelation function for a periodic signal $n(t)$ is seen to be

$$\phi_{nn}(\tau) = \frac{1}{T} \int_{-T/2}^{T/2} n(t)n(t+\tau)\, dt \qquad (14.44)$$

Similarly, from Eq. (14.38) it follows that the cross-correlation between the noise $n(t)$ and output $c(t)$ is

$$\phi_{nc}(\tau) = \frac{1}{T} \int_{-T/2}^{T/2} n(t - \tau)c(t) \, dt \tag{14.45}$$

As indicated by the preceding equations, because of the repetitive nature of a periodic signal it suffices to consider one period only. A particularly desirable feature is that the integration time is now limited to one period.

In Fig. 14.22, it is to be noted that if t_1 is very small compared to the period T, then the autocorrelation function for periodic DIBN approaches a train of impulses. That is,

$$\phi_{nn}(\tau) \approx \sum_{k=-\infty}^{\infty} Ku_1(\tau + kT) \tag{14.46}$$

where $K = t_1 x_0{}^2$ is the area of each impulse. The substitution of this result into Eq. (14.40) gives

$$\phi_{nc}(\tau) \approx K \int_{-\infty}^{\infty} g(x) \sum_{k=-\infty}^{\infty} u_1(\tau - x + kT) \, dx$$

Because the impulse exists at $x = \tau + kT$ only, evaluation of the preceding integral gives

$$\phi_{nc}(\tau) = K \sum_{k=-\infty}^{\infty} g(\tau + kT) \tag{14.47}$$

In Fig. 14.23 is shown a typical impulse response $g(t)$. Because $g(t)$ is zero for negative time, then for $0 < \tau < T$ the lower summation index

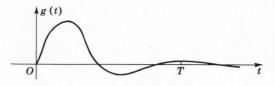

Fig. 14.23. Impulse response.

$k = -\infty$ may be changed to $k = 0$. Thus

$$\phi_{nc}(\tau) = K[g(\tau) + g(\tau + T) + g(\tau + 2T) + \cdot \cdot \cdot]$$

By making the period T sufficiently long such that the impulse response has essentially died out by time T, then

$$\phi_{nc} \approx Kg(\tau) \qquad 0 < \tau < T \tag{14.48}$$

In Fig. 14.24 is shown the schematic diagram of an adaptive control system developed by Anderson, Buland, and Cooper.[1] The output of

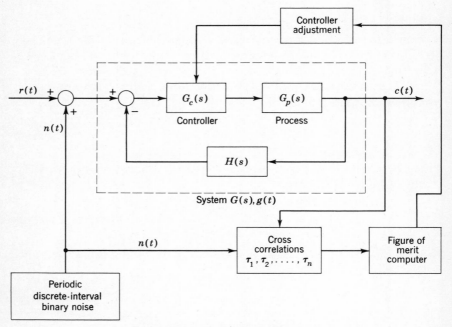

FIG. 14.24.   Adaptive control system.

the cross-correlators gives the value of the impulse response at n equally spaced stations $0 < \tau < T$. By measuring the area of the response curve above the horizontal axis (positive area) and the area below the axis (negative area), then a figure of merit which is an indication of the damping ratio, ζ, may be obtained. For a second-order system this figure of merit is

$$\text{F.M.} = A_+ - kA_- = \frac{1 - k \exp\left(-\zeta\pi/\sqrt{1 - \zeta^2}\right)}{1 - \exp\left(-\zeta\pi/\sqrt{1 - \zeta^2}\right)} \tag{14.49}$$

where A_+ = positive area

  A_- = negative area

  k = constant chosen such that F.M. = 0 at the desired damping ratio

[1] G. W. Anderson, R. N. Buland, and G. R. Cooper, "Use of Cross-correlation in an Adaptive Control System," *Proc. Natl. Electronics Conference*, **15**: (October, 1959).

For a damping ratio $\zeta = 0.5$, then F.M. $= 0$ when $k = 0.61$. When the figure of merit is negative, then $\zeta < 0.5$; and when the figure of merit is positive, then $\zeta > 0.5$. Thus, depending upon the sign of the figure of merit, the controller is changed so as to return the damping ratio of the system to 0.5.

In Fig. 14.25 is shown a generalized schematic diagram of an adaptive control system. Three basic functions performed by the adaptive con-

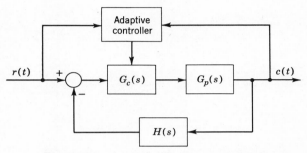

Fig. 14.25. General adaptive control system.

troller are identification, decision, and modification. The identification of the system dynamics is by far the most difficult of these functions. In the preceding, techniques for obtaining complete identification with the aid of a test signal have been discussed. For many applications, partial identification is adequate, and thus the identification mechanism is simplified accordingly. The literature contains many fine references with regard to various identification schemes. Because a test signal will have some effect upon the operation of a system, for some applications a test signal cannot be used. Interesting techniques for obtaining identification without the aid of a test signal have also been devised.

The identification information is usually in a form that cannot be used directly. Thus, the second function of an adaptive controller, decision, is to decide what to do with the information. The third function, modification, is the problem of how to modify the system so as to obtain the desired behavior.

14.5 Model-reference Systems. Because of the complex nature and many diverse schemes developed as adaptive control systems, it is sometimes difficult to distinguish if a system is actually an adaptive control system or a variation thereof. For example, in Fig. 14.26a is shown a model-reference system which is not regarded as an adaptive control system. The output of the actual system is compared to the output of a model; the error is then fed back to the input of the actual system so as

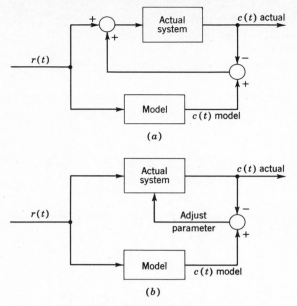

Fɪɢ. 14.26.   Model reference systems.

to minimize the error between the actual system and the model.   By block-diagram algebra it may be shown that such a system may be converted to the form of a conventional feedback control system.

The model-reference system shown in Fig. 14.26b is regarded as an adaptive control system.   The reason is that a system parameter is adjusted so as to obtain some reference, or optimum, performance.   It should be pointed out that the model system need not be actual hardware; it suffices to construct the optimum, or model, response on a computer. Model reference systems have been used with good success to obtain excellent performance in some very difficult control situations.

14.6 Computer-controlled Systems.   An important contribution to the field of adaptive control systems is the computer-controlled system developed by R. E. Kalman.[1]   In Fig. 14.27 is shown a schematic diagram of a process.   Feeding $m(t)$ and $c(t)$ to a digital computer is equivalent to sampling these signals periodically and then retaining these sampled values by a hold circuit.   The values m_k and c_k during the kth sampling interval, $kT < t < (k + 1)T$, are

$$m_k = m(kT)$$
$$c_k = c(kT)$$
$$(14.50)$$

[1] R. E. Kalman, "Design of a Self-optimizing Control System," *Trans. ASME,* **80:** 468–478 (February, 1958).

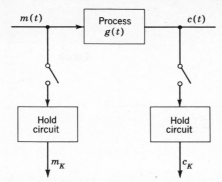

FIG. 14.27. Feeding $m(t)$ and $c(t)$ to a digital computer.

where T is the sampling period. From the convolution integral, the time relationship between $m(t)$ and $c(t)$ is

$$c(t) = \int_{-\infty}^{t} g(t - \tau)m(\tau)\, d\tau$$

In terms of sampled values this relationship is

$$c_k = \sum_{j=-\infty}^{k} g_{k-j}m_j \qquad (14.51)$$

In general, it may be shown that $G(z)$ has the form

$$G(z) = \frac{C(z)}{M(z)} = \frac{a_0 + a_1 z^{-1} + a_2 z^{-2} + \cdots + a_l z^{-l}}{1 + b_1 z^{-1} + b_2 z^{-2} + \cdots + b_n z^{-n}} \qquad (14.52)$$

where n is the order of the transfer function. Carrying out the division indicated in Eq. (14.52) shows that

$$G(z) = g_0 + g_1 z^{-1} + g_2 z^{-2} + \cdots \qquad (14.53)$$

where $g_0 = a_0$. Equation (14.53) has the same form as Eq. (13.3); hence $g_0 = g(0)$ is the impulse response at $t = 0$, $g_1 = g(T)$ is the impulse response at $t = T$, $g_2 = g(2T)$, etc. Because a physically realizable system cannot respond instantaneously, then $g_0 = a_0 = 0$.

As a numerical example, suppose that $H(s) = 3/(s + 1)(s + 3)$ for the plant of Fig. 14.28. The transfer function for the zero-order hold is $(1 - e^{-Ts})/s$. Thus,

$$G(s) = \frac{1 - e^{-Ts}}{s} \frac{3}{(s + 1)(s + 3)} = 1 - e^{-Ts}\left[\frac{1}{s} - \frac{1.5}{(s + 1)} + \frac{0.5}{(s + 3)}\right]$$

Using Eq. (13.54) to obtain the inverse z transform and evaluating for the case in which $T = 1$ gives

$$G(z) = \frac{0.474z^{-1} + 0.127z^{-2}}{1 + 0.418z^{-1} + 0.018z^{-2}}$$

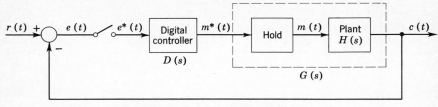

FIG. 14.28. Computer-controlled system.

From Sec. 13.5, the difference equation corresponding to Eq. (14.52) is

$$c_k + b_1c_{k-1} + b_2c_{k-2} + \cdots + b_nc_{k-n} = a_1m_k + a_2m_{k-1} + \cdots + a_lm_{k-l}$$

Kalman has built a special-purpose digital computer for analyzing a general second-order system in which $n = l = 2$. The corresponding difference equation is

$$c_k = a_1m_{k-1} + a_2m_{k-2} - b_1c_{k-1} - b_2c_{k-2} \qquad (14.54)$$

The a and b coefficients could be evaluated by taking four successive samples of the preceding equation and then solving simultaneously for a_1, a_2, b_1, and b_2. However, because of measurement errors the accuracy would not be very good. Errors due to measurements are minimized by basing the calculations on many measurements instead of just a few. Thus, as is described in the following, the a and b coefficients are selected so as to minimize the squared error between actual past values and calculated past values.

The values of the most recently calculated coefficients are designated $a_i(N)$ and $b_i(N)$ where N denotes the sampling instant at which these latest coefficients have been calculated. The past values of c at the kth sampling instant calculated from these coefficients are designated $c_k^*(N)$. Thus,

$$c_k^*(N) = a_1(N)m_{k-1} + a_2(N)m_{k-2} - b_1(N)c_{k-1} - b_2(N)c_{k-2}$$
$$k = 0, 1, 2, \ldots, N \qquad (14.55)$$

With the equipment available in his computer, Kalman can conveniently determine the mean square error. That is,

$$\frac{1}{N} \sum_{k=0}^{N} e_k{}^2(N) = \frac{1}{N} \sum_{k=0}^{N} [c_k - c_k^*(N)]^2 \qquad (14.56)$$

where $e_k{}^2(N)$ is the calculated value of the squared error at the kth sampling instant based on the most recent coefficients $a_i(N)$ and $b_i(N)$, and c_k is the actual (measured) past value.

Calculating the coefficients after every third sample, rather than after every sample, simplifies the computer considerably. Substituting $c_k^*(N)$

from Eq. (14.55) into Eq. (14.56) and replacing k by $3j$ gives the error squared at every third sampling instant.

$$
\begin{aligned}
e_{3j}{}^2(N) = [c_{3j} - c_{3j}^*(N)]^2 &= c_{3j}{}^2 + b_1{}^2(N)c_{3j-1}^2 + b_2{}^2(N)c_{3j-2}^2 \\
&+ 2b_1(N)c_{3j}c_{3j-1} + 2b_2(N)c_{3j}c_{3j-2} + 2b_1(N)b_2(N)c_{3j-1}c_{3j-2} \\
&- 2a_1(N)c_{3j}m_{3j-1} - 2a_2(N)c_{3j}m_{3j-2} - 2a_1(N)b_1(N)c_{3j-1}m_{3j-1} \\
&- 2a_2(N)b_1(N)c_{3j-1}m_{3j-2} - 2a_1(N)b_2(N)c_{3j-2}m_{3j-1} \\
&\qquad\qquad\qquad\qquad\qquad\qquad\qquad - 2a_2(N)b_2(N)c_{3j-2}m_{3j-2} \\
&+ a_1{}^2(N)m_{3j-1}^2 + a_2{}^2(N)m_{3j-2}^2 + 2a_1(N)a_2(N)m_{3j-1}m_{3j-2}
\end{aligned}
$$
$$(14.57)$$

More recent data should have more importance than older data. Thus, the mean squared error is modified (weighted) by introducing a weighting function w as follows

$$
E(N) = \sum_{j=0}^{N/3} e_{3j}{}^2(N)w_{N-3j}
\tag{14.58}
$$

For the weighting function Kalman uses

$$
w_{N-3j} = \alpha^{(N-3j)/3} \qquad 0 < \alpha < 1
$$

The value of the weighting function at the most recent $3j = N$ sampling instant is $\alpha^0 = 1$. The weighting function gets progressively smaller at preceding sampling instants. The substitution of $e_{3j}{}^2$ from Eq. (14.57) into Eq. (14.58) gives for the weighted mean squared error:

$$
\begin{aligned}
E(N) = \ &\phi_N^{cc}(0) + b_1{}^2(N)\phi_{N-1}^{cc}(0) + b_2{}^2(N)\phi_{N-2}^{cc}(0) \\
&+ 2b_1(N)\phi_N^{cc}(-1) + 2b_2(N)\phi_N^{cc}(-2) \\
&+ 2b_1(N)b_2(N)\phi_{N-1}^{cc}(-1) - 2a_1(N)\phi_N^{cm}(-1) \\
&- 2a_2(N)\phi_N^{cm}(-2) - 2b_1(N)a_1(N)\phi_{N-1}^{cm}(0) \\
&- 2b_1(N)a_2(N)\phi_{N-1}^{cm}(-1) - 2b_2(N)a_1(N)\phi_{N-2}^{cm}(1) \\
&- 2b_2(N)a_2(N)\phi_{N-2}^{cm}(0) + a_1{}^2(N)\phi_{N-1}^{mm}(0) + a_2{}^2(N)\phi_{N-2}^{mm}(0) \\
&+ 2a_1(N)a_2(N)\phi_{N-1}^{mm}(-1)
\end{aligned}
$$
$$(14.59)$$

where

$$
\phi_{N-r}^{cc}(r - s) = \sum_{j=1}^{N/3} c_{3j-r}c_{3j-s}w_{N-3j}
$$
$$
\phi_{N-r}^{cm}(r - s) = \sum_{j=1}^{N/3} c_{3j-r}m_{3j-s}w_{N-3j}
$$
$$
\phi_{N-r}^{mm}(r - s) = \sum_{j=1}^{N/3} m_{3j-r}m_{3j-s}w_{N-3j}
$$

These are seen to be pseudocorrelation functions.

By writing out separately the term for $3j = N$, the first pseudocorrelation function may be written in the form

$$\phi_{N-r}^{cc}(r - s) = c_{3j-r}c_{3j-s} + \sum_{j=1}^{(N-3)/3} c_{3j-r}m_{3j-s}w_{N-3j} \qquad (14.60)$$

The preceding calculated value, three sampling periods earlier, is

$$\phi_{N-3-r}^{cc}(r - s) = \sum_{j=1}^{(N-3)/3} c_{3j-r}m_{3j-s}w_{N-3-3j}$$

Because $w_{N-3j} = w_3 w_{N-3-3j} = \alpha w_{N-3-3j}$, Eq. (14.60) may be written in the form

$$\phi_{N-r}^{cc}(r - s) = c_{3j-r}c_{3j-s} + \alpha\phi_{N-3-r}^{cc}(r - s) \qquad (14.61)$$

This difference equation shows that to determine ϕ^{cc}, it is only necessary to know the preceding calculated value of ϕ^{cc} (three sampling periods earlier) plus c_N, c_{N-1}, c_{N-2}, m_{N-1}, and m_{N-2}. The pseudocorrelation functions for ϕ^{cm} and ϕ^{mm} also satisfy a difference equation of the same form as Eq. (14.61). Once the pseudocorrelation functions have been computed, all past data may be discarded except for the preceding calculated values of a_2, b_1, and b_2. That is, $a_2(N - 3)$, $b_1(N - 3)$, and $b_2(N - 3)$. The values of $a_1(N)$, $a_2(N)$, $b_1(N)$, and $b_2(N)$ are now chosen to make $E(N)$ of Eq. (14.59) a minimum. This is accomplished by satisfying the relationships

$$\frac{\partial E(N)}{\partial a_i} = 0 \quad \text{and} \quad \frac{\partial E(N)}{\partial b_i} = 0 \qquad i = 1, 2$$

This yields four equations from which the coefficients may be determined. Because the coefficients change slowly, the Gauss-Seidel[1] iteration procedure which uses the preceding values as a starting point may be employed to obtain the result more quickly. Thus, it is found that

$$a_1(N) = \frac{-a_2(N - 3)\phi_{N-1}^{mm}(-1) + b_1(N - 3)\phi_{N-1}^{cm}(0) + b_2(N - 3)\phi_{N-2}^{cm}(1) + \phi_N{}^{cm}(-1)}{\phi_{N-1}^{mm}(0)}$$

$$a_2(N) = \frac{-a_1(N)\phi_{N-1}^{mm}(-1) + b_1(N - 3)\phi_{N-1}^{cm}(-1) + b_2(N - 3)\phi_{N-2}^{cm}(0) + \phi_N{}^{cm}(-2)}{\phi_{N-2}^{mm}(0)}$$

$$b_1(N) = \frac{a_1(N)\phi_{N-1}^{cm}(0) + a_2(N)\phi_{N-1}^{cm}(-1) - b_2(N - 3)\phi_{N-1}^{cc}(-1) - \phi_N{}^{cc}(-1)}{\phi_{N-1}^{cc}(0)}$$

$$b_2(N) = \frac{a_1(N)\phi_{N-1}^{cm}(1) + a_2(N)\phi_{N-2}^{cm}(0) - b_1(N)\phi_{N-1}^{cc}(-1) - \phi_N{}^{cc}(-2)}{\phi_{N-2}^{cc}(0)}$$

This set of equations completes the identification.

[1] F. B. Hildebrand, "Introduction to Numerical Analysis," McGraw-Hill Book Company, New York, 1956.

It remains to determine the characteristics of the controller so as to obtain optimum performance. Any one of numerous optimum-performance criterion could be used. In the following, the method developed by Kalman[1] for obtaining the controller characteristics to yield a desired transient behavior is described. In Fig. 14.28 is shown a schematic diagram of the overall system. For illustrative purposes, assume that the transfer function of the plant is

$$H(s) = \frac{ab}{(s + a)(s + b)}$$

The transient behavior is considered optimum when the system responds to a step function in minimum time with no overshoot. In addition, there should be no steady-state error.

In Fig. 14.29, the optimum response $c(t)$ is indicated by the heavy line. The unit-step input is $r(t) = 1$. During the first interval $0 \leq t < T$, the

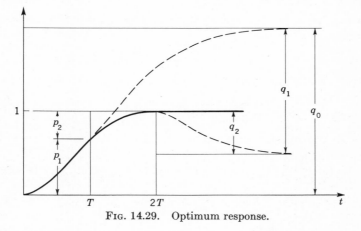

FIG. 14.29.   Optimum response.

input to the plant $m(t) = q_0$ is large so as to accelerate the system rapidly toward its final value. The first dotted extension in Fig. 14.29 shows the subsequent response if the plant input was not changed after the first sampling period. Thus, at time $t = T$, it is necessary to begin to decelerate the response so as to achieve the desired final value $c(t) = r(t) = 1$. During the second interval $T \leq t < 2T$ the plant input is changed by an amount q_1 so that $m(t) = q_0 + q_1$. As drawn in Fig. 14.29, the term q_1 is a negative constant. The response $c(t)$ reaches the final value at the end of the second interval $t = 2T$. The second dotted extension shows the path of the response if the plant input were not changed after the second

[1] R. E. Kalman (discussion of) "Sampled-data Processing Techniques for Feedback Control Systems," Bergen and Ragazzini, *Trans. AIEE*, **73**: (2), 245–246 (1954).

interval. Thus, for the third and subsequent intervals, the plant input is $q_0 + q_1 + q_2 = c(t) = r(t) = 1$.

A desirable feature of this performance criterion is that the error is reduced exactly to zero after two periods. The error then remains zero not only at the sampling points but also in between. This criterion thus eliminates the possibility of ripple (i.e., undesirable oscillations between sampling instants).

Because $m(t)$ is the output of a zero-order hold, it follows that the z transform of the sampled input $m^*(t)$ is

$$M(z) = q_0 + (q_0 + q_1)z^{-1} + (q_0 + q_1 + q_2)(z^{-2} + z^{-3} + \cdots)$$

Dividing $M(z)$ by the z transform of the unit-step input $[R(z) = 1 + z^{-1} + z^{-2} + \cdots]$ reveals that

$$\frac{M(z)}{R(z)} = q_0 + q_1 z^{-1} + q_2 z^{-2} \qquad (14.62)$$

Similarly, from Fig. 14.29 the z transform of the response at the sampling instants is

$$C(z) = p_1 z^{-1} + (p_1 + p_2)(z^{-2} + z^{-3} + \cdots)$$

Division by $R(z)$ shows that

$$\frac{C(z)}{R(z)} = p_1 z^{-1} + p_2 z^{-2} \qquad (14.63)$$

The pulsed transform for the process $G(z)$ is

$$G(z) = \frac{C(z)/R(z)}{M(z)/R(z)} = \frac{p_1 z^{-1} + p_2 z^{-2}}{q_0 + q_1 z^{-1} + q_2 z^{-2}} = \frac{a_1 z^{-1} + a_2 z^{-2}}{1 + b_1 z^{-1} + b_2 z^{-2}} \qquad (14.64)$$

where $a_1 = p_1/q_0$, $a_2 = p_2/q_0$, $b_1 = q_1/q_0$, and $b_2 = q_2/q_0$.

The pulsed transform for the digital controller is

$$D(z) = \frac{M(z)/R(z)}{E(z)/R(z)} = \frac{M(z)/R(z)}{1 - C(z)/R(z)} = \frac{q_0 + q_1 z^{-1} + q_2 z^{-2}}{1 - p_1 z^{-1} - p_2 z^{-2}}$$

$$= \frac{1 + b_1 z^{-1} + b_2 z^{-2}}{(1/q_0) - a_1 z^{-1} - a_2 z^{-2}}$$

By noting that $a_1 + a_2 = (p_1 + p_2)/q_0 = 1/q_0$, then $D(z) = M(z)/E(z)$ may be expressed as the following difference equation

$$[a_1(N) + a_2(N)]m_k - a_1(N)m_{k-1} - a_2(N)m_{k-2} = e_k + b_1(N)e_{k-1} + b_2(N)e_{k-2} \qquad (14.65)$$

This is the desired relationship for the digital controller which results in optimum response for the system.

As is indicated in the preceding analysis, the controller for a digital control system is programmed to yield a desired behavior. Because of the flexibility of programming, a digital controller is more versatile than a controller for a continuous system which is limited to some action described by a differential operator.

Problems

14.1 In Fig. P14.1 is shown the probability distribution for a discrete random variable. Construct the corresponding cumulative distribution function, and then determine the probability that $2 < X \leq 4$.

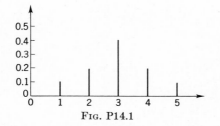

FIG. P14.1

14.2 The kth moment about the mean of the probability distribution for a discrete random variable is given by the equation

$$m_k = \sum_{i=1}^{n} (x_i - x_{av})^k P(x_i)$$

The standard deviation, $\sigma = \sqrt{m_2}$ is a measure of central tendency. The nondimensional quantity $\alpha_3 = m_3/\sigma^3$ is a measure of the skewness. Determine σ and α_3 for the probability distribution shown in Fig. P14.1.

14.3 The probability density function for a continuous random variable is shown in Fig. P14.3. Construct the corresponding cumulative distribution function, and then determine the probability that $4 < X \leq 7$.

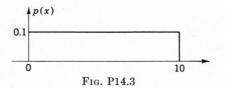

FIG. P14.3

14.4 The kth moment about the mean of the probability density function for a continuous random variable is

$$\mu_k = \int_{-\infty}^{\infty} (x - x_{av})^k p(x) \, dx$$

The standard deviation $\sigma = \sqrt{\mu_2}$ is a measure of the central tendency. The nondimensional quantity $\alpha_3 = \mu_3/\sigma^3$ is a measure of the skewness. Determine σ and α_3 for the probability density function shown in Fig. P14.3.

14.5   In Fig. P14.5 is shown the exponential probability density function

$$p(x) = \begin{cases} e^{-x} & x \geq 0 \\ 0 & x < 0 \end{cases}$$

Such a function is employed as an approximation of the density function for the life of vacuum tubes, light bulbs, etc.   Construct the corresponding cumulative

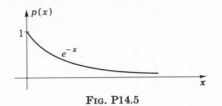

FIG. P14.5

distribution function and then determine:
  (a) the average life x_{av};
  (b) the standard deviation σ;
  (c) the measure of skewness α_3.
See the preceding problem for the definition of σ and α_3; also note that

$$\int_0^\infty x^k e^{-x}\, dx = k!$$

14.6   In Fig. P14.6a is shown a plot of the Gaussian or normal density function. The equation for this function is

$$p(x) = \frac{1}{\sigma \sqrt{2\pi}} \exp\left[-\frac{(x - x_{\text{av}})^2}{2\sigma^2} \right]$$

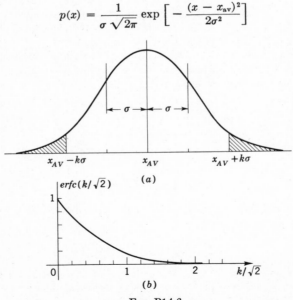

FIG. P14.6

Because of the symmetry of this function, the area shown shaded is

$$A = 2 \int_{x_{av}+k\sigma}^{\infty} p(x)\,dx = \frac{2}{\sqrt{\pi}} \int_{k/\sqrt{2}}^{\infty} e^{-y^2}\,dy$$

where $y = (x - x_{av})/\sigma\sqrt{2}$. This last integral is the well-known complementary error function which is shown plotted in Fig. P14.6b. Verify that the area under the normal density function between $x_{av} \pm \sigma = 0.68$, the area between $x_{av} \pm 2\sigma = 0.95$, and the area between $x_{av} \pm 3\sigma = 0.997$.

14.7 The addition law of probabilities is

$$P(A \text{ or } B) = P(A) + P(B) - P(AB)$$

where $P(A \text{ or } B)$ is the probability of either the event A occurring or the event B occurring, $P(A)$ is the probability of event A, $P(B)$ the probability of event B, and $P(AB)$ the probability of event A and event B both occurring.

(a) If a card is pulled from a deck, what is the probability that it will be either red or a spade?

(b) What is the probability of rolling either a 3 or a 5 with one dice?

(c) Show that

$$P(A \text{ or } B \text{ or } C) = P(A) + P(B) + P(C) - P(AB) - P(AC) - P(BC) + P(ABC)$$

14.8 The multiplication law of probabilities is

$$P(A \text{ and then } B) = P(A,B) = P(A)P(B/A)$$

where $P(A \text{ and } B) = P(A,B)$ is the probability of event A and then event B occurring, and $P(B/A)$ is the probability of event B occurring provided that event A has occurred.

(a) Determine the probability of drawing a red card and then a spade from a deck of cards when the first card is replaced.

(b) Same as part (a) except without replacement.

(c) Show that

$$P(A,B,C) = P(A)P(B/A)P(C/A,B)$$

14.9 In Fig. P14.9 are diagrammatically illustrated r slots. Any one of n things may fill the first slot, any one of $n-1$ things the second slot, etc. The pos-

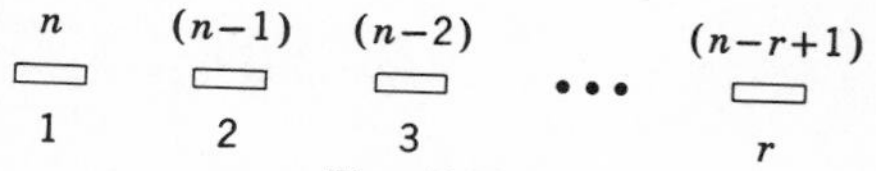

n	$(n-1)$	$(n-2)$		$(n-r+1)$
1	2	3	$\cdots$	r

Fig. P14.9

sible number of permutations (i.e. arrangements) of n things taken r at a time is:

$$P_r{}^n = n(n-1)\,\cdots\,(n-r+1)$$

(a) List the permutations of the numbers 1, 2, 3 taken 2 at a time.

(b) List the permutations of the numbers 1, 2, 3 taken 3 at a time.

14.10 All of the permutations that contain the same elements are regarded as but one combination (i.e., a combination disregards order). Thus, the number of permutations is equal to the number of combinations times the number of permutations per combination. That is,

$$P_r{}^n = C_r{}^n P_r{}^r$$

or $\qquad C_r{}^n = \dfrac{P_r{}^n}{P_r{}^r} = \dfrac{n(n-1)\cdots(n-r+1)}{r!} = \dfrac{n!}{r!(n-r)!}$

(a) What is the number of combinations of 3 things taken 2 at a time?

(b) What is the number of combinations of 3 things taken 3 at a time?

14.11 Consider an event for which the probability of success is p. The probability that the first x of n events will all be successful is p^x. The probability that the remaining $n-x$ events will all fail is $(1-p)^{n-x}$. The number of ways in which x successes and $n-x$ failures may occur is $n!/[x!(n-x)!]$. Thus, the probability of obtaining exactly x successes in n trials is

$$P(X = x) = \frac{n!}{x!(n-x)!}\, p^x(1-p)^{n-x}$$

This is the binomial distribution. The distribution function for obtaining 0, 1, or 2 heads in 2 tosses of a coin is shown in Fig. P14.11.

(a) Plot the distribution function for obtaining 0, 1, 2, or 3 heads.

(b) Plot the distribution function for obtaining 0, 1, 2, 3, or 4 heads.

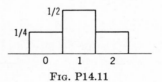

Fig. P14.11

It may be shown that for $p = \frac{1}{2}$, then as n becomes infinite the binomial distribution approaches the Gaussian or normal distribution.

14.12 When the probability of success is small and the number of events is large, then the binomial distribution may be approximated by Poisson's distribution. That is

$$P(X = x) = \frac{\mu^x e^{-\mu}}{x!}$$

where $\mu = np$ is the average value.

(a) When throwing two dice, what is the probability of not tossing a double six in 36 throws?

(b) At a given intersection, it has been observed that on the average one accident occurs every 70 days. What is the probability that no accidents will occur for 7 days, 70 days, 700 days?

14.13 Statistical averages for probability distributions are analogous to centroidal distances and radii of gyration for mass distributions. To develop the mass analog, consider a rod stretched along the x axis. The mass per unit length of the rod is $p(x)$. Thus, show that

(a) The expected value $E(x)$ is the distance from the origin to the center of mass.

(b) $E(x^2)$ is the moment of inertia (i.e., square of the radius of gyration) about the origin.

(c) σ^2 is the centroidal moment of inertia, and thus σ is the centroidal radius of gyration.

14.14 To develop the mass analog (see Prob. 14.13) for second-order probability distributions, consider a plate in the (x,y) plane. The mass per unit area is $p(x,y)$. Thus, show that

(a) $E(x)$ and $E(y)$ are the coordinates of the center of mass.

(b) $E(x^2)$ and $E(y^2)$ are the moments of inertia about the y and x axes respectively.

(c) σ_x^2 and σ_y^2 are the moments of inertia with respect to the centroidal axes (parallel to the x and y axes).

(d) The autocorrelation function $E(x,y)$ is the product of inertia with respect to the origin.

15

Hydraulic systems

Hydraulic devices are used extensively in control systems. With high-pressure hydraulic systems, very large forces are obtained. Such forces provide power for rapid accelerations, accurate positioning of heavy loads, etc. Because hydraulic motors are much smaller than equivalent electric motors, considerable size and weight savings can be realized.

In electrical systems, magnetic devices such as motors, solenoids, etc., are used to provide the "muscle" for doing work. The operation of magnetic equipment is characterized by relatively long time lags. In general, hydraulic components are very rapid-acting. Another feature is that hydraulic equipment is more rugged than corresponding electrical components. This can be a major factor in applications such as aircraft, where vibrations and shock may cause fine wires and delicate tubes or transistors to fail. In addition, the noise pickup from such vibrations may adversely effect the normal operation of electrical equipment.

Electrical equipment is better suited for applications in which components must be located far apart, as in remote-control positioning systems. The reason for this is that electrical signals may be transmitted long distances via wires or microwaves.

In general, pneumatic and hydraulic systems are quite similar. An advantage of pneumatic equipment is the accessibility and convenience of using air. However, because of the compressibility of air, pneumatic systems do not have the positive action afforded by hydraulic systems, which employ an incompressible fluid as the working medium.

Electrical components are inherently better suited for certain operations, hydraulic components for others, and pneumatic components for still others. However, for many applications, it is possible to accomplish a desired function almost equally well by electric, hydraulic, or pneumatic equipment. Thus, the designer must weigh the relative importance of size, weight, cost, accuracy, ruggedness, reliability, etc. Frequently, it is necessary to make a detailed design analysis of corresponding electric, hydraulic, or pneumatic components to obtain a good evaluation of these various factors. Sometimes, it may even be necessary to build models for testing before a final decision can be made. It is not uncommon to utilize all three types, i.e., electric, hydraulic, and pneumatic equipment, in one control system.

To be able to select the components which are best suited to his particular requirements, a designer must be familiar with all types of commonly used control apparatus. Characteristics of pneumatic and electric apparatus are presented in the next two chapters, respectively. This chapter presents basic considerations involved in the design of hydraulic systems. Emphasis is given to explaining the basic laws and equations which govern the operation of hydraulic equipment. Typical examples of commonly used hydraulic devices and the manner in which their performance may be evaluated are also presented. These basic principles and techniques may then be applied to any hydraulic equipment. In one chapter it is not possible to indicate the innumerable practical applications and uses for hydraulic systems.[1-4] Thus, of necessity, the primary effort of this chapter is limited to basic considerations.

Three major classifications of elements for hydraulic circuits are pumps, valves, and receiving units. The basic functions of these elements are distinguished as follows: pumps supply the high-pressure fluid for the system, valves control the direction and amount of flow, and receiving units utilize this flow of fluid to accomplish the desired objective.

15.1 Pumps and Power Supplies. The three types of pumps most commonly used for hydraulic power purposes are the gear pump, vane pump, and piston pump.

Gear Pump. A gear pump is shown in Fig. 15.1. Because of the direction of rotation of the gears, the inlet fluid is carried around the outer periphery of the gears to the high-pressure discharge side of the pump. The meshing gear teeth provide a seal to prevent return of the fluid to the low-pressure side of the pump. This type of pump is less expensive than other pumps and is also very rugged. Its best efficiency occurs at lower speeds and operating pressures than those for vane or piston pumps.

There is a leakage between the tips of the gear teeth and the housing and also between the sides or faces of the gear blanks and housing. At

---

[1] Publishers of *Applied Hydraulics*, "Fluid Power Directory 1958/1959," Industrial Publishing Corp., Cleveland, 1957.

[2] J. J. Pippenger and R. F. Koff, "Fluid-power Controls," McGraw-Hill Book Company, New York, 1959.

[3] J. G. Truxal, "Control Engineers' Handbook," McGraw-Hill Book Company, New York, 1958.

[4] I. McNeil, "Hydraulic Operation and Control of Machines," The Ronald Press Company, New York, 1958.

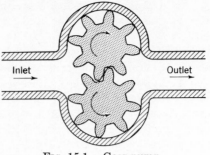

Fig. 15.1.   Gear pump.

high pressures and operating speeds, this leakage increases considerably, which tends to decrease the overall efficiency of this pump.

Vane Pump.   A vane pump is shown in Fig. 15.2.   The centrifugal force on each of the vanes is usually sufficient to maintain contact between

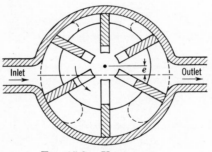

Fig. 15.2.   Vane pump.

the vanes and the housing.   For a counterclockwise rotation of the rotor as shown in Fig. 15.2, a large amount of fluid is carried from the inlet side of the pump to the discharge side.   Because of the eccentricity e of the center of the rotor with respect to the housing, more fluid is carried to the high-pressure side of the pump than is returned to the low-pressure side.   The net flow is seen to depend upon the amount of eccentricity e.   By varying the eccentricity, a vane pump can be used as a variable-delivery pump.

Axial Piston Pump.   An axial piston pump is shown in Fig. 15.3.   The pistons are located in the rotor (i.e., rotating cylinder block), which is driven by the drive shaft.   Because the pistons are parallel to the drive shaft, this type of pump is called an axial piston pump.   The wobble plate

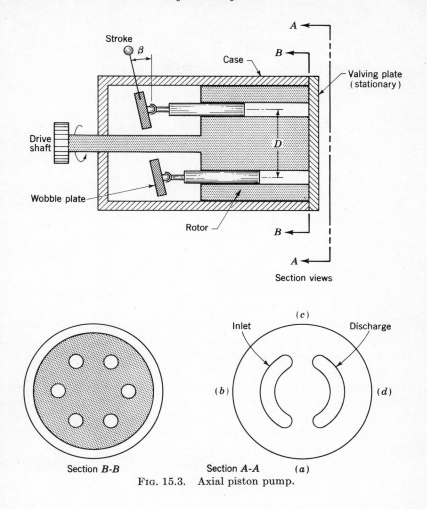

Fig. 15.3. Axial piston pump.

does not rotate, and furthermore its angle of inclination β is set by the position of the stroke-adjusting lever. The axial displacement of each piston ($X = D \tan \beta$) is varied by changing the angle of inclination β of the wobble plate. As a piston in the cylinder block rotates in a clockwise direction from (a) to (b) to (c) (pump viewed from right end), fluid is being admitted as the stroke is increasing. Then in going from (c) to (d) to (a) the fluid is forced out to the high-pressure, or discharge, side of the pump as the stroke is decreasing.

Radial Piston Pump. The pistons of a radial piston pump move in a radial direction, as is illustrated in Fig. 15.4. The inner shaft (i.e.,

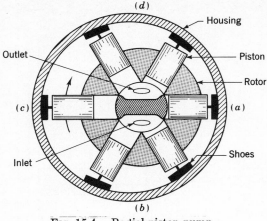

Fɪɢ. 15.4.   Radial piston pump.

pintle), which contains the inlet and discharge passageways, is fixed, as
is the housing.   As a piston in the rotor rotates clockwise from (*a*) to
(*b*) to (*c*), fluid is being admitted as the stroke increases.   Then in going
from (*c*) to (*d*) to (*a*) fluid is forced out at high pressure as the stroke is
decreasing.   The stroke and thus the amount of fluid delivered are varied
by changing the eccentricity between the center of the housing and the
center of the rotor.

The selection of a pump for a particular application depends upon
many factors, such as quantity of fluid to be delivered, discharge pressure, reliability desired, cost, operating efficiency, size, etc.   As is the
case with most specific equipment, a manufacturer's catalogue should
be consulted to obtain data regarding such details.

In general, the power output for any pump may be computed from the
equation

$$\text{hp} = \frac{Q(P_o - P_{\text{in}})}{(12)(550)} \tag{15.1}$$

where Q = net rate of flow delivered, in.³/sec
$P_o - P_{\text{in}}$ = change in pressure, psi

The overall pump efficiency is equal to the hydraulic power output of
the pump as given by Eq. (15.1) divided by the power supplied to drive
the pump.

15.2 Valves and Circuits.   From the time the fluid leaves the pump
until it reaches the receiving units, the flow is controlled and directed by
valves.

Relief Valve. A relief valve is shown in Fig. 15.5. When the pressure P_1 in the main flow passage is high enough to overcome the spring force

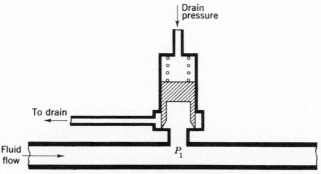

Fig. 15.5. Relief valve.

tending to close the valve, the valve opens. This connects the main flow passage to the return to sump (i.e., pump reservoir), which is at drain pressure. This relief valve remains open until the pressure P_1 decreases to the value that was required to open the valve. In effect, then, a relief valve limits the maximum obtainable pressure P_1. Because of its function, this type of valve is often referred to as a pressure-regulating valve.

If A is the cross-sectional area of the plunger in the relief valve, then the pressure force P_1A tends to raise the valve. The force F_c is the force exerted on the plunger by the spring when the valve is closed. When the plunger is raised a distance X from its closed position, an additional force KX is exerted by the spring. Thus

$$P_1A = F_c + KX \qquad (15.2)$$

or

$$P_1 = \frac{F_c}{A} + \frac{KX}{A} \qquad (15.3)$$

To minimize the variation in pressure P_1 due to the opening X, then K/A should be as small as possible. In addition, by making the diameter D of the plunger large, the plunger does not have to open so wide to bypass the flow. This minimizes the opening X. For most applications, the pressure P_1 may be regarded as the cracking pressure F_c/A, that is, the pressure at which the valve just opens or cracks.

In Fig. 15.6 is shown the fluid supply system for a typical hydraulic circuit. The oil in the sump is strained before going to the pump, which is driven by a motor. A fixed-displacement pump is indicated by the circle with PF in it. The representation for the spring-loaded relief valve

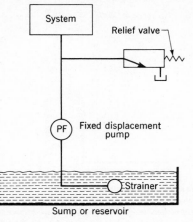

FIG. 15.6.   Relief valve used to provide a constant-pressure power supply.

indicates that the pressure in the main line is opposed by the spring
shown on the opposite side of the rectangle.   The arrow in the box indicates the direction of flow through the valve.   The arrow is drawn in
the position that indicates the flow when the spring force is greater than
the opposing pressure.   In this case, the flow is blocked off.   When the
opposing pressure exceeds the spring force, it is connected to the sump.
The drain, or return to sump, is indicated by drawing a little sump under
the valve.

A fixed-displacement pump which is driven at a constant speed delivers
a relatively constant amount of flow regardless of the discharge pressure.
The excess flow not used by the system is bypassed by the relief valve.
This bypass flow represents wasted power because it was supplied at
high pressure.   The resulting wasted energy increases the temperature
of the fluid in the system.   If the rise in temperature is sufficient, it may
be necessary to provide a cooler.

Accumulator and Unloading Valve.   A constant-pressure supply may
also be obtained by the use of an accumulator and an unloading valve,
as is shown in Fig. 15.7a.   The accumulator holds the supply of fluid
at constant pressure for use as the system needs it.   An accumulator
has an elastic diaphragm or bladder to separate the top portion, which
contains a gas under pressure, from the supply of fluid on the bottom
side.   The purpose of the gas is to maintain the fluid pressure.   As the
fluid level drops, the gas expands and the pressure of the fluid decreases
slightly.   The same effect may also be obtained by using a spring to
load the top side of the diaphragm.

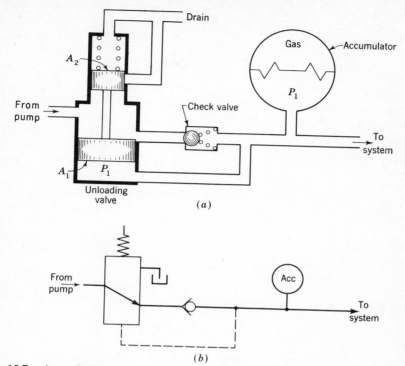

Fig. 15.7. Accumulator and unloading valve used to provide a constant-pressure power supply.

The unloading valve in Fig. 15.7a is drawn in the position in which the pump flow is refilling the accumulator. The check valve offers no resistance to flow to the accumulator, but it closes off to prevent reverse, or leakage, flow. As the accumulator fills, the pressure P_1 increases and the plunger rises. Just before the drain port is uncovered, the pressure P_1 is acting on both sides of the bottom land. The net upward force on the valve is $P_1 A_2$. After the drain is uncovered, both sides of the top land are connected to drain, as is the top side of the bottom land, so that the upward force is now $P_1 A_1$. Because A_1 is greater than A_2, the upward force suddenly increases to unload the pump by opening the drain port wide. Thus the pump is unloaded when

$$P_{1,\max} = \frac{F_c}{A_2} \tag{15.4}$$

where F_c is the force of the spring when the drain port is just uncovered and $P_{1,\max}$ is the maximum value of P_1. As the fluid in the accumulator is used, the pressure P_1 decreases and the plunger moves down to close off the drain. Just before the drain is closed off, the forces acting on the plunger are

$$P_{1,\text{min}} = \frac{F_c}{A_1} \tag{15.5}$$

where $P_{1,\text{min}}$ is the minimum value of P_1.   After the drain port is closed off, the pressure force is suddenly decreased from $P_1 A_1$ to $P_1 A_2$.   The spring then pushes the plunger down to open wide the passageway to the accumulator in order to refill it.   For a large accumulator, more fluid can be used before the supply of fluid must be replenished.   The purpose of employing a differential-area plunger is to prevent the pump from continually being unloaded and then loaded, i.e., to provide a spread between $P_{1,\text{max}}$ and $P_{1,\text{min}}$.

In the symbolic representation of the unloading valve in Fig. 15.7b, the pressure of the fluid in the accumulator opposes the spring force. The arrow indicates the direction of flow through the valve when the spring force is greater than the pressure force, i.e., when the accumulator is being refilled.   When the pressure force exceeds the spring force, the pump is connected to drain.

The use of a variable-delivery pump to provide a constant pressure supply is illustrated in Fig. 15.8.   When the pressure to the system

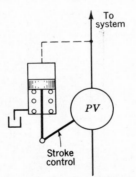

To
system

PV

Stroke
control

FIG. 15.8.   Variable-delivery pump to provide a constant-pressure power supply.

exceeds the nominal value, the piston in the cylinder is forced down. This actuates the pump-delivery control linkage to decrease the flow. The maximum variation in supply pressure is equal to the variation in pressure required to move the pump-delivery control linkage (e.g., wobble-plate control) from maximum to no flow.   There are numerous types of hydraulic power supplies; most of these, by far, are of the constant-pressure type.

Much time and effort are saved by using the line-diagram method for drawing hydraulic circuits.   In Fig. 15.9 is shown a partial listing of symbolic representations for various circuit elements.   These are stand-

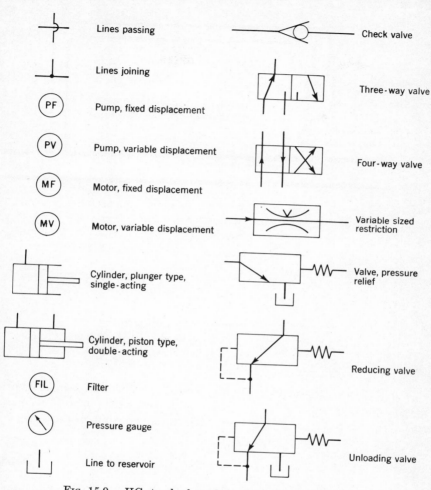

FIG. 15.9.   JIC standard symbols for hydraulic circuits.

ard symbols which have been adopted for hydraulic circuits by the Joint Hydraulic Industrial Conference (JIC).

Differential-pressure-regulating Valve.   A differential-pressure-regulating valve maintains a constant pressure difference $P_1 - P_2$ between two points in a system.   In Fig. 15.10a, the pressure P_2 is determined by the downstream characteristics of the system.   This system must be supplied by a constant-flow power supply such as is obtained by the use of a fixed-displacement pump.   When $P_1 - P_2$ exceeds the nominal value set by the spring, the plunger rises to bypass more flow to drain.   The flow

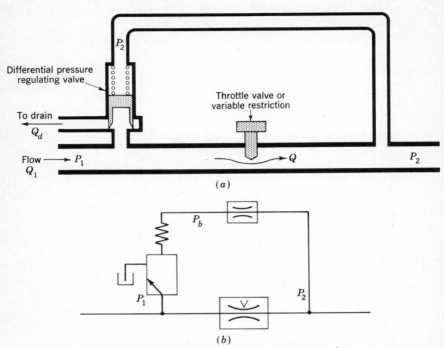

Fig. 15.10.   Differential-pressure-regulating valve.

through the throttle valve is decreased because of this additional bypass
flow.   This decrease in flow through the throttle valve in turn decreases
the pressure drop $P_1 - P_2$ across it.   The force equation for the plunger is

$$(P_1 - P_2)A = F_c + KX$$

or

$$P_1 - P_2 = \frac{F_c}{A} + \frac{KX}{A} \tag{15.6}$$

As for the case of the relief valve, the quantity K/A should be small
and the diameter D of the plunger should be large to minimize the variation $P_1 - P_2$ from the cracking value F_c/A.   The pressure drop $P_1 - P_2$
may be regarded as remaining essentially constant.   Thus, the flow
across the variable-sized restriction, or throttle valve, is controlled
entirely by the area of the throttle valve.   In effect, a flow control
device results.

   If one writes the equation of motion for the plunger and considers
the mass M of the plunger, it follows that

$$MD^2X = (P_1 - P_2)A - KX - F_c$$

or

$$X = \frac{1/M[(P_1 - P_2)A - F_c]}{D^2 + K/M} \tag{15.7}$$

The term in brackets is the difference between the pressure force acting on the valve and the spring force at cracking. From Eq. (15.7), it follows that the plunger will tend to oscillate or chatter at its natural frequency $\omega_n = \sqrt{K/M}$. This undesirable effect is avoided by inserting a viscous damper in the line between the spring side of the plunger and the discharge line at pressure P_2, as illustrated in the symbolic representation of Fig. 15.10b. Viscous damping is provided by an orifice whose length is sufficiently greater than its diameter so as to cause laminar flow. The flow through such a restriction is given by the equation

$$Q = \frac{\pi D^4 \, \Delta P}{128 \mu L} = C \, \Delta P \tag{15.8}$$

where Q = rate of flow, in.^{3}/sec
$\quad D$ = diameter of restriction, in.
$\quad \Delta P$ = pressure drop across restriction, psi
$\quad L$ = length of restriction, in.
$\quad \mu$ = absolute viscosity, reyns (lb-sec/in.^{2})

If the pressure behind the plunger between the spring and restriction is designated as P_b, the pressure drop across the restriction is $\Delta P = P_b - P_2$. Because the fluid is incompressible, the flow through this restriction is equal to the change of volume $A (dX/dt)$, on the spring side of the plunger. Thus

$$C(P_b - P_2) = ADX \tag{15.9}$$

The force equation for the plunger is now

$$MD^2X + KX = (P_1 - P_b)A - F_c \tag{15.10}$$

Eliminating P_b from Eqs. (15.9) and (15.10) and solving for X gives

$$X = \frac{1/M[(P_1 - P_2)A - F_c]}{D^2 + (A^2/CM)D + K/M} \tag{15.11}$$

whence $\omega_n = \sqrt{K/M}$ and $\zeta = A^2/(2C\sqrt{KM})$. The viscous damper thus provides a convenient means for eliminating the chatter. For steady-state operation, there is no flow through the damper so that $P_b = P_2$. Thus, the basic function of maintaining a constant pressure drop $P_1 = P_2$ is not altered by the damper.

Reducing Valve. A reducing valve is used to lower the pressure to a predetermined value. That is, it regulates the outlet pressure from the valve. A reducing valve is shown in Fig. 15.11a. When the outlet pressure is equal to the cracking value set by the spring, the plunger just shuts off the outlet from the inlet passageway. A decrease in the outlet pressure lowers the valve to admit high-pressure fluid, which in turn

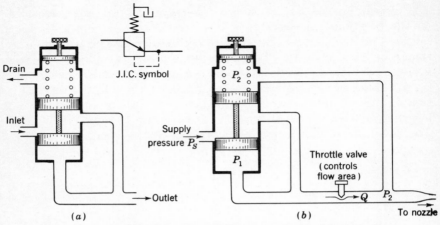

Fig. 15.11.   (a) Reducing valve; (b) flow control with reducing valve.

increases the outlet pressure.   This then returns the valve to its line-on-line position.   An increase in the outlet pressure closes off the outlet passageway.   Thus, the outlet pressure is maintained at its cracking value.

Although a relief valve could be used to regulate the outlet pressure, such a valve would also lower the inlet pressure.   A pressure-reducing valve regulates the outlet pressure independently of the inlet.   Relief valves and reducing valves are readily distinguished as follows: The spring of a relief valve tends to close it, while that of a reducing valve tends to open it.   The pressure force acting on a relief valve tends to open it, while that of a reducing valve tends to close it.   In the symbolic representation for the reducing valve, the outlet pressure opposes the spring force.   When the outlet pressure gets high enough, the inlet is disconnected from the outlet.

The use of a reducing valve is illustrated by the flow control system shown in Fig. 15.11b.   The discharge pressure P_2 is controlled independently by the nozzle characteristics which are downstream from the flow control portion of the system shown in Fig. 15.11b.   To have the flow Q a function of the position of the throttle valve only, it is desired to maintain a constant pressure drop across the throttle valve.   From Fig. 15.11b, it is seen that the pressure drop P_1-P_2 across the throttle valve acts across the reducing valve.   The reducing valve tends to maintain this pressure drop constant because if P_1 decreases, then the valve opens the outlet-pressure port wider to increase P_1.   Similarly, if P_1-P_2 exceeds the nominal value determined by the spring force, the reducing valve moves up to close off the outlet port, which in turn returns P_1-P_2 to its nominal value.   For this system, the value of the inlet pressure is independent of the operation of the system, whereas with the differential-pressure-regulating valve the inlet pressure was $P_s = P_1$. To eliminate chatter of the plunger of the reducing valve, it is necessary to insert a viscous damper in the line connecting the spring side of the plunger to the discharge line at pressure P_2, as was done for the differential-pressure-regulating valve.

15.3 Three-way Valve Amplifiers. The purpose of a pilot valve is to control the direction and amount of flow to a receiving unit. A spool-type pilot valve is one in which the shape of the valve resembles that of a spool. A circuit which utilizes a spool-type valve is illustrated in Fig. 15.12a. This valve has three external ports: a high-pressure (or

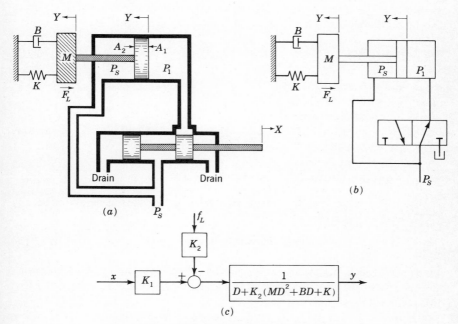

Fig. 15.12. Three-way-valve-cylinder circuit.

supply) port, a cylinder port, and a drain port. Thus, this valve is further classified as a three-way pilot valve. Pilot valves are sometimes referred to as control valves, servo valves, or proportional valves. When the valve is moved to the right, the high-pressure line is connected to the cylinder port and the drain is blocked off. Although high pressure is now connected to both sides of the piston, there is a larger area exposed to this pressure on the right side of the piston than on the left. Thus, the greater force on the right side causes the piston and load to move to the left.   When the valve is moved to the left of its line-on-line position, the cylinder port is connected to drain.   The high pressure which always acts on the left side of the piston now forces the piston and load to move to the right.

The symbolic representation for this circuit is shown in Fig. 15.12*b*. The right half of the valve representation indicates the line connections when the valve is moved to the right.   The direction of the arrow indicates the direction of flow from the high-pressure port to the cylinder. The drain connection is blocked off.   It is not necessary to reproduce the location of the ports for the left position.   With the valve in its left position, the arrow indicates that the direction of flow is from the cylinder port to drain.   The high-pressure port is blocked off in this position.

Because turbulent flow exists at a sharp-edged orifice such as a valve, the flow equation when the valve is moved to the right is

$$Q = C_d W X \sqrt{\frac{2g}{\rho}(P_s - P_1)} = K_d X \sqrt{P_s - P_1} \qquad X > 0 \quad (15.12)$$

where $K_d = C_d W \sqrt{2g/\rho}$
Q = flow through valve
C_d = discharge coefficient
WX = port area in which X = length of opening and W = circumference
ρ = fluid density
g = gravitational conversion constant

When the valve is to the left of its line-on-line position, the flow rate is given by the equation

$$Q = K_d X \sqrt{P_1} \qquad X < 0 \qquad\qquad (15.13)$$

From Eq. (15.12), it is to be noted that flow into the cylinder is represented as a positive quantity.   Because X is negative in Eq. (15.13), the return flow is also negative.

From Fig. 15.12*a*, it is to be seen that the flow rate through the valve is equal to the area A_1 of the right side of the piston times the piston velocity DY.   Thus

$$Q = A_1 D Y = A_1 \dot{Y} \qquad\qquad (15.14)$$

The pressure force acting on the piston is

$$F = P_1 A_1 - P_s A_2 \qquad\qquad (15.15)$$

For positive values of X, the overall equation relating F, X, and $\dot{Y}$ is obtained by substituting P_1 from Eq. (15.15) into Eq. (15.12) and then substituting Q from this resulting expression into Eq. (15.14). Thus

$$\dot{Y} = \frac{Q}{A_1} = \frac{K_d X}{A_1} \sqrt{P_s - \frac{F + P_s A_2}{A_1}}$$

$$= \frac{K_d X}{A_1^{3/2}} \sqrt{P_s(A_1 - A_2) - F} \qquad X > 0 \qquad (15.16)$$

For negative values of X, Eq. (15.13) must be used rather than Eq. (15.12). Thus, substituting P_1 from Eq. (15.15) into Eq. (15.13) and then substituting Q from this resulting expression into Eq. (15.14) gives

$$\dot{Y} = \frac{Q}{A_1} = \frac{K_d X}{A_1} \sqrt{\frac{F + P_s A_2}{A_1}}$$

$$= \frac{K_d X}{A_1^{3/2}} \sqrt{F + P_s A_2} \qquad X < 0 \qquad (15.17)$$

In both Eqs. (15.16) and (15.17), it is to be noticed that $\dot{Y}$ is a function of X and F. Thus, linearization of Eqs. (15.16) and (15.17) gives

$$\dot{y} = Dy = \frac{\partial \dot{Y}}{\partial X}\Big|_i x + \frac{\partial \dot{Y}}{\partial F}\Big|_i f$$

or
$$y = \frac{K_1 x - K_2 f}{D} \qquad (15.18)$$

where for $X > 0$

$$\frac{\partial \dot{Y}}{\partial X}\Big|_i = \frac{K_d}{A_1^{3/2}} \sqrt{P_s(A_1 - A_2) - F}\Big|_i = K_1 \qquad (15.19)$$

$$\frac{\partial \dot{Y}}{\partial F}\Big|_i = \frac{-K_d X}{2 A_1^{3/2} \sqrt{P_s(A_1 - A_2) - F}}\Big|_i = -K_2 \qquad (15.20)$$

and for $X < 0$

$$\frac{\partial \dot{Y}}{\partial X}\Big|_i = \frac{K_d}{A_1^{3/2}} \sqrt{F + P_s A_2}\Big|_i = K_1 \qquad (15.21)$$

$$\frac{\partial \dot{Y}}{\partial F}\Big|_i = \frac{K_d X}{2 A_1^{3/2} \sqrt{F + P_s A_2}}\Big|_i = -K_2 \qquad (15.22)$$

In the general case, the pressure force F acting on the piston is resisted by the inertia MD^2Y of the load, viscous friction BDY, a spring force KY, and external load F_L, thus,

$$F = (MD^2 + BD + K)Y + F_L$$

Linearization gives

$$f = (MD^2 + BD + K)y + f_L \qquad (15.23)$$

The substitution of f from Eq. (15.23) into Eq. (15.18) yields the following overall equation of operation for the valve-cylinder circuit:

$$[D + K_2(MD^2 + BD + K)]y = K_1 x - K_2 f_L \qquad (15.24)$$

The block-diagram representation for Eq. (15.24) is shown in Fig. 15.12c.

For smooth operation, it is desirable that K_1 be the same for positive as well as negative values of X, and in addition K_2 should be the same for positive or negative values of X. By comparison of Eqs. (15.19) and (15.21) and by comparison of Eqs. (15.20) and (15.22) it follows that both the preceding conditions are satisfied when the square-root terms are the same, i.e.,

$$P_s A_1 - P_s A_2 - F = F + P_s A_2$$

or
$$P_s A_1 = 2(P_s A_2 + F) \qquad (15.25)$$

When the nominal load F is quite small, the preceding result is satisfied when $A_2 = A_1/2$. For this case, it follows from Eq. (15.15) that $P_1 = P_s/2$, and thus Eqs. (15.19) and (15.21) reduce to

$$K_1 = \frac{K_d}{A_1} \sqrt{\frac{P_s}{2}} = \frac{C_1}{A_1} \qquad (15.26)$$

The normal operation of most valves is about the reference point $X_i = 0$. In this case $K_2 = 0$ in accordance with Eqs. (15.20) and (15.22). When $K_2 = 0$ and Eq. (15.26) is applicable for K_1, Eq. (15.18) reduces to the result that was given by Eq. (2.101), i.e.,

$$y = \frac{C_1}{A_1 D} x$$

In Fig. 15.13a is shown a typical family of curves of F versus $\dot{Y}$ with constant valve positions X. These curves may be obtained analytically from Eqs. (15.16) and (15.17). If an actual valve is available, it is possible to obtain the curves experimentally.

One method of obtaining the curves experimentally is to disconnect the cylinder and place a flowmeter in the P_1 pressure line. Then vary the pressure P_1, and plot the flow through the valve for various fixed (constant) positions X of the valve. A typical family of flow curves is shown in Fig. 15.13b (note that $\dot{Y} = Q/A_1$). For a given $\dot{Y}$ and X, the corresponding value of P_1 may be determined, whence F may be computed in accordance with Eq. (15.15). This process is repeated to obtain corresponding values of $\dot{Y}$, X, and F for plotting Fig. 15.13a. The family of curves shown in Fig. 15.13a is a plot of $\dot{Y}$ as a function of X and F. Linearization of $\dot{Y} = f(X,F)$ again yields Eq. (15.18). The value of $K_1 = \partial \dot{Y}/\partial X \big|_i$ is obtained directly from a vertical interpolation of the curves about the reference operating point. Similarly

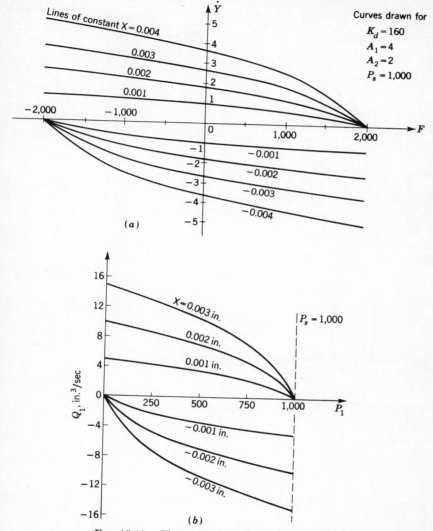

FIG. 15.13. Flow curves for three-way valve.

$K_2 = \partial \dot{Y}/\partial F \big|_i$ is the slope of the line of constant X at the reference point. Thus, these curves provide a very convenient means for evaluating K_1 and K_2 for a particular valve.

Overlapped or Underlapped Valves. Because of manufacturing tolerances, it is not possible to achieve an idealized line-on-line valve. An actual valve will either be overlapped as shown in Fig. 15.14a or underlapped as illustrated in Fig. 15.15a. For an overlapped valve, a dead zone occurs for $-X_0/2 < X < X_0/2$. The plot of uncovered port area

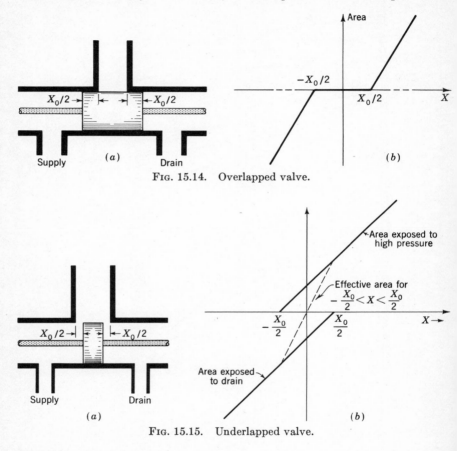

FIG. 15.14. Overlapped valve.

FIG. 15.15. Underlapped valve.

A versus X is shown in Fig. 15.14b. The flow equations for an overlapped valve are

$$Q = K_d W\left(X - \frac{X_0}{2}\right)\sqrt{P_s - P_1} \qquad X \geq \frac{X_0}{2}$$

$$Q = 0 \qquad \frac{-X_0}{2} \leq X \leq \frac{X_0}{2} \quad (15.27)$$

$$Q = K_d W\left(X + \frac{X_0}{2}\right)\sqrt{P_1} \qquad X \leq -\frac{X_0}{2}$$

For the underlapped valve of Fig. 15.15a, the valve must be moved to the left a distance $-X_0/2$ in order to close off the high-pressure, or inlet, passageway. In Fig. 15.15b, the inlet port area increases linearly for $X > -X_0/2$. To close off the return flow, the valve must be moved to the right a distance $X_0/2$. As illustrated by the dashed line of Fig. 15.15b, the effective port area for the underlapped region is the sum of that exposed to inlet flow and that exposed to return flow so that the resulting slope doubles in this region. For $-X_0/2 \leq X \leq X_0/2$ the flow equation is

$$Q = K_d \left(X + \frac{X_0}{2} \right) \sqrt{P_s - P_1} + K_d \left(X - \frac{X_0}{2} \right) \sqrt{P_1} \quad (15.28)$$

When Q is positive, there is a net flow into the cylinder, and when Q is negative, there is a net flow from the cylinder. In Fig. 15.16 are shown

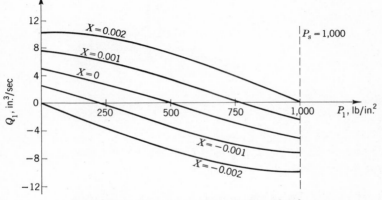

FIG. 15.16. Flow curves for underlapped valve.

the flow curves in the underlapped region for the case in which

$$\frac{X_0}{2} = 0.001 \text{ in.}$$

If an underlapped or overlapped valve is used, the partial derivatives K_1 and K_2 must be evaluated from the appropriate equations. Nothing else is affected in the preceding analysis of the valve-piston circuit. When experimental curves are available for the valve, K_1 and K_2 may be evaluated graphically from these curves.

For control applications in which X is proportional to the error signal, it is usually undesirable to have a dead zone. The reason is that, for small errors such that X is within the dead zone, changes have no effect. The error must become sufficiently large before it is detected. Control valves are usually dimensioned to ensure a slight underlapped condition.

This increases the valve sensitivity when X is within the underlapped region.

Spring-loaded Piston. In Fig. 15.12a, the high-pressure line which bypasses the valve and acts on the left side of the piston serves to provide a constant force P_sA_2. This force moves the piston to the right when the cylinder line is connected to drain. This high-pressure bypass line can be eliminated as shown in Fig. 15.17 by inserting a large spring

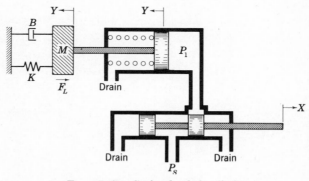

FIG. 15.17.   Spring-loaded cylinder.

behind the piston. The preceding analysis applies equally well to this circuit except that the spring rate K of the load is increased by that of the spring inserted behind the piston.

15.4 Four-way Valve Amplifiers. A four-way pilot valve is illustrated in Fig. 15.18a. The four ports are the high-pressure (or supply) port, a port each for both ends of the cylinder, and a drain port. When the

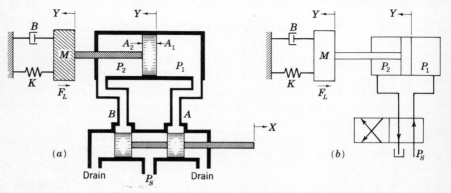

FIG. 15.18.   Four-way-valve-cylinder circuit.

valve is moved to the right, port A is connected to high pressure and port B to drain. This causes the piston to move to the left. When the valve is moved to the left, the reverse action occurs. The receiving unit shown in Fig. 15.18a is called a double-acting cylinder. Because of the four-way valve, it is possible to have the full supply pressure acting on either side of the piston with the other side connected to drain. The cylinders used with a three-way valve are single-acting. With a single-acting cylinder essentially a constant force is applied to one side. This force is generally about one-half the maximum force that can be applied to the other side. Thus, with the single-acting piston which is necessitated by the use of a three-way valve, only about one-half the force can be developed as for the case of a double-acting cylinder. Consequently, four-way valves, which permit the use of double-acting cylinders, are more commonly employed than three-way valves.

To analyze the operation of this circuit, it should first be noted that the velocity $DY = \dot{Y}$ of the piston is

$$\dot{Y} = \frac{Q_1}{A_1} = \frac{K_d X \sqrt{P_s - P_1}}{A_1} \qquad X > 0 \qquad (15.29)$$

$$\dot{Y} = \frac{Q_1}{A_1} = \frac{K_d X \sqrt{P_1}}{A_1} \qquad X < 0 \qquad (15.30)$$

where Q_1 is the rate of flow through port A. In addition, it follows that

$$\dot{Y} = \frac{Q_2}{A_2} = \frac{K_d X \sqrt{P_2}}{A_2} \qquad X > 0 \qquad (15.31)$$

$$\dot{Y} = \frac{Q_2}{A_2} = \frac{K_d X \sqrt{P_s - P_2}}{A_2} \qquad X < 0 \qquad (15.32)$$

where Q_2 is the flow rate at port B.

The resultant pressure force on the piston is

$$F = P_1 A_1 - P_2 A_2 \qquad (15.33)$$

For $X > 0$, the desired functional relationship between $\dot{Y}$, X, and F is obtained by eliminating P_1 and P_2 from Eqs. (15.29), (15.31), and (15.33). Thus

$$\dot{Y} = K_d X \sqrt{\frac{P_s A_1 - F}{A_1{}^3 + A_2{}^3}} \qquad X > 0 \qquad (15.34)$$

Similarly, the corresponding relationship for $X < 0$ is obtained by eliminating P_1 and P_2 from Eqs. (15.30), (15.32), and (15.33). Thus

$$\dot{Y} = K_d X \sqrt{\frac{P_s A_2 + F}{A_1{}^3 + A_2{}^3}} \qquad X < 0 \qquad (15.35)$$

In both Eqs. (15.34) and (15.35), $\dot{Y}$ is a function of X and F; thus linearization gives

$$y = \frac{K_1 x - K_2 f}{D}$$

The preceding result is the same as that given by Eq. (15.18) except that the constants K_1 and K_2 are as follows:

For $X > 0$
$$\left. \frac{\partial \dot{Y}}{\partial X} \right|_i = K_d \sqrt{\frac{P_s A_1 - F}{A_1{}^3 + A_2{}^3}} \bigg|_i = K_1$$

$$\left. \frac{\partial \dot{Y}}{\partial F} \right|_i = -\frac{K_d X}{2} \sqrt{\frac{A_1{}^3 + A_2{}^3}{P_s A_1 - F}} \bigg|_i = -K_2$$

(15.36)

For $X < 0$
$$\left. \frac{\partial \dot{Y}}{\partial X} \right|_i = K_d \sqrt{\frac{P_s A_2 + F}{A_1{}^3 + A_2{}^3}} \bigg|_i = K_1$$

$$\left. \frac{\partial \dot{Y}}{\partial F} \right|_i = \frac{K_d X}{2} \sqrt{\frac{A_1{}^3 + A_2{}^3}{P_s A_2 + F}} \bigg|_i = -K_2$$

(15.37)

From the preceding expressions, it follows that the term K_1 will be the same for positive or negative values of X and so will the term K_2, if

$$P_s A_1 - F = P_s A_2 + F$$
or
$$P_s(A_1 - A_2) = 2F$$

(15.38)

For the case in which the nominal load F is quite small and $A_1 = A_2$, the resulting expression for K_1 reduces to that given by Eq. (15.26). If, in addition, $K_2 = 0$, as is the case for $X_i = 0$, the equation of operation for this valve and cylinder reduces to the result that was given by Eq. (2.101).

A plot of the family of curves determined by Eqs. (15.34) and (15.35) is shown in Fig. 15.19a. This plot greatly facilitates the determination of $K_1 = \partial \dot{Y}/\partial X$ and $K_2 = \partial \dot{Y}/\partial F$. The curves for an underlapped valve are as shown in Fig. 15.19b. To determine these curves for a valve experimentally, first disconnect the cylinder, and then install a flowmeter in the line for port A and one in the line for port B. For port A, vary the pressure P_1, and obtain the flow curves of $\dot{Y} = Q_1/A_1$ versus P_1 for constant values of X. Similarly for port B obtain the flow curves of $\dot{Y} = Q_2/A_2$ versus P_2 for constant valve positions. Then by assuming a $\dot{Y}$ and X, the corresponding value of P_1 is obtained from the curves for port A and the value of P_2 from the port B curves. The force can now be evaluated from Eq. (15.33). Thus, repeating this process to obtain corresponding values of $\dot{Y}$, F, and X gives the desired curves shown in Fig. 15.19b.

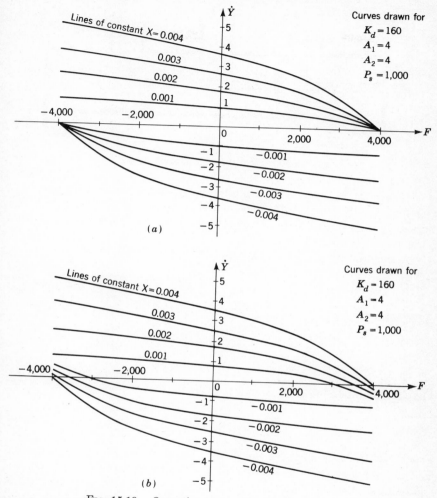

FIG. 15.19. Operating curves for a four-way valve.

15.5 Valve Forces. When fluid is flowing through a spool valve as shown in Fig. 15.20, an axial force is exerted on the valve spool due to the change in momentum of the fluid.[1,2] As is shown in the following analysis, this hydraulic force is always such as to tend to close the valve.

[1] J. F. Blackburn, G. Reethof, and J. L. Shearer, "Fluid Power Control," Technology Press, M.I.T., Cambridge, Mass., and John Wiley & Sons, Inc., New York, 1960.

[2] J. E. Gibson and F. B. Tuteur, "Control System Components," McGraw-Hill Book Company, New York, 1958.

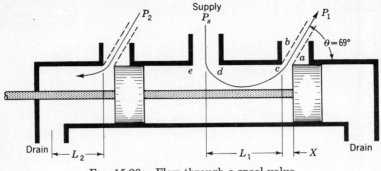

FIG. 15.20.   Flow through a spool valve.

This reactive force acts as a spring in that it increases linearly with the opening X of the valve.   Because of the large inlet port of width de for the supply pressure, the inlet velocity is negligible, as is the change in momentum.   For the right, or exit, port, the effective width ab is small so that the fluid leaves with a very high velocity.   The change in momentum is

$$\frac{d}{dt}(Mv) = \rho\frac{QV}{g} \tag{15.39}$$

where Mv = momentum
 ρ = density
 Q = flow rate
 V = exit velocity at vena contracta, ab

The axial component of force exerted on the valve spool is

$$F_1 = -\frac{Q\rho V}{g}\cos\theta \tag{15.40}$$

where θ is the exit angle of the fluid.   Lee and Blackburn[1] have found that for the type valve shown in Fig. 15.20, in which the valve is square, the value of θ is 69°.   In their analysis, it was assumed that the flow is irrotational, nonviscous, and incompressible and that there is no radial clearance.   The velocity V is given by Bernoulli's equation

$$V = \sqrt{\frac{2g}{\rho}(P_s - P_1)} \tag{15.41}$$

By noting that $Q = C_dAV = C_dWXV$, then

$$F_1 = -2C_dWX(P_s - P_1)\cos\theta \tag{15.42}$$

[1] S. Y. Lee and J. F. Blackburn, Contributions to Hydraulic Control, I, Steady-state Axial Forces on Control Valve Pistons, *Trans. ASME*, **74**: 1005 (1952).

The force F_1 acts as a spring which is extended to its free length when X is zero. When the valve is to the right of center and X is positive, the force acts to the left to tend to close the valve. When the valve is to the left of center and X is negative, the force acts in the opposite direction, again to close the valve. The axial force may be written in the form

$$F_1 = -K_{h_1}X \tag{15.43}$$

where $K_{h_1} = 2C_dW(P_s - P_1)\cos 69°$ is the equivalent hydraulic spring rate. Similarly, it may be shown that the hydraulic force acting on the left land is

$$F_2 = -2C_dWXP_2\cos\theta = -K_{h_2}X \tag{15.44}$$

where $K_{h_2} = 2C_dWP_2\cos 69°$. Thus, the total axial force is

$$F = -(K_{h_1} + K_{h_2})X = -K_hX \tag{15.45}$$

where $K_h = 2C_dW[P_s - (P_1 - P_2)]\cos 69°$.

Lee and Blackburn[1] have also investigated the case of a valve with radial clearance and with land edge of a finite radius. These factors tend to increase the flow area and decrease the exit angle θ so that the axial force tends to be somewhat greater than the analytical predictions indicate.

In addition to the axial valve force which depends on the opening X, Lee and Blackburn[2] have shown that a force is developed due to a velocity dx/dt of the valve. This force may be visualized as follows: Consider the right valve land in Fig. 15.20, in which the supply flow is moving from left to right. With the valve at rest, this fluid has some average velocity. If the valve is in motion to the left so as to close it, the amount of flow is being decreased by the closing of the port, thus decreasing the average velocity of the fluid in the chamber. The force exerted on the valve because of this decrease of momentum tends to resist the motion of the valve. When the valve is in motion to the right, the change in momentum of the fluid also tends to resist the motion of the valve.

If the direction of flow across the valve land is in the opposite direction, as is the case for the left valve land, then the change in momentum is in the opposite direction. The resulting force acting on the valve now aids rather than resists the motion. Lee and Blackburn have shown that the reactive force due to motion of the valve is

$$F' = -\frac{\rho}{g}L\frac{dQ}{dt} \tag{15.46}$$

---

[1] *Ibid.*

[2] S. Y. Lee and J. F. Blackburn, Contributions to Hydraulic Control, II, Transient Flow Forces and Valve Instability, *Trans. ASME*, **74**: 1013–1016 (1952).

where L is the axial distance between the inlet and discharge ports as shown in Fig. 15.20. This distance L is positive when the flow exits from a port (for example, L_1), and the distance L is negative when flow enters the chamber through a port (for example, L_2).[1] This force may be expressed as a function of the velocity of the valve as follows,

$$\frac{dQ}{dt} = \frac{d}{dt}\left(C_d W X \sqrt{\frac{2g}{\rho}}\, P\right) = C_d W \sqrt{\frac{2g}{\rho}}\, P\, Dx \qquad (15.47)$$

where P is the pressure drop across the restriction. In this analysis, it is assumed that the pressure drop across the valve may be considered to remain constant. If P is not constant, the preceding differentiation yields an additional term proportional to the rate of change of the pressure drop. Substitution of the preceding value for dQ/dt in Eq. (15.46) gives

$$F' = -C_d W L \sqrt{\frac{2\rho}{g}}\, P\, Dx \qquad (15.48)$$

Because this force is proportional to the velocity, then in effect a positive-damping term results for positive values of L and negative damping for negative L. The coefficient of viscous damping is $C_d W L \sqrt{(2\rho/g)P}$. Negative damping tends to decrease the valve stability and may cause the valve to sing (high-frequency chatter). The total hydraulic forces acting on the four-way valve of Fig. 15.20 are

$$F = -[(K_{h_1} + K_{h_2}) + C_d W \sqrt{(2\rho/g)P}\,(L_1 + L_2)D]x \qquad (15.49)$$

For the valve shown in Fig. 15.21a, $L_1 > L_2$ so that this valve has more positive damping than the valve in Fig. 15.21b, in which $L_2 > L_1$. Thus,

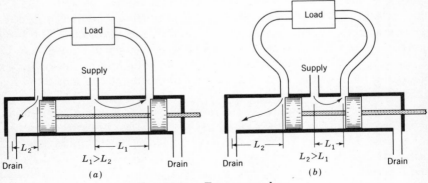

FIG. 15.21.   Four-way valves.

[1] When the force F' is written in the form $F' = (\rho/g)L(dQ/dt)$, then L must be regarded as negative when the flow exits and positive when the flow enters. The advantage of the form given by Eq. (15.46) is that positive L corresponds to positive damping and negative L results in negative damping.

the valve in Fig. 15.21a tends to be more stable than that in Fig. 15.21b. The spring rate and damping caused by hydraulic forces should be taken into account when a change in the external forces acting on a valve causes a corresponding change in the position, as is the case in Figs. 3.16, 4.6, and 4.9. When the valve is, in effect, positively or manually positioned, as is the case in Fig. 3.9, hydraulic reactions on the valve have a negligible effect.

15.6 Flapper Valves. Flapper valves have been developed in an effort to eliminate some of the disadvantages of spool valves. For instance, spool valves are quite expensive to manufacture because axial tolerances between valve lands must be held very closely. Also, the radial clearance must be kept as small as possible, and the corners of the valve lands should be very sharp. If a particle of dirt gets stuck in the small radial clearance, the valve becomes inoperative. The combination of friction, hydraulic forces, inertia forces, changes in fluid viscosity due to changes in temperature, etc., can cause a spool-type valve to chatter, or sing, under various operating conditions.

A flapper valve as shown in Fig. 15.22a is one in which small changes in the position X of the flapper cause large variations in the controlled

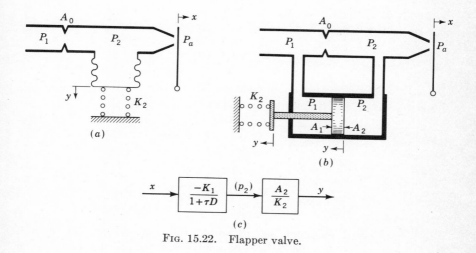

Fig. 15.22. Flapper valve.

pressure P_2 in the chamber. When the flapper is closed off so that there is no flow, the pressure in the chamber is equal to the supply pressure P_1. If the flapper is opened wide, the chamber pressure approaches the ambient pressure P_a. In the following analysis, it is assumed that the fluid flowing through this system is a hydraulic, or an incompressible, fluid. By attaching a spring-loaded bellows which is free to expand as the chamber pressure changes, this becomes a position control device as well as a pressure controller.

In Fig. 15.22b is shown a flapper valve, which serves the same purpose as the three-way valve previously discussed. The following analysis applies equally well to the systems of Fig. 15.22a and b.

Usually the area A_0 of the inlet orifice and the inlet pressure P_1 are held constant so that the pressure P_2 is controlled by the position of the flapper only. Thus, with A_0 and P_1 constant, the volume rate of flow Q_{in} into the chamber is a function of the chamber pressure only. That is,

$$Q_{in} = F(P_2) = C_{d_0}A_0 \sqrt{\frac{2g}{\rho}(P_1 - P_2)} \qquad (15.50)$$

where C_{d_0} is the discharge coefficient for orifice A_0. Linearization of Eq. (15.50) gives

$$q_{in} = \frac{\partial Q_{in}}{\partial P_2}\bigg|_i p_2 = -C_1 p_2 \qquad (15.51)$$

where

$$\frac{\partial Q_{in}}{\partial P_2}\bigg|_i = \frac{-C_{d_0}A_0\sqrt{2g/\rho}}{2\sqrt{P_1 - P_2}}\bigg|_i = -C_1$$

Because the ambient or discharge pressure is usually constant, the volume rate of flow Q_o leaving the chamber is seen to be a function of the position of the flapper X and also the chamber pressure P_2.

$$Q_o = F(X,P_2) = C_{d_f}WX\sqrt{\frac{2g}{\rho}P_2} \qquad (15.52)$$

where C_{d_f} is the discharge coefficient for the flapper orifice and W is the circumference of the flapper hole. Linearization gives

$$q_o = \frac{\partial Q_o}{\partial X}\bigg|_i x + \frac{\partial Q_o}{\partial P_2}\bigg|_i p_2 = C_2 x + C_3 p_2 \qquad (15.53)$$

where

$$\frac{\partial Q_o}{\partial X}\bigg|_i = C_{d_f}W\sqrt{\frac{2g}{\rho}P_2}\bigg|_i = C_2$$

and

$$\frac{\partial Q_o}{\partial P_2}\bigg|_i = \frac{C_{d_f}WX\sqrt{2g/\rho}}{2\sqrt{P_2}}\bigg|_i = C_3$$

When equilibrium exists at the reference condition, $Q_{in}|_i = Q_o|_i$ and the variation $q_{in} - q_o$ is the net rate of flow into or out of the chamber. This net rate of flow is equal to the rate of change of volume of the chamber. For Fig. 15.22a, the rate of change of volume is the effective area of the bellows A_2 times the velocity Dy, and for Fig. 15.22b this is the area A_2 of the piston times the velocity Dy. Thus

$$q_{in} - q_o = A_2 Dy \qquad (15.54)$$

The substitution of q_{in} from Eq. (15.51) and q_o from Eq. (15.53) into Eq. (15.54) gives

$$-C_2x - (C_1 + C_3)p_2 = A_2Dy \qquad (15.55)$$

Flapper valves are frequently employed in applications where the load is primarily a spring. For Fig. 15.22a, it follows that

$$P_2A_2 = K_2Y \qquad (15.56)$$

Similarly for Fig. 15.22b, the summation of forces acting on the piston is

$$P_2A_2 - P_1A_1 = K_2Y \qquad (15.57)$$

Because P_1A_1 is a constant, linearization of Eq. (15.56) or Eq. (15.57) gives the same result, i.e.,

$$y = \frac{A_2}{K_2}p_2 \qquad (15.58)$$

The substitution of p_2 from Eq. (15.58) into Eq. (15.55) yields the following overall equation of operation,

$$y = \frac{A_2(-K_1)x}{K_2(1 + \tau D)} \qquad (15.59)$$

where

$$K_1 = \frac{C_2}{C_1 + C_3}$$

and

$$\tau = \frac{A_2{}^2}{K_2(C_1 + C_3)}$$

The block-diagram representation for Eq. (15.59) is shown in Fig. 15.22c.

The $-K_1$ indicates that, as X increases, Y decreases. This fact is evident from Fig. 15.22a or b because as X increases, the pressure P_2 decreases and thus Y moves in the negative direction. For most flapper valves C_1 and C_3 are very large so that the time constant τ may generally be regarded as negligible.

Equilibrium Operation. Equilibrium exists for a flapper valve when the flow in is equal to the flow out, or

$$Q_{in} = Q_o = C_{d_o}A_0 \sqrt{\frac{2g}{\rho}(P_1 - P_2)} - C_{d_f}WX \sqrt{\frac{2g}{\rho}P_2} = 0 \quad (15.60)$$

Solving for P_2 gives

$$P_2 = \frac{P_1}{1 + (C_{d_f}WX/C_{d_o}A_0)^2} \qquad (15.61)$$

In Fig. 15.23 is shown a typical plot of P_2 versus X for a flapper valve. For steady-state or equilibrium operation, it follows from Fig. 15.22c that $p_2 = -K_1x$. Thus, the constant $-K_1$ is equal to the slope of the

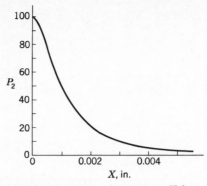

Fig. 15.23. Equilibrium curve of P_2 versus X for a flapper valve.

curve of P_2 versus X, which as shown in Fig. 15.23 remains quite constant over a considerable portion of the operating range. The fact that the slope of this curve is equal to $-K_1$ may also be ascertained as follows: For the implicit function F as given by Eq. (15.60), it follows from calculus that

$$\frac{p_2}{x} \approx \frac{\partial P_2}{\partial X} = -\frac{\partial F/\partial X}{\partial F/\partial P_2} = \frac{-C_2}{C_1 + C_3} = -K_1 \qquad (15.62)$$

where $\partial F/\partial X = -C_2$ and $\partial F/\partial P_2 = -(C_1 + C_3)$.

Although flapper valves find numerous applications in hydraulic systems, they are more extensively used in pneumatic controls. A major reason for this is that spool valves do not lend themselves to pneumatic applications because of the excessive leakage of air that is a result of the very low viscosity of air. Various types of pneumatic flapper valves are treated in detail in Chap. 16.

15.7 Receiving Units. The most commonly employed receiving units for hydraulic circuits are cylinders and motors. Cylinders may be single- or double-acting. Only motors are discussed in the following, because cylinders were included in preceding sections.

Motors. When a pump is supplied with a high-pressure fluid, the pressure force acting on the pistons, vanes, or gears causes the drive shaft to rotate. This is the reverse process of supplying power to the drive shaft of a pump to obtain a flow of high-pressure fluid. Thus, hydraulic motors are basically pumps which are supplied with a flow of high-pressure fluid which transmits power to the drive shaft. When pumps are used as motors, it is usually necessary to modify the design to reduce undesirable unbalanced forces.

In Fig. 15.24 is shown a hydraulic transmission in which the receiving unit is a fixed-displacement motor. Hydraulic transmissions are com-

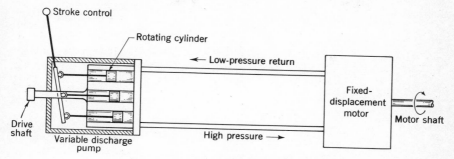

FIG. 15.24. Hydraulic transmission.

monly used as the power element for hydraulic servomechanisms to provide a very fast and accurate control of speed.[1,2] As is shown in Fig. 15.24, a hydraulic transmission consists of a variable-displacement pump which supplies high-pressure oil to a fixed-displacement motor. The direction of rotation is reversed by moving the stroke adjustment to the other side of its neutral position.

The operational representation for this hydraulic transmission is obtained as follows: The ideal volume of flow Q_i coming from the pump is

$$Q_i = na\,\frac{\dot{\theta}_p}{2\pi}\,X = K_p X \tag{15.63}$$

where Q_i = ideal pump flow, in.^{3}/sec
n = number of pistons in pump
a = area of each piston, in.^{2}
$\dot{\theta}_p/2\pi$ = pump speed, rps
X = length of stroke, in.

Because of the pressure drop across the pistons in the pump, a portion of this ideal flow leaks back past the pistons. For a given pump, the leakage flow Q_L is proportional to the pressure P developed by the pump. That is,

$$Q_L = K_L P \tag{15.64}$$

For a fixed-displacement motor, the volume rate of fluid flow Q_n delivered to the motor is

$$Q_n = D_m \dot{\theta}_m \tag{15.65}$$

[1] Blackburn, Reethof, and Shearer, *op. cit.*
[2] Gibson and Tuteur, *op. cit.*

where D_m is the volumetric displacement of the motor per radian and $\dot{\theta}_m$ is the motor speed (radians per second). The mechanical power developed by a motor, $T_m\dot{\theta}_m$, is equal to the hydraulic power delivered to the motor, PQ_n.

$$PQ_n = T_m\dot{\theta}_m \tag{15.66}$$

By substituting Q_n from Eq. (15.65) into Eq. (15.66), it follows that the pump discharge pressure P is proportional to the motor torque T_m, that is,

$$P = \frac{1}{D_m} T_m \tag{15.67}$$

Substitution of the preceding result into Eq. (15.64) shows that the leakage flow Q_L is also proportional to the motor torque T_m,

$$Q_L = \frac{K_L}{D_m} T_m \tag{15.68}$$

In addition to leakage through the pump, the net volume rate of flow Q_n delivered to the motor is less than the ideal volume flow Q_i displaced by the pump because of compressibility effects.

$$Q_n = Q_i - Q_L - Q_c \tag{15.69}$$

Compressibility of a hydraulic fluid may usually be considered negligible except when the fluid is at a very high pressure and when there is a large quantity of fluid in the system. The change in volume ΔV_c of a volume of fluid V is given by the equation

$$\Delta V_c = \frac{V}{B} \Delta P \tag{15.70}$$

where B = bulk modulus of the fluid. The equivalent compressibility flow is the rate of change of volume ΔV_c with respect to time.

$$Q_c = \lim_{\Delta t \to 0} \frac{\Delta V_c}{\Delta t} = \frac{V}{B}\frac{dP}{dt} = \frac{V}{BD_m}\frac{dT_m}{dt} = \frac{K_c}{D_m}DT_m \tag{15.71}$$

where $K_c = V/B$. Substitution of Eqs. (15.63), (15.65), (15.68), and (15.71) into Eq. (15.69) gives

$$D_m\dot{\theta}_m = K_pX - \frac{K_L}{D_m}T_m - \frac{K_c}{D_m}DT_m \tag{15.72}$$

If the load on the motor shaft consists of inertia, viscous damping, and an arbitrary load torque,

$$T_m = (JD + B_v)\dot{\theta}_m + T_L \tag{15.73}$$

Substitution of T_m from Eq. (15.73) into Eq. (15.72) and solving for θ_m yields

$$\theta_m = \frac{D_m K_p X - (K_L + K_c D) T_L}{K_c J D^2 + (K_c B_\nu + K_L J) D + (D_m{}^2 + K_L B_\nu)} \quad (15.74)$$

After making the coefficient of the D^2 term unity by factoring $K_c J$ out of the denominator, the natural frequency ω_n for the second-order characteristic equation is found to be

$$\omega_n = \sqrt{\frac{D_m{}^2 + K_L B_\nu}{K_c J}} \quad (15.75)$$

and similarly it follows that

$$2\zeta\omega_n = \left(\frac{B_\nu}{J} + \frac{K_L}{K_c}\right) \quad (15.76)$$

whence the damping ratio may be evaluated.

The preceding hydraulic transmission is primarily a speed control device. The position of the stroke control lever determines the flow to the fixed-displacement motor and thus controls the speed of rotation. Slight variations in speed result because of leakage and compressibility effects.

Numerous circuits are available for utilizing fluid motors. For example, if a fixed-displacement motor is supplied from a constant-pressure power supply, a constant torque is exerted on the motor. Thus a constant-torque drive results. The addition of a pressure-regulating device to vary the pressure permits torque control. In a similar manner, a constant-horsepower drive may be obtained by supplying a variable-displacement motor with a fixed-displacement pump.

Problems

15.1 The ideal torque required to produce a pressure rise $P_o - P_{in}$ across a pump is equal to the product of the pressure rise and the ideal pump displacement D_i per radian of pump rotation. The torque efficiency of a pump is the ratio of the ideal torque to the actual torque T required to drive the pump $[\eta_T = (P_o - P_{in}) D_i / T]$. The volumetric efficiency η_v is the ratio of actual net rate of flow Q discharged per second to the ideal discharge $D_i \omega$, where ω is the angular velocity of the pump. Show that the overall pump efficiency is equal to the product of the torque efficiency and volumetric efficiency of the pump.

15.2 A hydraulic damper, or dashpot, is shown in Fig. P15.2. The force F causes a pressure drop ΔP across the piston so that $F = A \Delta P$, where A is the net piston area. The leakage flow Q between the piston and cylinder is given by the equation

$$Q = \frac{\pi}{12} \frac{D d^3 \Delta P}{L \mu}$$

where Q = rate of flow, in.^{3}/sec

D = diameter of piston, in.

d = mean clearance = $\frac{1}{2}$ difference between cylinder and piston diameters, in.

L = length of piston, in.

ΔP = pressure drop across piston, psi

μ = absolute viscosity, reyns (lb-sec/in.^{2})

The velocity of the piston is $dx/dt = Q/A$. Show that the equation of operation for this damper may be written in the form $F = B(dx/dt)$. What is the resultant expression for the coefficient of viscous damping B?

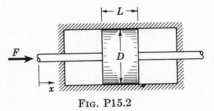

FIG. P15.2

15.3 A modification of the viscous damper of Fig. P15.2 is shown in Fig. P15.3. As in Prob. 15.2, the force F is resisted by the pressure drop ΔP, which acts on the diaphragm. Because the diaphragm prevents leakage, the flow Q must travel through the viscous restriction. The equation for the flow through a viscous restriction is given by Eq. (15.8). The velocity of the diaphragm is $dx/dt = Q/A$. Show that the equation of operation for this damper may be written in the form $F = B(dx/dt)$. Determine the resulting expression for the coefficient of viscous damping B.

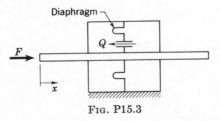

FIG. P15.3

15.4 For the flow control system shown in Fig. 15.10a, the net flow Q going through the throttle valve is equal to the flow Q_1 supplied by the pump minus the flow Q_d which is bypassed through the differential-pressure-regulating valve to drain (that is, $Q = Q_1 - Q_d$). Because the pump supply Q_1 is constant, for variations about some reference operating condition it follows that $q = -q_d$. The flow through the throttle valve is given by the equation $Q = C_d A_t \sqrt{P_1 - P_2}$. Linearization gives $q = C_1 a_t + C_2(p_1 - p_2)$. Similarly, the amount of flow which is bypassed is given by the expression $Q_d = K_d X \sqrt{P_1}$, where X is the opening of the valve plunger. Linearization gives $q_d = C_3 x + C_4 p_1$. The force balance for the valve plunger is $(P_1 - P_2)A = MD^2X + KX + F_c$, so that linearization gives $(p_1 - p_2)A = (MD^2 + K)x$. Combining the preceding linearized expressions yields the block diagram shown in Fig. P15.4a.

Because P_2 rather than P_1 is the independent variable which acts as the external disturbance, the block diagram of Fig. P15.4a should be modified as shown in Fig. P15.4b.

By means of block-diagram algebra, eliminate the minor feedback loop of Fig. P15.4b and determine the resulting characteristic equation for this system.

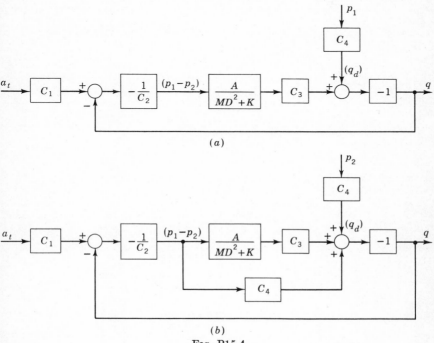

(a)

(b)

FIG. P15.4

15.5 For Prob. 15.4, suppose that a viscous damper is inserted as shown in Fig. 15.10b. The equation for the flow through this damper is given by Eq. (15.9), and the force balance for the plunger is given by Eq. (15.10). Determine the resulting characteristic equation for this system.

15.6 For the flow control system of Fig. 15.11b, the flow $Q = K_d X \sqrt{P_s - P_1}$ goes from the supply line through the unloading valve. This same flow passes through the throttle valve so that $Q = C_d A_t \sqrt{P_1 - P_2}$. Linearization of the preceding expressions gives $q = C_1 x - C_2 p_1$ and $q = C_3 a_t + C_4(p_1 - p_2)$. The force balance for the plunger is $(P_1 - P_2)A = MD^2 X + KX + F_c$; thus for small variations $(p_1 - p_2)A = (MD^2 + K)x$. Construct the block diagram for this system in which a_t is the input, q the output, and p_2 the external disturbance. What is the resulting characteristic equation?

15.7 Same as Prob. 15.6, except that a viscous damper is inserted between the spring-loaded side of the plunger and the downstream side of the throttle valve.

15.8 Determine the block-diagram representation for the hydraulic servomotor of Fig. 3.5 in which the operation of the four-way valve and cylinder is given by Eq. (15.18) rather than Eq. (2.101).

15.9 Determine the block-diagram representation for each of the hydraulic power amplifiers shown in Fig. P15.9a and b. The spring K in Fig. P15.9b represents flexibility in the linkage between the power output and the load. Determine the characteristic equation for each system.

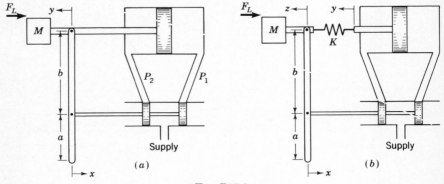

Fig. P15.9

15.10 A hydraulic servo system used to control the traverse feed of a machine tool is shown in Fig. P15.10. Each angular position of the cam corresponds to

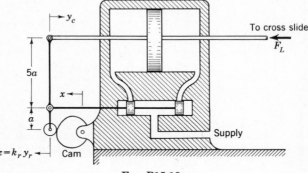

Fig. P15.10

a desired reference position y_r such that $z = k_r y_r$. For steady-state operation, the valve must be line on line, in which case $x = 0$. Because of the 5:1 lever ratio, it follows that $y_c = 5z = 5(k_r y_r)$. Thus, the value of k_r should be 0.2 in order to have $y_c = y_r$ during steady-state operation. The load on the piston is that due to the tool reactive force on the cross-slide mechanism.

Operation of the valve and cylinder is described by Eq. (15.24). Complete the block diagram for this system. What are the necessary conditions such that there will be no steady-state error due to variations in the external load?

15.11 In Fig. P15.11 is shown a machine tool with a tape-controlled traverse feed. (The longitudinal and rotational axes may also be tape-controlled if so

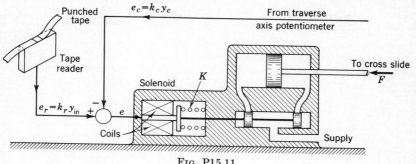

Fig. P15.11

desired.) The tape reader converts the signal on the punched tape to an electrical voltage $e_r = k_r y_r$ which is proportional to the desired traverse position y_r. A voltage signal $e_c = k_c y_c$ which is proportional to the actual position is fed back and compared with the reference signal. The error signal goes to the coils of a solenoid valve which gives a magnetic force ($f_m = k_m e$) in proportion to the error. This force is resisted by a spring such that $f_m = Kx$. The load on the piston is due to the tool reactive force acting on the cross-slide mechanism. Thus, operation of the valve and cylinder may be described by Eq. (15.24). Complete the block diagram for this system. What are the necessary conditions such that there will be no steady-state error due to variations in the external load?

15.12 The fluid power source for a hydraulic motor may be a variable-delivery pump (i.e., hydraulic transmission) or a servo valve as shown in Fig. P15.12.

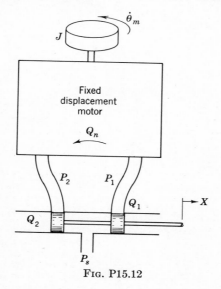

Fig. P15.12

The net flow delivered to the motor is

$$Q_n = Q_1 - Q_{c_1} - Q_L = D_m \dot{\theta}_m \qquad (a)$$

where $Q_{c_1} = \dfrac{V}{B}\dfrac{dP_1}{dt} = K_c D P_1$ is the equivalent compressibility flow in the P_1 pressure line and $Q_L = K_L(P_1 - P_2) = (K_L/D_m)T_m$ is the leakage flow through the motor.

The return flow Q_2 is the net flow Q_n minus the equivalent compressibility flow Q_{c_2} of the P_2 pressure line

$$Q_2 = Q_n - Q_{c_2} = D_m \dot{\theta}_m - K_c D P_2 \qquad (b)$$

The torque developed by the motor is

$$T_m = D_m(P_1 - P_2) \qquad (c)$$

Write the flow equations for Q_1 and Q_2 as a function of the respective pressure drops, across the valve and X. Linearize Eqs. (a) to (c), and then eliminate p_1 and p_2 to obtain the functional relationship between $\Delta\dot{\theta}_m$, t_m, and x. Construct the block diagram for the case in which the load consists of an inertia $JD^2\theta_m$ and external torque T_L.

16

Pneumatic systems

Pneumatic systems are distinguished from hydraulic systems in that the fluid medium for pneumatic systems is a compressible fluid (usually air) and that for hydraulic systems is an incompressible liquid. An advantage of using air as the working medium is its availability. After completion of its work cycle, the air may be exhausted to the atmosphere so that there is no need for return lines as there is with hydraulic fluid. Most hydraulic fluids are flammable so that leaks in such systems present fire hazards. No such danger results when air is employed as the working medium. Because the viscosity of hydraulic fluids changes considerably with temperature, variations in temperature of the working fluid have a marked effect upon the performance of such systems. The change of viscosity of the working medium used in pneumatic systems is usually negligible.

A fundamental advantage of hydraulic systems is that the incompressibility of the fluid results in positive action, or motion, and faster response. With pneumatic systems some of the flow is used to change the density of the fluid (i.e., to compress the fluid) so that pneumatic systems are characterized by longer time delays and less positive action. These disadvantages are diminished by the use of higher operating pressures.

The analysis of pneumatic systems is similar to that for hydraulic systems. The main difference is that the mass rate of flow of the fluid must be considered in pneumatic systems, whereas the volume rate of flow suffices for hydraulic systems.[1] It is not uncommon to have the same type of component used for both high-pressure pneumatic systems and hydraulic systems. To account for the increase in volume at the low-pressure outlets of a pneumatic component, the outlet ports are larger than the inlet ports.

[1] J. F. Blackburn, G. Reethof, and J. L. Shearer, "Fluid Power Control," Technology Press, M.I.T., Cambridge, Mass., and John Wiley & Sons, Inc., New York, 1960.

16.1 Pneumatic Power Supplies. Although there are many different forms and kinds of air compressors used to supply pneumatic power, usually such compressors may be classified as centrifugal, axial-flow, or positive-displacement compressors.

In Fig. 16.1 is shown a centrifugal air compressor. The air enters at the center, or eye, of the impeller. By centrifugal action the

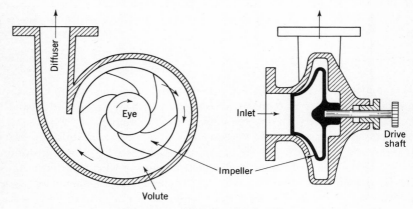

Fig. 16.1. Centrifugal compressor.

impeller throws the fluid into the volute, whence it goes to the diffuser. The fluid leaving the impeller has considerable kinetic energy, which is gradually changed to static pressure as the fluid travels through the volute and the diffuser. Such compressors deliver relatively small amounts of flow. The discharge pressure from a centrifugal compressor seldom exceeds 50 psia.

An axial-flow compressor is shown in Fig. 16.2. The annular area at the inlet to an axial-flow compressor is much larger than the rela-

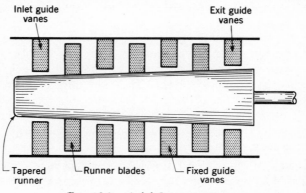

Fig. 16.2. Axial-flow compressor.

tively small area at the eye of the impeller of a centrifugal compressor. Thus, an axial compressor can deliver much more flow than a centrifugal compressor. The blades that are attached to the rotor of an axial compressor impart kinetic energy to the fluid, and the fixed blades in the housing act as diffusers to change this kinetic energy to static pressure. Because the fluid is continually being compressed as it flows through the compressor, the blades gradually become smaller to account for the decrease in specific volume of the fluid. The discharge pressure for such compressors is usually less than 100 psia.

Positive-displacement compressors are used to supply pneumatic power for high-pressure systems. In Fig. 16.3a is shown the PV diagram

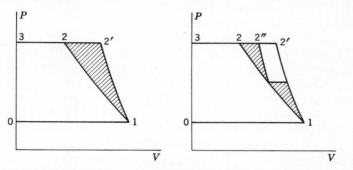

Fig. 16.3. PV diagram for ideal positive-displacement compressor.

for an ideal positive-displacement compressor which has no clearance. Air is brought into the cylinder as indicated by the line 0-1. If the compression is accomplished isothermally (i.e., the temperature of the air remains constant), then the line 1-2 is the path of compression. The equation for this line is

$$PV = \text{constant} \tag{16.1}$$

To have the compression occur isothermally, the heat due to compression must be continuously extracted. Actually, the cylinder, or housing, around the piston insulates the fluid so that the actual compression process is nearly adiabatic (i.e., no heat is transferred). The equation of adiabatic compression which follows the path 1-2' is

$$PV^{1.4} = \text{constant} \tag{16.2}$$

When the discharge pressure $P_2 = P_2'$ is reached, the discharge valve opens and air is expelled from the cylinder until the end of the stroke as indicated by point 3. Most compressor discharge valves are pressure-operated, so that when the air is compressed to the desired discharge pressure, the exhaust valve is forced open.

The total work of compression is equal to the area enclosed by the closed path of the compression cycle. The shaded area 1-2'-2-1 in Fig. 16.3*a* is the additional work needed for adiabatic compression as compared with isothermal compression. By using interstage cooling as represented in Fig. 16.3*b*, the ideal isothermal compression is more closely approximated. This requires the use of a multistage compressor in which the air is first compressed to some intermediate pressure in the low-pressure stage. Then the air is directed through an intercooler before it enters the high-pressure stage to complete the compression. For pressures of 500 psia or higher, three or more stages of compression may be used. To obtain clean, dry air, an intake filter and dehydrator are used. The filter removes foreign particles, dust, and dirt, while the dehydrator removes excess moisture.

16.2 Flapper Amplifiers. When the flapper valves of Fig. 15.22*a* and *b* are supplied with high-pressure air, pneumatic flapper amplifiers result. The basic operation of a pneumatic amplifier is the same as that for the corresponding hydraulic amplifier. That is, the pressure P_2 in the chamber is controlled by the position X of the flapper. When X is zero so that the flapper is closed, the pressure P_2 is equal to the supply pressure P_1. When the flapper is opened wide so that X is large, P_2 approaches the ambient pressure P_a. A typical graph of P_2 versus X is shown in Fig. 16.4. Small changes in the input motion X cause large changes in

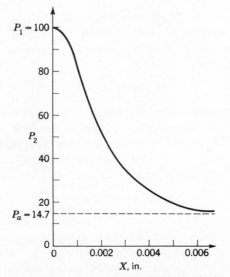

FIG. 16.4.   Graph of P_2 versus X for pneumatic flapper valve.

the controlled pressure P_2.   A position controller is obtained by providing a spring-loaded bellows or piston.

The procedure used to obtain the operational form of the differential equation for this pneumatic amplifier is similar to that used for the hydraulic amplifier, with the exception that, because of compressibility effects, the mass rate of flow must be considered rather than the volume rate.   With a constant supply pressure P_1 and fixed area of inlet orifice, A_0, the mass rate of flow into the chamber, M_{in}, is a function of the chamber pressure P_2 only.   Thus,

$$M_{in} = F(P_2)$$

and
$$m_{in} = \frac{\partial M_{in}}{\partial P_2}\bigg|_i p_2 = -C_1 p_2 \qquad (16.3)$$

In Sec. 16.6, equations for the flow of a compressible fluid through an orifice are developed, whence the corresponding partial derivatives may be evaluated.   It is also shown how to determine the equilibrium or reference operating conditions such as are illustrated by Fig. 16.4.

The mass rate of flow out from the chamber, M_o, is a function of X and P_2.   Thus

$$M_o = F(X,P_2)$$

and
$$m_o = \frac{\partial M_o}{\partial X}\bigg|_i x + \frac{\partial M_o}{\partial P_2}\bigg|_i p_2 = C_2 x + C_3 p_2 \qquad (16.4)$$

The change in mass w of air in the chamber is the integral of $m_{in} - m_o$, that is,

$$w = \frac{-C_1 p_2 - C_2 x - C_3 p_2}{D} \qquad (16.5)$$

From the equation of state, the pressure P_2 in the chamber is

$$P_2 = \frac{WRT_2}{V_2} \qquad (16.6)$$

where V_2 is the volume of the chamber and T_2 is the stagnation temperature of the air in the chamber.   For the usual case of adiabatic flow, the stagnation temperature T_2 is equal to the stagnation temperature T_1 of the supply, which is constant.   Linearization of Eq. (16.6) yields the following expression for the variation p_2 of pressure in the chamber:

$$p_2 = \frac{\partial P_2}{\partial W}\bigg|_i w + \frac{\partial P_2}{\partial V_2}\bigg|_i v_2 = C_4 w - C_5 v_2 \qquad (16.7)$$

The change of pressure in the chamber depends upon the change of mass w and the change of volume v_2.   By use of Eq. (16.6) to evaluate the partial derivatives, it follows that

$$\frac{\partial P_2}{\partial W}\bigg|_i = \frac{RT_2}{V_2}\bigg|_i = C_4 \tag{16.8}$$

$$\frac{\partial P}{\partial V}\bigg|_i = \frac{-WRT_2}{V_2{}^2}\bigg|_i = \frac{-P_2}{V_2}\bigg|_i = -C_5 \tag{16.9}$$

The change in volume v_2 of the chamber is equal to the area A_2 times the change in length y. That is,

$$v_2 = A_2 y \tag{16.10}$$

The change in the pressure force $p_2 A_2$ is equal to the change in spring force $K_2 y$. Thus

$$p_2 A_2 = K_2 y \tag{16.11}$$

The overall relationship between the input x and output y is obtained by substituting w from Eq. (16.5), v_2 from Eq. (16.10), and p_2 from Eq. (16.11) into Eq. (16.7). Thus

$$y = \frac{A_2}{K_2} \frac{-K_1}{1 + \tau D} x \tag{16.12}$$

where $K_1 = C_2/(C_1 + C_3)$ and $\tau = (1 + C_5 A_2{}^2/K_2)/[(C_1 + C_3)C_4]$. Equation (16.12) has the same general form as Eq. (15.59), and thus the block-diagram representation for this pneumatic amplifier is the same as that for the corresponding hydraulic amplifier drawn in Fig. 15.22c. The constant $-K_1$ is the slope of Fig. 16.4 at the reference operating condition. Although τ is slightly larger for a pneumatic amplifier than for a corresponding hydraulic amplifier, it is still extremely small and is generally regarded as negligible.

16.3 Two-stage Amplifiers. For the control of large industrial processes where it is necessary to have large quantities of a controlled pneumatic pressure, it is customary to use a two-stage amplifier as shown in Fig. 16.5a. The first stage of amplification consists of a flapper-type amplifier in which the pressure P_2 is controlled by the flapper position X. The controlled pressure P_2 determines the position Y of the metering valve for the second amplifier. The second stage of amplification is capable of handling large quantities of flow. This second unit is called an air relay.

The actuating signal e coming from the comparator is the input signal for the two-stage controller shown in Fig. 16.5a. An increase in the actuating signal moves the top of the error link to the right, and thus the flapper also moves to the right. This in turn decreases the pressure P_2, which causes the metering valve to move up to admit more flow to the main part of the system. If the actuating signal decreases, then

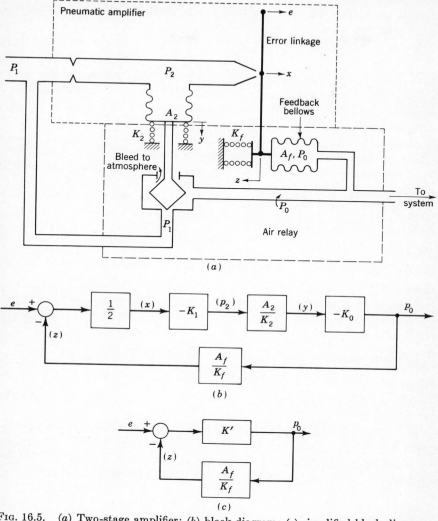

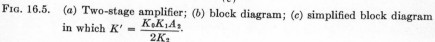

FIG. 16.5. (a) Two-stage amplifier; (b) block diagram; (c) simplified block diagram in which $K' = \dfrac{K_0 K_1 A_2}{2K_2}$.

the metering valve moves down to block off the supply flow and open wider the bleed passageway. Bleeding off more flow to the atmosphere in turn causes P_o to decrease. By proper contouring of the metering valve, a linear relationship may be obtained between the actuating signal e and the output pressure P_o.

The first stage (i.e., flapper amplifier) for a two-stage amplifier is usually such that the time constant τ is negligibly small, in which case Eq. (16.12) becomes

$$y = \frac{A_2}{K_2}(-K_1)x \tag{16.13}$$

Because of the compressibility of air, a certain time lag is associated with the change of pressure in any portion of the system. However, pneumatic systems are generally proportioned so that the time constants associated with certain portions are negligibly small, and thus the larger time constants have the predominant effect on the system behavior.

The position Y of the air relay determines the pressure P_o, or $P_o = F(Y)$. Because the air relay handles a large quantity of flow, the pressure P_o changes almost instantaneously for changes in the position Y of the metering valve, and hence there is a negligible time delay associated with this device. Thus, the equation of operation is

$$p_o = -K_o y \tag{16.14}$$

where $-K_o = \partial P_o/\partial Y \big|_i$ is the slope of the curve of P_o versus Y for the air relay.

For the error linkage

$$x = \frac{e - z}{2} \tag{16.15}$$

The summation of forces acting on the feedback bellows gives

$$K_f Z = A_f P_o$$

or

$$z = \frac{A_f}{K_f} p_o \tag{16.16}$$

From Eqs. (16.13) through (16.16), the block-diagram representation for this controller is drawn as shown in Fig. 16.5b. By letting $K' = K_o K_1 A_2/2K_2$ the block diagram of Fig. 16.5c results. The relationship between the output p_o and the input e for this controller is

$$p_o = \frac{K'}{1 + K'(A_f/K_f)} e \tag{16.17}$$

This is recognized as a proportional controller because

$$G_1(D) = \frac{K'}{[1 + K'(A_f/K_f)]}$$

is a constant. For the usual case in which $K'A_f/K_f \gg 1$, the preceding expression reduces to

$$p_o \approx \frac{K'}{K'(A_f/K_f)} e = \frac{K_f}{A_f} e \tag{16.18}$$

The relationship given by Eq. (16.18) can be deduced directly from a closer examination of Fig. 16.5a. The position x changes only a very small amount to produce a large change in P_2, which in turn controls P_o. Because of the very small motion at x, this point may be considered as a fixed pivot point, or

$$z \approx e \qquad (16.19)$$

The substitution of $z = (A_f/K_f)p_o$ into Eq. (16.19) gives the result of Eq. (16.18).

Proportional plus Derivative Action. The proportional controller of Fig. 16.5a is changed to a proportional plus derivative controller by inserting a restriction between the outlet line P_o and the feedback bellows, as is shown in Fig. 16.6a. The area of this restriction is small so that the

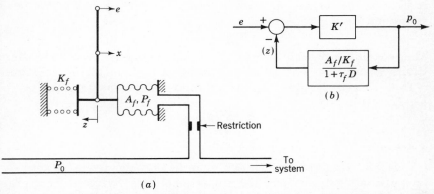

(a)

(b)

FIG. 16.6. (a) Two-stage amplifier with proportional plus derivative action; (b) block diagram.

time constant associated with changing the feedback pressure P_f in the bellows is appreciable. The equation relating the pressure P_f in this bellows to the pressure P_o on the other side of the restriction is obtained as follows: For a given sized restriction at the input to this bellows, the mass rate of flow, M, going to the bellows is a function of the pressure P_o and the pressure P_f in the bellows.

$$M = F(P_o, P_f)$$

Linearization gives

$$m = \frac{\partial M}{\partial P_o}\bigg|_i p_o + \frac{\partial M}{\partial P_f}\bigg|_i p_f = C_1 p_o - C_2 p_f \qquad (16.20)$$

where $\partial M/\partial P_o\big|_i = C_1$ and $\partial M/\partial P_f\big|_i = -C_2$. The fact that C_1 is equal to C_2 is ascertained as follows: Suppose that p_o and p_f are changed by the same amount so that there is no resulting pressure drop and no flow ($m = 0$) across the restriction. From Eq. (16.20), it follows that C_1 must equal C_2 to substantiate the known result that m is zero. The pressure P_f is obtained from the equation of state, i.e.,

$$P_f = \frac{WRT_f}{V_f} \tag{16.21}$$

where V_f is the volume of the bellows and T_f is the corresponding temperature. The change of pressure p_f is

$$p_f = \frac{\partial P_f}{\partial W}\bigg|_i w + \frac{\partial P_f}{\partial V_f}\bigg|_i v_f = C_3 w - C_4 v_f \tag{16.22}$$

The change in volume v_f is equal to the effective area of the bellows times the displacement z.

$$v_f = A_f z \tag{16.23}$$

A force balance on the feedback bellows gives $A_f P_f = K_f Z$ or for small variations

$$A_f p_f = K_f z \tag{16.24}$$

The overall relationship between z and p_o is obtained as follows: Substitute w, which is obtained by integration of Eq. (16.20), substitute v_f from Eq. (16.23) into Eq. (16.22), and then eliminate p_f by use of Eq. (16.24). Thus

$$z = \frac{(A_f/K_f)p_o}{1 + \tau_f D} \tag{16.25}$$

where $\qquad\qquad \tau_f = (1 + C_4 A_f{}^2/K_f)/C_2 C_3$

This relationship between z and p_o is the only difference between the proportional controller and the proportional plus derivative controller. Thus, the insertion of the block diagram for Eq. (16.25) into the feedback path between p_o and z of Fig. 16.5c gives the overall block diagram for the proportional plus derivative controller shown in Fig. 16.6b. The overall equation of operation for this controller is

$$p_o = \frac{K'e}{1 + (K'A_f/K_f)/(1 + \tau_f D)} = \frac{K'(1 + \tau_f D)e}{(1 + K'A_f/K_f) + \tau_f D} \tag{16.26}$$

Because K' is very large, $1 + K'A_f/K_f \approx K'A_f/K_f \gg 1$, in which case Eq. (16.26) becomes

$$p_o = \frac{(K_f/A_f)(1 + \tau_f D)e}{1 + [\tau_f/(K'A_f/K_f)]D} \tag{16.27}$$

Because $K'A_f/K_f \gg 1$, the time constant in the denominator may be regarded as negligible. Thus

$$p_o = \frac{K_f}{A_f}e + \frac{K_f \tau_f}{A_f} De \tag{16.28}$$

The preceding expression shows the proportional plus derivative action of this controller.

Proportional plus Integral Action. The proportional controller of Fig. 16.5a is changed to a proportional plus integral controller by the addition of a second bellows as shown in Fig. 16.7a. The effective area

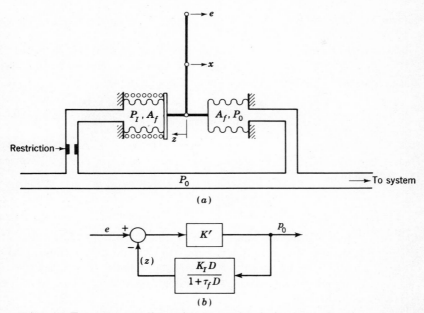

Fig. 16.7. (a) Two-stage amplifier with proportional plus integral action; (b) block diagram.

A_f of this bellows is the same as that of the feedback bellows. Because the bellows on the left provides the integrating action, it is called the integrating bellows. The pressure inside of this bellows is P_I. The feedback bellows on the right has no restriction, so that its pressure is always P_o. The equation of operation for this proportional plus integral controller is obtained by applying the method of analysis just described for the proportional plus derivative controller. Thus

$$m = \frac{\partial M}{\partial P_o}\bigg|_i p_o + \frac{\partial M}{\partial P_I}\bigg| p_I = C_1 p_o - C_2 p_I$$

where

$$C_1 = C_2$$

$$p_I = \frac{\partial P_I}{\partial W}\bigg| w + \frac{\partial P_I}{\partial V_I}\bigg| v_I = C_3 w - C_4 v_I \qquad (16.29)$$

where

$$P_I = \frac{WRT_I}{V_I}$$

$$v_I = -A_f z$$

and

$$(p_o - p_I)A_f = K_f z$$

From the preceding expressions, the overall relationship between z and p_o is found to be

$$z = \frac{K_I D}{1 + \tau_f D} p_o \tag{16.30}$$

where $\qquad K_I = \dfrac{A_f}{C_2 C_3 K_f} \qquad$ and $\qquad \tau_f = \dfrac{1 + C_4 A_f{}^2/K_f}{C_2 C_3}$

Figure 16.7*b* shows the overall block diagram for this controller, in which Eq. (16.30) is seen to describe the operation of the internal feedback elements. The overall equation of operation is

$$p_o = \frac{K'e}{1 + K'K_I D/(1 + \tau_f D)} = \frac{K'(1 + \tau_f D)e}{1 + (\tau_f + K'K_I)D} \tag{16.31}$$

Because the time constant for the denominator $\tau_f + K'K_I \approx K'K_I \gg 1$, then $1 + (\tau_f + K'K_I)D$ is closely approximated by $K'K_I D$. Thus Eq. (16.31) becomes

$$p_o = \frac{(1 + \tau_f D)e}{K_I D} = \frac{1}{K_I D} e + \frac{\tau_f D}{K_I D} e \tag{16.32}$$

The first term on the right-hand side of Eq. (16.32) provides the integrating effect, and the second term contributes the proportional action.

By adding derivative action to this proportional plus integral controller, a proportional plus integral plus derivative controller is obtained, as is shown in Fig. 16.8.

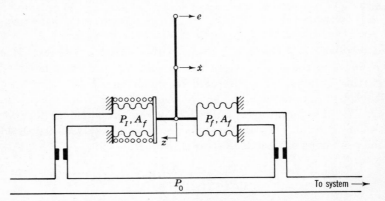

Fig. 16.8. Proportional plus integral plus derivative controller.

16.4 Pneumatic Controllers. A force-type pneumatic controller operates only on pressure signals, and so it is necessary to convert the reference input and controlled variable to corresponding pressures. Simple adjustments make it easy to modify the operating characteristics of a force-type controller. Such industrial controllers are sometimes called "stack controllers."[1,2]

In Fig. 16.9a is shown a force-type controller which has proportional action. The subscripts refer to the signal to which the pressure corresponds, i.e.,

P_r = pressure corresponding to reference input
P_c = pressure corresponding to controlled variable
P_o = pressure corresponding to output of controller
P_f = pressure corresponding to an internal-feedback signal

The operation of the controller shown in Fig. 16.9a may be summarized as follows: An increase in the pressure P_r which is proportional to the reference input causes the valve stem to move down to close off the bleed restriction for P_o. This in turn causes the output pressure P_o to increase.

To obtain the equation of operation for this controller, first sum up the forces acting on the pilot stem.

$$P_f A_2 + P_r(A_1 - A_2) - P_c(A_1 - A_2) - P_o A_2 = 0 \qquad (16.33)$$

or

$$(P_r - P_c)(A_1 - A_2) + P_f A_2 = P_o A_2 \qquad (16.34)$$

The block-diagram representation for Eq. (16.34) is given in Fig. 16.9b. This shows that the comparator which produces the actuating signal e is automatically incorporated into this controller. The two-stage amplifier was separately excited by the actuating signal e. To complete the feedback between the output signal P_o and the feedback signal P_f, it is necessary to determine the relationship between p_o and p_f. On the assumption that there is a negligible time lag between p_f and p_o, it follows that

$$p_f = C_1 p_o \qquad (16.35)$$

where

$$C_1 = \frac{\partial P_f}{\partial P_o}\bigg|_i$$

Because p_f is less than p_o, the value of C_1 is less than 1. The completed block diagram is shown in Fig. 16.9c. Because of the one linearized relationship, Eq. (16.35), the entire block diagram must be linearized. The overall relationship between p_o and e is

$$p_o = \frac{(1/A_2)e}{1 - C_1} = \frac{1}{A_2(1 - C_1)}\, e = K'e \qquad (16.36)$$

---

[1] D. P. Eckman, "Automatic Process Control," John Wiley & Sons, Inc., New York, 1958.

[2] J. E. Gibson and F. B. Tuteur, "Control System Components," McGraw-Hill Book Company, New York, 1958.

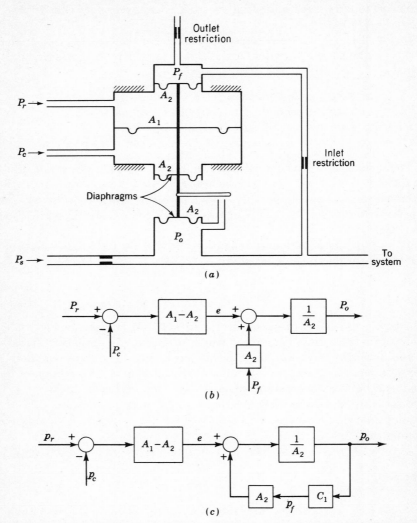

FIG. 16.9. (a) Force-type controller with proportional action; (b) block diagram of force balance for force-type controller; (c) overall block diagram for force-type controller.

This is recognized as the operating equation for a proportional controller. The value of K' increases as C_1 approaches unity. This is accomplished by making the inlet restriction to the P_f chamber large compared with the outlet restriction.

This controller is converted to a proportional plus integral controller by closing off the outlet restriction as shown in Fig. 16.10a. For this

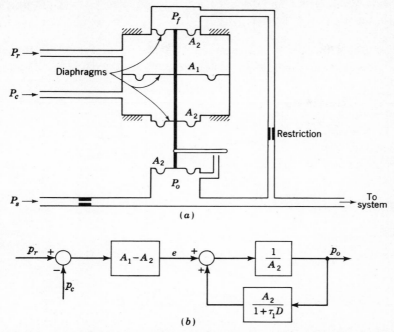

FIG. 16.10. (a) Force-type controller with proportional plus integral action; (b) overall block diagram.

case, it may be demonstrated that

$$p_f = \frac{p_o}{1 + \tau_1 D} \tag{16.37}$$

The block-diagram representation for this controller is given in Fig. 16.10b, from which it follows that

$$p_o = \frac{(1/A_2)e}{1 - 1/(1 + \tau_1 D)} = \frac{1}{A_2}\frac{1 + \tau_1 D}{\tau_1 D} e$$

$$= \left(\frac{1}{A_2 \tau_1 D} + \frac{D}{A_2 D}\right)e \tag{16.38}$$

The preceding expression describes the operation of a proportional plus integral controller.

Caldwell[1] has compiled a table of numerous force-type controllers which may be used to obtain proportional plus integral action, proportional plus derivative action, or proportional plus integral plus derivative

[1] W. I. Caldwell, Generating Control Functions Pneumatically, *Control Eng.*, **1**: (1), 58 (1954).

action.   Williamson[1] has designed a compact "plug-in" type of unit for obtaining compound action.

16.5 Receiving Units.   A commonly employed receiving unit for position control is the pneumatic actuator shown in Fig. 16.11a.   The pres-

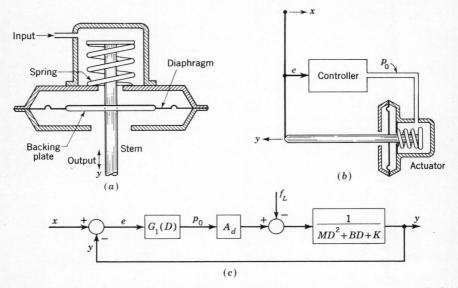

FIG. 16.11.   (*a*) Pneumatic actuator; (*b*) pneumatic position control system; (*c*) block diagram for pneumatic position control system.

sure force acting on the diaphragm is $A_d P_o$, where A_d is the area of the diaphragm.   For the general case in which this actuator is used to position a load of mass M, coefficient of viscous damping B, and spring constant K and upon which an external load F_L acts it follows that

$$A_d P_o = (MD^2 + BD + K)Y + F_L$$

Because the preceding expression is linear, then for small variations

$$A_d p_o = (MD^2 + BD + K)y + f_L$$

or
$$y = \frac{A_d p_o - f_L}{MD^2 + BD + K} \tag{16.39}$$

A typical control system utilizing an actuator is shown in Fig. 16.11b. The reference input signal is x, and the controlled variable is y.   The error signal e could be the input signal to a two-stage pneumatic amplifier.

[1] H. Williamson, Theory and Design of Compound Action Pneumatic Controllers, *Trans. Soc. Instrument Technol.*, **6** : (4), 153 (1954).

The overall block diagram for such a controller is given in Fig. 16.11c.

Single- or double-acting cylinders similar to the hydraulic cylinders discussed in Chap. 15 are also frequently employed as pneumatic receiving units. Actually, a pneumatic actuator is basically a single-acting cylinder in which the piston has been replaced by a diaphragm. In pneumatic systems, as was the case with hydraulic systems, double-acting cylinders are usually directed by a four-way valve. However, the four-way valve may in turn be positioned by the output pressure P_o of a pneumatic controller, as is illustrated in Fig. 16.12. The analysis

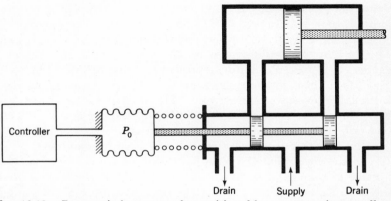

FIG. 16.12. Pneumatic four-way valve positioned by a pneumatic controller.

of a pneumatic four-way valve and cylinder combination is similar to that for the corresponding hydraulic unit with the exception that mass rate of flow must be considered rather than volume rate of flow. When the variation of pressure is small, compressibility effects become negligible. In this case, the analysis of the pneumatic system is the same as that for the corresponding hydraulic system.

Another type of receiving unit is the pneumatic motor. Although theoretically it should be possible to utilize a gear or piston motor, only the vane motor is now commercially available. A characteristic feature of a vane motor is that the torque developed by the motor is proportional to the supply pressure P_o and is independent of the speed of rotation, i.e.,

$$T = KP_o \tag{16.40}$$

This result is not astonishing, because a force balance on the blades shows clearly that the torque depends only on the pressure that is acting against them. The use of such a motor is illustrated in the speed control system shown in Fig. 16.13.

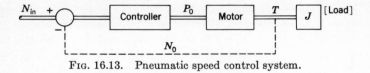

Fig. 16.13.   Pneumatic speed control system.

16.6 Equilibrium Flow.   Many pneumatic components use two orifices in series to obtain a controlled pressure in the chamber between the orifices.   If the component is available, the chamber pressure may be experimentally determined for various operating conditions.   However, in the initial design stages, before any parts have been manufactured, it is desirable to be able to predict the value of the chamber pressure.   This may be accomplished by use of the nondimensional family of curves shown in Fig. 16.14a.   As is illustrated by the insert above Fig. 16.14a, the pressures P_1, P_{1_t}, P_2, P_{2_t}, and P_3 represent the inlet pressure, throat pressure at first orifice, chamber pressure, throat pressure at second orifice, and discharge pressure, respectively.   The symbol A_{1_t} is the area of the first orifice times the coefficient of discharge, and A_{2_t} is the area of the second orifice times the coefficient of discharge.

Usually, the overall pressure ratio P_1/P_3 is known, and also the ratio A_{2_t}/A_{1_t} is known, so that the ratio P_2/P_1 can be found from Fig. 16.14a. The value of the chamber pressure P_2 is then computed as the product of the ratio P_2/P_1 and the value of the inlet pressure P_1.   In using Fig. 16.14a, it is necessary to use absolute pressures.   Because these are non-dimensional curves, any consistent set of units may be used.

The derivation of this nondimensional family of curves is accomplished as follows: By assuming that the fluid is a perfect gas and that the kinetic energy at the inlet is negligible compared with other terms in the energy equation, the mass rate of flow through the first orifice is

$$M_1 = \frac{A_{1_t}P_1}{\sqrt{T_1}} \left\{ 2g\, \frac{k}{k-1}\, \frac{1}{R} \left[\left(\frac{P_{1_t}}{P_1}\right)^{2/k} - \left(\frac{P_{1_t}}{P_1}\right)^{(k+1)/k} \right] \right\}^{\frac{1}{2}} \quad (16.41)$$

where T_1 = stagnation temperature at inlet
g = gravitational conversion factor
k = ratio of specific heat at constant pressure to that at constant volume
R = gas constant

By replacing the subscript 1_t in Eq. (16.41) by 2_t and the subscript 1 by 2, the equation for the mass rate of flow through the second orifice is obtained.   For equilibrium to exist, the mass rate of flow in equals that

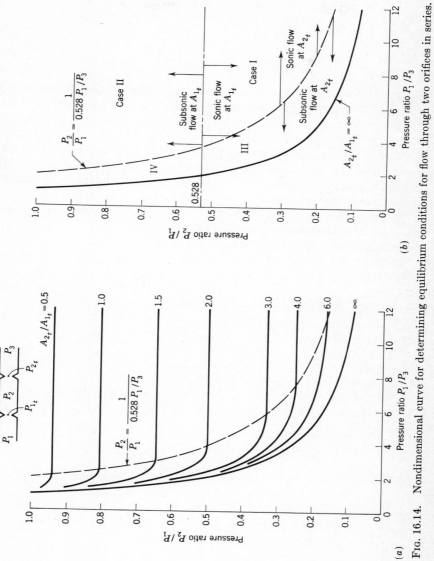

FIG. 16.14. Nondimensional curve for determining equilibrium conditions for flow through two orifices in series.

out, so that

$$\frac{A_{1_t}P_1}{\sqrt{T_1}}B_1^{1/2} = \frac{A_{2_t}P_2}{\sqrt{T_2}}B_2^{1/2} \tag{16.42}$$

where

$$B_1 = \left(\frac{P_{1_t}}{P_1}\right)^{2/k} - \left(\frac{P_{1_t}}{P_1}\right)^{(k+1)/k}$$

$$B_2 = \left(\frac{P_{2_t}}{P_2}\right)^{2/k} - \left(\frac{P_{2_t}}{P_2}\right)^{(k+1)/k}$$

Because there is little time for heat transfer to take place, the flow may be considered to be adiabatic so that $T_1 = T_2$. Thus Eq. (16.42) becomes

$$A_{1_t}P_1B_1^{1/2} = A_{2_t}P_2B_2^{1/2} \tag{16.43}$$

In the following analysis, it is assumed that the fluid is air, for which $k = 1.4$, and the critical pressure ratio is $P_2/P_1 = P_3/P_2 = 0.528$. By using the appropriate value of k and the critical ratio, this analysis is applicable for any gas.

When sonic flow exists at the first orifice, $B_1^{1/2} = 0.259$ and similarly for sonic flow at the second orifice $B_2^{1/2} = 0.259$. Thus, for sonic flow at both orifices Eq. (16.43) reduces to

$$\frac{P_2}{P_1} = \frac{1}{A_{2_t}/A_{1_t}} \tag{16.44}$$

When sonic flow exists at the first orifice,

$$\frac{P_2}{P_1} \leq 0.528$$

Above the line $P_2/P_1 = 0.528$ shown in Fig. 16.14b, subsonic flow exists at A_{1_t}, and below this line sonic flow exists at A_{1_t}.

The equation for the line of separation between subsonic and sonic flow at A_{2_t} is obtained by noting that the critical ratio is $P_3/P_2 = 0.528$; thus

$$\frac{P_2}{P_1} = \frac{1}{(P_3/P_2)(P_1/P_3)} = \frac{1}{0.528(P_1/P_3)} \tag{16.45}$$

The curve defined by the preceding expression is shown in Fig. 16.14b. To the right of this curve sonic flow exists at A_{2_t}, and to the left of this curve subsonic flow exists at A_{2_t}. The regions in which each of the four possible combinations of sonic or subsonic flow may exist at the first and second orifices are shown in Fig. 16.14b, that is,

Case I   sonic flow at both orifices
Case II   subsonic flow at the first orifice and sonic at the second
Case III sonic flow at the first orifice and subsonic at the second
Case IV   subsonic flow at both orifices

For case I, from Eq. (16.44) it follows that the lines of constant values of A_{2_t}/A_{1_t} are horizontal straight lines as shown in Fig. 16.14a.

For case II, $P_2 = P_{1_t}$, and $B_2^{1/2} = 0.259$, so that Eq. (16.43) reduces to

$$\frac{P_2}{P_1} \frac{1}{B_1^{1/2}} = \frac{1}{0.259(A_{2_t}/A_{1_t})} \tag{16.46}$$

For a given area ratio A_{2_t}/A_{1_t}, there is but one value of P_2/P_1 which makes the left-hand side of Eq. (16.46) equal to the right-hand side. Thus, for case II, lines of constant A_{2_t}/A_{1_t} are also horizontal.

By applying these techniques to case III and case IV, the complete family of curves shown in Fig. 16.14a is obtained. This method of analysis may be extended to determine equilibrium flow conditions for three or more orifices in series.[1]

Equation (16.41) is in an awkward form for computing partial derivatives. However, for the case of sonic flow, this expression reduces to

$$M_1 = \frac{0.53}{\sqrt{T_1}} A_{1_t} P_1 \tag{16.47}$$

where the preceding expression has units of inches, pounds, degrees Rankine, and seconds. For the usual design case in which the stagnation temperature of the inlet air is 60°F or 520°R, then $M_1 = 0.0074 A_{1_t} P_1$.

For the case of subsonic flow $P_{1_t} = P_2$, Eq. (16.41) may be approximated by noting that a plot of the function B_1 versus $(P_1 - P_2)P_2/P_1^2$ is very nearly a straight line. The slope of this line is such that

$$B_1 \approx \frac{0.261(P_1 - P_2)P_2}{P_1^2} \tag{16.48}$$

Substitution of the preceding approximation into Eq. (16.41) gives

$$M_1 \approx \frac{2.06}{\sqrt{T_1}} A_{1_t} \sqrt{0.261(P_1 - P_2)P_2}$$

$$= \frac{1.05}{\sqrt{T_1}} A_{1_t} \sqrt{(P_1 - P_2)P_2} \tag{16.49}$$

where $\sqrt{\dfrac{2g}{R}\dfrac{k}{k-1}} = 2.06$ when units of inches, pounds, degrees Rankine, and seconds are employed. For a stagnation temperature of 520°R, Eq. (16.49) is

$$M_1 = 0.046 A_{1_t} \sqrt{(P_1 - P_2)P_2} \tag{16.50}$$

---

[1] The author wishes to express his appreciation to Mr. Stanley Best, Chief of Analysis, Hamilton Standard Division, United Aircraft Corporation, Windsor Locks, Conn., for his fine comments and suggestions concerning the development of the preceding method for determining equilibrium flow conditions.

Problems

16.1 Derive the equation relating p_o and z for each of the pneumatic control elements shown in Fig. P16.1a to d. Explain the significance of each partial derivative which occurs in these equations.

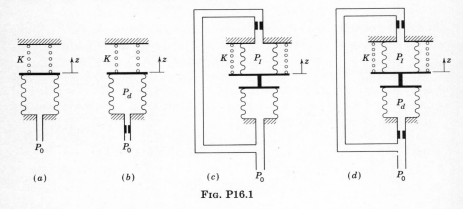

FIG. P16.1

16.2 In Fig. P16.2 is shown a flapper amplifier in which the controlled pressure is P_o. Determine the overall block diagram which results when this pressure P_o is connected to each of the pneumatic control elements shown in Fig. P16.1a to d. The position z is fed back to the walking-beam linkage as indicated. Note that for this overall block diagram the input is the error e and the output is the variation in the controlled pressure p_o. (The time constant for the flapper amplifier may be considered negligible.) Identify the mode of control for each case.

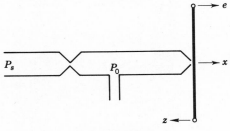

FIG. P16.2

16.3 The block diagram of a pneumatic position control system is shown in Fig. P16.3. The controlled position is θ_c, and the reference position is θ_r. Construct the resulting root-locus plot for each of the following:

(a) Proportional controller $p_o = K_c e$
(b) Proportional plus derivative controller $p_o = K_c(1 + s)e$
(c) Proportional plus integral controller $p_o = K_c(1 + 1/s)e$
(d) Proportional plus derivative plus integral controller $p_o = K_c(1 + s + 1/s)e$

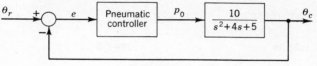

Fig. P16.3

16.4 Same as Prob. 16.3*b*, but use

(*a*) $p_o = K_c(10 + s)e$ (*b*) $p_o = K_c(0.1 + s)e$

16.5 Same as Prob. 16.3*c*, but use

(*a*) $p_o = K_c(1 + 10/s)e$ (*b*) $p_o = K_c(1 + 0.1/s)e$

16.6 For the pneumatic flapper amplifier shown in Fig. 15.22*a* plot a curve of P_2 versus X. The diameter of the fixed orifice is 0.05 in., the diameter of the flapper opening is 0.20 in., and the supply pressure is 100 psia. Determine K_1 at $P_2 = $ 30, 50, and 70 psia.

17

Electrical systems

The availability of electrical power and the ease of transmitting signals via wires or microwaves are desirable aspects of electrical equipment. The characteristics of an electrical component may usually be altered by a simple adjustment such as changing the size of a resistor or a capacitor, as was the case for the general-purpose analog computer discussed in Chap. 8. Thus, electrical equipment tends to be versatile and convenient to use.

This chapter discusses the characteristics of electrical components which are frequently used in automatic control systems. It is shown how to obtain the operational form of the differential equation for commonly used electrical devices such as motors, generators, vacuum tubes, transistor amplifiers, etc.[1-3]

17.1 DC Motors. A major reason for the use of dc machines in electromechanical control systems is the ease with which speed can be controlled. The polarity of the applied voltage determines the direction of rotation. Also dc machines are capable of providing large power amplifications.

The field and armature windings of dc motors may be shunt-connected, series-connected, compounded, or separately excited. The motors used in control systems are generally separately excited. There are two types of separate excitation, field control with fixed armature current, and armature control with fixed field.

Field Control. A separately excited motor in which the armature current I_a is maintained constant is shown in Fig. 17.1a. The constant

---

[1] J. E. Gibson and F. B. Tuteur, "Control System Components," McGraw-Hill Book Company, New York, 1958.

[2] N. R. Ahrendt and C. J. Savant, "Servomechanism Practice," 2d ed., McGraw-Hill Book Company, New York, 1960.

[3] J. G. Truxal, "Control Engineers' Handbook," McGraw-Hill Book Company, New York, 1958.

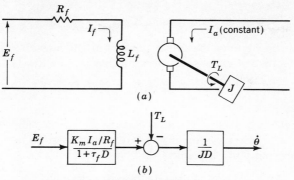

(a)

(b)

Fig. 17.1. Field-controlled dc motor.

current I_a may be supplied by a d-c generator or from an ac line. The latter method requires the use of transformers and rectifiers to obtain the proper rectification. The voltage E_f applied to the field is obtained from the output of an amplifier in low-power application or from a dc generator when greater power is needed. In the field circuit, the resistance of the windings is R_f, and the inductance is designated by L_f. The torque T developed by a motor is proportional to the product of the armature current I_a and the magnetic flux ϕ of the field.

$$T = K_1 \phi I_a \tag{17.1}$$

where K_1 is a constant for any motor and depends upon the total number of armature conductors, the number of field poles, etc.

A typical curve of flux ϕ versus field current I_f is shown in Fig. 17.2. When the field current I_f becomes great enough to cause the iron to saturate, the flux ϕ no longer increases linearly with the current. Motors used in control systems usually operate over the linear portion of this

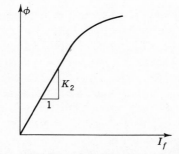

Fig. 17.2. Plot of flux vs. field current.

curve, in which case

$$\phi = K_2 I_f \tag{17.2}$$

where K_2 is the slope of the linear portion of the curve as shown in Fig. 17.2. The substitution of the preceding result into Eq. (17.1) yields

$$T = K_1 K_2 I_a I_f = K_m I_a I_f \tag{17.3}$$

where $K_m = K_1 K_2$.

If the moment of inertia of the armature is J, the coefficient of viscous friction B_ν, and the load torque T_L, then from a summation of torques acting on the armature it follows that

$$T = (B_\nu D + J D^2)\theta + T_L \tag{17.4}$$

where θ is the angular position of the armature, or motor shaft.

The equation for the field current I_f is obtained from the equivalent field circuit of Fig. 17.1a.

$$I_f = \frac{E_f}{R_f + L_f D} = \frac{E_f}{R_f(1 + \tau_f D)} \tag{17.5}$$

where $\tau_f = L_f/R_f$ is the time constant of the field circuit.

Substituting T from Eq. (17.4) and I_f from Eq. (17.5) into Eq. (17.3) and solving for θ gives

$$\theta = \frac{1}{D(B_\nu + JD)}\left[\frac{(K_m I_a/R_f)E_f}{1 + \tau_f D} - T_L\right] \tag{17.6}$$

Multiplication of the preceding expression by D gives the angular velocity $\dot\theta = D\theta$,

$$\dot\theta = \frac{1}{B_\nu + JD}\left[\frac{(K_m I_a/R_f)E_f}{1 + \tau_f D} - T_L\right] \tag{17.7}$$

Generally, the damping B_ν is negligible, so that the block-diagram representation for the speed of this field-controlled dc motor is as shown in Fig. 17.1b.

Because of the difficulty and expense of obtaining a constant-current source, this type of motor is often operated with an approximately constant-current source. This is accomplished by supplying the armature with a constant voltage V_a and inserting a very large resistance in series with the armature. The resulting schematic representation is shown in Fig. 17.3a. The resistance R_a is the sum of the inserted series resistance and that of the armature. The term L_a represents the inductance of the armature. The voltage E_c is the counter emf induced by the rotation of the armature windings in the magnetic field. The counter emf is proportional to the product of the armature speed $\dot\theta$ and the field

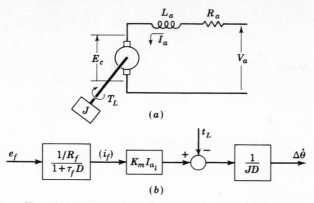

FIG. 17.3. Approximately constant current source.

strength ϕ. Thus

$$E_c = K_3 \phi \dot\theta \tag{17.8}$$

where K_3 is a constant for any particular motor. The substitution of ϕ from Eq. (17.2) into Eq. (17.8) yields

$$E_c = K_2 K_3 I_f \dot\theta = K_c I_f \dot\theta \tag{17.9}$$

where $K_c = K_2 K_3$. Solving the circuit of Fig. 17.3a for the armature current I_a yields

$$I_a = \frac{V_a - E_c}{R_a + L_a D} \tag{17.10}$$

Equation (17.9) is nonlinear in that I_f and $\dot\theta$ multiply. To obtain a linear representation for this system, it is necessary to linearize the equations which describe its operation. The linearized form of Eq. (17.9) is

$$e_c = \frac{\partial E_c}{\partial \dot\theta}\Big|_i \Delta\dot\theta + \frac{\partial E_c}{\partial I_f}\Big|_i i_f = K_c I_{f_i} \Delta\dot\theta + K_c \dot\theta_i i_f \tag{17.11}$$

where from Eq. (17.9) it follows that

$$\frac{\partial E_c}{\partial \dot\theta}\Big|_i = K_c I_{f_i} \qquad \text{and} \qquad \frac{\partial E_c}{\partial I_f}\Big|_i = K_c \dot\theta_i$$

Because Eq. (17.10) is linear, all that is necessary is to replace the capital-letter representation of the independent variables by their lower-case counterparts.

$$i_a = \frac{v_a - e_c}{R_a + L_a D} \tag{17.12}$$

From the assumption that the armature supply voltage V_a is constant,

v_a is zero. The preceding expression thus becomes

$$i_a = \frac{-e_c}{R_a + L_a D} \tag{17.13}$$

The torque T developed by a motor as given by Eq. (17.3) is linearized as follows,

$$t = \frac{\partial T}{\partial I_f}\Big|_i i_f + \frac{\partial T}{\partial I_a}\Big|_i i_a = K_m I_{a_i} i_f + K_m I_{f_i} i_a \tag{17.14}$$

where from Eq. (17.3) it follows that

$$\frac{\partial T}{\partial I_f}\Big|_i = K_m I_{a_i} \quad \text{and} \quad \frac{\partial T}{\partial I_a}\Big|_i = K_m I_{f_i}$$

The torque balance for the armature as given by Eq. (17.4) is already linear. Replacing the independent variable terms designated by capital letters in Eq. (17.4) by their lowercase counterparts yields the following torque balance for small departures:

$$t = (B_\nu + JD)\,\Delta\dot\theta + t_L \tag{17.15}$$

By substituting e_c from Eq. (17.11) into Eq. (17.13), and then substituting i_a from this resulting equation into Eq. (17.14), one obtains an equation for the torque variation t as a function of i_f and $\Delta\dot\theta$. Equating this value of t to Eq. (17.15) and solving for $\Delta\dot\theta$ yields

$$\Delta\dot\theta = \frac{K_m[(I_{a_i}R_a - K_c I_{f_i}\dot\theta_i) + I_{a_i}L_a D]i_f - (R_a + L_a D)t_L}{(R_a + L_a D)(B_\nu + JD) + K_m K_c I_{f_i}{}^2} \tag{17.16}$$

For the usual case in which the equilibrium operating condition is about the point $\dot\theta_i = I_{f_i} = 0$ and the damping B_ν is negligible, the preceding expression reduces to

$$\Delta\dot\theta = \frac{1}{JD}(K_m I_{a_i} i_f - t_L) \tag{17.17}$$

From Eq. (17.17) and the linearized form of Eq. (17.5), the overall block-diagram representation for this field-controlled motor which is supplied by an approximately constant armature current may be constructed as shown in Fig. 17.3b.

Armature Control. A dc motor with armature control is one in which the speed is controlled by the armature voltage E_a. An armature-controlled motor is shown in Fig. 17.4a, in which the field current I_f is kept constant. It is much easier to maintain a constant field current I_f than a constant armature current I_a because there is no counter emf generated in the fixed field windings. The armature voltage E_a is usually supplied by a generator, which in turn may be supplied by an amplifier.

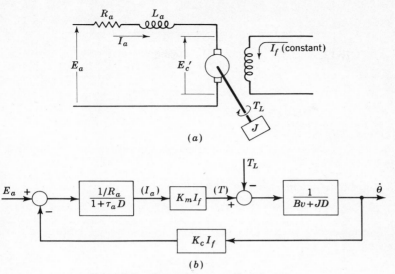

FIG. 17.4. Armature-controlled dc motor.

The circuit equation for the armature portion of Fig. 17.4a is

$$E_a - K_c I_f \dot{\theta} = R_a I_a + L_a D I_a = R_a (1 + \tau_a D) I_a \qquad (17.18)$$

where $\tau_a = L_a / R_a$ and the term $K_c I_f \dot{\theta}$ is the counter emf developed in the armature. The torque developed by the motor is given by the equation

$$T = K_m I_f I_a \qquad (17.19)$$

and the torque balance for the output shaft is

$$T = (B_r D + J D^2)\theta + T_L \qquad (17.20)$$

The block-diagram representation for this armature-controlled motor is obtained by combining the block-diagram representations for Eqs. (17.18), (17.19), and (17.20) as shown in Fig. 17.4b. The counter emf is responsible for the minor feedback.

A complete generator and armature-controlled motor combination is shown in Fig. 17.5. This is in effect a Ward Leonard system, or motor-generator set. The voltage E supplied to the generator may be quite small, as in the case of that coming from an amplifier. The resistance of the field of the generator is R_{fg}, and the inductance is L_{fg}. The armature of the generator is driven at a constant speed by a prime mover. The output voltage of the generator, E_g, goes directly to the armature of the motor so that $E_g = E_a$.

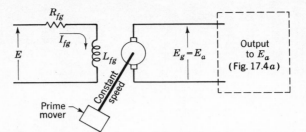

FIG. 17.5.   Complete generator and armature-controlled motor combination.

The circuit equation for the generator field is

$$E = (R_{fg} + L_{fg}D)I_{fg} \tag{17.21}$$

The voltage induced in the armature is the generated voltage $E_g = E_a$, which is

$$E_a = K_{cg}\dot{\theta}_g I_{fg} = K_c' I_{fg} \tag{17.22}$$

where $\dot{\theta}_g$ is the angular velocity of the prime mover, which is constant, so that $K_{cg}\dot{\theta}_g = K_c'$. The substitution of I_{fg} from Eq. (17.21) into Eq. (17.22) yields

$$E_a = \frac{K_c'E}{R_{fg} + L_{fg}D} = \frac{(K_c'/R_{fg})E}{1 + \tau_{fg}D} \tag{17.23}$$

where $\tau_{fg} = L_{fg}/R_{fg}$ is the time constant of the generator field.

The overall block diagram relating the input voltage E and the velocity $\dot{\theta}$ of this armature-controlled motor-generator system is obtained by connecting the block-diagram representation for the output E_a from Eq. (17.23) to that for E_a in Fig. 17.4b.

DC Tachometer.   A dc tachometer is a generator in which the magnetic flux is supplied by a permanent magnet.   Because the flux is maintained constant, the equation of operation for a tachometer is obtained from Eq. (17.8) as follows,

$$E_c = E_g = K_3\phi\dot{\theta} = K_g\dot{\theta} \tag{17.24}$$

where $K_g = K_3\phi$ is a constant and E_g is the generated voltage.

Thus a tachometer is seen to supply a voltage E_g which is proportional to the speed at which it is driven.

Rototrol Generator.   When very large power amplification is required, it is customary to place two generators in series.   The Rototrol generator is a combination of two generators in which part of the field for the first, or pilot, generator is in series with the armature.   In Fig. 17.6 this

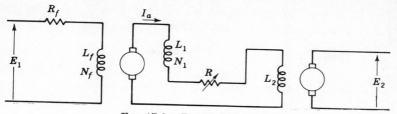

FIG. 17.6. Rototrol generator.

series portion of the field is designated by L_1, and the portion with separate excitation is L_f. The series field L_1 causes a self-energizing effect in that as the armature current I_a increases so also does the flux caused by the series winding L_1. An analysis of the system shown in Fig. 17.6 yields the following equation relating the output voltage E_2 to the input E_1,

$$E_2 = \frac{K_v K_p/R_f}{(1 + \tau_f D)(R - K_p N_1/N_f + LD)} E_1 \qquad (17.25)$$

where K_v is the constant relating the voltage output E_2 of the main generator to the armature current I_a (that is, $E_2 = K_v I_a$) and K_p is the corresponding constant for the pilot generator. The term $L = L_1 + L_2$ is the total inductance of the armature circuit, and R is the total resistance. The number of turns on the series field winding is N_1, and that on the separately excited winding is N_f. The time constant of the separately excited pilot-generator field is $\tau_f = L_f/R_f$.

The critical value of R is

$$R = R_c = \frac{K_p N_1}{N_f} \qquad (17.26)$$

When the total resistance R is adjusted to the critical value, Eq. (17.25) becomes

$$\frac{E_2}{E_1} = \frac{K_v K_p}{R_f L} \frac{1}{D(1 + \tau_f D)} \cdot \qquad (17.27)$$

The primary advantage of the Rototrol is the integrating effect that is obtained when it is critically tuned; otherwise there would be little if any advantage in using a Rototrol in preference to two simple generators in series.

Amplidyne. An amplidyne is essentially a two-stage generator, but the two stages are combined in a single machine. The main advantage of an amplidyne is that it is smaller and more compact than a Rototrol of the same rating. Because of coupling effects and various interactions which take place in the one machine, the performance of the amplidyne is poorer than that obtained with two separate machines.   Also, the use of two generators permits greater flexibility in the adjustment of operating characteristics.

Remote-control Positional Servomechanism.   A remote-control positional servomechanism is shown in Fig. 17.7a.   The wiper arm of the input

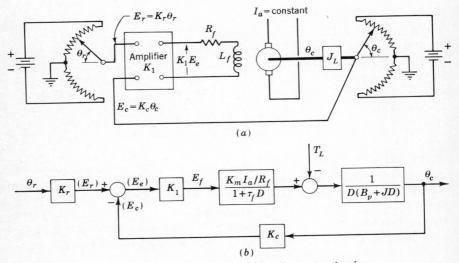

FIG. 17.7.   Remote-control positional servomechanism.

potentiometer is positioned by the desired input position θ_r, so that the voltage E_r is proportional to θ_r (that is, $E_r = K_r\theta_r$).   Similarly, the controlled shaft position θ_c determines the position of the wiper arm for the other potentiometer so that $E_c = K_c\theta_c$.   The error signal $E_e = E_r - E_c$ is amplified by the amplifier, and the resultant voltage is applied to the field of a field-controlled motor so that $E_f = K_1E_e$.   The operational representation of the differential equation for the motor is given by Eq. (17.6).   The over all block diagram for this system is shown in Fig. 17.7b.

The motor must be located at the output shaft, while the input potentiometer is usually situated in any convenient location.   A major advantage in using such electrical equipment for position control systems is the ease of connecting the input and output by means of wires.

The preceding position controller may be converted to a speed control system by connecting the output shaft to a tachometer rather than to a potentiometer.   In this case, the voltage signal E_c coming from the tachometer is proportional to the speed $\dot{\theta}_c$ (that is, $E_c = K'_c \dot{\theta}_c$). Similarly, each wiper position of the input potentiometer corresponds to a desired speed setting $\dot{\theta}_r$ rather than position θ_r, so that the reference voltage is $E_r = K'_r \dot{\theta}_r$.

17.2 AC Two-phase Motors.

An ac two-phase motor is used for simple low-power applications. One of the phases is supplied with a fixed ac voltage which acts as the reference voltage. The other phase is connected to the controlled voltage. A schematic representation of a two-phase motor is shown in Fig. 17.8a. Because the reference voltage

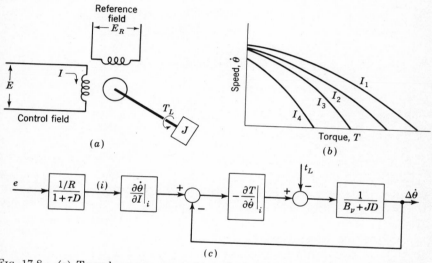

FIG. 17.8. (a) Two-phase ac motor; (b) typical performance curves; (c) block-diagram representation.

E_R is constant, the speed depends upon the control voltage E. The direction of rotation is reversed by changing the polarity of the control voltage.

As is shown in Fig. 17.8a, the reference and control windings are displaced by 90° in the stator of the motor. Thus, although the voltage applied to each winding has the same frequency, there is a 90° phase shift of one with respect to the other.

Typical performance curves relating the developed motor torque T and the angular velocity $\dot{\theta}$ for constant values of control current I are shown in Fig. 17.8b. The equation describing the operation of a two-phase motor about some equilibrium point of operation is derived as follows: From Fig. 17.8b it is to be noticed that the speed is a function of

T and I.

$$\dot{\theta} = F(T,I) \tag{17.28}$$

$$\Delta\dot{\theta} = \frac{\partial\dot{\theta}}{\partial T}\bigg|_i t + \frac{\partial\dot{\theta}}{\partial I}\bigg|_i i \tag{17.29}$$

The torque balance for the armature is

$$T = (B_\nu + JD)\dot{\theta} + T_L \tag{17.30}$$

The form of the preceding equation for small departures is

$$t = (B_\nu + JD)\,\Delta\dot{\theta} + t_L \tag{17.31}$$

The circuit equation for the control winding is

$$E = (R + LD)I = R(1 + \tau D)I \tag{17.32}$$

For small departures this expression becomes

$$e = R(1 + \tau D)i \tag{17.33}$$

The block-diagram representation for this two phase ac motor is obtained from Eqs. (17.29), (17.31), and (17.33) as shown in Fig. 17.8c.

17.3 Synchro Error-detecting Devices. Synchro systems are usually employed as error-sensing devices. A synchro system as shown in Fig. 17.9a consists of a synchro generator and synchro motor. The rotor of both the generator and motor is connected to the same ac supply. When the rotors are in the same relative position such that θ_1 is equal to θ_2, identical flux patterns are set up in each stator. Because the stator winding for each unit is connected as shown in Fig. 17.9b, the voltage induced in each corresponding phase will be the same for the generator and the motor. In this case, the voltage induced in the first stator winding S_1' of the generator is the same as that induced in the first winding S_1 of the motor, etc. Because all corresponding coils have the same induced voltage, no current flows through the stator coils for this balanced position.

When the rotors are rotated with respect to one another so that θ_1 is not equal to θ_2, different voltages are induced across corresponding phases of the stator windings. This causes currents to flow through the stator windings. The reaction of the rotor flux and the current produces a torque on each rotor which tends to align them. In many applications, the rotor of the generator is held in a fixed, or reference, position; thus the relative position of the rotor in the motor will depend upon the torque applied to the motor shaft. The relation between torque and relative angular position is reasonably linear up to about 75° and is given by the

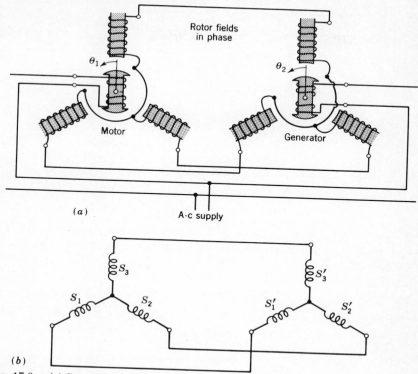

Fig. 17.9. (a) Synchro generator and motor combination; (b) wiring of synchro units in correspondence.

equation

$$T = k(\theta_2 - \theta_1) \qquad (17.34)$$

A device that produces a voltage which is a function of the relative rotor positions may be obtained by a slight modification of the synchro generator-motor system. Such a system is called a synchro control transformer and is shown in Fig. 17.10. The generator is the same as before, but the motor has been replaced by a synchro control transformer. Only the rotor of the generator is connected to the ac supply. The stator of the generator and that of the control transformer are identical, as shown in Fig. 17.10. Thus, the field produced in the stator of the control transformer is the same as that of the generator. The voltage E_o induced in the rotor of the control transformer is a maximum, E_m, when the two rotors are aligned. The voltage decreases sinusoidally as the rotors are displaced. When the rotors are 90° apart, the control transformer rotor is at right angles to the field and the output voltage E_o is zero. To take into account the fact that the output is zero when the rotors are displaced

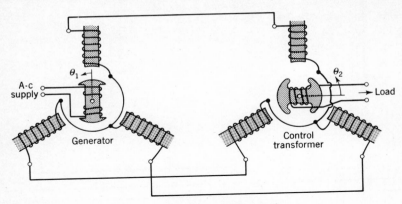

FIG. 17.10.   Synchro control transformer.

by 90°, it is convenient to measure θ_2 from a reference position which is at right angles to the reference position for θ_1, as shown in Fig. 17.10. The operation of the synchro control transformer is then described by the equation

$$E_o = E_m \sin (\theta_2 - \theta_1') \tag{17.35}$$

In Fig. 17.11 is shown a typical remote-control positional servo-mechanism in which the error-sensing device is a synchro control trans-

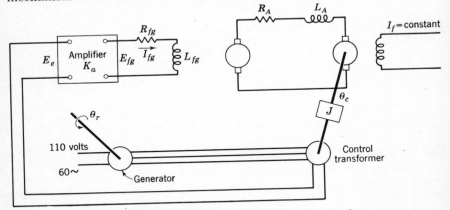

FIG. 17.11.   Remote-control positional servomechanism.

former.   The output voltage coming from the control transformer is a measure of the error

$$E_e = E_m \sin (\theta_r - \theta_c) \tag{17.36}$$

For normal operation in which the error $\theta_r - \theta_c$ is small, the preceding expression becomes

$$E_e \approx E_m(\theta_r - \theta_c) \tag{17.37}$$

17.4 Vacuum-tube Amplifiers. Vacuum tubes are frequently used to amplify voltage signals in electrical control systems. A triode, as shown in Fig. 17.12a, is the simplest type of vacuum-tube amplifier. The three

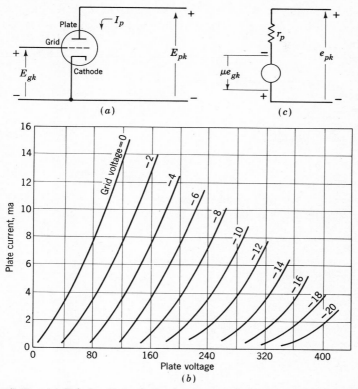

FIG. 17.12. (*a*) Triode; (*b*) typical tube characteristics; (*c*) equivalent circuit.

basic elements of a triode are the cathode, grid, and plate. The cathode serves as the source of electrons. A heater element is incorporated in the cathode for the purpose of increasing the number of free electrons on the surface of the cathode. Because electrons are negatively charged particles and the plate is charged positively with respect to the cathode, the number of electrons flowing from the cathode to the plate will depend upon the value of the voltage drop from the plate to the cathode, E_{pk}. (In accordance with standard practice, the direction of current flow is opposite to that of the flow of electrons.) When the grid is charged negatively with respect to the cathode (that is, E_{gk} is negative), electrons on the cathode are repelled, which decreases the current flow. Because the grid is located close to the cathode, a small negative charge E_{gk} will cause a rather substantial decrease in current flow. For example, in Fig. 17.12b with the plate voltage E_{pk} held constant at 80 volts, changing the grid voltage E_{gk} from 0 to -2 volts results in a change in the plate current I_p from 7.8 to 3.4 ma.

For a vacuum-tube amplifier, the plate current I_p is a function of the voltage drop E_{pk} from the plate to the cathode and also the grid-bias voltage E_{gk}, that is,

$$I_p = F(E_{pk}, E_{gk}) \tag{17.38}$$

Linearization of the preceding expression yields

$$i_p = \frac{\partial I_p}{\partial E_{pk}}\bigg|_i e_{pk} + \frac{\partial I_p}{\partial E_{gk}}\bigg|_i e_{gk} \tag{17.39}$$

Solving for e_{pk} gives

$$e_{pk} = \frac{\partial E_{pk}}{\partial I_p}\bigg|_i i_p - \frac{\partial E_{pk}}{\partial I_p}\bigg|_i \frac{\partial I_p}{\partial E_{gk}}\bigg|_i e_{gk} \tag{17.40}$$

The product of the partial derivatives in the last term may be simplified by first writing Eq. (17.38) in the implicit form

$$G(I_p, E_{pk}, E_{gk}) = 0 \tag{17.41}$$

From calculus, it is known that the product of the three partial derivatives for an implicit function is equal to -1, that is,

$$\frac{\partial I_p}{\partial E_{pk}} \frac{\partial E_{pk}}{\partial E_{gk}} \frac{\partial E_{gk}}{\partial I_p} = -1 \tag{17.42}$$

Thus, $$\frac{\partial E_{pk}}{\partial E_{gk}} = -\frac{\partial E_{pk}}{\partial I_p} \frac{\partial I_p}{\partial E_{gk}} \tag{17.43}$$

Substitution of the preceding result into Eq. (17.40) gives

$$e_{pk} = \frac{\partial E_{pk}}{\partial I_p}\bigg|_i i_p + \frac{\partial E_{pk}}{\partial E_{gk}}\bigg|_i e_{gk}$$

or $$e_{pk} = r_p i_p - \mu e_{gk} \tag{17.44}$$

where $\partial E_{pk}/\partial I_p = r_p$ is the change in voltage across the plate per change in current, which is the effective resistance of the plate. Thus, r_p is called the dynamic plate resistance. The term $\partial E_{pk}/\partial E_{gk} = -\mu$ is the change in voltage drop across the plate per change in grid to cathode voltage, with I_p remaining constant. Because E_{pk} increases as E_{gk} decreases, the negative sign is used so that μ will always be a positive number. The term μ is called the amplification factor. The equation for the operation of the circuit shown in Fig. 17.12c is the same as Eq. (17.44). Thus, Fig. 17.12c is the equivalent circuit for a vacuum-tube amplifier.

In Fig. 17.13a is shown a vacuum tube in which the load is a pure

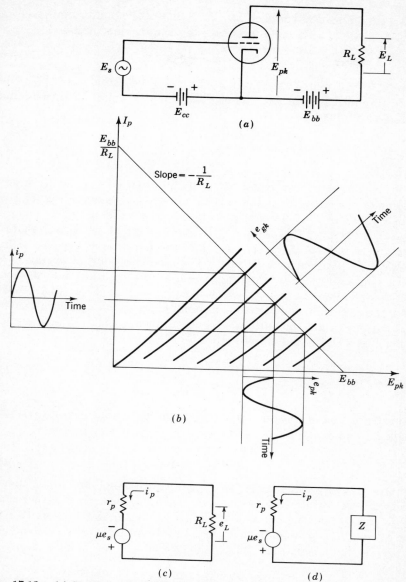

FIG. 17.13. (a) Vacuum tube with resistive load; (b) load line superimposed upon operating curves; (c) equivalent amplifier circuit with a resistive load; (d) equivalent amplifier circuit with a general impedance load.

resistance. The d-c voltage E_{cc} determines the equilibrium value of the grid bias E_{gk}. The total grid bias is given by the equation

$$E_{gk} = E_s - E_{cc} \qquad (17.45)$$

where E_s is the input-voltage signal which is to be amplified. The plate bias is provided by the dc voltage E_{bb}. The loop equation for load and plate circuit is

$$E_{bb} = I_p R_L + E_{pk}$$

or
$$I_p = -\frac{1}{R_L} E_{pk} + \frac{E_{bb}}{R_L} \qquad (17.46)$$

Equation (17.46) is the equation of the straight line which is superimposed on the curve for the tube characteristics as shown in Fig. 17.13b. From Eq. (17.46), it follows that with I_p as the ordinate and E_{pk} as the abscissa, the slope of this line is $-1/R_L$, the I_p intercept is E_{bb}/R_L (that is, when $E_{pk} = 0$, then $I_{pk} = E_{bb}/R_L$), and the E_{pk} intercept is E_{bb}. This straight line is called the load line. The reference point of operation of the tube is determined by the intersection of this load line and the tube-characteristic line for $E_s = 0$, which is $E_{gk} = -E_{cc}$. From Fig. 17.13b, it is to be seen that, for a small sinusoidal input e_{gk}, the variation in the plate current i_p and the variation e_{pk} are also sinusoidal. The linearization of Eqs. (17.45) and (17.46) yields

$$e_{gk} = e_s$$
$$i_p = -\frac{e_{pk}}{R_L} \qquad (17.47)$$

The substitution of the preceding results for e_{gk} and e_{pk} into Eq. (17.44) yields

$$-R_L i_p = r_p i_p - \mu e_s$$

or
$$\mu e_s = (r_p + R_L) i_p \qquad (17.48)$$

Equation (17.48) is the basis for the equivalent amplifier circuit shown in Fig. 17.13c. When the load is some general impedance Z rather than a pure resistance, the equivalent circuit is that shown in Fig. 17.13d. The overall voltage amplification for a tube is the ratio of output voltage e_L to the input signal e_s. Thus, the overall voltage amplification, or gain, is

$$\text{Gain} = \frac{e_L}{e_s} = \frac{-R_L i_p}{e_s} \qquad (17.49)$$

The substitution of i_p from Eq. (17.48) into the preceding expression yields

$$\text{Gain} = -R_L \frac{\mu e_s}{(r_p + R_L)/e_s} = \frac{-\mu R_L}{r_p + R_L} = -K \qquad (17.50)$$

The minus sign in the preceding expression indicates that the voltage e_L decreases as e_s increases (i.e., there is a 180° phase shift).

Tetrode and Pentode. A tetrode, which is a four-element tube, and a pentode, which has five elements, both have much higher gains than a triode, which has only three elements. A tetrode has a screen grid in addition to the usual cathode, grid, and plate of a triode. A tetrode is shown in Fig. 17.14a, and typical tube characteristics are shown in

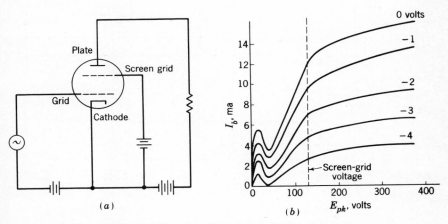

(a) (b) E_{pk}, volts

FIG. 17.14. (a) Tetrode; (b) typical tube characteristics.

Fig. 17.14b. When the plate-to-cathode voltage E_{pk} is less than the screen-grid voltage, the tube characteristics become quite erratic. Thus, tetrodes are usually operated in the range where the voltage E_{pk} is greater than the screen-grid voltage.

A pentode has a fifth element, the suppressor grid, in addition to the four elements of the tetrode. A pentode tube is shown in Fig. 17.15a, and a family of curves of typical tube characteristics is shown in Fig. 17.15b. Because of the suppressor grid the pentode does not have the irregular tube characteristics that were found in the tetrode when the voltage E_{pk} was less than the screen-grid voltage. The suppressor grid is located between the plate and the screen grid. Because the suppressor grid is at cathode potential, it is negative with respect to the plate. Thus, it repels the flow of electrons from the plate to the screen grid even when the plate voltage is less than that of the screen grid.

The plate resistance r_p for a pentode is much greater than that for a triode, so that for a pentode r_p is generally much greater than R_L. Thus, for a pentode $r_p + R_L$ may be approximated by r_p, in which case from

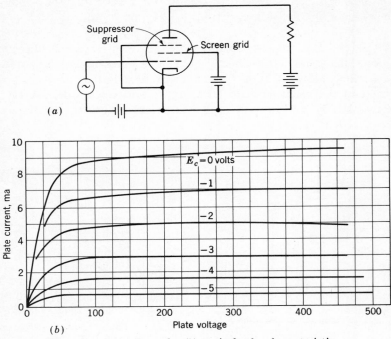

FIG. 17.15.   (*a*) Pentode; (*b*) typical tube characteristics.

Eq. (17.50) it is seen that the amplifier gain K for a pentode is

$$K \approx \frac{\mu}{r_p} R_L \qquad (17.51)$$

where $\mu/r_p = (\partial E_{pk}/\partial E_{gk})/(\partial E_{pk}/\partial I_{pk}) = -\partial I_{pk}/\partial E_{gk} = g_m$ is the change in plate current I_p per change in grid-to-cathode voltage E_{gk}, with E_{pk} held constant. This coefficient is called the mutual conductance, or the transconductance, of the tube. The pentode is capable of much greater amplification than is a triode.

Coupling. To obtain a greater amplification, it is customary to place amplifiers in series so that the voltage output from the first tube is the input to the second, etc. The overall gain is the product of the gain of each amplifier. For ac amplifiers, a capacitor C as shown in Fig. 17.16*a* is frequently used as the coupling. Only the ac component e_L at the output of the first amplifier is transmitted through the capacitor to the second amplifier. For example, the voltage at point A is E_{bb}, and that at point B is $E_{bb} - e_L$. Because it is desired to have only e_L appear

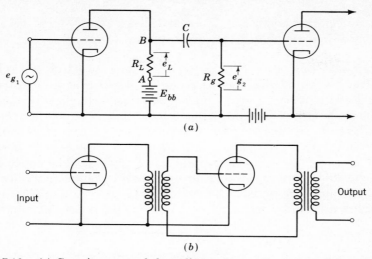

FIG. 17.16. (*a*) Capacitance-coupled amplifiers; (*b*) transformer-coupled amplifiers.

as the input signal to the second tube rather than e_L plus the dc bias E_{bb}, it is necessary to block the dc component by means of the capacitor. For practical purposes the value of e_{g2} may be assumed equal to e_L if the resistor R_g is at least ten times greater than R_L and the reactance of the capacitor is one-tenth or less of the value of R_g.

Another method for isolating the ac component e_L of the output tube is to use a transformer. Two amplifiers which are coupled through a transformer are shown in Fig. 17.16*b*. An advantage of transformer coupling is that the overall gain per stage is increased by the turns ratio. However, flux leakage soon becomes excessive for a large turns ratio. The major disadvantage to transformer coupling is that at higher frequencies leakage reactance and capacitance between turns limit the operation. Resistance-capacitance-coupled amplifiers have a greater frequency range than transformer-coupled amplifiers.

When the input signal is a direct current or a very low frequency, the voltage e_L cannot be isolated by the preceding techniques. To amplify dc or very-low-frequency signals, it is customary to use chopper stabilization to achieve high performance. In Fig. 17.17 is shown a chopper-stabilized dc amplifier. The modulator, or chopper, converts the input signal to a relatively high-frequency ac signal, which may be amplified

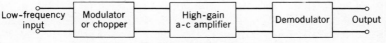

FIG. 17.17. Chopper-stabilized d-c amplifier.

by a standard ac amplifier. The demodulator then restores this amplified signal to its original dc, or low-frequency, form.

Push-pull Amplifier. A push-pull amplifier is in effect two tubes in parallel. When considerable ac power is required, as is often the case with electrical control systems, a push-pull type of amplifier is capable of doubling the power output. A more important factor is that the non-linearities of one tube tend to be compensated for by the second, with the result that distortion is minimized. This enables the push-pull amplifier to be operated over a wider range than would be possible with a single tube, thus permitting an even greater power gain. Often a push-pull amplifier is used as the last stage of a high-gain amplifier system in order to reduce distortion. In Fig. 17.18a is shown a push-pull

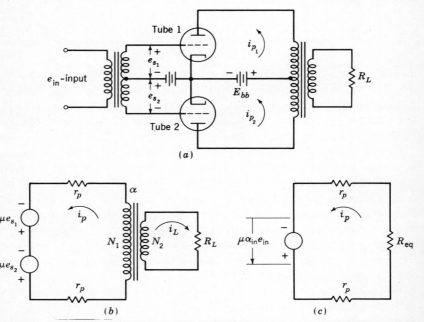

FIG. 17.18. (a) Push-pull amplifier; (b) equivalent circuit; (c) simplified equivalent circuit.

amplifier. If there is no input voltage e_{in}, then the grid-to-cathode bias for each tube is $-E_{cc}$. Thus, each tube has the same initial equilibrium point of operation. An input voltage causes a signal voltage e_{s_1} of the polarity indicated to appear on the grid of tube 1 so that the resultant grid-to-cathode voltage is $E_{gk_1} = e_{s_1} - E_{cc}$. This causes a current i_{p_1} to flow in the direction indicated. The signal voltage $e_{s_2} = -e_{s_1}$ applied to tube 2 is of the opposite polarity. Thus the current i_{p_2} flows through the second tube in the opposite direction to that in the first. However, the directions of the currents flowing through the output transformer are additive. In Fig. 17.18b is shown the equivalent circuit for a push-pull amplifier, in which $i_p = i_{p_1} = i_{p_2}$. Because the current i_{p_2} flowing through the power supply E_{bb} is opposite to i_{p_1}, there is no net ac current flowing through E_{bb}. Thus, the E_{bb} line is omitted in the equivalent-circuit representation.

For an ideal transformer, the sum of the magnetomotive forces (mmfs) around the core is zero. Thus for the output transformer it follows that

$$i_p N_1 - i_L N_2 = 0$$

or
$$i_L = \frac{N_1}{N_2} i_p = \frac{i_p}{\alpha} \tag{17.52}$$

where α is the ratio of the total secondary turns N_2 to the total primary turns N_1 (that is, $\alpha = N_2/N_1$). The power delivered to the load resistor is

$$P = i_L^2 R_L = i_p^2 R_{\text{eq}} \tag{17.53}$$

Thus, the equivalent resistance R_{eq} is

$$R_{\text{eq}} = \left(\frac{i_L}{i_p}\right)^2 R_L = \frac{R_L}{\alpha^2} \tag{17.54}$$

Similarly, if it is assumed that the input transformer is also ideal,

$$e_{s_1} = \frac{\alpha_{\text{in}}}{2} e_{\text{in}} \quad \text{and} \quad e_{s_2} = \frac{\alpha_{\text{in}}}{2} e_{\text{in}} \tag{17.55}$$

Thus, the voltage signal in Fig. 17.18b may be written as

$$\mu(e_{s_1} + e_{s_2}) = \mu \alpha_{\text{in}} e_{\text{in}} \tag{17.56}$$

The resulting equivalent ac circuit is shown in Fig. 17.18c.

17.5 Transistor Amplifiers. In many respects transistors are superior to vacuum-tube amplifiers, as is evidenced by their increasing use in electronic controls. An obvious advantage is their small size. In addition, they require much less power than vacuum tubes. For example, low-level transistor amplifier stages operate with collector voltages of only a few volts, whereas vacuum-tube plate voltages are usually several hundred volts. Another source of power savings is that transistors have no heater element such as is required for the cathode of vacuum tubes. A strong feature is that the life of a well-designed transistor is about 50,000 hr, as compared with 2,000 hr for a vacuum tube.

A disadvantage of transistors is that their characteristics are sensitive to temperature variations. Also, there is a rather large variation in characteristics of successive transistor units as they come from the production line. However, these disadvantages are continually being minimized as manufacturing techniques are improved.

The three major parts of a junction transistor are the emitter, collector, and base. A junction transistor is, in effect, a sandwich of three sections of semiconductor crystal. The section in the center is the base, while the outer sections are the emitter and collector, respectively.[1-3]

As is shown in Fig. 17.19a, a transistor is represented by a circle with a dash in it. The base is indicated by the line which is perpendicular to the

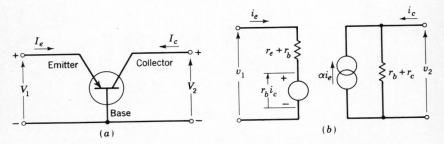

FIG. 17.19. (a) Grounded-base connection; (b) equivalent circuit.

dash. The emitter is the line with the arrowhead pointing toward the dash. The collector is represented by the line which is symmetrical to the emitter, but the collector does not have an arrowhead.

In Fig. 17.19a is shown a transistor circuit in which the base is grounded. The current I_e is the current which flows from the emitter through the base, and the current I_c flows from the collector through the base. The emitter voltage with respect to ground is V_1, and the collector voltage is V_2. As is indicated in Fig. 17.19a, the emitter current I_e is a function of the emitter-to-ground voltage V_1 and the current I_c flowing through the collector, thus,

$$I_e = F(V_1, I_c) \tag{17.57}$$

For small variations, the preceding expression becomes

$$i_e = \frac{\partial I_e}{\partial V_1}\bigg|_i v_1 + \frac{\partial I_e}{\partial I_c}\bigg|_i i_c \tag{17.58}$$

The equivalent-circuit representation for the preceding expression in

[1] Gibson and Tuteur, *op. cit.*

[2] L. P. Hunter, "Handbook of Semiconductor Electronics," McGraw-Hill Book Company, New York, 1956.

[3] R. F. Shea, "Transistor Circuit Engineering," John Wiley & Sons, Inc., New York, 1957.

which v_1 is the applied voltage is obtained by first solving for v_1.

$$v_1 = \frac{\partial V_1}{\partial I_e}\Big|_i i_e - \frac{\partial V_1}{\partial I_e}\Big|_i \frac{\partial I_e}{\partial I_c}\Big|_i i_c \qquad (17.59)$$

By writing Eq. (17.57) in the implicit form $G(I_e, V_1, I_c) = 0$ and utilizing the fact that the product of the three partial derivatives for an implicit function is equal to -1, it follows that

$$\frac{\partial I_e}{\partial V_1} \frac{\partial V_1}{\partial I_c} \frac{\partial I_c}{\partial I_e} = -1$$

or

$$\frac{\partial V_1}{\partial I_c} = - \frac{\partial V_1}{\partial I_e} \frac{\partial I_e}{\partial I_c} \qquad (17.60)$$

Substitution of the preceding result into Eq. (17.59) gives

$$v_1 = \frac{\partial V_1}{\partial I_e}\Big|_i i_e + \frac{\partial V_1}{\partial I_c}\Big|_i i_c = (r_b + r_e)i_e + r_b i_c \qquad (17.61)$$

where

$$r_b + r_e = \frac{\partial V_1}{\partial I_e}\Big|_i \qquad \text{and} \qquad r_b = \frac{\partial V_1}{\partial I_c}\Big|_i \qquad (17.62)$$

The equivalent-circuit representation for Eq. (17.61) is shown on the left side of Fig. 17.19b. The resistances r_b and r_e do not exist physically in the transistor but are defined by Eq. (17.62). The dynamic resistance $r_b + r_e$ is, in effect, the ratio of the change in voltage from the emitter to the base per change in current. The collector current does not flow through the emitter, so that the change in voltage per change in collector current is designated as r_b.

From Fig. 17.19a, it follows that the current I_c is a function of the voltage drop V_2, from the collector to the base, and the emitter current I_e, that is,

$$I_c = F(V_2, I_e) \qquad (17.63)$$

Linearizing and solving for v_2 gives

$$v_2 = \frac{\partial V_2}{\partial I_c}\Big|_i i_c - \frac{\partial V_2}{\partial I_c}\Big|_i \frac{\partial I_c}{\partial I_e}\Big|_i i_e = (r_b + r_c)i_c + (r_b + r_c)\alpha i_e \qquad (17.64)$$

where

$$r_b + r_c = \frac{\partial V_2}{\partial I_c}\Big|_i \qquad \text{and} \qquad \alpha = - \frac{\partial I_c}{\partial I_e}\Big|_i \qquad (17.65)$$

The reason for the minus sign in the preceding equation for α is that, with the collector voltage V_2 held constant, I_c decreases as I_e increases. The equivalent circuit for the collector as described by Eq. (17.64) is shown in the right portion of Fig. 17.19b. The two interlocking circles represent a constant-current source of αi_e. The term α is a very important transistor parameter. For junction transistors, the value of α is usually slightly less than unity. Typical values of α range from 0.95 to 0.98. For a grounded-base transistor, it follows from Eq. (17.65) that the current amplification ratio I_c/I_e can never exceed unity because α is always less than 1.

To achieve a high amplification ratio, the grounded-emitter transistor connection shown in Fig. 17.20a is commonly used. The input current

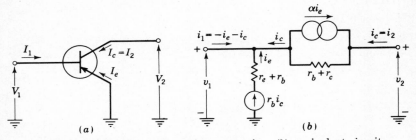

FIG. 17.20. (a) Grounded-emitter connection; (b) equivalent circuit.

is I_1, and the output current I_2 is also the collector current I_c. The potential of the collector, or output voltage, is V_2 volts. As is indicated in Fig. 17.20a, the collector current I_c is a function of the voltage drop $V_2 - V_1$ from the collector to the base, and also of the current I_e which flows through the emitter.

$$I_c = F(V_2 - V_1, I_e) \tag{17.66}$$

Linearization yields

$$i_c = \frac{\partial I_c}{\partial (V_2 - V_1)}\bigg|_i (v_2 - v_1) + \frac{\partial I_c}{\partial I_e}\bigg|_i i_e \tag{17.67}$$

Solving for the voltage drop $v_2 - v_1$ gives

$$v_2 - v_1 = \frac{\partial (V_2 - V_1)}{\partial I_c}\bigg|_i i_c - \frac{\partial (V_2 - V_1)}{\partial I_c}\bigg|_i \frac{\partial I_c}{\partial I_e}\bigg|_i i_e \tag{17.68}$$

$$= (r_b + r_c)(i_c + \alpha i_e) \tag{17.69}$$

where $\quad r_b + r_c = \dfrac{\partial (V_2 - V_1)}{\partial I_c}\bigg|_i \quad$ and $\quad \alpha = -\dfrac{\partial I_c}{\partial I_e}\bigg|_i \tag{17.70}$

As is indicated in Fig. 17.20a, the emitter current I_e is a function of the voltage drop from the emitter to the base, $-V_1$, and also of the collector current I_c. Thus

$$I_e = F(V_1, I_c) \tag{17.71}$$

In the preceding general functional relationship for I_e, it is not necessary to introduce the minus sign in front of V_1. The correct sign in the final linearized expression is automatically accounted for in the evaluation of the partial derivatives. The resultant linearized expression for v_1 is

$$v_1 = \frac{\partial V_1}{\partial I_c}\Big|_i i_c + \frac{\partial V_1}{\partial I_e}\Big|_i i_e = -r_b i_c - (r_b + r_e)i_e \qquad (17.72)$$

where
$$-r_b = \frac{\partial V_1}{\partial I_c}\Big|_i \qquad \text{and} \qquad -(r_b + r_e) = \frac{\partial V_1}{\partial I_e}\Big|_i \qquad (17.73)$$

The reason for the minus signs in Eq. (17.73) is that v_1 decreases as either i_c or i_e increases. Equations (17.69) and (17.72) form the basis for the equivalent grounded-emitter circuit shown in Fig. 17.20b.

The much simplified equivalent circuit of Fig. 17.21a is obtained in

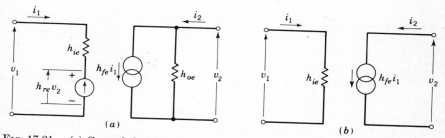

FIG. 17.21. (a) Grounded emitter in terms of h parameters; (b) approximate circuit.

the following manner: From Fig. 17.20a, it is to be noted that

$$I_1 = -(I_e + I_c) \qquad (17.74)$$
$$\text{or} \qquad i_1 = -(i_e + i_c) \qquad (17.75)$$

It should also be noted that $I_c = I_2$, and thus

$$i_c = i_2 \qquad (17.76)$$

h Parameters for the Grounded-emitter Connection. By rearranging Eqs. (17.69) and (17.72) so that v_1 and i_2 are the dependent variables and i_1 and v_2 are the independent variables, it is found that

$$v_1 = h_{ie}i_1 + h_{re}v_2 \qquad (17.77)$$
$$i_2 = h_{fe}i + h_{oe}v_2 \qquad (17.78)$$

The simplified equivalent circuit of Fig. 17.21a follows directly from Eqs. (17.77) and (17.78). The values of the constant-h parameters are obtained as follows: Substituting i_e from Eq. (17.75) into Eq. (17.72) and noting that $i_c = i_2$ yields

$$v_1 = -r_b i_2 + (r_b + r_e)(i_1 + i_2) = (r_b + r_e)i_1 + r_e i_2 \qquad (17.79)$$

Similarly, substituting v_1 from Eq. (17.79) into Eq. (17.69) and noting that $i_e = -(i_1 + i_2)$ yields

$$v_2 = [r_b + r_e - \alpha(r_b + r_c)]i_1 + [r_b + r_c + 'r_e - \alpha(r_b + r_c)]i_2 \quad (17.80)$$

The elimination of i_2 from Eqs. (17.79) and (17.80) yields Eq. (17.77), in which it is seen that

$$h_{ie} = r_e + r_b - \frac{r_e[r_e + r_b - \alpha(r_b + r_c)]}{r_b + r_c + r_e - \alpha(r_b + r_c)} \approx \frac{r_e}{1 - \alpha} + r_b \quad (17.81)$$

and $\quad h_{re} = \dfrac{r_e}{r_b + r_c + r_e - \alpha(r_b + r_c)} \approx \dfrac{r_e}{r_c(1 - \alpha)} \quad (17.82)$

In making these approximations, use is made of the fact that r_c is much larger than r_b or r_e. The h-parameter subscripts i, r, f, and o refer to input, reverse, forward, and output, respectively, while the second subscript, e, indicates that these parameters are defined for the grounded-emitter transistor. A second subscript e could also be added to the voltage and current terms of Eqs. (17.77) and (17.78).

Because Eq. (17.80) is in the same general form as Eq. (17.78), all that is necessary is to solve Eq. (17.80) for i_2 and compare coefficients of like terms to obtain directly

$$h_{fe} = -\frac{r_b + r_e - \alpha(r_b + r_c)}{r_b + r_c + r_e - \alpha(r_b + r_c)} \approx \frac{\alpha}{1 - \alpha} \quad (17.83)$$

$$h_{oe} = \frac{1}{r_b + r_c + r_e - \alpha(r_b + r_c)} \approx \frac{1}{r_c(1 - \alpha)} \quad (17.84)$$

A further simplification in the equivalent circuit shown in Fig. 17.21a is obtained by utilizing the fact that h_{ie} is generally much greater than $h_{re}v_2$. Also, the load resistance R_L is usually much less than h_{oe} so that h_{oe} is effectively shunted and may thus be neglected. The resulting equivalent circuit for a grounded-emitter transistor amplifier is shown in Fig. 17.21b. The input circuit and output circuit are seen to be decoupled. For the output circuit, it is seen that

$$i_2 = h_{fe}i_1$$

or $\qquad\qquad\qquad \dfrac{i_2}{i_1} = h_{fe} \qquad\qquad\qquad (17.85)$

Thus, the current gain is simply h_{fe}.

The voltage gain is obtained by substituting $i_2 = -v_2/R_L$ into Eq. (17.78) and solving Eqs. (17.77) and (17.78) simultaneously. Thus

$$\frac{v_2}{v_1} = \frac{-h_{fe}(R_L/h_{ie})}{1 + R_L h_{oe}(1 - h_{fe}h_{re}/h_{oe}h_{ie})} \quad (17.86)$$

For most amplifiers $R_L h_{oe} \ll 1$, and $0 < (h_{fe} h_{re}/h_{oe} h_{ic}) < 1$, so that the voltage amplification is approximately

$$\frac{v_2}{v_1} \approx -h_{fe} \frac{R_L}{h_{ie}} \tag{17.87}$$

The resulting power amplification is the product of the current and voltage amplifications.

An important advantage of the h-parameter designation is that the values of h may be obtained directly from characteristic curves which are usually supplied by the manufacturer. A typical set of curves for a grounded-emitter connection is shown in Fig. 17.22. The geometric

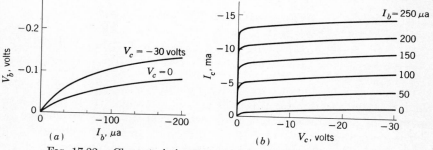

FIG. 17.22. Characteristic curves for grounded-emitter connection.

interpretation of the h parameters from Fig. 17.22a and b gives, respectively,

$$V_b = F(I_b, V_c)$$
$$I_c = F(I_b, V_c)$$

From Fig. 17.23a, it is to be seen that for a grounded-emitter connection, the base is the input and the collector the output, so that the sub-

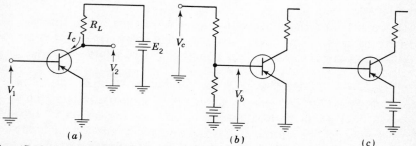

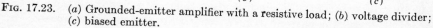

FIG. 17.23. (a) Grounded-emitter amplifier with a resistive load; (b) voltage divider; (c) biased emitter.

scripts 1 and b may be used interchangeably, as well as the subscripts 2 and c. Thus,

$$V_1 = F(I_1, V_2) \tag{17.88}$$
$$I_2 = F(I_1, V_2)$$

Linearization of the preceding equations yields

$$v_1 = \frac{\partial V_1}{\partial I_1}\Big|_i \, i_1 + \frac{\partial V_1}{\partial V_2}\Big|_i \, v_2 \tag{17.89}$$

$$i_2 = \frac{\partial I_2}{\partial I_1}\Big|_i \, i_1 + \frac{\partial I_2}{\partial V_2}\Big|_i \, v_2 \tag{17.90}$$

Equating coefficients of like terms of Eqs. (17.89) and (17.77) and also coefficients of Eqs. (17.90) and (17.78) yields

$$
\begin{aligned}
h_{ie} &= \frac{\partial V_1}{\partial I_1}\Big|_i = \frac{\partial V_b}{\partial I_b}\Big|_i & h_{re} &= \frac{\partial V_1}{\partial V_2}\Big|_i = \frac{\partial V_b}{\partial V_c}\Big|_i \\
h_{fe} &= \frac{\partial I_2}{\partial I_1}\Big|_i = \frac{\partial I_c}{\partial I_b}\Big|_i & h_{oe} &= \frac{\partial I_2}{\partial V_2}\Big|_i = \frac{\partial I_c}{\partial V_c}\Big|_i
\end{aligned}
\tag{17.91}
$$

The problem of coupling transistor amplifiers is usually much simpler than that for vacuum-tube amplifiers. For example, it is possible to operate the base of a second stage directly from the collector voltage V_c of the preceding stage, etc. If the quiescent collector voltage V_{co} of the first stage is different from the desired value V_{bo} for the second stage, V_{co} may be run through a biased voltage divider as shown in Fig. 17.23b to achieve the proper V_{bo}. Another technique is to bias the emitter as illustrated in Fig. 17.23c. A biased emitter in effect decreases V_b and V_c for the particular transistor by the amount of the biasing voltage.

The direction of current flow and the signs for the various voltages used in the preceding discussion are appropriate for the p-n-p type of transistors. In a p-n-p transistor, the current is carried through the emitter and the collector by positive carriers called holes, while the current in the base is transmitted by means of negative carriers, or electrons. For the other transistor type, the n-p-n transistor, the current is carried in the emitter and the collector by negative carriers, while the base has positive carriers. To convert from a p-n-p to an n-p-n transistor, all that is necessary is to reverse the polarity of the battery voltages.

h Parameters for the Grounded-collector and the Grounded-base Connections. Figure 17.24a, b, and c shows the grounded-emitter, grounded-collector, and grounded-base transistor circuits, respectively. Each of these circuits may be represented by the equivalent four-terminal network shown in Fig. 17.24d. Table 17.1 gives the equations for the voltage gain $G_v = v_2/v_1$ and the current gain $G_i = i_2/i_1$ for each of these circuits.

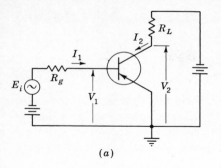

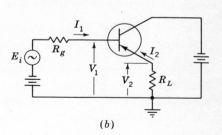

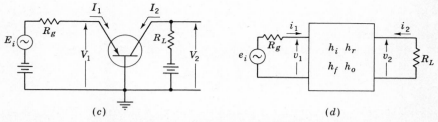

FIG. 17.24. (a) Grounded-emitter connection; (b) grounded-collector connection; (c) grounded-base connection; (d) equivalent four-terminal network.

TABLE 17.1

Circuit	G_v	G_i	Approximation
Grounded emitter	$-h_{fe}\dfrac{R_L}{h_{ie}}$	h_{fe}	$R_L h_{oe} \ll 1$ $\dfrac{R_g}{h_{ie}} \gg 1$ $0 < \dfrac{h_{fe}h_{re}}{h_{ie}h_{oe}} < 1$
Grounded collector	1	$-(1 + h_{fe})$	$R_L h_{oe} \ll 1$ $\dfrac{R_g}{h_{ie}} \gg 1$ $\dfrac{(1 + h_{fe})R_L}{h_{ie}} \gg 1$ $\dfrac{1 + h_{fe}}{R_g h_{oe}} \gg 1$
Grounded base	$h_{fe}\dfrac{R_L}{h_{ie}}$	$-\dfrac{h_{fe}}{1 + h_{fe}}$	$R_L h_{oe} \ll 1$ $\dfrac{R_g}{h_{ie}} \gg 1$ $0 < \dfrac{h_{fe}h_{re}}{h_{ie}h_{oe}} < 1$

By comparison of Fig. 17.24a and b, it follows that the voltage drop from the base to the emitter is

$$V_{1e} = V_{1c} - V_{2c}$$

and thus $\qquad\qquad v_{1e} = v_{1c} - v_{2c}$ (17.92)

The second subscript refers to the type of circuit, that is, e for grounded emitter and c for grounded collector. Similarly, corresponding values of the voltage drop from the collector to the emitter, the current flowing through the base, and the current flowing through the collector are, respectively,

$$\begin{aligned} v_{2e} &= -v_{2c} \\ i_{1e} &= i_{1c} \\ i_{2e} &= -i_{1c} - i_{2c} \end{aligned}$$ (17.93)

Substitution of these results into Eqs. (17.77) and (17.78) gives

$$\begin{aligned} v_{1c} &= h_{ie}i_{1c} + (1 - h_{re})v_{2c} \\ i_{2c} &= -(1 + h_{fe})i_{1c} + h_{oe}v_{2c} \end{aligned}$$ (17.94)

Thus, the h parameters for a grounded-collector circuit are obtained in terms of the h parameters for a grounded-emitter circuit, that is,

$$\begin{aligned} h_{ic} &= h_{ie} \\ h_{rc} &= 1 - h_{re} \\ h_{fc} &= -(1 + h_{fe}) \\ h_{oc} &= h_{oe} \end{aligned}$$ (17.95)

Similarly, the characteristics of a grounded-base circuit may be expressed as a function of the h parameters for a grounded-emitter circuit. An advantage of using h parameters is that the characteristics of the grounded-emitter circuit (which are usually supplied by the manufacturer) may be used to evaluate the performance of the grounded-collector or grounded-base connections.

Problems

17.1 A field-controlled dc motor is shown in Fig. P17.1. The motor drives the load through a gearbox so that $\omega_c = n\omega$, where n is the gear ratio, ω is the motor speed, and ω_c is the speed of the load (i.e., the controlled speed). The output shaft is connected to a tachometer, which produces a voltage proportional to the controlled speed ($E_c = K_c\omega_c$). An electronic amplifier is used to amplify the error signal by a factor K_a, that is, $E_f = K_a(E_r - E_c)$. Complete the overall block-diagram representation for this system. What is the characteristic equation for this system? Sketch the root-locus plot for the case in which the time constant τ_f is 0.1 sec and the viscous friction B_v is negligible.

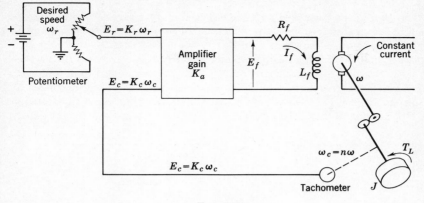

Fig. P17.1

17.2 (*a*) In Fig. P17.2 is shown a generator which is used as a voltage amplifier. The prime mover drives the generator at a constant speed. Determine the equation of operation for the amplification ratio E_2/E_1.

(*b*) Derive Eq. (17.25).

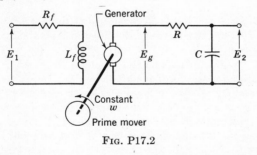

Fig. P17.2

17.3 Obtain the overall block-diagram representation for the positioning servomechanism shown in Fig. 17.11. What is the characteristic equation for this system? Sketch the resulting root-locus plot for the case in which $\tau_{fg} = 0.5$, $\tau_a = 0.1$, and B_r is negligible.

17.4 A Wheatstone bridge as shown in Fig. P17.4 is commonly used as a comparator for electrical systems. The resistance R_r of the input potentiometer varies in proportion to the reference input. Similarly the resistance R_c is varied

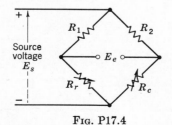

Fig. P17.4

in proportion to the controlled variable. The supply voltage E_s and resistances R_1 and R_2 are maintained constant. Determine the equation for the voltage E_e which is a measure of the error.

17.5 The gain K of a high-gain amplifier is affected by variations in the tube characteristics due to temperature changes, variations in the supply voltages, etc. Also, slight irregularities in the input signal become greatly magnified at the output (i.e., noise). The use of feedback around an amplifier as illustrated in Fig. P17.5 tends to make the amplifier insensitive to these changing influences.

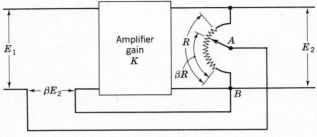

FIG. P17.5

For this feedback amplifier, the total resistance of the potentiometer across the output is R, and the resistance between the wiper arm and point B is βR. Thus, the potential between points A and B is βE_2, which is fed back. The input to the amplifier is $E_{\text{in}} = E_1 + \beta E_2$, and the output is $E_2 = KE_{\text{in}}$. Determine the equation of operation for this feedback amplifier.

17.6 When the amplifier shown in Fig. P17.5 is operated with the recommended supply voltage, the voltage amplification (without feedback) is 30 per stage. For three stages of amplification, $K = -27,000$ at full supply voltage. The negative sign occurs because of the odd number of stages of amplification. When the supply voltage drops 20 percent, the amplification without feedback is reduced to $K = -20,000$.

Determine the voltage amplification E_2/E_1 under the two preceding conditions for this amplifier with feedback in which $\beta = 0.001$. What is the resulting percent change in overall amplification?

17.7 Determine the overall voltage amplification E_2/E_1 for the feedback amplifier shown in Fig. P17.7.

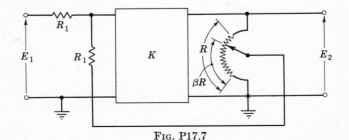

FIG. P17.7

17.8 Typical values for a transistor are base resistance $r_b = 1,000$ ohms, emitter resistance $r_e = 25$ ohms, collector resistance $r_c = 2$ megohms, and $\alpha = 0.975$.

(a) Determine the corresponding values for h_{ie}, h_{fe}, h_{re}, and h_{oe}.

(b) Determine each value of G_i and G_v in Table 17.1 for the case in which $R_L = 20,000$ ohms.

17.9 Show that for a grounded-base transistor circuit

$$h_{ib} = \frac{h_{ie}}{1 + h_{fe}}$$

$$h_{rb} = \frac{h_{ie}h_{oe}}{1 + h_{fe}} - h_{re}$$

$$h_{fb} = -\alpha = -\frac{h_{fe}}{1 + h_{fe}}$$

$$h_{ob} = \frac{h_{oe}}{1 + h_{fe}}$$

(To obtain these relationships, it is necessary to utilize the approximations that $h_{re} \ll 1$ and $h_{ie}h_{oe} \ll h_{fe}$.)

17.10 Use Eqs. (17.81) to (17.84) to express the values of G_v and G_i in Table 17.1 as a function of the equivalent circuit resistances and α.

17.11 Verify the equations for G_v and G_i given in Table 17.1.

17.12 In working with the four-terminal network of Fig. 17.24d it is convenient to use the term $Z_i = v_1/i_1$ and the term $Z_o = v_2/i_2$. Determine equations for Z_i and Z_o in terms of the grounded-emitter h parameters for a:

(a) Grounded-emitter connection
(b) Grounded-collector connection
(c) Grounded-base connection

(Note that $v_1 = R_g i_1$.)

18

Inertial guidance

Gyroscopes are basically the position-measuring or -indicating devices for inertial-guidance systems. The ability of a controlled vehicle to maintain its desired path depends upon the accuracy with which the gyroscopes indicate its position.

As is shown in Fig. 18.1, a gyroscope consists of a spinning disk (i.e., gyrowheel) which is supported by linkages called gimbals. The axis of

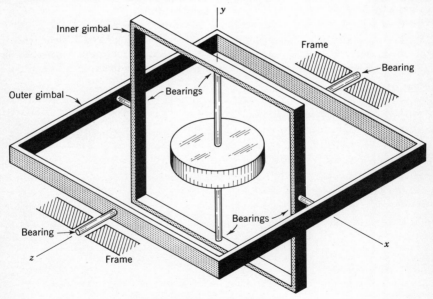

FIG. 18.1. Free gyroscope.

rotation of the gyrowheel is referred to as the rotor spin axis. This is the y axis in Fig. 18.1.

18.1 Free Gyros. A basic characteristic of gyroscopes is that the rotor spin axis always points in the same direction unless it is acted upon by an external torque. The term "free gyro" is used to describe a gyro-wheel which is suspended in such a manner that external torques cannot be transmitted to it. The gimbals for the free gyro shown in Fig. 18.1 are supported by bearings so that, regardless of the motion of the frame, the direction of the spin axis tends to remain fixed in space.

This tendency for the rotor spin axis to maintain a fixed direction in inertial space is illustrated in Fig. 18.2. Initially, the spin axis of this

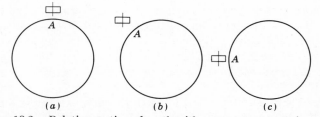

Fig. 18.2. Relative motion of earth with respect to rotor spin axis.

gyroscope is perpendicular to the earth, as is shown in Fig. 18.2a. If the vehicle in which the gyroscope is mounted is not moving relative to the earth (i.e., remains at point A, which is fixed), in 3 hr the earth turns one-eighth its daily revolution, or 45°. Thus, in 3 hr, the angle of inclination of the spin axis is 45° with respect to the earth, as shown in Fig. 18.2b. The gyroscope is still located at point A, and its rotor spin axis has not changed direction in inertial space. The angle of inclination is due to the earth's rotation in space. After 6 hr, the spin axis is tangent to the earth, as shown in Fig. 18.2c.

In a practical gyro, the spin axis tends to drift slowly from its initial direction because of torque acting on the gyrowheel due to friction in the gimbal bearings. This phenomenon is referred to as drift. It should be noted that the angle of inclination of the spin axis with respect to the earth depends not only on the rotation of the earth and drift but also on the movement relative to the earth of the vehicle in which the gyro-scope is mounted.

18.2 Vertical and Directional Gyros. A vertical gyro is one in which the spin axis is aligned with the gravitational field of the earth (i.e., perpendicular to the earth's surface). To compensate for the effects of drift, earth's rotation, and motion of the gyroscope relative to the earth, it is necessary to reset the reference position of the spin axis. This is generally accomplished by applying an external torque to realign the gyrowheel to the desired reference position. An external torque can be applied to the gyrowheel shown in Fig. 18.1 by extending the gimbal axes and connecting torque motors to these shaft extensions, rather than letting them rotate freely in bearings. The rotor of the torque motor is wound around the shaft extension and is free to rotate inside its stator, which is fixed to the adjoining gimbal or frame. An electrical signal applied to the torque motor causes a torque to be exerted on the shaft extension.

A gyro used to establish a vertical reference can automatically be controlled by, or slaved to, a more accurate primary reference such as the average position of a pendulum. This is accomplished by comparing the direction of the gyro spin axis with the direction of the pendulum and using the resulting error signal to make the gyro position correspond to that of the pendulum. By having a small torque applied to the gyro so that the spin axis cannot follow rapid fluctuations of the pendulum, the gyro spin axis tends to remain aligned to the average pendulum position (i.e., the vertical).

A directional gyroscope is one in which the spin axis lies in a horizontal plane and holds a given direction, which is usually north-south. A directional gyroscope may be slaved to a magnetic compass, which provides the primary north-south reference.

By maintaining the spin axis in some reference direction, then it is possible to measure the angular displacement of the frame (which is the angular displacement of the vehicle to which the frame is mounted). Gyroscopes which are used to measure such displacements of a vehicle from some reference direction, as a vertical or a north-south orientation, are frequently called displacement gyroscopes.

A vertical gyroscope can measure pitch and roll, while a directional gyroscope can measure yaw (azimuth). From Fig. 18.3 it is to be noted

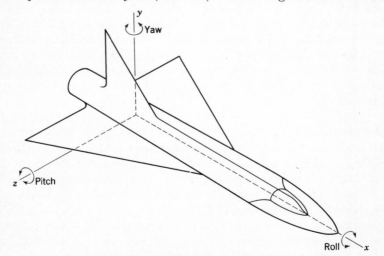

FIG. 18.3. Pitch, roll, and yaw motions of a vehicle.

that pitch is angular motion about the lateral, or z, axis, roll is angular motion about the longitudinal, or x, axis, and yaw is angular motion about the normal, or y, axis. The frame and the pitch and roll scales of the vertical gyroscope shown in Fig. 18.4 are fastened to the vehicle.

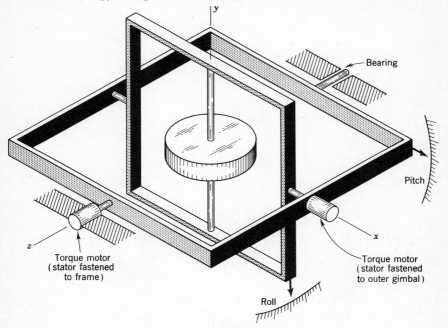

FIG. 18.4. Vertical gyroscope.

A rotation of the vehicle about the x, y, or z axis causes a corresponding rotation of the frame and the attached pitch and roll scales. For example, a rotation of the vehicle about the z axis causes a corresponding rotation of the pitch scale, but the outer gimbal and attached pointer cannot rotate about the z axis, because the spin axis is maintained in a vertical position. Thus the relative motion between the pitch scale, which rotates with the vehicle, and the pointer on the outer gimbal is a measure of the angle of inclination, or pitch, of the vehicle. The pointer and scale may be replaced by an electrical pick-off in order to obtain a voltage signal proportional to the pitch angle. This change in pitch also causes the roll scale to rotate about the z axis, while the inner gimbal remains fixed. However, there is no change in the scale reading, because this motion is perpendicular to the pointer on the inner gimbal. For a rotation about the x axis the roll scale rotates relative to the pointer on the inner gimbal, which maintains its vertical inclination. This relative motion is a measure of the roll. The pitch reading is unaffected, because both the outer gimbal and the pitch scale rotate the same amount, and thus there is no relative motion. Similarly, a motion of the vehicle about the y axis (i.e., yaw) has no effect upon either the roll or the pitch readings.

For the directional gyroscope shown in Fig. 18.5, the rotor spin axis maintains a fixed horizontal direction (usually a north-south direction).

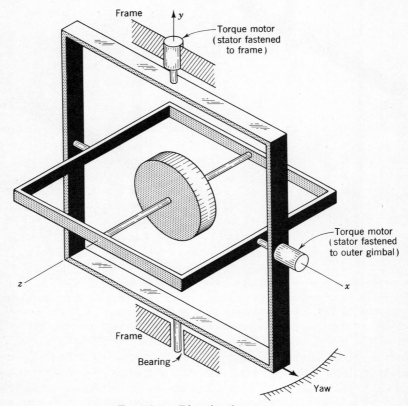

Fig. 18.5.   Directional gyroscope.

A rotation of the vehicle about the y axis is seen to cause a corresponding rotation of the attached yaw scale. However, the outer gimbal and attached pointer cannot rotate, because the spin axis is maintained in its reference direction. This relative motion is thus a measure of the direction of heading, or yaw. Other motions of the vehicle have no effect upon the measured angle of yaw.

Vertical and directional gyros are used in automatic pilots, roll-stabilizing equipment, artificial horizons, inertial-navigation equipment, etc. To obtain a better understanding of the operation of other types of gyroscopes which play an essential role in inertial navigation, some attention is first given to the dynamics of gyroscopes.

18.3 Dynamics of Gyroscopes. A gyrowheel is essentially a spinning wheel, as is shown in Fig. 18.6. Frequently, the gyrowheel is the rotor

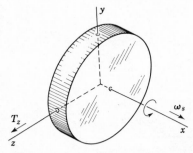

FIG. 18.6. Free-body diagram of a gyrowheel.

of a synchronous motor which rotates the rotor at a constant angular velocity. The disk, or rotor, rotates about the x axis (i.e., its spin axis) with an angular velocity ω_s. In accordance with standard procedure, the vector representing the angular velocity ω_s is in the direction in which a right-hand thread would move if the thread were rotating in the same direction as the gyrowheel. Thus, the vector representing ω_s is in the positive direction of the x axis. If a positive torque $\mathbf{T}_z$ is applied about the z axis as shown in Fig. 18.6, from Newton's law this torque is equal to the time rate of angular momentum. That is,

$$\mathbf{T}_z = \lim_{\Delta t \to 0} \frac{\Delta \mathbf{H}}{\Delta t} = \lim_{\Delta t \to 0} \frac{\Delta(J_s \omega_s)}{\Delta t} = \lim_{\Delta t \to 0} \frac{J_s \, \Delta \omega_s}{\Delta t} \tag{18.1}$$

where J_s is the polar moment of inertia of the gyrowheel about its spin axis and $\mathbf{H} = J_s \omega_s$ is the angular momentum of the disk. Because J_s and Δt are scalar quantities, $\Delta \omega_s$ is in the same direction as $\mathbf{T}_z$ and $\Delta \mathbf{H}$, as shown in Fig. 18.7a. In this figure, the y axis is perpendicular to the plane of the paper and coming out from the paper. From the geometry of Fig. 18.7a, it follows that

$$\tan(-\Delta\theta_y) = \frac{T_z \, \Delta t}{J_s \omega_s} \tag{18.2}$$

Because $\tan(-\Delta\theta_y) \approx -\Delta\theta_y$,

$$\omega_y = \lim_{\Delta t \to 0} \frac{\Delta\theta_y}{\Delta t} = -\frac{T_z}{J_s \omega_s} \tag{18.3}$$

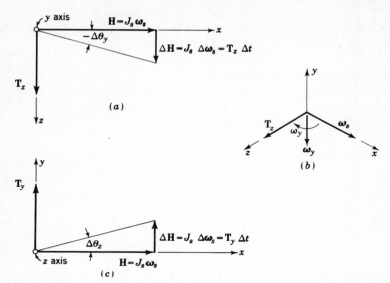

FIG. 18.7.   (a) Gyroscopic precession caused by T_z; (b) precession velocity; (c) gyroscopic precession caused by T_y.

The angular velocity imparted to a gyrowheel because of an external torque is referred to as the velocity of precession.   The vector representing the velocity of precession is perpendicular to the plane determined by the spin vector and the torque vector.   In general, *the direction of rotation of the precession velocity is the same as that required to rotate the spin vector* ω_s *into the torque vector* $\mathbf{T}_z$, as is shown in Fig. 18.7b.

For a positive torque T_y applied about the y axis, the resultant vector diagram is as shown in Fig. 18.7c.   From the geometry of this figure, it follows that

$$\tan (\Delta\theta_z) = \frac{T_y \, \Delta t}{J_s \omega_s} \tag{18.4}$$

and therefore

$$\omega_z = \frac{d\theta_z}{dt} = \frac{T_y}{J_s \omega_s} \tag{18.5}$$

where ω_z is the velocity of precession about the z axis.   Again, it is to be noted that the gyro tends to precess so as to line up the spin axis with the direction of the torque vector.

In a practical gyroscope, torque is not applied directly to the gyrowheel but rather is applied to the gimbals, usually by means of either the y-axis torque motor or the z-axis torque motor.   Thus, Eqs. (18.3) and (18.5) must be modified to include the effects of the gyro rest inertia and viscous friction of the gimbal bearings.   That is, in addition to causing the precession, a torque T_y applied by the y-axis torque motor is utilized in accelerating the rest inertia $J_y(d^2\theta_y/dt^2)$ of the gyro about the y axis and in overcoming the viscous friction of the y-axis gimbal bearings, $B_y(d\theta_y/dt)$.   Thus

$$T_y = J_y \frac{d^2\theta_y}{dt^2} + B_y \frac{d\theta_y}{dt} + J_s\omega_s \frac{d\theta_z}{dt} \tag{18.6}$$

Similarly, it follows that the torque T_z applied by the z-axis torque motor is

$$T_z = J_z \frac{d^2\theta_z}{dt^2} + B_z \frac{d\theta_z}{dt} - J_s\omega_s \frac{d\theta_y}{dt} \tag{18.7}$$

where J_y and J_z are the rest inertias of the gyro and gimbals about the y and z axes, respectively.   Similarly, B_y and B_z are the coefficients of viscous damping for rotation about the y axis and the z axis, respectively.

18.4 Restrained Gyros.   A restrained gyro is one which has constraints such as springs or dampers attached to the gimbals in such a manner that a motion of the gimbal tends to precess the gyro.

For the gyro shown in Fig. 18.8, it is to be noticed that with the frame

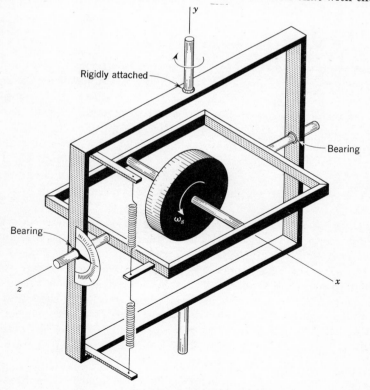

Fig. 18.8.   Rate gyro.

held fixed the gyrowheel is free to rotate about the z axis but not about the y axis. Such a gyroscope, which can pivot about only one axis, has one degree of freedom. Gyroscopes such as those shown in Figs. 18.1, 18.4, and 18.5 are free to pivot about the two mutually perpendicular y and z axes and have two degrees of freedom.

Rate Gyro. A rate gyro is one in which the motion of a gimbal is restrained by means of springs, as shown in Fig. 18.8. When the frame rotates about the y axis, the y-axis torque is transmitted through the gimbal arrangement to the gyrowheel. This causes a precession about the z axis, which is seen to be resisted by the restraining springs. Because the torque T_z exerted by the restraining springs opposes the precession θ_z, it follows that

$$T_z = -K_z\theta_z \tag{18.8}$$

The substitution of the preceding value of T_z into Eq. (18.7) yields the following equation of operation for a rate gyro,

$$K_z\theta_z + B_zD\theta_z + J_zD^2\theta_z = J_s\omega_sD\theta_y$$

or
$$\theta_z = \frac{J_s\omega_s}{J_zD^2 + B_zD + K_z}\dot{\theta}_y \tag{18.9}$$

By designing the rate gyro so that the first two terms in the denominator may be considered negligible, the angular position θ_z is a measure of the angular velocity $\dot{\theta}_y$ of the input shaft. In addition, by having the angular momentum $J_s\omega_s$ of the gyrowheel very large, a rate gyro is capable of measuring small angular velocities quite accurately. The value of θ_z can be measured by attaching a scale to the outer gimbal and a pointer to the shaft extension of the inner gimbal, as shown in Fig. 18.8. Usually, it is desired to have an electrical output signal which is proportional to θ_z. This is accomplished by using a synchro pick-off.

Integrating Rate Gyro. The integrating rate gyroscope shown in Fig. 18.9a is referred to as an HIG gyro (hermetically sealed integrating gyro).[1] This single-degree-of-freedom gyroscope is very rugged and extremely accurate. The inner gimbal, or can, is hermetically sealed and filled with an inert gas which acts as a neutral atmosphere. The outer case is filled with a viscous fluid whose density is such that the inner gimbal neither floats nor sinks but rather remains suspended. Thus, the load on the jeweled bearings is negligibly small in order to minimize the effects of drift. A schematic diagram for the operation of

---

[1] C. S. Draper, W. Wrigley, and L. R. Grohe, The Floating Integrating Gyro and Its Application to Geometrical Stabilization Problems on Moving Bases, *Aeronaut. Eng. Rev.*, **15**: (6), (June, 1956).

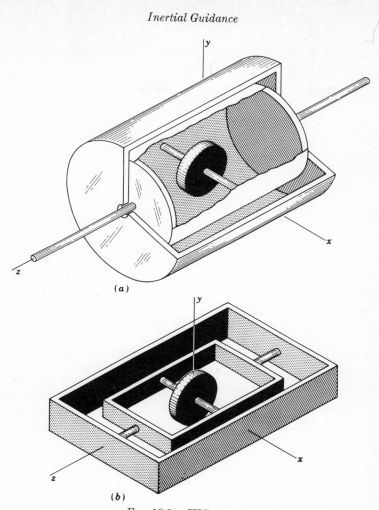

(a)

(b)

Fig. 18.9.   HIG gyro.

an integrating rate gyro is shown in Fig. 18.9*b*.   This illustrates that a
rotation of the outer case about the *y* axis causes a precession of the
gyrowheel about the *z* axis.   By placing an electrical pickup on the
output shaft, a signal is obtained which is a measure of the angular
position θ_y.   Although at first glance the integrating rate gyro looks
quite different from the rate gyro of Fig. 18.8, actually both gyros are
quite similar in many respects.   A motion about the *y* axis of an integrating rate gyro causes the gyro to precess about the *z* axis, as was the
case for the rate gyro.   The major distinction is that an integrating rate
gyro does not have a restraining spring, but rather the viscous friction
of the fluid between the inner gimbal, which is a cylinder, and the outer

gimbal, which is also a cylinder, produces a torque T_z which opposes precession. That is,

$$T_z = -B \frac{d\theta_z}{dt} \qquad (18.10)$$

where B is the coefficient of viscous friction between the inner gimbal and the outer case. Substituting T_z from Eq. (18.10) into Eq. (18.7) and noting that the viscous friction B_z of the bearings is negligible compared with B gives

$$J_z D^2 \theta_z + BD\theta_z = J_s \omega_s D\theta_y$$

Solving for θ_z yields

$$\theta_z = \frac{J_s\omega_s}{J_z D + B}\,\theta_y = \frac{J_s\omega_s/B}{\tau D + 1}\,\theta_y \approx \frac{J_s\omega_s}{B}\,\theta_y \qquad (18.11)$$

where $\tau = J_z/B$. By making the value of B large and the value for J_z small so that the time constant is negligible, the output angle θ_z is proportional to the input θ_y rather than the rate of change of θ_y, as is the case for the rate gyro. Thus, this device is called an integrating rate gyro or sometimes an "integrating gyro."

18.5 Stable Platform. The primary member of a stable platform is the stable element. The stable element is orientated so that one axis always points in a north-south direction, another in an east-west direction. and a third in a vertical direction, as is shown in Fig. 18.10. Three

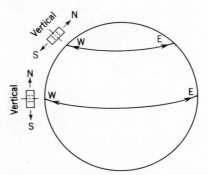

F1G. 18.10.   Orientation of the stable element relative to the earth.

accelerometers are mounted on this stable element at right angles to each other to measure acceleration in the north-south, east-west, and vertical directions. Successive integration of the output of each accelerometer yields velocity and then displacement. The three components of displacement determine the position of the vehicle. Because the accelerometers cannot distinguish acceleration of the vehicle from the acceleration of gravity, it is essential that the north-south and east-west accelerometers be mounted in a horizontal plane. Otherwise, each accelerometer would measure a component of the acceleration due to gravity, which would be interpreted by the computer as an acceleration in the direction of motion of the particular accelerometer whence the signal came. Similarly, the vertical accelerometer would yield an erroneous signal if it did not maintain its vertical direction. Thus, it is essential that the stable element be maintained in its proper orientation to obtain an accurate measurement of position.

As is shown in Fig. 18.11a, a stable platform utilizes a set of gimbals mounted in bearings so that the motion of the vehicle is not transmitted to the stable element. However, because of bearing friction and other extraneous disturbances, it is possible for the stable element to rotate from its reference orientation. Such motion is detected by the use of three gyroscopes, as is shown in Fig. 18.11b. The plane of the inner gimbal and gyrowheel for each gyroscope is perpendicular to the axis about which rotation is to be detected. For example, a rotation about the vertical axis causes a corresponding precession of the vertical gyro. In turn, the electrical pick-off sends a signal to the azimuth gimbal servomotor, which applies a torque to return the stable element to its reference position.

To maintain a fixed attitude as shown in Fig. 18.10, it is necessary to compensate the orientation of the stable element for the effect of the rotation of the earth and motion of the vehicle relative to the earth. A computer automatically corrects the reference orientation for rotation of the earth by sending an electrical signal to each torque motor which is incorporated in each gyro. The torque motor of a gyro applies a torque to precess the gyro which thus changes the reference position, or orientation, of the gyroscope. The electrical pick-off detects this change and sends an electrical signal to the appropriate gimbal servomotor so that the stable element follows the reference position determined by each gyroscope. In addition to compensating for rotation of the earth, it is also necessary for the computer to take into account the motion of the vehicle with respect to the earth. This motion is obtained by integrating the three mutually perpendicular accelerations of the vehicle, as was previously discussed.

In the design of a stable platform,[1] often a considerable savings in weight and space may be realized by using the internal-gimbaling scheme shown in Fig. 18.12a rather than the external gimbaling illustrated in Fig. 18.11a. The outer gimbal is seen to be the same for either internal

[1] R. H. Cannon and D. P. Chandler, Stable Platforms for High Performance Aircraft, *Aeronaut. Eng. Rev.*, **16:** (12), 42–47 (Dec., 1957).

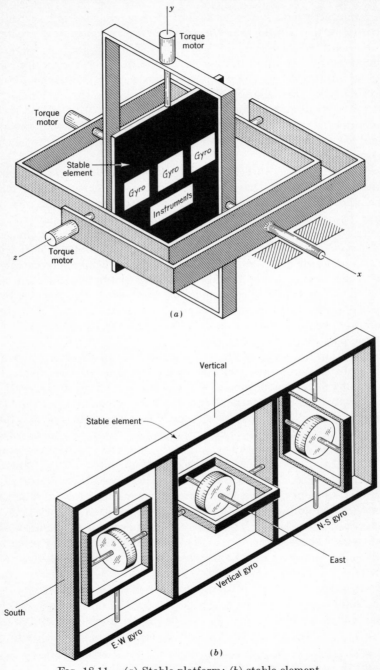

FIG. 18.11.   (a) Stable platform; (b) stable element.

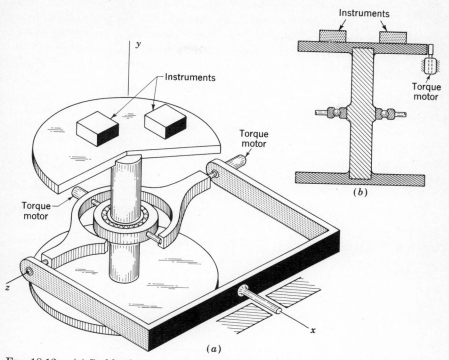

FIG. 18.12. (*a*) Stable platform with internal gimbaling; (*b*) stable element of a stable platform with internal gimbaling.

or external gimbaling. However, the middle gimbal now becomes a split beam, and the inner gimbal is simply a sleeve. The stable element consists of two tables connected by a solid post, as is shown separately in Fig. 18.12*b*.

18.6 The Control Loop. From Figs. 18.11 and 18.12, it is to be noted that a basic similarity exists in the control of the position of the stable element due to roll, pitch, or azimuth. A rotation of the stable element is sensed by the appropriate gyro, which sends an electrical signal to the corresponding torque motor to return the stable element to its reference position. The effect of roll, pitch, or azimuth may be considered independently.

In the following, it is shown how to obtain the block diagram describing the control of the azimuth position of the stable element.[1] Similar techniques may be used to determine the response due to roll or pitch. By

[1] R. H. Cannon, Jr., Root-locus Analysis of Structural Coupling in Control Systems, *Trans. ASME, J. Appl. Mechanics*, **81**: E(2) (1959).

designating the reference direction of the azimuth gyro as ϕ_r and the angular position of the stable element as ϕ_c, then $\phi_c - \phi_r$ is the rotation of the stable element from the reference or desired direction. This error causes a precession of the gyro, which in turn sends a signal to the azimuth torque motor to correct the orientation of the stable element, i.e.,

$$T_m = -K_m(\phi_c - \phi_r) = K_m(\phi_r - \phi_c) \qquad (18.12)$$

where K_m is the gain for the corrective action of the torque motor.

Because of the precision bearings which support the stable element, the damping may be considered as negligible. The motor torque T_m applied to the table is resisted by the inertia of the table and the load torque.

$$T_m = JD^2\phi_c + T_L \qquad (18.13)$$

where T_L is the sum of the extraneous torques such as that due to gimbal-bearing friction. The block-diagram representation for the overall control loop is obtained by combining Eqs. (18.12) and (18.13) and substituting s for D, as shown in Fig. 18.13a. This is the basic control

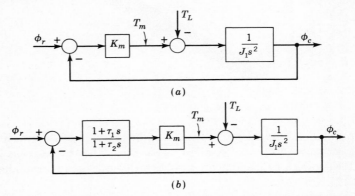

(a)

(b)

FIG. 18.13.   Block diagram for azimuth control of a stable element with a rigid post: (a) uncompensated system; (b) system with lead compensation.

loop whose characteristic equation is

$$Js^2 + K_m = 0$$

or

$$s^2 + \frac{K_m}{J} = s^2 + K = 0 \qquad (18.14)$$

where $K = K_m/J$ and $J = J_1 + J_2$ is the combined inertia of the upper table J_1 plus that of the lower table J_2. The $G(j\omega)H(j\omega)$ polar plot for this system is seen to lie entirely along the negative real axis, as is shown by the solid line in Fig. 18.14a. The corresponding root-locus plot is shown in Fig. 18.14b.

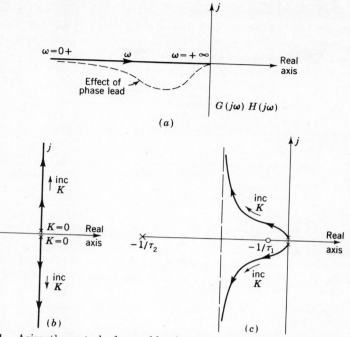

Fig. 18.14. Azimuth control of a stable element with a rigid post: (a) vector loci plot; (b) root-locus plot for uncompensated system; (c) root-locus plot for system with lead compensation.

To stabilize the operation of this system, it is necessary to use lead compensation to reshape the $G(j\omega)H(j\omega)$ plot, as is shown by the dashed-line loci in Fig. 18.14a. The addition of lead compensation to the servo controller results in the block diagram shown in Fig. 18.13b, for which the characteristic equation is

$$Js^2(\tau_2 s + 1) + K_m(\tau_1 s + 1) = 0$$

or

$$s^2\left(s + \frac{1}{\tau_2}\right) + K\left(s + \frac{1}{\tau_1}\right) = 0 \qquad (18.15)$$

where $K = \tau_1 K_m / \tau_2 J$. The resultant root-locus plot is shown in Fig. 18.14c.

In the preceding analysis, the azimuth post connecting the upper and lower tables was considered to be rigid. An investigation of the effects of the limberness of the post is accomplished as follows: The summation of torques acting on the upper table is

$$\Sigma T_e = T_m - T_L + K_s(\phi_{c_2} - \phi_{c_1}) = J_1 s^2 \phi_{c_1}$$

or

$$(J_1 s^2 + K_s)\phi_{c_1} - K_s\phi_{c_2} = T_m - T_L \qquad (18.16)$$

where K_s is the torsional spring constant for the azimuth post. The angular position of the upper table is designated by ϕ_{c_1} and that of the lower table by ϕ_{c_2}. Similarly, from the summation of torques acting on the lower table, it is found that

$$\Sigma T_e = -K_s(\phi_{c_2} - \phi_{c_1}) = J_2 s^2 \phi_{c_2}$$

or
$$(J_2 s^2 + K_s)\phi_{c_2} - K_s \phi_{c_1} = 0 \qquad (18.17)$$

Elimination of ϕ_{c_2} between Eqs. (18.16) and (18.17) gives

$$\phi_{c_1} = \frac{J_2(s^2 + K_s/J_2)}{J_1 J_2 s^2 [s^2 + K_s(J_1 + J_2)/J_1 J_2]} (T_m - T_L)$$

$$= \frac{(s + j\omega_{n_2})(s - j\omega_{n_2})}{J_1 s^2 (s + j\omega_{n_1})(s - j\omega_{n_1})} (T_m - T_L) \qquad (18.18)$$

where
$$\omega_{n_1} = \sqrt{\frac{K_s(J_1 + J_2)}{J_1 J_2}} \qquad \text{and} \qquad \omega_{n_2} = \sqrt{\frac{K_s}{J_2}}$$

The block-diagram representation for Eqs. (18.12) and (18.18) is shown in Fig. 18.15a. The characteristic equation for this system is

$$s^2(s + j\omega_{n_1})(s - j\omega_{n_1}) + K(s + j\omega_{n_2})(s - j\omega_{n_2}) = 0 \qquad (18.19)$$

where $K = K_m/J_1$. The corresponding root-locus plot is shown in Fig.

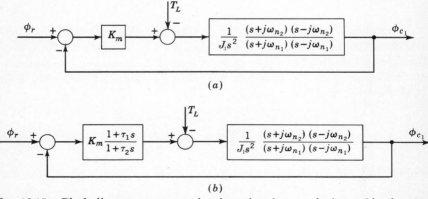

(a)

(b)

FIG. 18.15. Block-diagram representation for azimuth control of a stable element with a limber post (torque applied to upper table): (a) uncompensated system; (b) compensated system.

18.16a. It is again necessary to use lead compensation to stabilize this system, as is indicated in Fig. 18.15b.

The corresponding characteristic equation which includes the effect

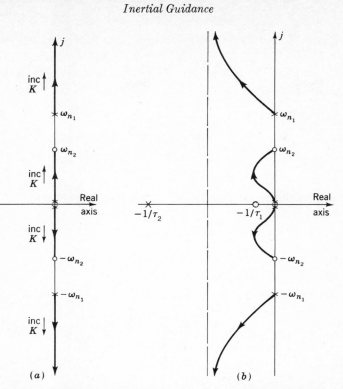

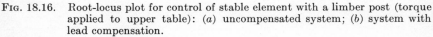

FIG. 18.16. Root-locus plot for control of stable element with a limber post (torque applied to upper table): (*a*) uncompensated system; (*b*) system with lead compensation.

of the lead compensation is

$$s^2(s + j\omega_{n_1})(s - j\omega_{n_1})\left(s + \frac{1}{\tau_2}\right) + K(s + j\omega_{n_2})(s - j\omega_{n_2})\left(s + \frac{1}{\tau_1}\right) = 0 \tag{18.20}$$

where $K = \dfrac{\tau_1}{\tau_2}\dfrac{K_m}{J_1}$. The root-locus plot for Eq. (18.20) is shown in Fig. 18.16*b*.

For a rigid post, it makes no difference whether the torque motor is attached to the upper or lower table. However, for a limber post, the torque motor must be attached to the upper table, on which the gyros are located, for otherwise it becomes impossible to stabilize the system by ordinary means. This is easily proved as follows:

With the torque motor connected to the bottom table, the summation of torques acting on the upper table gives

$$(J_1 s^2 + K_s)\phi_{c_1} - K_s\phi_{c_2} = 0 \tag{18.21}$$

and similarly the summation of torques acting on the lower table is

$$(J_2s^2 + K_s)\phi_{c_2} - K_s\phi_{c_1} = T_m - T_L \tag{18.22}$$

Elimination of ϕ_{c_2} gives

$$\phi_{c_1} = \frac{K_s/J_1J_2}{s^2(s^2 + \omega_n^2)}(T_m - T_L) \tag{18.23}$$

where

$$\omega_n = \sqrt{\frac{K_s(J_1 + J_2)}{J_1J_2}}$$

The root-locus plot for this system in which torque is applied to the lower table is shown in Fig. 18.17. This is a system which cannot be

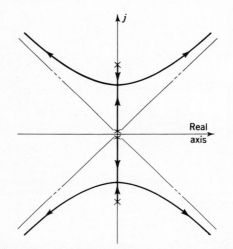

FIG. 18.17.   Root-locus plot for uncompensated control of stable element with a limber post (torque applied to lower table).

stabilized by simple compensation. Thus, it is interesting to note that, for a rigid post, it makes no difference whether the correcting torque is applied to the lower or upper platform, whereas for a limber system the effect is somewhat astonishing.

18.7 Missile in Flight. When a missile is in flight, it is subjected to a number of forces such as aerodynamic forces, gravitational forces, and the thrust which propels it, as is shown in Fig. 18.18. Aerodynamic forces are conveniently handled by resolving them into a component parallel to and a component perpendicular to the direction of motion, or heading, of the missile. The aerodynamic component parallel to the direction of motion is designated as the drag D_r, and the perpendicular

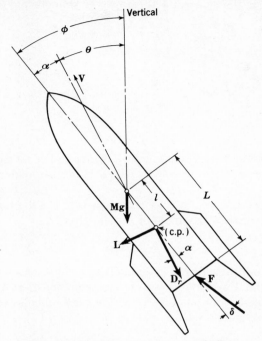

FIG. 18.18. Forces acting on a missile.

component is called the lift L. The intersection of the line of action of D_r and L is called the center of pressure (c.p.).

Although the vehicle is pointed at an angle ϕ with respect to the vertical, the direction of motion is inclined at an angle θ from the vertical. Because $e^{j(\theta+90°)}$ is a unit vector in the direction of motion, as is shown in Fig. 18.19a, the velocity may be written

$$\mathbf{V} = Ve^{j(\theta+90°)} \tag{18.24}$$

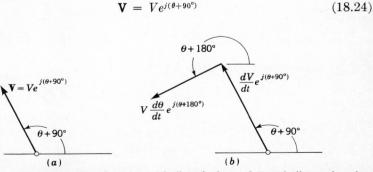

FIG. 18.19. Vector representation of (a) missile velocity and (b) missile acceleration.

Differentiation of the velocity with respect to time yields the acceleration

$$\mathbf{A} = \frac{d\mathbf{V}}{dt} = V \frac{d}{dt} e^{j(\theta+90°)} + e^{j(\theta+90°)} \frac{dV}{dt} \qquad (18.25)$$

Noting that

$$\frac{d}{dt} e^{j(\theta+90°)} = j \frac{d\theta}{dt} e^{j(\theta+90°)} = \frac{d\theta}{dt} e^{j90°} e^{j(\theta+90°)}$$

then

$$\mathbf{A} = \frac{dV}{dt} e^{j(\theta+90°)} + V \frac{d\theta}{dt} e^{j(\theta+180°)} \qquad (18.26)$$

The acceleration has a component dV/dt parallel to the direction of motion and a component $V(d\theta/dt)$ which is perpendicular, as shown in Fig. 18.19b.

For small angles of attack (i.e., less than 10°) the lift force is approximately proportional to the angle of attack, that is,

$$L = K_L \alpha$$

where K_L is the lift coefficient (pounds lift per unit α).

Unlike lift, the drag force D_r tends to remain constant for small angles of attack. The summation of forces acting perpendicular to the direction of motion of the missile yields

$$MV \frac{d\theta}{dt} = K_L \alpha + F \sin (\alpha + \delta) + Mg \sin \theta \qquad (18.27)$$

which for small values of $\alpha + \delta$ and θ becomes

$$MV \frac{d\theta}{dt} - Mg\theta = (K_L + F)\alpha + F\delta \qquad (18.28)$$

where δ is the angle between the thrust force F and the centerline of the missile, as shown in Fig. 18.18.

Similarly, the summation of torques acting about the center of gravity yields

$$\sum T_\epsilon = J \frac{d^2\phi}{dt^2} = -K_L \alpha \cos \alpha - D_r \sin \alpha - FL \sin \delta - B_\nu \frac{d\phi}{dt} \qquad (18.29)$$

which for small values of α and δ gives

$$J \frac{d^2\phi}{dt^2} + B_\nu \frac{d\phi}{dt} = -K_L \alpha - D_r \alpha - FL\delta \qquad (18.30)$$

From Fig. 18.18, it follows that

$$\phi = \theta + \alpha \qquad (18.31)$$

Thus, from Eqs. (18.28), (18.30), and (18.31) the overall relationship between ϕ and δ is

$$\phi = \frac{-F[LMVD + (K_L + F - Mg)L - (K_L + D_r)]\delta}{JMVD^3 + [J(K_L + F - Mg) + B_\nu MV]D^2} \quad (18.32)$$
$$+ [B_\nu(K_L + F - Mg) + (K_L + D_r)MV]D$$
$$- (K_L + D_r)Mg$$

The characteristic equation for the preceding result is seen to be of the third order.

A typical block diagram for controlling the flight of a missile is shown in Fig. 18.20. The servomotor controls the direction of the angle of

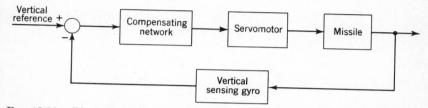

Fig. 18.20. Block-diagram representation for control of missile in vertical flight.

thrust, and the vertical sensing gyro measures the angle of inclination ϕ of the missile with respect to the vertical.

Problems

18.1 In Fig. P2.5 is shown a linear accelerometer in which y is the motion of the mass relative to the frame and x is the motion of the frame. In the differential equation relating x and y, replace the acceleration term d^2x/dt^2 by a_x (where a_x is the acceleration of the frame). Obtain the resulting transfer function for $Y(s)/A(s)$. Note that because the input is an acceleration the output displacement y will be proportional to the acceleration. Explain why it is desirable to have ω_n very high and ζ between 0.4 and 0.7.

HINT: Sketch the log-magnitude diagram.

18.2 A single-degree-of-freedom gyroscope is shown in Fig. P18.2. A rotation of the frame about the z axis causes the gyrowheel to precess about the y axis. This precession is resisted by a spring and damper which provide an opposing torque such that $T_y = -(K + BD)\theta_y$. With the aid of Eq. (18.6), determine the equation relating the input motion θ_z to the output θ_y (neglect inertia J_y and damping B_y).

When the opposing torque is provided by the spring only (i.e., no damper), a rate gyro results. What is the equation of operation for this rate gyro? When the resisting torque is provided by the damper only (i.e., the spring K is removed), the device becomes an integrating rate gyro. Determine the resulting equation of operation.

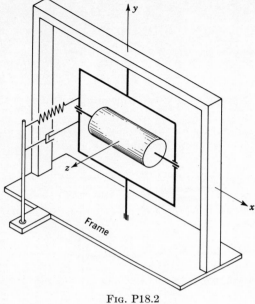

Fig. P18.2

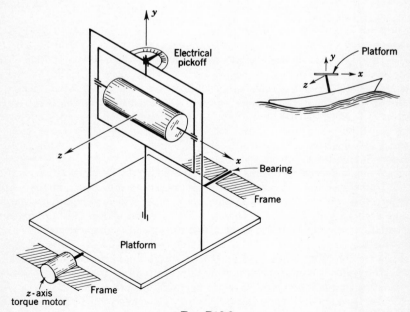

Fig. P18.3

18.3 In Fig. P18.3 is shown the application of a one-degree-of-freedom gyroscope to provide a stable reference plane. Because of the bearings, motion of the ship is not transmitted to the platform. However, extraneous torques T_{ze} may be transmitted to the platform because of friction in the bearings, inertia forces, etc. Such external disturbing torques tend to rotate the platform about the z axis away from its reference orientation. A rotation of the platform from its reference position causes the gyroscope to precess about the y axis. An electrical pick-off then detects the error.

For an integrating rate gyroscope which is sensitive to torque about its z axis, it follows that $\theta_y \approx (J_s\omega_s/B)\theta_z$. The electrical pick-off sends a signal to the motor to provide a corrective torque such that $T_m = K_m(\theta_r - \theta_y)$, where θ_r is the desired reference position. From Eq. (18.7) it follows that

$$T_z = T_m - T_{ze} = J_zD^2\theta_z + B_zD\theta_z + J_s\omega_sD\theta_y$$

where T_{ze} is the external disturbing torque tending to rotate the platform from its reference position.

Determine the overall block-diagram representation for this system in which θ_r is the reference input and θ_z the output.

18.4 Sketch the root-locus plot for the characteristic equation of the system of Prob. 18.3. Assume that the viscous friction $B_zD\theta_z$ is negligibly small.

Add lead compensation of the form $(1 + \tau_1s)/(1 + \tau_2s)$, where $\tau_1 > \tau_2$, to this system. Sketch the resulting root-locus plot. Does lead compensation improve the general stability? Could stability be improved by the use of lag compensation?

18.5 By the addition of another gimbal and an x-axis torque motor, it is possible to make the platform of Fig. P18.3 insensitive to rotations about the x axis as well as being insensitive to rotations about the z axis. The gyroscope of Fig. P18.3 detects rotation about the z axis only. To detect rotations about the x axis, it is necessary to mount another gyroscope on the platform. Make a sketch of the resulting system. Determine the block-diagram representation in which θ_x is the output and θ_r is the reference input.

18.6 In Fig. P18.6 is shown the block-diagram representation of an autopilot system for controlling the pitch angle θ_c of an airplane. Determine the required value of the gain K such that the resulting system will have an M_m of 1.4.

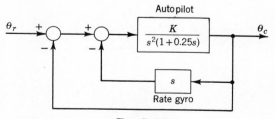

FIG. P18.6

APPENDIX **I**

Fourier series, Fourier integral, and the Laplace transform

A greater understanding of the Laplace transform $F(s)$ of a time function $f(t)$ may be obtained by examining the similarities which exist between Laplace transforms and the more familiar Fourier series and Fourier integral.

Fourier Series. A periodic function as shown in Fig. I.1 may be represented by the series

$$f(t) = K + \sum_{n=1}^{\infty} (A_n \cos n\omega_0 t + B_n \sin n\omega_0 t) \qquad (\text{I.1})$$

where $\omega_0 = 2\pi/T$, in which T is the period. The constant K is evaluated

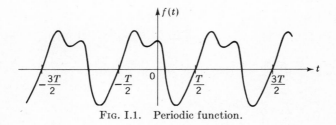

FIG. I.1. Periodic function.

as follows: Integration of each term in Eq. (I.1) over a complete period causes each term in the summation on the right-hand side to vanish. Thus

$$\int_{-T/2}^{T/2} f(t)\,dt = K \int_{-T/2}^{T/2} dt + 0 = KT$$

or

$$K = \frac{1}{T} \int_{-T/2}^{T/2} f(t)\,dt \qquad (\text{I.2})$$

The value of K is seen to be equal to the average value of the function over a period.

To evaluate A_n each term of Eq. (I.1) is multiplied by $\cos m\omega_0 t$ and

613

then integrated over a period.   Because

$$\int_{-T/2}^{+T/2} \cos n\omega_0 t \, \cos m\omega_0 t \, dt = \begin{cases} 0 & \text{for } m \neq n \\ \dfrac{T}{2} & \text{for } m = n \end{cases} \tag{I.3}$$

and

$$\int_{-T/2}^{+T/2} \sin n\omega_0 t \, \cos m\omega_0 t \, dt = 0 \tag{I.4}$$

it follows that

$$A_n = \frac{2}{T} \int_{-T/2}^{+T/2} f(t) \cos n\omega_0 t \, dt \tag{I.5}$$

Similarly, multiplication of each term of Eq. (I.1) by $\sin m\omega_0 t$ and integration over the period yields the following result for B_n

$$B_n = \frac{2}{T} \int_{-T/2}^{+T/2} f(t) \sin n\omega_0 t \, dt \tag{I.6}$$

Equation (I.1) may be telescoped into a more convenient form by using Eqs. (5.37) and (5.38) to express the cosine and sine in exponential form.

$$A_n \cos n\omega_0 t = \frac{A_n}{2} \left(e^{jn\omega_0 t} + e^{-jn\omega_0 t} \right)$$

and

$$B_n \sin n\omega_0 t = -j \frac{B_n}{2} \left(e^{jn\omega_0 t} - e^{-jn\omega_0 t} \right)$$

Thus $$f(t) = K + \frac{1}{2} \sum_{n=1}^{\infty} (A_n - jB_n)e^{jn\omega_0 t} + (A_n + jB_n)e^{-jn\omega_0 t} \tag{I.7}$$

By also writing Eqs. (I.5) and (I.6) in exponential form, it can be seen that

$$A_n - jB_n = \frac{2}{T} \int_{-T/2}^{T/2} f(t)(\cos n\omega_0 t - j \sin n\omega_0 t) \, dt$$

$$= \frac{2}{T} \int_{-T/2}^{T/2} f(t)e^{-jn\omega_0 t} \, dt \tag{I.8}$$

and

$$A_n + jB_n = \frac{2}{T} \int_{-T/2}^{T/2} f(t)(\cos n\omega_0 t + j \sin n\omega_0 t) \, dt$$

$$= \frac{2}{T} \int_{-T/2}^{T/2} f(t)e^{jn\omega_0 t} \, dt \tag{I.9}$$

Substitution of the preceding results into Eq. (I.7) gives

$$f(t) = K + \frac{1}{T} \sum_{n=1}^{\infty} e^{jn\omega_0 t} \int_{-T/2}^{+T/2} f(t)e^{-jn\omega_0 t} \, dt$$

$$+ \frac{1}{T} \sum_{n=1}^{\infty} e^{-jn\omega_0 t} \int_{-T/2}^{+T/2} f(t)e^{jn\omega_0 t} \, dt \tag{I.10}$$

By noting that the last summation is unaltered by changing the sign of n, the Fourier series becomes

$$f(t) = K + \sum_{n=1}^{\infty} \frac{e^{jn\omega_0 t}}{T} \int_{-T/2}^{+T/2} f(t)e^{-jn\omega_0 t}\, dt$$

$$+ \sum_{n=-1}^{-\infty} \frac{e^{jn\omega_0 t}}{T} \int_{-T/2}^{+T/2} f(t)e^{-jn\omega_0 t}\, dt \quad \text{(I.11)}$$

Because the value of the summation for $n = 0$ is K,

$$f(t) = \sum_{n=-\infty}^{\infty} \frac{e^{jn\omega_0 t}}{T} \int_{-T/2}^{+T/2} f(t)e^{-jn\omega_0 t}\, dt \quad \text{(I.12)}$$

Equation (I.12) is frequently written in the form

$$f(t) = \sum_{n=-\infty}^{\infty} C_n e^{jn\omega_0 t} \quad \text{(I.13)}$$

where
$$C_n = \frac{1}{T} \int_{-T/2}^{+T/2} f(t)e^{-jn\omega_0 t}\, dt$$

Fourier Integral. As the period T becomes infinite, the Fourier series expression given by Eq. (I.12) is

$$f(t) = \lim_{T \to \infty} \left[\sum_{n=-\infty}^{\infty} \frac{e^{jn\omega_0 t}}{T} \int_{-T/2}^{+T/2} f(t)e^{-jn\omega_0 t}\, dt \right] \quad \text{(I.14)}$$

For large values of T it is more appropriate to use the following notation:

$$\lim_{T \to \infty} \omega_0 = \lim_{T \to \infty} \frac{2\pi}{T} = \Delta\omega$$

and
$$\lim_{T \to \infty} n\omega_0 = n\,\Delta\omega = \omega$$

Thus, Eq. (I.14) becomes

$$f(t) = \lim_{\substack{\Delta\omega \to 0 \\ T \to \infty}} \left[\frac{1}{2\pi} \sum_{n=-\infty}^{\infty} e^{j\omega t}\,\Delta\omega \int_{-T/2}^{+T/2} f(t)e^{-j\omega t}\, dt \right] \quad \text{(I.15)}$$

The limit of Eq. (I.15) is the Fourier integral

$$f(t) = \frac{1}{2\pi} \int_{-\infty}^{\infty} e^{j\omega t} \left[\int_{-\infty}^{\infty} f(t)e^{-j\omega t}\, dt \right] d\omega \quad \text{(I.16)}$$

The Fourier integral is frequently expressed by the Fourier transform pair

$$f(t) = \frac{1}{2\pi} \int_{-\infty}^{\infty} F(j\omega)e^{j\omega t}\, d\omega \quad \text{(I.17)}$$

$$F(j\omega) = \int_{-\infty}^{\infty} f(t)e^{-j\omega t}\, dt \quad \text{(I.18)}$$

Equation (I.18) is referred to as the direct Fourier transformation, and Eq. (I.17) is the inverse Fourier transformation.

For most physical problems, it is desired to know the solution for $t > 0$. Thus, if the initial conditions are known, then the lower limit of integration in Eq. (I.18) may be taken as zero.

To illustrate the use of the Fourier transform, consider the function

$$f(t) = e^{at} \qquad t \geq 0 \tag{I.19}$$

Application of the direct Fourier transform gives

$$F(j\omega) = \int_0^\infty e^{at} e^{-j\omega t}\, dt = \frac{e^{at} e^{-j\omega t}}{a - j\omega}\bigg|_0^\infty \tag{I.20}$$

If the exponent a is less than zero, the preceding expression becomes

$$F(j\omega) = 0 - \frac{1}{a - j\omega} = \frac{1}{j\omega - a} \qquad a < 0 \tag{I.21}$$

However, if the exponent a is positive, e^{at} becomes infinite when evaluated at $t = \infty$ and thus $F(j\omega)$ diverges.

Laplace Transform. To extend the usefulness of the Fourier transform so that it is applicable to divergent functions, a converging factor $e^{-\sigma t}$ is introduced. Thus, the general transform equation is

$$F(\sigma + j\omega) = \int_0^\infty f(t) e^{-\sigma t} e^{-j\omega t}\, dt$$

$$= \int_0^\infty f(t) e^{-(\sigma + j\omega)t}\, dt \tag{I.22}$$

The transform for the time function given by Eq. (I.19) is

$$F(\sigma + j\omega) = \frac{e^{(a - \sigma - j\omega)t}}{a - \sigma - j\omega}\bigg|_0^\infty$$

$$= \frac{1}{(\sigma + j\omega) - a} \qquad \sigma > a \tag{I.23}$$

The preceding expression is seen to converge when σ is greater than a. To ensure convergence of the Fourier transform, it was necessary that $\int_0^\infty |f(t)|\, dt < \infty$. However, the transform indicated by Eq. (I.22) converges when $\int_0^\infty |f(t)| e^{-\sigma t}\, dt < \infty$ for some finite σ.

The substitution of $s = \sigma + j\omega$ and $F(s) = F(\sigma + j\omega)$ into Eq. (I.22) yields the Laplace transform equation.

$$F(s) = \int_0^\infty f(t) e^{-st}\, dt \tag{I.24}$$

It is only necessary that some finite value of σ exists such that $\int_0^\infty |f(t)| e^{-\sigma t}\, dt < \infty$ in order to verify the existence of the transform indicated by Eq. (I.24).   For most functions $f(t)$ encountered in engineering work, the transform $F(s)$ is convergent.   It should also be noted that, to solve differential equations by Laplace transforms, it is not necessary to determine the value or values of σ over which $F(s)$ is convergent.   It suffices to know that such a value or values of σ exist.

In effect, Eq. (I.24) is the result of substituting s for $j\omega$ and $F(s)$ for $F(j\omega)$ in Eq. (I.18).   The use of these same substitutions in Eq. (I.17) yields the inverse transform, i.e.,

$$f(t) = \frac{1}{2\pi j} \int_{\sigma-j\infty}^{\sigma+j\infty} F(s)e^{st}\,ds \qquad (I.25)$$

The new limits of integration are obtained by noting that, when $\omega = \pm\infty$, then $s = \sigma \pm j\omega = \sigma \pm j\infty$.   Equation (I.25) is a line integral for which the path of integration is a vertical line which is displaced a distance σ from the imaginary axis, as is shown in Fig. I.2.   For con-

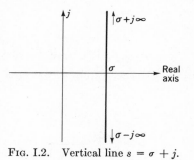

FIG. I.2.   Vertical line $s = \sigma + j$.

vergence, it is necessary that σ be such that all the values of s which make $F(s)$ infinite [i.e., poles of $F(s)$] lie to the left of the vertical line shown in Fig. I.2.

Response of system to an arbitrary input

For some input functions $f(t)$, such as an arbitrary input, the transform $F(s)$ is not easily obtained or is a very complicated expression. For such cases, it is desired to be able to determine the transient response without knowing the value of $F(s)$.

The arbitrary input $f(t)$ shown in Fig. II.1 could be approximated by a sum of pulses, i.e.,

$$f(t) \approx f_1[u(t) - u(t - t_1)] + f_2[u(t - t_1) - u(t - t_2)]$$
$$+ \cdots + f_n[u(t - t_{n-1}) - u(t - t_n)] \quad \text{(II.1)}$$

For this case, the response of the system $y(t)$ at time t is obtained by add-

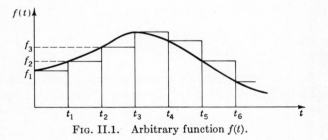

Fig. II.1. Arbitrary function $f(t)$.

ing the individual responses due to each pulse, as is shown graphically in Fig. II.2; i.e.,

$$y(t) = y_1(t) + y_2(t) + \cdots \quad \text{(II.2)}$$

where $y_1(t)$ is the response due to the first pulse, etc. With the preceding method, accuracy is increased by using more pulses of a smaller width to approximate the input. In a similar manner, it is possible to approximate the input by a series of step changes.

A considerable saving in computational time and effort is realized by the use of the convolution integral. In addition, the convolution-integral method yields an exact rather than an approximate solution. It should

618

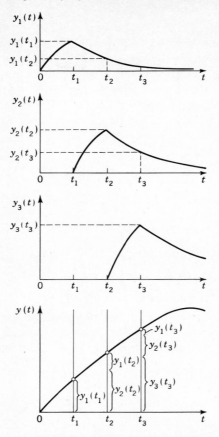

Fig. II.2. Response at time t_n.

first be noted that the general transformed expression for $Y(s)$ is

$$Y(s) = \frac{L_m(s)F(s)}{L_n(s)} + \frac{I(s)}{L_n(s)} = W(s)F(s) + \frac{I(s)}{L_n(s)} \qquad \text{(II.3)}$$

where $W(s) = L_m(s)/L_n(s)$.

The inverse transformation of Eq. (II.3) yields the desired time response

$$y(t) = \mathcal{L}^{-1}[W(s)F(s)] + \mathcal{L}^{-1}\left[\frac{I(s)}{L_n(s)}\right] \qquad \text{(II.4)}$$

The last term of the preceding expression is evaluated directly from a knowledge of the initial conditions. For an arbitrary input for which $F(s)$ is not known, the first term may be determined by application of the following convolution integral,

$$\mathcal{L}^{-1}[W(s)F(s)] = \int_0^\infty w(\lambda)f(t - \lambda)\, d\lambda \qquad \text{(II.5)}$$

where $w(\lambda) = \mathcal{L}^{-1}\{[L_m(s)/L_n(s)](1)\} = \mathcal{L}^{-1}[W(s)]$ is the unit impulse response of the system and may be computed directly since $W(s)$ is known. It is necessary to introduce the symbol λ to distinguish the two time terms which appear in Eq. (II.5). A plot of the impulse response $w(t)$ versus t would be identical to a plot of $w(\lambda)$ versus λ.

The convolution integral given by Eq. (II.5) is verified as follows: First take the Laplace transform of the right-hand side of Eq. (II.5).

$$\mathcal{L}\left[\int_0^\infty w(\lambda)f(t-\lambda)\,d\lambda\right] = \int_0^\infty \left[\int_0^\infty w(\lambda)f(t-\lambda)\,d\lambda\right]e^{-st}\,dt$$
$$= \int_0^\infty w(\lambda)\left[\int_0^\infty f(t-\lambda)e^{-st}\,dt\right]d\lambda \quad (II.6)$$

Application of the real-translation theorem to the integral in brackets in Eq. (II.6) gives

$$\int_0^\infty f(t-\lambda)e^{-st}\,dt = F(s)e^{-s\lambda} \tag{II.7}$$

Substitution of this result into Eq. (II.6) yields

$$\mathcal{L}\left[\int_0^\infty w(\lambda)f(t-\lambda)\,d\lambda\right] = \left[\int_0^\infty w(\lambda)e^{-s\lambda}\,d\lambda\right]F(s)$$
$$= W(s)F(s) \tag{II.8}$$

Taking the inverse transform of both sides of the preceding expression yields the result given by Eq. (II.5). A direct physical interpretation of the convolution integral is shown in Fig. II.3. The response of the sys-

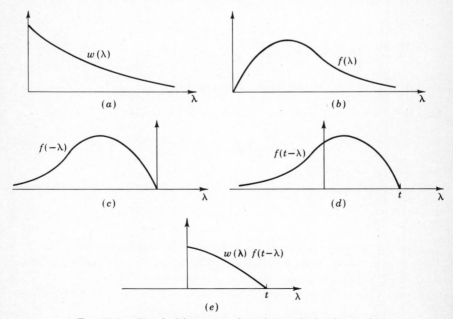

Fig. II.3. Physical interpretation of convolution integral.

tem $w(\lambda)$ to a unit impulse is shown in Fig. II.3*a*. The arbitrary input is drawn in Fig. II.3*b*. The plot of $f(\lambda)$ versus λ is identical to the graph of the input function $f(t)$ versus t. The input is reflected about the $\lambda = 0$ axis to yield $f(-\lambda)$ in Fig. II.3*c*. Translating Fig. II.3*c* by t sec yields the $f(t - \lambda)$ plot shown in Fig. II.3*d*. Multiplication of corresponding values of $w(\lambda)$ and $f(t - \lambda)$ yields the curve of $w(\lambda)f(t - \lambda)$ as shown in Fig. II.3*e*. The desired response $y(t)$ at time t is equal to the area under this latter graph. From Fig. II.3*e*, it is apparent that the value of the integral given by Eq. (II.5) is zero for values of λ greater than t. Thus, the upper limit of integration may be taken as t rather

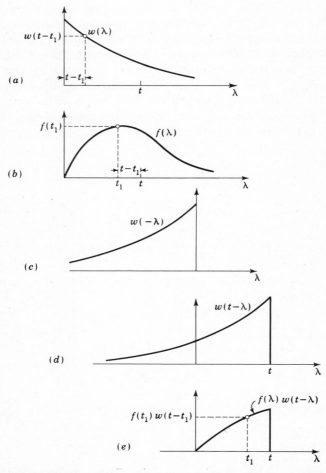

FIG. II.4. Physical interpretation of the alternate form of the convolution integral.

than infinity, i.e.,

$$\mathcal{L}^{-1}[W(s)F(s)] = \int_0^t w(\lambda)f(t - \lambda)\,d\lambda \tag{II.9}$$

The complete time-response expression is

$$y(t) = \int_0^t w(\lambda)f(t - \lambda)\,d\lambda + \mathcal{L}^{-1}\left[\frac{I(s)}{L_n(s)}\right] \tag{II.10}$$

By employing techniques similar to those used in deriving Eq. (II.5), it may also be shown that

$$\mathcal{L}^{-1}[W(s)F(s)] = \int_0^t f(\lambda)w(t - \lambda)\,d\lambda \tag{II.11}$$

where, as before, $w(\lambda)$ is the unit impulse response and $f(\lambda)$ the arbitrary input. The graphical interpretation of the preceding expression is shown in Fig. II.4. It is interesting to consider the portion of the total response $y(t)$ due to the portion of the input which occurs at time t_1, as shown in Fig. II.4b. In effect the abscissa $f(t_1)$ is multiplied by the value of $w(t - t_1)$ to give $f(t_1)w(t - t_1)$. Thus, the multiplication factor for each portion of the input depends on the value of $w(\lambda)$ at $\lambda = t - t_1$. The impulse response $w(\lambda)$ is also called the *weighting function because it weights the past values of the input.*

APPENDIX ▌▌▌

Obtaining the frequency response from the transient response

Several techniques are available[1] for determining the frequency response of a system when the transient response is known. The method now to be described was developed by Guillemin.[2] This method possesses the advantage that the accuracy obtained with only a few terms (computational effort thus being minimized) is better than that obtained by other techniques.

Guillemin's procedure is based primarily upon a graphical interpretation of the following equation:

$$Y(j\omega) = \frac{1}{(j\omega)^n} \int_0^\infty y^{(n)}(t)e^{-j\omega t}\,dt \tag{III.1}$$

The preceding expression is derived as follows: The transform for the nth derivative of a function $y(t)$ for which the initial conditions are zero is given by

$$\mathcal{L}[y^{(n)}(t)] = \int_0^\infty y^{(n)}(t)e^{-st}\,dt = s^n Y(s)$$

or

$$Y(s) = \frac{1}{s^n} \int_0^\infty y^{(n)}(t)e^{-st}\,dt \tag{III.2}$$

The substitution of $j\omega$ for s in the preceding expression yields the result given by Eq. (III.1). By comparison of Eq. (III.1) and Eq. (I.18) it follows that differentiation of $y(t)$ with respect to time corresponds to multiplication of $Y(j\omega)$ by $j\omega$.

The application of Eq. (III.1) for obtaining the frequency response is next demonstrated. In Fig. III.1a is shown a typical function $y(t)$. The straight-line approximation to this function is indicated by $y^*(t)$. The first derivative $y^{*(1)}(t)$ shown in Fig. III.1b is seen to be a series of steps. The height of each step is equal to the slope of the corresponding

---

[1] R. C. Seaman, Jr., B. P. Blasingame, and G. C. Clementson, The Pulse Method for Determination of Aircraft Performance, *Aeronaut. Sci.*, **17**: (1), 22–38 (Jan., 1950).

[2] E. A. Guillemin, Computational Techniques Which Simplify the Correlation between Steady-state and Transient Responses of Filters and Other Networks, *Proc. Natl. Electronics Conf., 1953*, **9**: (1954).

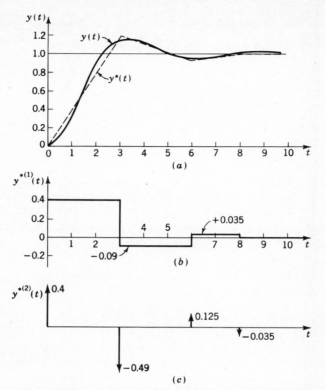

FIG. III.1. Differentiation of $y^*(t)$ to obtain a train of impulses.

portion of $y^*(t)$. The second derivative $y^{*(2)}(t)$ yields the train of impulses shown in Fig. III.1c. The area of each impulse is equal to the vertical distance between steps of Fig. III.1b.

The second derivative $y^{*(2)}(t)$ may be written in the form

$$y^{*(2)}(t) = \sum_{k=1}^{\nu} a_k u_1(t - t_k) \tag{III.3}$$

where a_k is the area of the kth impulse, $u_1(t - t_k)$ is the symbolic designation for a unit impulse which occurs at time t_k, and ν is the total number of impulses.

Substituting Eq. (III.3) into Eq. (III.1) and noting that $n = 2$ gives

$$Y^*(j\omega) = \frac{1}{(j\omega)^2} \int_0^\infty \sum_{k=1}^{\nu} a_k u_1(t - t_k) e^{-j\omega t} \, dt$$

$$= \frac{1}{(j\omega)^2} \sum_{k=1}^{\nu} a_k e^{-j\omega t_k} \tag{III.4}$$

Application of Eq. (III.4) to the function shown in Fig. III.1 gives

$$Y^*(j\omega) = \frac{1}{(j\omega)^2} (0.40 - 0.49e^{-j3\omega} + 0.125e^{-j6\omega} - 0.035e^{-j8\omega}) \quad \text{(III.5)}$$

For a given input $f(t)$ and corresponding output $y(t)$, the frequency response is $G^*(j\omega) = Y^*(j\omega)/F^*(j\omega)$. For example, if the response $y(t)$ is given by the function $y(t)$ of Fig. III.1 and $f(t)$ is a unit step function, $f^{*(1)}(t)$ is a unit impulse occurring at $t = 0$. Thus, $F^*(j\omega) = 1/j\omega$, and

$$G^*(j\omega) = \frac{Y^*(j\omega)}{F^*(j\omega)} = \frac{1}{j\omega} (0.40 - 0.49e^{-j3\omega} + 0.125e^{-j6\omega} - 0.035e^{-j8\omega})$$

$$\text{(III.6)}$$

Improved accuracy is obtained by determining $y^{(1)}(t)$ exactly and then approximating this derivative by straight lines rather than the original function $y(t)$. In effect, the function $y(t)$ is now being approximated by a series of parabolas. For this case, the second derivative $y^{*(2)}(t)$ is a series of steps, and the third derivative is a train of impulses. The approximation $Y^*(j\omega)$ now becomes

$$Y^*(j\omega) = \frac{1}{(j\omega)^3} \sum_{k=1}^{\nu} a_k e^{-j\omega t_k} \quad \text{(III.7)}$$

APPENDIX **IV**

Obtaining the transient response from the frequency response

Essentially the same approach described in Appendix III may be used to determine the transient response when the frequency response of a system is known. The general operational representation for a differential equation is

$$y(t) = G(D)f(t) \tag{IV.1}$$

For the case in which the initial conditions are zero and the input $f(t)$ is a unit impulse, the transform is

$$Y(s) = G(s) \tag{IV.2}$$

The inverse transformation of Eq. (IV.2) is

$$y(t) = w(t) = \frac{1}{2\pi j} \int_{\sigma-j\infty}^{\sigma+j\infty} G(s)e^{st}\, ds \tag{IV.3}$$

where $w(t)$ is the symbol for the impulse response. The substitution of $j\omega$ for s in Eq. (IV.3) gives

$$w(t) = \frac{1}{2\pi} \int_{-\infty}^{\infty} G(j\omega)e^{j\omega t}\, d\omega \tag{IV.4}$$

Integrating the right-hand side of the preceding expression by parts and letting $u = G(j\omega)/2\pi$ and $dv = e^{j\omega t}\, d\omega$ gives

$$w(t) = \frac{G(j\omega)e^{j\omega t}}{2\pi jt}\bigg|_{-\infty}^{\infty} + \frac{1}{2\pi(-jt)} \int_{-\infty}^{\infty} G^{(1)}(j\omega)e^{j\omega t}\, d\omega \tag{IV.5}$$

For any realizable function, $G(j\omega)$ goes to zero for infinite values of ω. Thus, the first term on the right-hand side of the preceding expression vanishes. Further integration by parts yields the following general expression for $w(t)$:

$$w(t) = \frac{1}{2\pi(-jt)^n} \int_{-\infty}^{\infty} G^{(n)}(j\omega)e^{j\omega t}\, d\omega \tag{IV.6}$$

By separating $G^{(n)}(j\omega)$ into its real part $G_R^{(n)}(j\omega)$ and its imaginary part $G_I^{(n)}(j\omega)$ and similarly by writing $e^{j\omega t}$ in its rectangular form $\cos \omega t + j \sin \omega t$, the preceding expression becomes

$$w(t) = \frac{1}{2\pi(-jt)^n} \int_{-\infty}^{\infty} [G_R^{(n)}(j\omega) \cos \omega t - G_I^{(n)}(j\omega) \sin \omega t] \, d\omega$$

$$+ \frac{j}{2\pi(-jt)^n} \int_{-\infty}^{\infty} [G_R^{(n)}(j\omega) \sin \omega t + G_I^{(n)}(j\omega) \cos \omega t] \, d\omega \quad (IV.7)$$

Examination of the coefficient $j/(-jt)^n$ in front of the second integral shows that for even values of $n(n = 2, 4, 6, \ldots)$ the second integral is imaginary. In order that $w(t)$ be real, the second integral must vanish for even values of n. Similarly, for odd values of n the first integral is imaginary and therefore must vanish.

The preceding result could also be ascertained as follows: In Fig. IV.1a is shown a typical polar plot of $G(j\omega)$. For any value of ω, $G_R(j\omega) = G_R(-j\omega)$ so that the real part $G_R(j\omega)$ is an even function of ω, as shown in Fig. IV.1b. However, from Fig. IV.1a it is to be noted that $G_I(j\omega) = -G_I(-j\omega)$, and thus the imaginary part $G_I(j\omega)$ is an odd function of ω, as shown in Fig. IV.1c. Differentiation of an even function yields an odd function, while differentiation of an odd function yields an even function. Thus, the nth derivative of $G_R(j\omega)$ is an even function when n is even and an odd function when n is odd. Similarly, the nth derivative of $G_I(j\omega)$ is an odd function when n is even and an even function when n is odd. In addition, the product of two even functions or the product of two odd functions gives an even function, while the product of an even function and an odd function is an odd function. Thus, since $\cos \omega t$ is an even function of ω and $\sin \omega t$ is odd, it follows that for even values of n the first integrand of Eq. (IV.7) is an even function, while the second integrand is odd. The integral of an odd function from $-\infty$ to $+\infty$ is zero so that the second term of Eq. (IV.7) vanishes for even values of n. Similarly, for odd values of n, the first integrand is an odd function and thus vanishes after integration.

Because the first integral of Eq. (IV.7) is an even function when n is even,

$$w(t) = \frac{1}{\pi(-jt)^n} \int_0^{\infty} [G_R^{(n)}(j\omega) \cos \omega t - G_I^{(n)}(j\omega) \sin \omega t] \, d\omega \qquad (n \text{ even})$$

$$(IV.8)$$

The first term in the integrand of Eq. (IV.8) is an even function of *time*, while the second is an odd function of *time*. In order that $w(t)$ be zero for negative values of time, the two components must be equal and opposite for negative values of t and hence equal for $t > 0$. Thus for

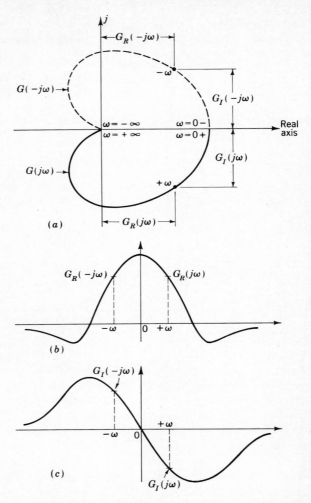

Fig. IV.1. (a) Polar plot $G(j\omega)$; (b) plot of $G_R(j\omega)$ versus ω; (c) plot of $G_I(j\omega)$ versus ω.

even values of n and $t > 0$

$$w(t) = \frac{-2}{\pi(-jt)^n} \int_0^\infty G_I^{(n)}(j\omega) \sin \omega t \, d\omega \qquad \text{(IV.9)}$$

$$w(t) = \frac{2}{\pi(-jt)^n} \int_0^\infty G_R^{(n)}(j\omega) \cos \omega t \, d\omega \qquad \text{(IV.10)}$$

By applying similar reasoning to the second integral of Eq. (IV.7), it may be shown that for odd values of n and $t > 0$

$$w(t) = \frac{2j}{\pi(-jt)^n} \int_0^\infty G_I^{(n)}(j\omega) \cos \omega t \, d\omega \qquad (IV.11)$$

$$w(t) = \frac{2j}{\pi(-jt)^n} \int_0^\infty G_R^{(n)}(j\omega) \sin \omega t \, d\omega \qquad (IV.12)$$

When the nth derivative is a train of impulses, Eqs. (IV.10) and (IV.12) become

$$w(t) = \frac{2}{\pi} \frac{(-1)^{n/2}}{t^n} \sum_{k=1}^\nu a_k \cos \omega_k t \qquad n \text{ even} \qquad (IV.13)$$

$$w(t) = \frac{2}{\pi} \frac{(-1)^{(n+1)/2}}{t^n} \sum_{k=1}^\nu a_k \sin \omega_k t \qquad n \text{ odd} \qquad (IV.14)$$

where a_k is the area of the kth pulse and ω_k is the angular velocity at which it occurs.

The procedure to use in applying Eq. (IV.13) or (IV.14) parallels that described for Eq. (III.4) or (III.7). A set of equations similar to Eqs. (IV.13) and (IV.14) can be obtained from Eqs. (IV.9) and (IV.11), in which the imaginary part $G_I(j\omega)$ is employed. Thus, one may work with either the real or the imaginary part of $G(j\omega)$ in order to find the impulse response. After the impulse response has been determined, the convolution technique presented in Appendix II may be used to find the response to any arbitrary input.

APPENDIX V

The complex convolution integral

The Laplace transforms of two functions $f_1(t)$ and $f_2(t)$ are

$$F_1(s) = \mathcal{L}[f_1(t)] = \int_0^\infty f_1(t)e^{-st}\,dt \qquad \text{Re } s > \sigma_1 \qquad (V.1)$$

$$F_2(s) = \mathcal{L}[f_2(t)] = \int_0^\infty f_2(t)e^{-st}\,dt \qquad \text{Re } s > \sigma_2 \qquad (V.2)$$

In order for $F_1(s)$ to exist, it is necessary that the real part of s in Eq. (V.1) be greater than σ_1. Similarly, in Eq. (V.2) it is necessary that the real part of s be greater than σ_2. The Laplace transform for the product $f_1(t)f_2(t)$ is

$$\mathcal{L}[f_1(t)f_2(t)] = \int_0^\infty f_1(t)f_2(t)e^{-st}\,dt \qquad \text{Re } s = \sigma > \sigma_1 + \sigma_2 \qquad (V.3)$$

From Eq. (I.25) in Appendix I, the inverse Laplace transform for $f_1(t)$ is

$$f_1(t) = \frac{1}{2\pi j} \int_{c-j\infty}^{c+j\infty} F_1(w)e^{wt}\,dw \qquad \text{Re } w = c > \sigma_1 \qquad (V.4)$$

where w is used as the Laplace operator to distinguish it from the operator s in Eq. (V.3). The substitution of $f_1(t)$ from Eq. (V.4) into Eq. (V.3) gives

$$\mathcal{L}[f_1(t)f_2(t)] = \frac{1}{2\pi j} \int_0^\infty \int_{c-j\infty}^{c+j\infty} F_1(w)e^{wt}\,dw f_2(t)e^{-st}\,dt$$

Interchanging the order of integration shows that

$$\mathcal{L}[f_1(t)f_2(t)] = \frac{1}{2\pi j} \int_{c-j\infty}^{c+j\infty} F_1(w) \int_0^\infty f_2(t)e^{-(s-w)t}\,dt\,dw$$

$$\text{Re } (s - w) > \sigma_2 \qquad (V.5)$$

The last integral is recognized as the Laplace transform of a delayed function. Thus

$$\mathcal{L}[f_1(t)f_2(t)] = \frac{1}{2\pi j} \int_{c-j\infty}^{c+j\infty} F_1(w)F_2(s - w)\,dw \qquad (V.6)$$

The integral on the right-hand side has the form of the convolution integral. Because s and w are complex, this is referred to as the complex

630

convolution integral. To evaluate this complex convolution integral by means of residues, it is necessary to take a closer look at the parameter c. From Eqs. (V.3) and (V.4) it follows that

$$\text{Re } (s - w) = \text{Re } (s) - \text{Re } (w) = (\sigma - c)$$

Comparison with Eq. (V.5) shows that

$$(\sigma - c) > \sigma_2 \qquad \text{or} \qquad c < (\sigma - \sigma_2)$$

Equation (V.4) shows that $\sigma_1 < c$, thus

$$\sigma_1 < c < \sigma - \sigma_2 \qquad\qquad\qquad (\text{V.7})$$

The meaning of the preceding result, Eq. (V.7), may be better understood by the following geometric interpretation. In Fig. V.1 is shown a

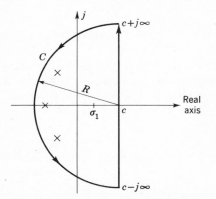

FIG. V.1. Closed path that encloses all the poles of $F_1(w)$.

closed path that encloses all of the poles (indicated by ×'s) of the function $F_1(w)$. Because σ_1 is to the right of all these poles, then $c > \sigma_1$ must also be to the right of all the poles.

In Fig. V.2a the poles of $F_2(w)$ are located to the left of the vertical

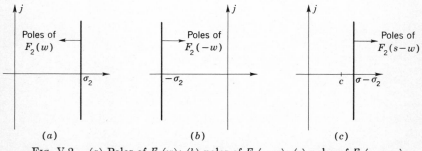

FIG. V.2. (a) Poles of $F_2(w)$; (b) poles of $F_2(-w)$; (c) poles of $F_2(s - w)$.

line through σ_2. The real part of the poles of $F_2(-w)$ are the same as $F_2(w)$ except that they are flipped about the imaginary axis as indicated in Fig. V.2b. Thus, the poles of $F_2(-w)$ are now to the right of the vertical line through $-\sigma_2$. The real part of the poles of $F_2(s - w)$ are translated a distance $\sigma = \text{Re}\ (s)$ to the right of the poles of $F_2(-w)$. Thus, as is illustrated in Fig. V.2c, the poles of $F_2(s - w)$ are located to the right of the vertical line through $\sigma - \sigma_2$. The value of σ is selected (σ may be chosen as large as desired but not infinite) such that the vertical line through $\sigma - \sigma_2$ lies to the right of c as shown in Fig. V.2c.

Because of the preceding selection of σ, the contour shown in Fig. V.1 encloses only the poles of $F_1(w)$. Thus, application of Cauchy's integral formula gives

$$\frac{1}{2\pi j} \int_{c-j\infty}^{c+j\infty} F_1(w)F_2(s - w)\ dw + \frac{1}{2\pi j} \int_C F_1(w)F_2(s - w)\ dw$$

$$= \sum \text{residues of } F_1(w)F_2(s - w) \text{ at poles of } F_1(w) \quad \text{(V.8)}$$

Because the contour in Fig. V.1 encloses all the poles of $F_1(w)$, the preceding summation is the residues due to all the poles of $F_1(w)$. For many applications such as in sampled-data systems, the integral around the infinite semicircle C vanishes.

Sampled-data Systems. To apply the complex convolution integral to sampled-data systems, first write the sampled function $f^*(t)$ in the form

$$f^*(t) = f(t)i(t)$$

where $i(t)$ is a train of unit impulses occurring every T seconds. That is,

$$i(t) = u_1(t) + u_1(t - T) + u_1(t - 2T) + \cdots$$

By letting $f_1(t) = f(t)$ and $f_2(t) = i(t)$, then $F_1(s) = F(s)$ is the Laplace transform of the continuous signal, and $F_2(s) = I(s)$ is the Laplace transform of $i(t)$. That is,

$$F_2(s) = I(s) = 1 + e^{-Ts} + e^{-2Ts} + \cdots = \frac{1}{1 - e^{-Ts}} \quad \text{(V.9)}$$

The function $F_2(s - w) = I(s - w)$ is

$$F_2(s - w) = I(s - w) = \frac{1}{1 - e^{-T(s-w)}} \quad \text{(V.10)}$$

For this case, it can be shown that the integral around C vanishes if

$$\lim_{s \to \infty} F_1(s) = 0$$

Thus, from Eqs. (V.6), (V.8), and (V.9) it follows that

$$\mathcal{L}[f^*(t)] = \mathcal{L}[f(t)i(t)] = \frac{1}{2\pi j} \int_{c-j\infty}^{c+j\infty} F(w) \, \frac{1}{1 - e^{-T(s-w)}} \, dw$$

$$= \sum \text{residues of } F(w) \, \frac{1}{1 - e^{-T(s-w)}} \text{ at poles of } F(w) \quad \text{(V.11)}$$

To obtain the z transform, let $z = e^{sT}$. Thus,

$$Z[f^*(t)] = \sum \text{residues of } F(w) \, \frac{1}{1 - e^{wT}/z} \text{ at poles of } F(w)$$

The dummy operator w may now be replaced by the Laplace operator s, thus

$$Z[f^*(t)] = \sum \text{residues of } F(s) \, \frac{1}{1 - e^{sT}/z} \text{ at poles of } F(s) \quad \text{(V.12)}$$

It is interesting to investigate the location of the poles of $F_2(s - w) = I(s - w)$. From Eq. (V.9), $F_2(w) = 1/(1 - e^{-Tw})$. Thus, the poles are the values of w such that $e^{-Tw} = 1$. That is,

$$w = j2\pi n \qquad n = 0, \pm 1, \pm 2, \ldots$$

Because the poles of $F_2(w)$ are equally spaced at intervals of 2π along the imaginary axis, the poles of $F_2(-w)$ are also located on the imaginary axis. Thus any $\sigma_2 > 0$ suffices.

As is illustrated in Fig. V.3, the poles of $F_2(s - w) = I(s - w)$ are translated a distance σ to the right of the imaginary axis.

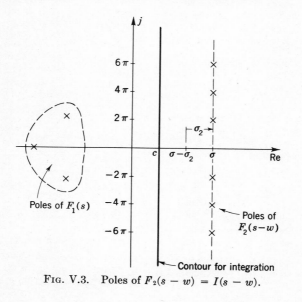

FIG. V.3. Poles of $F_2(s - w) = I(s - w)$.

APPENDIX VI

Frequency-response tables

FREQUENCY RESPONSE FOR $G(j\omega) = \dfrac{1}{j\omega}$

ω	$\angle G(j\omega)$	$|G(j\omega)|$	$\log |G(j\omega)|$
0.10000	−90.00000	10.00000	1.00000
0.15000	−90.00000	6.66667	0.82391
0.20000	−90.00000	5.00000	0.69897
0.25000	−90.00000	4.00000	0.60206
0.30000	−90.00000	3.33333	0.52288
0.40000	−90.00000	2.50000	0.39794
0.50000	−90.00000	2.00000	0.30103
0.60000	−90.00000	1.66667	0.22185
0.70000	−90.00000	1.42857	0.15490
0.80000	−90.00000	1.25000	0.09691
1.00000	−90.00000	1.00000	0.00000
1.20000	−90.00000	0.83333	−0.07918
1.40000	−90.00000	0.71429	−0.14613
1.60000	−90.00000	0.62500	−0.20412
1.80000	−90.00000	0.55556	−0.25527
2.00000	−90.00000	0.50000	−0.30103
2.20000	−90.00000	0.45455	−0.34242
2.40000	−90.00000	0.41667	−0.38021
2.60000	−90.00000	0.38462	−0.41497
2.80000	−90.00000	0.35714	−0.44716
3.00000	−90.00000	0.33333	−0.47712
3.20000	−90.00000	0.31250	−0.50515
3.40000	−90.00000	0.29412	−0.53148
3.60000	−90.00000	0.27778	−0.55630
3.80000	−90.00000	0.26316	−0.57978
4.00000	−90.00000	0.25000	−0.60206
5.00000	−90.00000	0.20000	−0.69897
6.00000	−90.00000	0.16667	−0.77815
7.00000	−90.00000	0.14286	−0.84510
8.00000	−90.00000	0.12500	−0.90309
9.00000	−90.00000	0.11111	−0.95424
10.00000	−90.00000	0.10000	−1.00000

FREQUENCY RESPONSE FOR $G(j\omega) = \dfrac{1}{1 + j\tau\omega}$

$\tau\omega$	$\angle G(j\omega)$	$|G(j\omega)|$	$\log |G(j\omega)|$
0.10000	−5.71059	0.99504	−0.00216
0.15000	−8.53077	0.98894	−0.00483
0.20000	−11.30993	0.98058	−0.00852
0.25000	−14.03624	0.97014	−0.01316
0.30000	−16.69924	0.95783	−0.01871
0.40000	−21.80141	0.92848	−0.03223
0.50000	−26.56505	0.89443	−0.04846
0.60000	−30.96376	0.85749	−0.06677
0.70000	−34.99202	0.81923	−0.08659
0.80000	−38.65981	0.78087	−0.10742
1.00000	−45.00000	0.70711	−0.15051
1.20000	−50.19443	0.64018	−0.19369
1.40000	−54.46232	0.58124	−0.23565
1.60000	−57.99462	0.53000	−0.27572
1.80000	−60.94540	0.48564	−0.31368
2.00000	−63.43495	0.44721	−0.34949
2.20000	−65.55604	0.41380	−0.38321
2.40000	−67.38013	0.38462	−0.41497
2.60000	−68.96249	0.35898	−0.44493
2.80000	−70.34618	0.33634	−0.47323
3.00000	−71.56505	0.31623	−0.50000
3.20000	−72.64597	0.29827	−0.52538
3.40000	−73.61046	0.28217	−0.54949
3.60000	−74.47589	0.26764	−0.57244
3.80000	−75.25644	0.25449	−0.59432
4.00000	−75.96376	0.24254	−0.61522
5.00000	−78.69007	0.19612	−0.70749
6.00000	−80.53768	0.16440	−0.78410
7.00000	−81.86990	0.14142	−0.84949
8.00000	−82.87498	0.12403	−0.90646
9.00000	−83.65981	0.11043	−0.95691
10.00000	−84.28941	0.09950	−1.00216

FREQUENCY RESPONSE FOR $G(j\omega) = 1 - \left(\dfrac{\omega}{\omega_n}\right)^2 + j2\zeta\left(\dfrac{\omega}{\omega_n}\right)$ WHEN $\zeta = 0$

ω/ω_n	$\measuredangle G(j\omega)$	$|G(j\omega)|$	$\log|G(j\omega)|$
0.10000	−0.00000	1.01010	0.00436
0.15000	−0.00000	1.02302	0.00988
0.20000	−0.00000	1.04167	0.01773
0.25000	−0.00000	1.06667	0.02803
0.30000	−0.00000	1.09890	0.04096
0.40000	−0.00000	1.19048	0.07572
0.50000	−0.00000	1.33333	0.12494
0.60000	−0.00000	1.56250	0.19382
0.70000	−0.00000	1.96078	0.29243
0.80000	−0.00000	2.77778	0.44370
1.00000	−90.00000	Infinite	Infinite
1.20000	−180.00000	2.27273	0.35655
1.40000	−180.00000	1.04167	0.01773
1.60000	−180.00000	0.64103	−0.19312
1.80000	−180.00000	0.44643	−0.35025
2.00000	−180.00000	0.33333	−0.47712
2.20000	−180.00000	0.26042	−0.58433
2.40000	−180.00000	0.21008	−0.67761
2.60000	−180.00000	0.17361	−0.76042
2.80000	−180.00000	0.14620	−0.83506
3.00000	−180.00000	0.12500	−0.90309
3.20000	−180.00000	0.10823	−0.96567
3.40000	−180.00000	0.09470	−1.02366
3.60000	−180.00000	0.08361	−1.07773
3.80000	−180.00000	0.07440	−1.12840
4.00000	−180.00000	0.06667	−1.17609
5.00000	−180.00000	0.04167	−1.38021
6.00000	−180.00000	0.02857	−1.54407
7.00000	−180.00000	0.02083	−1.68124
8.00000	−180.00000	0.01587	−1.79934
9.00000	−180.00000	0.01250	−1.90309
10.00000	−180.00000	0.01010	−1.99564

Frequency Response for $G(j\omega) = 1 - \left(\dfrac{\omega}{\omega_n}\right)^2 + j2\zeta\left(\dfrac{\omega}{\omega_n}\right)$ when $\zeta = 0.2$

ω/ω_n	$\angle G(j\omega)$	$\lvert G(j\omega)\rvert$	$\log \lvert G(j\omega)\rvert$
0.10000	−2.31372	1.00928	0.00401
0.15000	−3.51247	1.02110	0.00907
0.20000	−4.76364	1.03807	0.01623
0.25000	−6.08853	1.06065	0.02557
0.30000	−7.51214	1.08947	0.03722
0.40000	−10.78430	1.16945	0.06798
0.50000	−14.93142	1.28831	0.11002
0.60000	−20.55604	1.46301	0.16525
0.70000	−28.76765	1.71878	0.23522
0.80000	−41.63354	2.07614	0.31726
1.00000	−90.00000	2.50000	0.39794
1.20000	−132.51045	1.53574	0.18632
1.40000	−149.74356	0.89977	−0.04587
1.60000	−157.69380	0.59306	−0.22690
1.80000	−162.18111	0.42501	−0.37160
2.00000	−165.06858	0.32208	−0.49204
2.20000	−167.09259	0.25384	−0.59545
2.40000	−168.59750	0.20594	−0.68626
2.60000	−169.76520	0.17085	−0.76739
2.80000	−170.70076	0.14428	−0.84080
3.00000	−171.46923	0.12362	−0.90792
3.20000	−172.11311	0.10720	−0.96980
3.40000	−172.66139	0.09392	−1.02724
3.60000	−173.13456	0.08301	−1.08086
3.80000	−173.54754	0.07393	−1.13116
4.00000	−173.91147	0.06629	−1.17855
5.00000	−175.23636	0.04152	−1.38171
6.00000	−176.07728	0.02850	−1.54509
7.00000	−176.66153	0.02080	−1.68198
8.00000	−177.09223	0.01585	−1.79990
9.00000	−177.42343	0.01249	−1.90353
10.00000	−177.68627	0.01009	−1.99599

Frequency Response for $G(j\omega) = 1 - \left(\dfrac{\omega}{\omega_n}\right)^2 + j2\zeta\left(\dfrac{\omega}{\omega_n}\right)$ when $\zeta = 0.4$

ω/ω_n	$\angle G(j\omega)$	$|G(j\omega)|$	$\log |G(j\omega)|$
0.10000	−4.61992	1.00682	0.00295
0.15000	−6.99873	1.01540	0.00664
0.20000	−9.46232	1.02749	0.01178
0.25000	−12.04257	1.04319	0.01836
0.30000	−14.77455	1.06257	0.02636
0.40000	−20.85446	1.11249	0.04629
0.50000	−28.07249	1.17647	0.07058
0.60000	−36.86990	1.25000	0.09691
0.70000	−47.67542	1.32025	0.12066
0.80000	−60.64224	1.36184	0.13413
1.00000	−90.00000	1.25000	0.09691
1.20000	−114.62356	0.94694	−0.02368
1.40000	−130.60129	0.67791	−0.16883
1.60000	−140.63068	0.49556	−0.30490
1.80000	−147.26477	0.37553	−0.42536
2.00000	−151.92751	0.29412	−0.53148
2.20000	−155.37643	0.23674	−0.62574
2.40000	−158.03275	0.19483	−0.71034
2.60000	−160.14478	0.16329	−0.78704
2.80000	−161.86713	0.13894	−0.85718
3.00000	−163.30075	0.11973	−0.92180
3.20000	−164.51427	0.10430	−0.98173
3.40000	−165.55596	0.09170	−1.03761
3.60000	−166.46079	0.08129	−1.08997
3.80000	−167.25471	0.07257	−1.13923
4.00000	−167.95743	0.06520	−1.18576
5.00000	−170.53767	0.04110	−1.38616
6.00000	−172.19100	0.02831	−1.54811
7.00000	−173.34557	0.02069	−1.68418
8.00000	−174.19937	0.01579	−1.80157
9.00000	−174.85724	0.01245	−1.90484
10.00000	−175.38007	0.01007	−1.99705

FREQUENCY RESPONSE FOR $G(j\omega) = 1 - \left(\dfrac{\omega}{\omega_n}\right)^2 + j2\zeta\left(\dfrac{\omega}{\omega_n}\right)$ WHEN $\zeta = 0.7$

ω/ω_n	$\angle G(j\omega)$	$|G(j\omega)|$	$\log|G(j\omega)|$
0.10000	-8.04906	1.00015	0.00007
0.15000	-12.12478	1.00020	0.00009
0.20000	-16.26020	1.00000	0.00000
0.25000	-20.47228	0.99930	-0.00031
0.30000	-24.77514	0.99776	-0.00097
0.40000	-33.69007	0.99054	-0.00413
0.50000	-43.02506	0.97474	-0.01111
0.60000	-52.69605	0.94694	-0.02368
0.70000	-62.50716	0.90517	-0.04327
0.80000	-72.18111	0.85003	-0.07057
1.00000	-90.00000	0.71429	-0.14613
1.20000	-104.67639	0.57582	-0.23972
1.40000	-116.09542	0.45820	-0.33895
1.60000	-124.85446	0.36634	-0.43611
1.80000	-131.63354	0.29659	-0.52784
2.00000	-136.97493	0.24369	-0.61317
2.20000	-141.26748	0.20314	-0.69219
2.40000	-144.78240	0.17163	-0.76540
2.60000	-147.70938	0.14676	-0.83339
2.80000	-150.18300	0.12684	-0.89673
3.00000	-152.30052	0.11067	-0.95595
3.20000	-154.13364	0.09738	-1.01152
3.40000	-155.73616	0.08633	-1.06383
3.60000	-157.14921	0.07705	-1.11323
3.80000	-158.40469	0.06918	-1.16001
4.00000	-159.52772	0.06246	-1.20443
5.00000	-163.73979	0.04000	-1.39794
6.00000	-166.50426	0.02778	-1.55623
7.00000	-168.46070	0.02041	-1.69011
8.00000	-169.91940	0.01563	-1.80610
9.00000	-171.04944	0.01235	-1.90841
10.00000	-171.95094	0.01000	-1.99993

FREQUENCY RESPONSE FOR $G(j\omega) = 1 - \left(\dfrac{\omega}{\omega_n}\right)^2 + j2\zeta\left(\dfrac{\omega}{\omega_n}\right)$ WHEN $\zeta = 1.0$

ω/ω_n	$\angle G(j\omega)$	$|G(j\omega)|$	$\log|G(j\omega)|$
0.10000	−11.42118	0.99010	−0.00432
0.15000	−17.06153	0.97800	−0.00966
0.20000	−22.61986	0.96154	−0.01703
0.25000	−28.07249	0.94118	−0.02633
0.30000	−33.39849	0.91743	−0.03743
0.40000	−43.60282	0.86207	−0.06446
0.50000	−53.13010	0.80000	−0.09691
0.60000	−61.92751	0.73529	−0.13354
0.70000	−69.98404	0.67114	−0.17319
0.80000	−77.31962	0.60976	−0.21484
1.00000	−90.00000	0.50000	−0.30103
1.20000	−100.38886	0.40984	−0.38739
1.40000	−108.92464	0.33784	−0.47129
1.60000	−115.98923	0.28090	−0.55145
1.80000	−121.89079	0.23585	−0.62737
2.00000	−126.86990	0.20000	−0.69897
2.20000	−131.11209	0.17123	−0.76641
2.40000	−134.76027	0.14793	−0.82995
2.60000	−137.92498	0.12887	−0.88986
2.80000	−140.69235	0.11312	−0.94645
3.00000	−143.13010	0.10000	−1.00000
3.20000	−145.29195	0.08897	−1.05077
3.40000	−147.22092	0.07962	−1.09899
3.60000	−148.95178	0.07163	−1.14489
3.80000	−150.51287	0.06477	−1.18865
4.00000	−151.92751	0.05882	−1.23045
5.00000	−157.38013	0.03846	−1.41497
6.00000	−161.07535	0.02703	−1.56820
7.00000	−163.73979	0.02000	−1.69897
8.00000	−165.74997	0.01538	−1.81291
9.00000	−167.31961	0.01220	−1.91381
10.00000	−168.57881	0.00990	−2.00432

index